D0903597

One Strong Voice

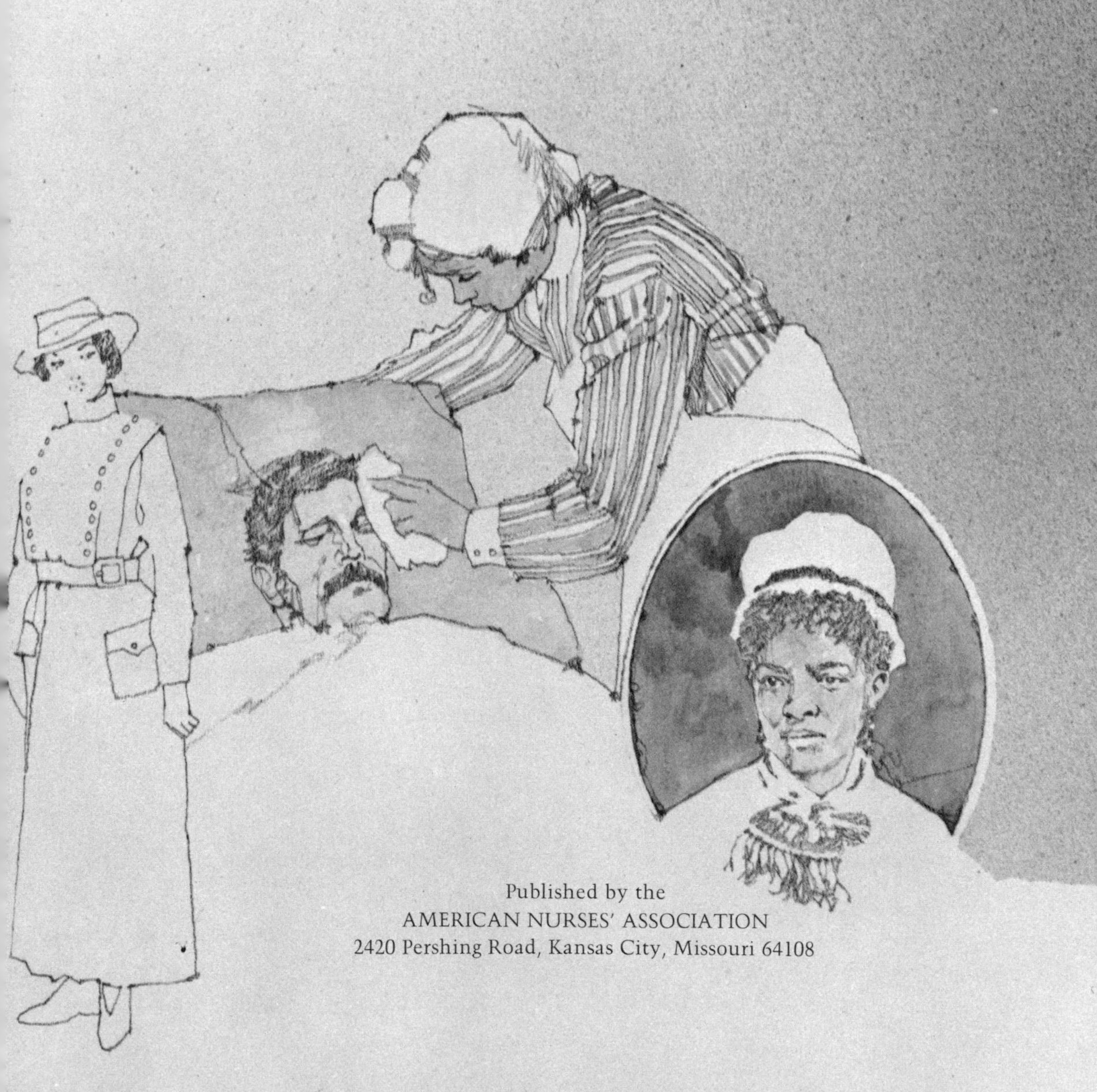

Published by the
AMERICAN NURSES' ASSOCIATION
2420 Pershing Road, Kansas City, Missouri 64108

One Strong Voice

The Story of the American Nurses' Association

Compiled by **Lyndia Flanagan**

First Edition

Printed in the United States of America
by The Lowell Press, Kansas City, Missouri
Library of Congress Catalog Card No. 76-13366
ISBN 0-913504-31-9

Dedication

This book contains the history of the American Nurses' Association. It is the story of individual and group efforts to maintain a viable professional association for nurses and to safeguard nursing's interests and the public's welfare.

This book is dedicated to the tens of thousands of elected and appointed officials who established policies and developed program plans to promote nursing and to serve nurses

and

the thousands of staff members who facilitated the growth and development of the association by effectively implementing its programs and activities.

Collectively, these individuals represent nursing's ONE STRONG VOICE.

Foreword

The nursing profession began to gain prominence in America when nurses banded together in 1896 to seek standardization of educational programs and laws to insure practitioner competency. Prior to that time, hospital committees and physicians dictated nursing duties and methods of training. In the last decade of the nineteenth century, nurses displayed a growing consciousness of the need to insure practitioner competency in order to improve nursing care. Recognizing the value of organized effort, pioneer leaders proposed the formation of a nursing organization to elevate the standards of nursing education, establish a code of ethics, and promote the interests of nurses.

The establishment of the American Nurses' Association was a direct outgrowth of an interest in the professional and educational advancement of nurses. Since its founding in 1896, ANA has had a significant impact on the growth and development of nurses and the quality of nursing care. Between 1896 and 1940, the American Nurses' Association took the necessary steps to secure a professional status for nurses. In the 1940s, the American Nurses' Association instituted measures to insure the adequate distribution of professional nursing services in the broader community. In the 1950s, the American Nurses' Association began to develop professional safeguards to insure quality nursing care. In the 1960s, the American Nurses' Association identified standards for nursing education of a "true professional calibre." More recently, the American Nurses' Association, working through the state nurses' associations, launched a campaign to actively involve nurses in the determination of matters relevant to the delivery of nursing care to the public and the welfare of the nurse in the employment setting.

In observance of the nation's bicentennial celebration and ANA's eightieth anniversary, a record has been compiled of the association's major accomplishments. *One Strong Voice,* the story of the American Nurses' Association, is a synopsis of the development of nursing in America since 1776 and the growth of the American Nurses' Association since its founding in 1896. *One Strong Voice* also contains a collection of the convention speeches of all the presidents of the American Nurses' Association. As "witnesses to nursing history," each president identified the key issues in nursing during her term in office. The observations of these individuals coupled with the historical narrative paints a distinct picture of the growth of modern nursing in America.

Much of the detailed information contained in this volume does not appear in any other account of nursing history. The material for *One Strong Voice* was compiled from the records and documents of the American Nurses' Association. An analysis of the minutes of early meetings, proceedings of the conventions, special reports, staff documents, and correspondence provided unique insight into the issues and problems which confronted the profession and the association during the past eighty years.

For other health professionals and consumers of health care, *One Strong Voice* presents a concise statement on the vital role of nurses in society. The nursing profession has been called the "conscience of the health care system." The development of trained nursing in the United States is the direct outgrowth of the efforts of women who were interested in public health reform. Through the years, nursing has assumed a leadership role among the health professions to secure the rights of the public to receive adequate health care.

For nurses, *One Strong Voice* provides an historical analysis of those issues and factors affecting the growth and development of nursing as a profession. There is a Chinese proverb which states that "one has to study the old to understand the new." It is the objective of the American Nurses' Association that this historical review will provide new insight into the resolution of current issues facing nursing and nurses.

Throughout the history of modern nursing in America, the profession has labored over three major concerns:

1) The need to develop criteria based on educational preparation and practical experience by which to judge a nurse's competency,

2) The need to establish laws which set forth certain standards deemed essential for nurses wishing to function in a professional capacity, and

3) The need to create descriptive terminology which reflects not only specific nursing functions, but also levels of competency.

In 1873, the profession established the first three schools of nursing, each of which was affiliated with a general hospital. The first training program lasted twenty-four months, with the first year devoted to instruction and practice and the second year devoted to practical experience. In 1973, there were nursing programs at the diploma, associate degree, baccalaureate degree, master's degree, and doctoral degree levels.

In 1900, nurses began to take the necessary measures to establish nurse registration or licensure. In 1970, the profession began considering more essential and extensive credentialing mechanisms, including certification and continuing education recognition.

In 1875, nurses became concerned about the semantic means for distinguishing the trained or graduate nurse from the untrained nursemaid. In 1975, nurses were concerned about the means for distinguishing not only levels of competencies, but also nursing roles. The professional glossary currently identifies practitioners, clinicians, specialists, and others.

In each period of nursing history, the profession's response to issues, including educational preparation and legal safeguards, has been tempered by societal needs and demands. At least two factors of change have necessitated role adaption on the part of the nurse practitioner:

1) The technological and scientific advances which have introduced complex methods of dealing with specific health problems as well as new approaches to the diagnosis and treatment of certain conditions, and

2) Changes in patterns of demand for health services which warrant provision of a more comprehensive continuum of care.

According to sociologist Dr. Robert K. Merton, the issues confronting a profession can be reduced to one basic issue: whether a profession will wait until societal demands force it to reluctant change or whether the profession will anticipate societal demands and be prepared to meet them. The issue is a choice between a course of action or reaction.

In order to maintain a viable position in the health care system and a professional vitality, nursing must begin today to forecast consumer needs of the future. Forecasting involves three steps: 1) a critical analysis of past and present developments in health care and nursing, 2) the identification of significant goals and priorities for nursing, and 3) the development and initiation of innovative programs in nursing aimed at satisfying projected health care needs for the next twenty to thirty years.

In compiling *One Strong Voice*, the American Nurses' Association has attempted to review past and present developments in nursing and health care and to identify some of the trends which may affect the provision of health care in the next three decades. It is now up to the nursing profession, working with and through ANA, to set the priorities for nursing and to develop and implement innovative programs to satisfy health care needs.

AMERICAN NURSES' ASSOCIATION
KANSAS CITY, MISSOURI

EILEEN M. JACOBI, ED.D., R.N.
EXECUTIVE DIRECTOR

Contents

One Strong Voice

Section I

Nursing's Key to Advancement

Introduction
Interest in Reform, 1776-1875
Earmarks of a Profession, 1875-1900
Struggle for Legal Safeguards, 1900-1910
Signs of Growth, 1912-1922
Professional Assessment, 1924-1934
Unprecedented Demands, 1936-1946
Blueprint for Action, 1948-1958
Four Major Concerns, 1960-1970
Tomorrow's Challenge, 1972-1976

Introduction

Eighty-three years ago a group of nurses with foresight met during the International Congress of Charities to chart a definite course for the nursing profession. The thesis of each speaker was most clearly enunciated by Edith Draper, who declared, "To advance we must unite." The interest and concern of these individuals in the advancement of nursing led to the establishment of the American Nurses' Association in 1897.

Nurses are fortunate that a representative association was organized at so early a period in nursing's development. As Annie Damer, the second president of the American Nurses' Association, observed: the establishment of the American Nurses' Association "brought nurses to where they were ready to work for the good of not the individual nurse or individual school of nursing, but the whole profession."

Created to promote the professional and educational advancement of nurses, the American Nurses' Association has given nurses the vehicle through which to present an effective, united front on issues affecting nursing and the general welfare of the nurse. The association has provided efficient mechanisms for promoting legislation and developing professional controls. Consequently, in the eighty years since the founding of ANA, nurses have made monumental strides in promoting nursing's role in the health care system. The American Nurses' Association has been and is "nursing's key to advancement."

Section One is not meant to be a comprehensive history of nursing in the United States. Rather, it is a synopsis of the development of nursing as a profession and the growth of the American Nurses' Association.

It has been suggested that the demands of the times shape individual needs for health care. It is significant to note that modern nursing began to develop during a period when social, economic, and industrial problems were colossal, and interest in the humane treatment of individuals was high. In adapting to demands for health care, pioneer nurses began to express concern for the individualistic needs of the sick. This was and is nursing's unique contribution to health care.

The growth of nursing in the United States since 1776 represents two centuries of advancement. Nursing care has developed from neighborly assistance rendered by untrained housekeepers to the present organized nursing services delivered by highly skilled practitioners. Chapters One and Two of this book deal with basic nursing accomplishments from the time of the Revolutionary War to the beginning of the twentieth century. Symbols of nursing achievement during this period include the growth and development of training schools for nurses, the establishment of a professional organization of nurses, and the publication of a national nursing journal.

When delegates met for the first annual convention of the American Nurses' Association in 1898, Isabel Hampton Robb, the first president of the association, observed:

> The objects as outlined in our constitution may seem simple and few in the reading; and yet concealed in each there lies folded up the seed of many a plan and purpose that can only come to maturity in the fullness of time....

In its eighty year history, the American Nurses' Association has fostered nursing research, promoted nursing practice legislation, encouraged development of advanced and continuing education programs, and stimulated the establishment and implementation of standards of nursing practice, nursing service, and nursing education. Chapters Three through Eight provide an accounting of the association's work in accomplishing its objectives. Each of these chapters highlights approximately one decade of ANA's history. It would be impossible to relate all of the association's efforts to promote the professional and educational advancement of nursing. Therefore, each chapter focuses on those endeavors of the association which have had a significant impact on the status of nurses and the quality of nursing care.

In recent years, the delivery of health care services has been greatly affected by a number of conditions, including growth of population, increase in family income, internal migration, overcrowding, and new techniques in the health sciences, to name only a few. As demands for health care services have grown, nurses have been expected to assume greater responsibility for the delivery of health care services. Today nurses function as clinical nurse specialists in intensive care units, independent nurse practitioners in rural and ghetto areas, and teachers and counselors to families experiencing health care crises. The final chapter of this section focuses on the current issues facing the nursing profession and the future plans of the American Nurses' Association.

1776-1875

Interest in Reform

By 1776, the thermometer had been perfected. A method for determining blood pressure had been discovered. Limited-scale inoculation and vaccination procedures had been introduced. Extensive studies into the utilization of oxygen were underway. The idea that diseases originated in localized areas of the body had been presented. A scientific basis for surgery was beginning to be identified.

Although these and other medical advances were being made, eighteenth century man still lacked an understanding of bacterial infection. Consequently, American colonists witnessed distressing outbreaks of diseases. During the Revolutionary War, the plight of the soldier was particularly alarming. As a result of a lack of adequate sanitation in the camps and insufficient food and clothing, infectious diseases such as cholera, pneumonia, typhus and dysentery spread in epidemic form.

Revolutionary War

George Washington was keenly aware of the need for organized care of his soldiers. Between 1775 and 1777, the Colonial Congress adopted legislation which would establish army hospitals. Included in the Congressional bills were provisions for a set number of 'nurses' proportionate to the number of sick and wounded.

The first reference to the employment of nurses in military hospitals in the United States can be found in *Continental Hospital Returns.*[1] These documents, dating back to 1777, not only list the names of hospitalized soldiers, but also the names of women who cared for the sick and wounded.

From scant records describing the care of the disabled, it is apparent that female "camp followers" engaged to nurse colonial soldiers, served as housekeepers. They did not function in roles requiring the technical knowledge and practical ability to actually "nurse" the injured or the sick. Little, if any, consideration was given to training individuals to provide nursing care. The prevailing attitude was that nurses were born, not trained.

While trained nurses were nonexistent during the Revolutionary War and nursing was not recognized as a distinct occupation, female camp followers performed a valuable service. They kept the sick and wounded clean and well fed, and comfortable, thus limiting the spread of disease and the frequency of infection. Nursing care, as it existed during this significant period in American history, was reflective of the basic needs of the colonial soldiers.

Following the Revolutionary War, little effort was exerted to establish an effective system of health care. In fact, provisions for medical and nursing care were neglected. The prevailing Puritan attitude was that illness represented God's punishment for sin. Penitential rather than curative approaches to the care of the ill were encouraged.

At the close of the Revolutionary War, there were only five permanent hospitals in colonial America: Bellevue Almshouse in New York, New York Hospital, Blockney and Pennsylvania Hospitals[2] in Philadelphia, and Eastern State Hospital for the insane at Williamsburg, Virginia. These barracks-type institutions generally served three purposes: almshouse, penitentiary, and hospital.

Civic indifference and poor administration often led to many shocking abuses in these multi-purpose settings. The sick were incarcerated with criminals, paupers, the insane, the orphaned, and the aged. Conditions were so crowded that as many as three individuals shared a single small bed. Failure to isolate the sick from other occupants of the institution enhanced the spread of disease. The death rate from epidemics exceeded fifty percent. Prejudice against hospitals arose because of the neglect and ill treatment of patients and the high death rate.

This was a dark period in the history of nursing in the United States. "Nurses" lacked moral standards and were unfeeling and unsympathetic. Nursing wages were so low that only people who could secure no other employment undertook nursing assignments. Nursing in city hospitals was done by inmates, who were frequently "ten-day women" detailed from the penitentiary for such work. In most instances, the women were over fifty years of age, and many were 70 and 80 years old.

Industrial Revolution

Between 1790 and 1860, the United States witnessed the effects of the Industrial Revolution, which not only brought about scientific, economic, and cultural expansion, but also conditions of poverty, overcrowding, disease, and many other social problems. During this period, the population doubled approximately every twenty-five years. Although the birth rate was high, the arrival of hundreds of thousands of immigrants accounted for a significant percentage of the increase. By 1790, immigrants entered the U.S. at the rate of approximately 60,000 a year. By 1840, this influx had tripled, and, by 1850, 240,000 persons immigrated to the U.S. annually. The rapid population growth complicated existing sanitation problems. Large city slums began to develop around factories where workers (ranging in age from four to seventy-four) labored six days a week, thirteen hours a day. Epidemics of cholera, yellow fever, malaria, typhoid fever, and other contagious diseases thrived in the crowded tenements and sweatshops. The need for methodical attendance to the health problems of the masses was great.

Early in the nineteenth century, the humanitarian movement gained momentum. Individuals sympathizing with the victims of the Industrial Revolution exposed the evils of the factory system and child labor. Public opinion was stirred by American and English novelists such as Charles Dickens who identified significant social problems of the times, including the questionable arrangements for nursing care. In *Martin Chuzzlewit* (1844), Dickens focuses attention on the nursing care administered by pardoned criminals and women of low moral standards. Unfortunately, much needed social reform was stymied by strong sentiments about slavery. The crusade against slavery overshadowed all other reform.

Nurse Training During the Period Preceding The Civil War

Limited advances were made in the area of nursing care in the United States between 1790 and 1860. Toward the end of the eighteenth century, with the general decline in superstition and religious prejudice, interest in the care of the sick was revived. The first American medical schools were organized. Numerous investigations were made of the conditions in various institutions. Attention was drawn to the need for therapeutic approaches to caring for mentally ill patients. A few progressive physicians appealed for better nursing care. These individuals were supported by men such as Benjamin Franklin who urged humane treatment of the sick in the interest of public welfare.

In 1798, Dr. Valentine Seaman organized and conducted a series of lectures on anatomy, physiology, care of children, and midwifery for the nursing staff of New York Hospital.

In 1809, the Sisters of Charity was founded by Mother Elizabeth Seton to give special attention to nursing and to the care of the poor in the United States.

Humanistic treatment of the sick was not attempted outside of religious orders until the formation of the Nurse Society of Philadelphia in 1839. Dr. Joseph Warrington organized the society and published *The Nurse's Guide* which contained a series of instructions on "nursing mother and child in the lying-in chamber." The society appealed to prudent young women to work as nurses. A short course of training was arranged for them in maternity nursing. These nurses were also required to assist in six cases before they could receive a "certificate of approbation" and become eligible for private duty under the general supervision of the society. Fifty nurses were employed between 1839 and 1850. Inasmuch as the training encompassed only a three month period and the nurse's hospital experience was restricted to obstetrical nursing, the society's training program was not considered a formal school for nurses.

The foundation for modern nursing education was laid by Florence Nightingale in 1860 with the opening of the Nightingale School for Nurses at St. Thomas Hospital in London. It was the first fully endowed school of nursing. The aims of the school were to train hospital nurses, to train nurses to train others, and to train district nurses in the care of sick poor. According to Miss Nightingale, who is considered the founder of modern nursing education, nursing the sick is an art requiring organized practical and scientific training. To this end, she encouraged the development of institutions specially organized to provide nurses with appropriate training.

The earliest attempt to establish a formal training school for nurses in the United States occurred in 1859 when Drs. Elizabeth and Emily Blackwell, close personal friends of Florence Nightingale, planned a training school as an adjunct to the New York Infirmary for Women and Children. Unfortunately, the outbreak of the Civil War interrupted their plans.

Civil War

When the Civil War began in 1861, there were virtually no trained nurses in the country. Nursing in most of the larger government hospitals was carried out under the auspices of religious orders. The utilization of religious nursing groups was preferred by many physicians, because members of religious orders were organized, were accustomed to discipline, and had helped in many epidemics. Although over 600 sisters from twelve religious orders volunteered for nursing duties, a much larger volunteer nursing corps was required to meet the nursing needs of sick and wounded soldiers.

The first voluntary nursing group was established by Dr. Elizabeth Blackwell and other lady managers of the New York Infirmary for Women and Children. As a result of a meeting at Cooper Union, where hundreds of women gathered to volunteer their help, the Women's Central Association for Relief was organized. This group concentrated their efforts on training individuals who could qualify as supervisors or chief nurses. More than 100 women were sent to Bellevue and New York Hospitals for a month's training by staff physicians.

The Women's Central Association for Relief banded together with similar groups to petition President Lincoln to establish an agency to administer care to the sick and wounded. Although President Lincoln initially rejected the association's proposal as presented by Rev. Henry Bellows and several physician representatives, he ultimately signed an order (June 13, 1861) creating the U.S. Sanitary Commission.[3] Its objective was to secure healthful conditions in military camps and hospitals.

The principle and course of action of the commission were nearly identical to the Red Cross Society which was first proposed in 1863 and founded in 1866. It is said that the establishment of the U.S. Sanitary Commission and the International Red Cross Society marked the beginning of the joint work of men and women in public enterprise.

During the Civil War, the U.S. Sanitary Commission spent over $5,000 in cash and distributed $15,000 worth of supplies, an unprecedented amount. At the time of the Civil War, there were only sixty-eight hospitals in the country. Most were ill-adapted to care for the hundreds of sick and wounded victims of the war. Temporary hospitals were organized in available buildings and other structures were hastily erected. The commission inaugurated both a floating hospital transport service and a hospital train. Its greatest achievement was the development of solders' aid societies, a comprehensive system of aid for the sick and wounded.

Many of the volunteer bodies of the U.S. Sanitary Commission were counseled and advised by Florence Nightingale, who had nursed the sick and wounded during the Crimean War (1853-1856). In October, 1854, she and thirty-eight nurses whom she had selected were given charge of 1,500 patients in the Barrack Hospital at Scutari, Turkey. Conditions in the hospital were so poor that the death rate was forty-two percent.

In addition to recognizing the needs of patients, and the nurse's role in ministering to these needs, she recognized the importance of the organizational framework in which patient care is delivered. In two months' time, she transformed the hospital into an efficiently managed institution. In six months' time, she had reduced the death rate to two percent.[4]

It is estimated that 2,000 women from the North and South undertook nursing duties during the Civil War. Early in the conflict, Dorothea Lynde Dix, a well-known crusader for psychiatric care, was appointed Superintendent of Women Nurses by the Secretary of War. She was assigned the responsibility and authority to recruit and equip a corps of army nurses. Miss Dix thus became the first woman appointed to an administrative position in the federal government.

She succeeded in having the army adopt a fairly systematic plan of regulations for nurses. Miss Dix outlined the requirements for army nurses as follows: they had to be 30 to 50 years of age; they had to have good health and endurance; they had to have a matronly demeanor and good character; and they had to be plainly dressed. Nurses bathed and dressed wounds, prepared and served food, and administered medications. Their responsibilities were similar to the tasks performed by women during the Revolutionary War.

The Confederate States did not establish an official organization comparable to the U.S. Sanitary Commission. A Women's Relief Society was organized, and individual states and volunteer groups organized hospitals for their own troops near the battlefields. Although the Confederate Army did not appoint a director of nursing, President Jefferson Davis authorized the rank of captain for Sally Tompkins. Miss Tompkins was placed in charge of Robertson Hospital. At the end of the Civil War, records indicated that only seventy-three patients died out of the 1,333 who received care in the hospital.[5]

Following the Civil War, urban industrial growth was rapid. Inexperience in governing people in densely populated areas gave rise to corrupt city governments, such as the Tammany organization in New York City. At the hands of unscrupulous men, a few individuals amassed great fortunes while a significant portion of the population existed at deplorable levels of poverty. The contrast between the wealthy and the poor was appalling.

Municipal utilities were the primary targets for corruption in such governments. Urban planning received little attention. As the movement into industial cities gathered momentum, water and sewer systems, police and fire services, and arrangements for public health programs quickly became antiquated.

During this period, the development of cast iron supports permitted the construction of multi-storied tenements which allowed for a much greater concentration of individuals. Machine-made jobs enticed Americans to move into "high-rise" tenements in areas close to factory employment. Immigrants flocked into the United States and settled in buildings with people of like backgrounds, establishing ethnic neighborhoods. As more people located in industrial cities, the tenement areas became more crowded, dirtier, and less healthful. Communicable diseases, such as tuberculosis, smallpox, diphtheria, scarlet fever, yellow fever, cholera, and dysentery, were rampant in the congested tenement districts.

The work of the U.S. Sanitary Commission during the Civil

War heightened interest in public sanitation. Citizens' associations developed to fight for sanitary and health reform. Public dispensaries were created to provide medical care for the poor. The need for health education was recognized. Pamphlets on child care, food preparation, ventilation, and disease prevention were made available. As these citizens' associations attempted health reform, the need for nurses prepared to teach and care for people in homes and hospitals[6] became more apparent.

Changing Status of Women

During the latter part of the nineteenth century, two factors provided impetus for the development of nursing education: growing support for educational opportunities and the crusade for women's rights.

The concept of tax-supported elementary schools was adopted on a nationwide basis before the Civil War, and public education continued to gain support after the Civil War. By 1870, more and more states were making grade school education compulsory.

The growth of higher education was spurred by the Morrill Act of 1862 which provided a generous grant of public lands to states for support of education. Teacher-training schools experienced a striking expansion. There was a sharp increase in professional and technical schools. During this period, women's colleges were gaining ground and universities were beginning to open their doors to both sexes. Traditional concepts of woman's role in society and her educational needs were changing.

The crusade for women's rights was eclipsed by the anti-slavery movement before the Civil War. During the Civil War, hospital work in the United States was conducted by women on a larger scale than it was in any other country. Historians assert that this was the beginning of an organized concentration of women in public duties in the United States.

Between 1865 and 1900, no single group was more profoundly affected by industrialization and urbanization than women. Technological advances provided both more time for women to participate in activities outside the home and the need for more workers in the industrial field. The inventions of the typewriter and telephone switchboard opened up jobs for millions of women, helping them achieve a new economic and social independence. Moreover, the depression which began in 1873 forced women of middle and upper income to seek employment in order to supplement the family earnings. During this period, women experienced a progressive liberation from household duties.

The speed with which nursing has gained stature in the health care field has been greatly affected by the status of women in society. This is evidenced by the fact that the dark period of nursing corresponds to a time in history when women were reduced to the lowest levels of self-expression. As women gained status in America and as educational opportunities for women increased, society grew more receptive to the establishment of training schools for nurses.

Early Schools of Nursing

The experiences of the Civil War focused attention on the weaknesses of the volunteer system of nursing and created a new interest in reform. During the Civil War, discerning women discovered that "motherly instinct" and good intentions did not adequately equip individuals to nurse the sick and wounded. Many historians assert that the establishment of trained nurses in the United States came as a direct result of the pioneering work done by women during the Civil War.

The earliest formal training programs owe their impetus to female physicians who undertook the responsibility of instructing nursing staffs. In 1861, the Woman's Hospital of Philadelphia established a six months' course in nurse training taught by women doctors. However, the school did not actually flourish until 1872 when it received an endowment, making it the first endowed school of nursing in America.

At the suggestion of Dr. Marie Zakrzewska, the 1863 charter of the New England Hospital for Women and Children in Boston included provision for a nursing school. Under the charge of Drs. Susan Dimock and Marie Zakrzewska, the school opened in 1872. On October 1, 1873, the school graduated Linda Richards, America's first trained nurse. On August 1, 1879, Mary Eliza Mahoney, America's first Negro nurse graduate, completed courses at the school.

During the 1868 annual meeting of the American Medical Association, founded in 1847, AMA's president, Dr. S. D. Gross, noted that nursing education had not received adequate attention from the majority of physicians in the country. As a result of Dr. Gross' remarks, the committee on recommendations offered a resolution that all hospitals and public institutions caring for the sick should only engage educated, well-trained nurses. It was strongly recommended that training institutions for nurses be established in all large cities. The resolution was referred to a committee for report at the 1869 annual meeting.

The committee's study revealed that the utilization of trained nurses in British hospitals had resulted in decreased mortality rates. The physicians gathered at the 1869 meeting adopted the committee's recommendations that district schools be formed under the guardianship of the county medical societies; that society members provide instruction in the art and science of nursing; and that homes for nurses be established and placed under the supervision of women administrators. Thus, the medical profession went on record favoring nurses' training. Unfortunately, no apparent action was undertaken by state or county medical societies to implement the recommendations.

In 1873 (just ten years after the founding of the Nightingale School of Nursing), the opening of schools in New York, New Haven, and Boston marked the recognition of nursing as a distinct occupation. The ultimate objective of those individuals who founded these early schools was the improvement of nursing care. As Florence Nightingale had pointed out, the purpose of training programs was to "teach the nurse to help the patient live."[7]

After the Civil War, a group of U.S. Sanitary Commission members formed the New York State Charities Aid Association. Within the framework of the association, the Bellevue Hospital Visiting Committee was initiated. After inspecting the conditions at Bellevue Hospital, the committee recommended establishment of a school for nurses in order to provide better nursing care. To insure the success of their endeavor, the women's committee sent Dr. Gill Wylie to seek the advice of Florence Nightingale. The Bellevue Training School for Nurses, founded in May, 1873, was the first school in the United States to utilize the principles of the Nightingale School.

Although the hospital's medical board initially disapproved the establishment of the school, improved patient care and a lower death rate convinced doctors of the value of trained nurses.

Among the early graduates of Bellevue were two presidents of the American Nurses' Association, Isabel Hampton (Robb) and Jane A. Delano.

Although the Connecticut Training School for Nurses received its charter before the Bellevue Training School, it was not opened until October, 1873. The school was founded as the result of a recommendation of a committee of New Haven Hospital doctors that a training school be established as a separate organization, with the hospital providing opportunities for practical experience. Both men and women served on the training board.

In 1879, a committee of doctors and nurses published a textbook for use by nursing students. *The New Haven Manual of Nursing* was the first text of its kind in the country and was widely used.

Like the Bellevue School, the Boston Training School was initiated by women who had been active during the Civil War and, afterwards, formed the Woman's Educational Union. The objective of the union was to advance women and prepare them to be self-supporting. The Boston Training School was opened in November, 1873. In 1896, it ceased to be an independent institution and was absorbed by Massachusetts General Hospital.

LINDA RICHARDS
America's First Trained Nurse

These three schools were purported to be patterned after the Nightingale School. According to Florence Nightingale's doctrine on nursing education:

1) A training school for nurses should be considered an educational institution to be supported by public funds,

2) A training school for nurses should be closely connected with a hospital, but administratively independent,

3) A professional nurse should assume responsibility for the administration and instruction of nursing students, and

4) A home should be established for student nurses.[8]

The revolutionary feature of the Nightingale plan was the mandate that the discipline and teaching of nursing staffs must be taken out of the control of hospital directors and medical personnel and placed in the hands of competent trained nurses.

In a *Century of Nursing*, written in 1876, Abby Woolsey stressed the desirability of elevating nursing to an educated and honorable profession. Miss Woolsey pleaded for quality educational programs. She expressed the opinion that nursing schools should be institutions of higher education. Unfortunately, the American public did not recognize the obligation or the benefit of financing programs to prepare nurses. Early schools had great difficulty surviving as independent schools. Because of lack of endowment, the early schools were absorbed into the hospitals with which they were connected. Under the aegis of the hospital, formal instruction of the nurse became a by-product of her service to the institution.

In early training schools, there were few lectures and limited textbook instruction. With the exception of manuals on nursing developed by the Bellevue and Connecticut training schools, the first nursing textbook in America was not written until 1885. Mrs. Clara Weeks-Shaw compiled *A Textbook of Nursing* which made the distinction between true nursing care and the mere execution of doctor's orders.

The first training programs were twelve months long. The

period was eventually extended to twenty-four months, with the first year devoted to instruction and practice and the second year devoted exclusively to practical experience. The first training schools based their curricula on the simple "job-analysis" of nursing duties which originated with Florence Nightingale.

By 1875, trained nurse graduates had three avenues of employment open to them: ward nursing in hospitals, the superintendentship of training schools, and private duty nursing. Toward the end of the century, district nursing also became an option.

During the latter part of the nineteenth century, the responsibilities of both the physician and the nurse underwent change. The development of the science of bacteriology drastically reduced infection and its dangers. Man had discovered that infectious disease was caused by specific micro-organisms. There was a tremendous impetus in the development of surgical medicine with the discoveries of anesthesia, ether, and chloroform and their uses; the x-ray and its application to the field of medicine; and the utilization of radium to destroy some types of malignant cells and tissues. Because of these advances and many more, patient care improved markedly.

As more patients discovered better and more convenient service in the hospitals, more duties were delegated to the trained nurse who was considered a distinctly *modern* addition to the hospital staff. Isabel Hampton Robb, first president of the Nurses' Associated Alumnae, pointed out:

> Just starting out on her career, without antecedents, without experience, with all before her, and all to learn. Her credentials had to be of her own making, her professional standing had to be evolved, she had to establish her own traditions and in all these undertakings, she had to maintain her own personal and professional dignity.[9]

REFERENCES

1. Julia C. Stimson, "Earliest Known Connection of Nurses with Army Hospitals in the United States," *American Journal of Nursing*, Vol. XXV (January, 1925), 18.
2. Pennsylvania Hospital, opened in 1752, is said to be the oldest hospital in the proper sense of the word. The hospital was designed solely for the purpose of providing curative care for the sick.
3. On September 5, 1861, the Western Sanitary Commission, an independent organization, was created. It had similar purposes and, in time, the two collaborated closely.
4. Josephine A. Dolan, *History of Nursing* (Philadelphia: W. B. Saunders, 1968), 214-216.
5. *Ibid.*, 228.
6. The Civil War made cities cognizant of the need for more hospitals, and the number of these institutions increased. At the outbreak of the war, there were 68 hospitals; by 1872, there were 178 hospitals in the country.
7. Florence Nightingale, "Sick Nursing and Health Nursing" in *Nursing of the Sick—1893* by Isabel Hampton and others (New York: McGraw-Hill Book Company, 1949), 26.
8. *Ibid.*, 24-37.
9. Isabel Hampton Robb, "President's Address," *Report of the Second Annual Convention of the Associated Alumnae of Trained Nurses*, 1899, 29.

1875-1900

Earmarks of a Profession

Although the establishment of schools of nursing made it possible to classify nursing as an occupation, nurses were still a most "indefinite quantity." As Isabel Hampton Robb pointed out: collectively, nurses in the late nineteenth century could not qualify as a profession because nursing lacked two essential elements—organization and legislation.[1]

Many books have been written on professionalism, yet it is difficult to find a succinct definition of "profession." The concept is best explained as a composite of characteristics. In 1910, Dr. Abraham Flexner identified several elements of a profession:

1) A profession involves a high degree of individual responsibility.

2) A profession possesses a body of specialized knowledge and skills.

3) A profession aims to provide a practical and definite service.

4) A profession is characterized by self-organization.

5) A profession's motivation tends to be altruistic.

Common elements of modern professions include specialized training programs, a unique service to society, standards of practice and education, a code of ethical conduct, an economic and general welfare program for its practitioners, appropriate public safeguards, and self-government.

Between 1873-1900, nursing lacked appropriate educational standards and legal safeguards. Nurses were at the mercy of hospital committees and groups of physicians who dictated their duties and methods of training. Nursing did not gain status until nurses began to band together to seek standardization of training programs and laws to insure practitioner competency. In the last decade of the nineteenth century, nurses displayed a growing consciousness of the need to upgrade nurse training and, in turn, improve nursing services.

Recognizing the need for nurses to determine the future of nursing, pioneer nursing leaders proposed the formation of a nursing organization which would establish a code of ethics, elevate the standards of nursing education, and promote the interests of nurses.

A survey of the history of modern professions shows that when a profession becomes clearly defined, competent practitioners form an association in an attempt to establish standards of practice and enforce a code of conduct based on ethical principles.[2] The establishment of a professional association is an expression of a growing consciousness of the need to promote a group's interests and aims. It is a clear indication of the maturity of a profession.

Early Proposals for Nurses' Organizations

The early nursing publications contain accounts of the development of American nursing organizations. In 1886, *The Nightingale,* the first nursing publication in the United States, recorded the establishment of the Philomena Society of New York. This was the first American society to be initiated by nurses. Unfortunately, the names of the founders were not preserved. Little is known about the activities of the society which ceased to exist between 1887 and 1888.

The earliest proposals to establish a national association of nurses are recorded in *The Trained Nurse,* the first American nursing journal. In 1888, *The Trained Nurse* absorbed *The*

Nightingale. The purpose of the new journal was to serve as a channel of communication between the ninety-four schools of nursing in existence in the United States.

A letter to Margaret E. Francis (Sirch), editor of *The Trained Nurse,* printed in January, 1889, outlined a proposal to band together the country's nurses in an "American Nurses' Association." The purpose of the association was to initiate an official registration of nurses.[3] In subsequent issues of *The Trained Nurse,* the editor solicited responses.

In October, 1889, *The Trained Nurse* printed a proposal that each state develop local nurses' organizations. Believing the establishment of state nursing groups would lead to formation of a national association, the editor of *The Trained Nurse* encouraged New York State to initiate the first state organization. In the December issue, the journal carried the rationale for establishment of the New York State Trained Nurses' Association, proposed bylaws, and a definition of a trained nurse. However, the issue of incorporation hampered establishment of the association. Although a bill was apparently drafted to incorporate the New York nurses' association, there was never any mention of the bill's introduction in the state legislature.

Finally in February, 1890, *The Trained Nurse* published a proposed constitution for an American Nurses' Association drawn up by several unidentified nurses. Unfortunately, later issues of the journal carried only occasional reference to the need for a nurses' organization.

An apparent obstacle to the establishment of a national nurses' organization was the lack of support from the large training schools.

Inasmuch as early nursing schools were financially dependent on hospitals, the development of trained nurses was closely linked to the growth of hospitals in America. Before the twentieth century, a hospital's operation was highly individualistic. The total identification of a training school with a hospital nursing service tended to isolate the school from similar schools in other hospital settings. Believing nurses were not capable of managing their own affairs, hospital authorities opposed any organizational efforts. Moreover, the lack of accepted standards for nursing education caused graduates of one nursing school to question the credentials of graduates of other nursing schools. For many years, nurses maintained an air of aloofness, believing it was neither possible nor desirable to work collectively. As Isabel Hampton Robb observed some time later, "As [the rapid increase in training programs] became more and more apparent, the older and better known schools with the instinct of self-preservation began to draw more closely within themselves, trusting in their own irreproachable names to protect their graduates, with the result that the members of one school were led to hold themselves aloof from those of another."[4]

The lack of interest in organizing nurses on a national scale during this period is reflected in the response to an 1892 proposal for a New York City association which would admit into membership trained nurses from the various training schools across the country. According to information appearing in several issues of *The Trained Nurse,* Lois Kunz of Orange, New Jersey, recommended that an association of qualified trained nurses be established in New York City; that a clubhouse be furnished with a good library and accommodations for nurses exposed to contagious diseases; and that a central registry be maintained for nurses who were not associated with the New York training schools. Superintendents of the New York training schools soundly rejected the idea of including nurses from other cities in a New York association. The editor of *The Trained Nurse* observed that the spirit of rivalry between different training schools severely hampered efforts to unite nursing forces. Ultimately, the proposal was killed.

Between 1888 and 1897, a number of temporary "clubs" were developed as places for nurses to rest between nursing assignments, to find reading materials, and, on occasion, to band together in support of city and state registries for nurses. The first permanent societies were three alumnae associations: Bellevue (1889),[5] Illinois Training School (1891), and Johns Hopkins (1892). Unfortunately, the alumnae groups maintained the singular objective of promoting their own schools.

The value of cooperation on a national scale was not realized until 1893 when nurses were faced with their first major problem—lack of standardization in nurse training as well as the need for laws to protect the public from poorly trained nurses.

In 1873, the schools of nursing were supported and managed by independent training school committees. When hospitals assumed financial responsibility for operation of these schools, training school committees had far less influence. The year 1890 heralded an uncontrolled expansion in the growth of schools of nursing. Most of these schools were void of standards, entrance requirements, and control by nursing. Moreover, as schools of nursing developed more rapidly, nursing students were exploited as a source of cheap labor by hospital authorities.

Deplorable working conditions further stimulated efforts to unite nurses. Hospital nurses worked an average eleven hours a day. Nurses assigned private duty worked twenty-four hour periods for weeks at a time, with only a few hours of rest. The demands of nursing duties during the 1880s caused individuals to speculate that the life span of a trained nurse would be no more than ten years.

Thus in 1893, some twenty years after the founding of American training schools of nursing, nursing leadership recognized the need to organize in order to establish standards of nursing education and nursing practice and to promote the general welfare of nurses.

American Society of Superintendents of Training Schools for Nurses

The first general meeting of nurses in the United States was held at the International Congress of Charities, Correction, and Philanthropy at the Chicago World's Fair in June, 1893. At the encouragement of Mrs. Ethel Gordon Fenwick, founder of the British Nurses' Association, the chairmen of the International Congress arranged for a subsection on nursing. Dr. John S. Billings, chairman of the section on hospital care, training of nurses, dispensary work, and first aid, appointed Miss Isabel Hampton (Robb) chairman of the subsection on nursing. Miss Hampton, with the help of M. Adelaide Nutting and Lavinia L. Dock, planned a program which focused on control of nurse training schools, registration of nurses, and the formation of a national organization of nurses.

In her keynote address, Miss Hampton, principal of the Training School at Johns Hopkins Hospital, observed that the term "trained nurse" meant "anything, everything or next to nothing" in the absence of educational standards.[6] Urging the establishment of a uniform system of instruction, she recommended that the course of instruction be lengthened to three years with eight hours a day of practical work.

Addressing the issue of control of schools of nursing, Lavinia L. Dock, Assistant Superintendent of Johns Hopkins Hospital, pointed out that the teaching, training, and discipline of nurses should not be at the discretion of medicine. Acknowledging the fact that the physician and the nurse represented different professions, Miss Dock explained that physicians could not comprehend the actual matter-of-fact realities of the training school. She concluded that training schools for nurses must be controlled by nurses.[7]

This same theme was reiterated in a paper on organization of training schools presented by Louise Darche, Superintendent of the New York City Training School. Itemizing the essential elements of proper training school organization, Miss Darche stressed the fact that nursing should be considered a distinct department within the hospital and should be organized and managed as such.[8]

Among other papers[9] presented during the nursing section were two papers on the organization of nursing associations. Edith A.

Draper, Superintendent of the Illinois Training School, spoke on the necessity of an American Nurses' Association to provide professional and financial assistance, promote lectures, and encourage creation of publications pertaining to nursing needs and free exchange of ideas.[10] Following Miss Draper's remarks, Isabel McIsaac, Assistant Superintendent of the Illinois Training School, identified some of the benefits of alumnae associations. At the conclusion of a discussion on these two presentations, Miss Hampton observed that the organization of alumnae associations and a superintendent's society were necessary before a larger national association could be established. To this she added that the delegates should hold a superintendents' meeting before the congress adjourned to discuss formation of a society of superintendents.

On June 15, 1893, eighteen superintendents attended a general meeting to select a committee to draw up resolutions for a society of superintendents. On June 16, 1893, these superintendents unanimously adopted resolutions to establish the American Society of Superintendents of Training Schools for Nurses which would 1) promote fellowship of members, 2) establish and maintain a universal standard of training, and 3) further the best interests of the nursing profession.

A convention of the society was called for January 10, 1894, in New York City. *The Trained Nurse* carried a notice of the meeting. Forty-four superintendents attended the meeting, chaired by Anna L. Alston, Superintendent of the Mount Sinai Training School for Nurses. The society's constitution and bylaws were approved and Linda Richards was elected president. Thus, the first national organization of superintendents of training schools for nurses in the United States was organized.

Nurses' Associated Alumnae of the United States and Canada

One of the first important projects undertaken by the society was to stimulate interest in the development of a national association of trained nurses. Two papers were prepared and presented: one by Sophia F. Palmer during the second annual convention (February, 1895) on "Training School Alumnae Associations;" the other by Lavinia L. Dock during the third annual convention (February, 1896) on "A National Association and Its Legal Organization."

Miss Palmer's address was aimed at stimulating the development of training school alumnae societies. Emphasizing the significance of the organization of nurses, Miss Palmer stated that the power of the nursing profession was dependent upon its ability to maintain the cooperation of individual nurses who had the ability to influence public opinion.[11]

The following year, Lavinia L. Dock focused her remarks on ways and means by which to establish a broad national association of nurses. Based on a careful study of the organization of national associations with local units and a review of the laws under which professional organizations could operate, Miss Dock made the following recommendations:

1) A national association of trained nurses should be based on a systematic division of responsibility. The national association should be a policy-making body which supports standards, sets forth principles of conduct, and promotes the goals and objectives of the nursing profession. The state organizations must be the working bodies.

2) Membership in a national association of trained nurses should include the graduates of those schools whose superintendents are members of the society. The graduates must be affiliated with an alumnae society.

3) It should be the responsibility of the associated alumnae of the schools of nursing to keep watch over the professional standing and general character of future candidates for membership in the organization.

4) Both the national association and state organizations should seek incorporation for purposes of stability and continuity. However, the national body should not seek a charter until the association is completely organized. (Organization would include

ISABEL HAMPTON ROBB
First President of the Nurses' Associated Alumnae

preparation of a national constitution and individual state constitutions, as well as a national code of ethics.

5) A national association of trained nurses should conform in goals and activities to professional and educational bodies.[12]

Following the discussion of Miss Dock's paper, the Committee for the Organization of a National Association for Nurses was appointed to prepare a constitution for a trained nurses' association which could be presented at the fourth annual convention of the society in 1897.[13] This committee met immediately after the close of the society's convention in February, 1896, to plan a September meeting at the Manhattan Beach Hotel in New York City. During the September meeting, ten delegates representing the oldest training school alumnae associations and five members of the organization committee: 1) selected a name for the association—Nurses' Associated Alumnae of the United States and Canada,[14] 2) set the date and place for the first meeting (February 11-12, 1897; Baltimore, Maryland), and 3) drafted a constitution and bylaws.

Nine delegates from alumnae associations and nine members of the Committee for the Organization of a National Association for Nurses were present for the 1897 meeting which was held during the society's fourth annual convention. It was agreed that these individuals and the alumnae associations they represented would be the charter members of the new organization.[15]

A constitution and bylaws were adopted. The objectives of the association were identified as follows: "To establish and maintain a code of ethics; to elevate the standard of nursing education; to promote the usefulness and honor, the financial and other interests of the nursing profession."[16] At the close of the meeting, Isabel Hampton Robb was elected president, a position she held until September, 1901.

During the association's first annual convention in 1898, Mrs. Robb reflected on the similarities and dissimilarities of the nurses' meeting during the 1893 International Congress of Charities and the first annual meeting of the Nurses' Associated

Alumnae of the United States and Canada:

> The occasions have a certain similarity, in that the former had the distinction of being the first occasion in the history of trained nursing in America on which nurses had met together to discuss affairs dealing with the various interests of their profession, while the second meeting heralds the beginning of organized work among nurses. But, from another point of view, the two meetings show a marked dissimilarity. The first presented an unorganized body of women with indefinite views and an uncertain future. To the present one we come as an organized, representative body with definite objects and ready to deal with some of the problems which, with the growth of the profession, have presented themselves for solution.[17]

Among those problems discussed at the early conventions were the establishment of an army nurse corps and the creation of an official nursing publication.

Spanish American War

An immediate problem faced by the Nurses' Associated Alumnae was the unexpected demand for wartime nursing services. Although over 400 training schools were in existence and more than 2,000 trained nurses were available, there was no organized army nurse corps at the outset of the Spanish American War in 1898. Moreover, there was no systematic method for organizing nurses for war service. A nursing force was desperately needed because of the communicable diseases (typhoid fever, malaria, and yellow fever) that afflicted many soldiers in the camps.

One of the initial acts of the delegates to the first annual convention of the Nurses' Associated Alumnae of the U.S. and Canada (April, 1898) was to offer the nursing services of representative trained nurses for any relief work that the army's medical department deemed necessary in connection with the war with Spain. When the Secretary of War failed to respond to this offer, President Isabel Hampton Robb, accompanied by a vice president, sought a personal interview with the Surgeon General. Unfortunately, they were informed that the nursing organization had not been given charge of the army's nursing department. "Visions of what splendid systematic work might be done if the nursing might only be in the hands of nurses themselves . . . floated before us, but it was not to be."[18]

At the suggestion of Dr. Anita Newcomb McGee, vice president of the Daughters of the American Revolution, the Surgeon General had authorized the DAR to act as a clearinghouse for nurse applicants.[19] During the summer of 1898, more than 8,000 nurses and non-nurses applied for nursing duty. Only nurses who were approved by the directors of the schools of nursing from which they had been graduated were accepted by a committee chaired by Dr. McGee. Some 1,200 nurses were contracted to care for patients in the general and field hospitals in the United States and Cuba.

In addition to those nurses secured by government contract, more than 200 nurses were recruited by the Red Cross Society for the Maintenance of Trained Nurses, also known as New York's Auxiliary No. 3. This auxiliary was organized for the express purpose of supplying and maintaining trained nurses in army hospitals.

Reflecting on the nursing services during the war, Mrs. Robb observed:

> The chaos and confusion that reigned supreme at first owing to the suddenness and greatness of the emergency was intensified and prolonged by the lack of experience on the part of those into whose hands the work was entrusted. This . . . resulted in much bad nursing, a worse morale, and in a total lack of standard or system . . . A certain amount of good nursing was done, but not half of what could have been accomplished with proper management.[20]

Disturbed by these nursing conditions, the Nurses' Associated

Alumnae called a meeting of women who had been actively engaged in relief work during the war. The purpose of the gathering held in New York City in December, 1898, was to explore the possibility and advisability of legislation which would place army nursing in the hands of trained nurses. Believing it would be inappropriate for the Nurses' Associated Alumnae to sponsor a bill, a special committee of nurse representatives was selected to formulate the Army Bill for Nurses.

Upon learning that Congress failed to enact this legislation, delegates to the 1900 convention of the Nurses' Associated Alumnae reaffirmed their support of the establishment of a permanent Army Nursing Service under the direction of a properly qualified trained nurse. Finally, with the enactment of the Army Reorganization Act of 1901, an army nurse corps was established under the direction of a graduate nurse.[21] This represented one of the earliest attempts of the nursing profession to promote legislation which established a standard or criteria of competency and ensured supervision of nurses by nurses.

At the same time that the association was waging a campaign to secure an army nurse corps, attempts were being made to establish a professional journal. The publication of a nursing magazine was viewed as a medium for voicing professional opinion.

American Journal of Nursing

Although magazines for nurses were visible as early as 1886, they were not published by nurses nor did they represent the views of the nursing profession as a body.[22] In 1893, Edith A. Draper addressed the need for an American nurses' association which would encourage creation of publications pertaining to nursing needs and the exchange of ideas. Miss Draper's remarks were delivered to delegates attending the nursing subsection of the International Congress of Charities, Correction, and Philanthropy. A group of these delegates was instrumental in the formation of the American Society of Superintendents of Training Schools for Nurses and the Nurses' Associated Alumnae. Establishment of a magazine to promote nursing, owned and controlled by the nursing profession, was an early objective of both organizations.

At the 1895 and 1896 annual meetings of the society, delegates informally discussed the need for a magazine for nurses. In 1896, Sophia Palmer and M. E. P. Davis sought the suggestions and recommendations of the J. B. Lippincott Company in order to formulate definite plans of action for such a magazine. Believing a nursing magazine should represent the entire profession, the society (which only represented the educational interests of nursing) refrained from spearheading the project. Plans for a nursing magazine were delayed until a representative nursing body was formed in 1897.

During the first session of the first annual convention of the Nurses' Associated Alumnae in 1898, a committee was appointed to establish a nursing magazine. As Lavinia Dock pointed out, the profession should consider a nursing periodical a necessary part of professional life.[23] Although this committee was unable to produce a working plan, they did survey different alumnae associations to determine the probable circulation of a nursing magazine. They also identified two methods for establishing a journal: formation of a joint stock company or the securement of private backing.

According to the proceedings of the association's second annual convention in 1899, delegates explored the possibility of developing a nursing department in some established periodical of known merit. A committee was even formed to investigate the feasibility of developing a supplemental nursing section in the *Philadelphia Medical Journal*. Unfortunately, no record exists of the activities of this committee.

During the same convention, a committee on ways and means of producing a magazine was reorganized.[24] As a result of planning meetings in January, 1900, the committee took the initiative to organize a stock company. Shares of $100 each were sold only to nurses or to nurses' alumnae associations, thus ensuring professional control of the magazine.[25] By May, 1900, the committee was able to guarantee the sale of twenty-four shares of stock, totaling $2,400.[26] Moreover, 462 individual nurses had promised to subscribe to the organization's journal. At the third annual convention of the Nurses' Associated Alumnae held on May 3-5, 1900, the committee presented its report. Acknowledging the fact that the committee had overstepped its authority by forming a stock company, committee chairman M. E. P. Davis asked delegates to entrust the committee with the power to act on the recommendation that: the printing, binding, proofreading, mailing, and copyrighting of the publication be turned over to an established publishing company which would furnish a business manager.

After a discussion of the subject, it was voted that the committee be given full authority to establish a magazine upon the lines which had been formulated, including the formation of a stock company.

The J. B. Lippincott Company of Philadelphia was chosen publisher of the magazine, titled the *American Journal of Nursing*. Sophia Palmer assumed the responsibilities of editor of the journal, a position she maintained for twenty years.

The first issue of the *American Journal of Nursing* was scheduled for mailing on October 1, 1900. It was discovered, however, that the magazine could not be mailed because the journal's stockholders were not incorporated. No one was authorized to distribute the magazine as required by the U.S. postal authorities. In order to expedite the mailing of 2,500 copies of the first issue, M. E. P. Davis and Sophia Palmer assumed personal responsibility for all liabilities of the journal.[27]

Although the journal was initially financed by alumnae associations and individual nurses, it was regarded the official organ of the nursing profession. It was assumed that, in time, the Nurses' Associated Alumnae would take over the stock. The first share of stock owned by the association was donated by Lavinia Dock at the convention in May, 1904. The association was not able to secure ownership of all journal stock until 1912.

By 1900, nursing was acquiring the basic earmarks of a profession, including a national organization and a journal controlled by nurses. In a short twenty-five year period, nurses were able to identify their major weaknesses as a profession and determine an effective course of action. As Isabel Hampton Robb pointed out, "We close . . . the first quarter of a century of our history with the knowledge that our chief weakness during these years has come from the rapid increase in numbers, from the want of a professional and educational standard and from the scattering of our forces from lack of organization . . ." Mrs. Robb concluded, "We are fortunate in having discovered our weakest points at so early a period in our career."[28]

REFERENCES

1. Isabel Hampton Robb, "President's Address," *Proceedings of the Third Annual Convention (May 3-5, 1900) of the Associated Alumnae of Trained Nurses* (Cleveland: J. B. Savage Print, 1900), 46.
2. A. M. Carr-Saunders, "Professionalization in Historical Perspective, " in *Professionalization* ed. by Howard Vollmer and Donald Mills (New Jersey: Prentice Hall, 1966), 6.
3. The establishment of a national association was complicated by interest in the creation of an organization which would assume responsibility for the registration of nurses. This stipulation infringed upon the role of the state to establish safeguards for the welfare of its citizenry.
4. Isabel Hampton Robb, "President's Address," *Proceedings of the Second Annual Convention (May 1-2, 1899) of the Associated Alumnae of Trained Nurses* (Cleveland: J. B. Savage, 1899), 30.
5. The first structured and incorporated association to be organized.
6. Isabel Hampton, "Educational Standards for Nurses," in *Nursing of the Sick—1893* by Hampton et al. (New York: McGraw-Hill Book Company, 1949), 5.
7. Lavinia L. Dock, "The Relation of Training Schools to Hospitals," in *Nursing of the Sick—1893* by Isabel Hampton et al. (New York: McGraw-Hill Book Company, 1949), 17.
8. Louis Darche, "Proper Organization of Training Schools in America," in *Nursing of the Sick—1893* by Isabel Hampton et al. (New York: McGraw-Hill Book Company, 1949), 101.
9. A highlight of the program was the reading of a paper prepared by Florence Nightingale on curative and preventive nursing.
10. The text of this paper appears in Appendix II.
11. Sophia F. Palmer, "Training School Alumnae Associations," *Reports of the First (Jan. 10, 1894) and Second (Feb. 13, 1895) Annual Conventions of the American*

Society of Superintendents of Training Schools for Nurses (Harrisburg, Pa.: Harrisburg Publishing Co., 1897), 56 (proceedings of second convention).
12. Lavinia L. Dock, "A National Association for Nurses and Its Legal Organization," *Trained Nurse,* Vol. XVI (April, 1896), 173-185.
13. The following individuals comprised the committee: Lavinia Dock (chairman), M. Isabel Merritt, Isabel McIsaac, M. B. Brown, Lucy Walker, M. Adelaide Nutting, Edith A. Draper, Mary Agnes Snively, Anne Maxwell, Florence Hutchinson, Isabel Hampton Robb and Sophia F. Palmer.
14. Also referred to as Associated Alumnae of Trained Nurses of the U.S. and Canada.
15. The list of names, as recorded in the minutes, is as follows: Members—M. B. Brown, Massachusetts General; L. L. Dock, Secretary and Chairman, Constitutional Convention; Edith Draper, formerly of the Royal Victoria; Isabel Merritt, Brooklyn City; Isabel McIsaac, Illinois; Anna Maxwell, Presbyterian of New York; Adelaide Nutting, Johns Hopkins, Isabel Hampton Robb, Cleveland; M. A. Snively, Toronto General. Alumnae association representatives—Phebe W. Brown, Illinois; Ella Clapp, New Haven; Laura Healy, Brooklyn City; Mrs. J. R. Hawley, Philadelphia; Margaret A. Mullen, Garfield; Miss Barnard, Johns Hopkins; M. W. Stevenson, Massachusetts General; C. Borden, Farrand, Lena Walden, New York.
16. *Nurses' Associated Alumnae of the U.S. and Canada, Minutes,* February 11-12, 1897, Baltimore, Maryland, 11.
17. Isabel Hampton Robb, "President's Address," *Proceedings of the First Annual Convention (April 28-29), 1898) of the Associated Alumnae of Trained Nurses* (New York: O'Donnell Bros., 1898), 18.
18. Isabel Hampton Robb, "President's Address," *Proceedings of the Second Annual Convention (May 1-2, 1899) of the Associated Alumnae of Trained Nurses* (Cleveland: J. B. Savage, 1899), 33.
19. Dr. McGee established standards of admission, as well as a system of record-keeping, which provided the basis for permanent records when the Army Nurse Corps was organized. In early autumn, 1898, she was appointed Acting Assistant Surgeon General in charge of the Army Nurse Division. At that time, she terminated the assistance of the DAR.
20. Isabel Hampton Robb, "President's Address," *Proceedings of the Second Annual Convention (May 1-2, 1899) of the Associated Alumnae of Trained Nurses* (Cleveland: J. B. Savage, 1899), 33.
21. Dr. McGee, at the request of the Surgeon General, had written the section of the act dealing with the Army Nurse Corps. Upon her resignation from the Army Nurse Division, Dita H. Kinney (a trained nurse) was appointed Superintendent of the U.S. Army Nurse Corps.
22. *The Trained Nurse,* established in 1888, served as the sounding board for nursing groups until the *American Journal of Nursing* distributed its first issue in 1900.
23. Lavinia L. Dock, "Discussion," *Proceedings of the First Annual Convention (April 28-29), 1898) of the Associated Alumnae of Trained Nurses* (New York: O'Donnell Bros., 1898), 10.
24. The committee was composed of M. E. P. Davis (chairman), Harriet Fulmer, M. Adelaide Nutting, Sophia Palmer, Isabel Hampton Robb and M. W. Stevenson.
25. Although the committee allowed individual nurses and alumnae associations to purchase stock, they considered the stock held in trust for the Nurses' Associated Alumnae until it could afford to own the company.
26. The first stockholders included: No. 1, Linda Richards; No. 2, Sophia Palmer; No. 3,

Ida Palmer; No. 4, Isabel Hampton Robb; No. 5, Lavinia Dock; and No. 6, M. Adelaide Nutting.

27. Finally, in October, 1902, the stockholders were incorporated and a board of directors was elected.

28. Isabel Hampton Robb, "President's Address," *Proceedings of the Second Annual Convention (May 1-2, 1899) of the Associated Alumnae of Trained Nurses* (Cleveland: J. B. Savage, 1899), 31.

1900-1910

Struggle for Legal Safeguards

Between 1900 and 1911, the nursing profession "came of age." As Annie Damer[1] so aptly explained, "Never in the history of nursing have there come times so auspicious for progress and betterment as those through which we are now passing."[2]

1) In 1900, members of the Nurses' Associated Alumnae received the initial issues of the *American Journal of Nursing,* the first American magazine for nurses, owned and operated by nurses.

2) In 1901, the Army Reorganization Act established a female army nurse corps under the direction of a graduate nurse. This legislation represented one of the earliest attempts to establish a standard of nursing performance and to ensure supervision of nurses by nurses. When Jane A. Delano, president of the Nurses' Associated Alumnae (1909-1911), became superintendent of the Army Nurse Corps in 1909, she organized the American Red Cross Nursing Service.[3] With the assistance of the Nurses' Associated Alumnae and the American Red Cross, a system was developed to maintain a nursing service which could be engaged in the event of national or international emergencies.

3) In 1901, the first state nurses' associations were organized to work toward state laws to control nursing practice. By 1903, legislation concerning registration for nurses had been enacted in

North Carolina, New York, New Jersey, and Virginia.

4) In 1901, American nurses took preliminary steps to branch out into international service. The Nurses' Associated Alumnae affiliated with the American Society of Superintendents of Training Schools for Nurses to form the American Federation of Nurses for the purpose of applying for membership in the National Council of Women. Membership in the national council lead to participation in the International Council of Women. Finally, in 1905, the American Federation of Nurses withdrew from the National Council of Women and became one of three charter members of the International Council of Nurses, founded in 1900 to promote self-government by nurses. It is now considered the oldest continuously functioning international council.

5) During the early part of the twentieth century, the Superintendent's Society and the Nurses' Associated Alumnae worked diligently to maintain a hospital economics course at Teachers' College (Columbia University).[4] In 1907, Columbia University established a department of household administration which included provisions for the hospital economics course. In the same year, Mary Adelaide Nutting was appointed professor of institutional administration, the first nurse to occupy a university chair. In 1909, the first complete university school of nursing was organized at the University of Minnesota.

Nursing made more professional strides in the first decade of the twentieth century than in all the years preceding this time.

The twentieth century has been labeled the century of social consciousness due to the fact that pioneer individualism gave way to group cooperation. The growth of the Nurses' Associated Alumnae is indicative of this trend. When the Nurses' Associated Alumnae held its first annual convention in 1898, twenty-nine delegates, representing twenty-three alumnae associations, attended. Membership in the association totaled 1,654 trained nurses.[5] By 1910, membership in the Nurses' Associated Alumnae numbered 14,997. Two hundred fifteen delegates, representing 135 alumnae associations, 31 state associations, and 22 county and city associations, attended the thirteenth annual convention in 1910.[6]

The expanding interests of the organization were reflected in the variety of convention programs presented between 1900 and 1911. By 1904, convention sessions were divided into program sections chaired by alumnae and state associations and, in 1910, a special convention session was established for private duty nurses. Delegates to these conventions considered such topics as "How to Bring Skilled Nursing to People of Moderate Means," "The Necessity for and Development of Post-Graduate Work for Graduate Nurses," "How to Organize for Registration," "Psychology and Nursing," and "Examining Boards of Nurses and Their Powers." Convention delegates not only dealt with professional problems, but also considered the implications of pressing social issues, including women's suffrage, child labor, and sex education. As Lavinia L. Dock pointed out at the association's tenth annual convention, it was essential that nurses, as trained workers, exercise social awareness.[7]

State Registration for Nurses

The most pressing problem confronting nurses at the turn of the twentieth century was the regulation of training schools. The increasing number of hospitals throughout the country had brought about a corresponding increase in the number of schools of nursing. Early investigations suggested that the practical and theoretical instruction in these institutions was inconsistent.

It became apparent to nursing leadership that if nurses were to assume professional roles, legislation was needed to protect the public from poorly prepared nurses. It was proposed that a system of registration be devised whereby nurse graduates would be required to conform to standards established by the profession before permission to practice nursing could be granted. In 1900, Isabel Hampton Robb, first president of the Nurses' Associated Alumnae, pointed out that nursing would be unable to attain "its full dignity as a recognized profession" until there was a complete system of registration.[8] This observation was reinforced in 1902 by her predecessor, Annie Damer, who stated that nurses had reached the time when they "should demand recognition as a profession through granting of a proper certificate by a state constituted and maintained board of examiners."[9] (An essential component of nursing legislation was provision for state boards of nurse examiners.)

The issue of enforcement of nursing education standards became so important that state nurses' associations were organized to work for the passage of nurse practice acts. As early as 1901, state societies were promoting legislation which would standardize nurse training as well as regulate nursing practice. More importantly, these societies began waging campaigns to convince state legislatures that the nursing profession should be responsible for determining standards of nursing education and nursing practice.

Since the first gathering of nurses in 1893, nursing leaders had focused on the establishment of a superintendent's society and alumnae associations as the basis for a larger national association. Membership in the national association was to include only nurses who were members of school alumnae associations. Consequently, when the Nurses' Associated Alumnae was formed in 1897, membership eligibility was spelled out as follows:

> Alumnae associations of schools of nursing connected with general hospitals of not less than one hundred beds, giving not less than two full years of training in the hospital, shall be eligible for membership in this association, by sending thereto accredited delegates and paying annual dues.[10]

As a result of the growth of state nurses' associations, the membership component of the Nurses' Associated Alumnae became a point of contention.[11] It was recognized that the main objectives of establishing a state association were distinctly different from those of an alumnae association which was developed to further the interests of the school, promote fellowship, assist nurses in times of sickness, and establish annuity funds. The purpose of the state association was to influence legislation affecting nursing and to provide nurses, no longer living near their alumnae chapters, an instrument through which to enunciate their opinions about nursing matters in their state of residence.

Although Article V of the Nurses' Associated Alumnae's first constitution provided guidelines for state and provincial associations, organization of such societies could come about only:

> Whenever there shall be not less than three eligible alumnae associations in a state or province it shall be the duty of these alumnae to organize a state or provincial association; provided that they shall first have joined this association . . .[12]

Changes in Membership Requirements

Two of the earliest proposed amendments to the constitution were: 1) the addition of the associate membership[13] consisting of duly elected delegates representing alumnae associations of small general hospitals whose superintendents were eligible for membership in the American Society of Superintendents of Training Schools for Nurses,[14] and 2) the admission of other local organizations and societies to full membership, provided that these groups have the same requirements for admission as the national alumnae (two full years of training in a general hospital).[15]

Inasmuch as the constitution was drawn up for alumnae associations, the president of the Nurses' Associated Alumnae, Isabel Robb, pointed out that the adoption of these amendments would involve massive reorganization, including a name change. She, therefore, proposed that New York State nurses come together to form a nucleus upon which a state society could be built; that the constitution be waived until 1901; and that the New York association report its requirements at the next convention and apply for affiliation with the national association.[16]

Although Mrs. Robb had originally proposed that the alumnae

association serve as the basic unit of the national nursing organization, she recognized the significance of the state society.

> Remember that our object in associating is to advance the interests of the whole nursing profession and not merely those of any one association. After deciding upon the formation of local associations we trust steps may very soon be taken to formulate state associations . . . Before we meet again, we look for the formation of at least one state association, *the last link in the chain of organization.*[17]

When the secretary of the Nurses' Associated Alumnae sent out information about the fourth annual convention (1901) in Buffalo, she also suggested that each alumnae association explore the advisability of establishing an auxiliary membership entitling nurses, who were not affiliated with an alumnae organization, privileges of the Nurses' Associated Alumnae, excluding voting rights. During the convention, only a limited amount of business was conducted and no papers or discussion were prepared. Instead delegates attended the program sessions of the International Congress of Nurses. No mention was made of the work to organize a New York State nurses' association. However, at the request of Isabel Hampton Robb, a five-member committee on bylaw revision was appointed to deal with the auxiliary membership question as well as other issues.

In 1902, Annie Damer, president of the Nurses' Associated Alumnae, observed:

> Our alumnae associations have multiplied all over the country, but with them have grown up a number of associations of equal standing, formed of nurses many of whom have removed from the neighborhood of their school and who feel the need of fellowship and mutual effort and aid. To many it seems advisable that these societies should become a part of our national association . . .[18]

By 1902, the Committee on the Revision of the Constitution

had rewritten the constitution and bylaws and presented the draft to the delegates of the fifth annual convention. The proposed eligibility clause read as follows:

> Nursing organizations whose members are graduates from general hospitals giving not less than two full years of training in the hospital shall be eligible for membership in this association by sending thereto accredited delegates and paying annual dues.[19]

Those who opposed the change in eligibility requirements argued that the organization was too young to make such a radical departure from the original plan of composition. Although the clause was amended to include the statement, "such societies to be acceptable to this society,"[20] delegates delayed action on the question of eligibility.[21]

Membership eligibility was still a burning issue during the sixth annual convention in 1903. In an effort to secure registration, state nurses' associations were forced to establish minimum standards which did not measure up to the eligibility criteria set by the Nurses' Associated Alumnae. Consequently, delegates were divided into two factions: those who supported the original standards of eligibility based on affiliation with alumnae associations and those who supported the union of state associations. The conflict was not resolved at the 1903 convention.

Finally, in 1904, the revisions of the bylaws were approved. The eligibility clause, as adopted, contained two unique features: 1) the period of training was lengthened to three years, and 2) it was acknowledged that nurse training could be obtained in one or more hospitals or include a term in a recognized technical school.[22]

Recognizing that the articles on eligibility might require periodic alteration, the committee on constitutional revision placed the membership criteria in the bylaws section. This made it possible to amend the requirements without seeking a change in the incorporation papers.[23]

The revised eligibility clause appeared to satisfy all delegates.

On the one hand, proponents of rigid standards were able to elevate the educational requirements. On the other hand, in the event state associations were prevented from affiliating with the national association, revision of the membership standards was now feasible.

Moreover, an apparent trend was beginning to develop which would enhance the affiliation of state associations with the national association. The issue of interstate reciprocity presented a natural lever for those state associations attempting to convince legislatures to upgrade nursing standards. As Mary Adelaide Nutting pointed out in a 1904 presentation on "State Reciprocity," it was the duty of the nursing organization to encourage state legislatures to establish a standard for nurses high enough to insure the interstate mobility of nurses.[24]

In 1906, convention delegates proposed the establishment of an interstate committee composed of state association presidents and secretaries of other affiliated societies. The purpose of the committee was to facilitate the dissemination of legislative information among states. Although the committee was short-lived, it reflected the desire to unite state associations. In the same year, the office of an interstate secretary was created to assist in organizing state associations.[25]

By 1907, there were twenty-eight state nurses' associations. Twenty-one were affiliated with the Nurses' Associated Alumnae and fifteen had secured state legislation setting guidelines for nursing education and nursing practice. It was becoming apparent to more members of the Nurses' Associated Alumnae that the state organization was the appropriate working unit of the national association.

Moreover, city and county associations were also gaining recognition. During the 1907 convention, a motion was adopted that the Board of Directors be instructed to recommend amendments to the bylaws which would provide for the admission of local organizations maintaining desired standards of eligibility. The proposal was prompted by the migration of many eastern nurses to western states where nurses had not organized. The delegate who presented the motion observed, "Why should we not become a representative body of all the nurses, not simply representing the schools, but representing the nurse body as a whole?"[26]

The following year the board of directors discussed the admission of city and county associations. Upon their recommendation, delegates to the 1908 convention amended the association's bylaws to include the admission of these local societies on the same basis as state associations.

By 1909, nurses were presented with several avenues of entry into the Nurses' Associated Alumnae. Delegates to the twelfth annual convention represented 136 alumnae associations, 28 state associations, and 18 county and city associations. Reorganization was the key issue of the 1909 convention. As the association president pointed out, "Our society has been growing up under the alumnae association. We had no state societies when our alumnae were first organized and now we are admitting city and county associations and we want some better plan of affiliation, so that we can work upon a better basis."[27]

A committee was appointed to develop a report on reorganization. Among the issues to be examined were individual and federated membership and state representation.[28]

Delegates to the thirteenth annual convention in 1910 voted that membership in the association remain federated. The recommendation concerning state representation was referred back to the committee on revision to be reintroduced the following year. Finally in 1911, delegates to the fourteenth annual convention took definite action to realign the membership component. The amendment to the article on eligibility, as adopted, read:

> Any state, county or city association or one of national character which shall be approved by the Eligibility Committee shall be eligible for membership. Any alumnae association from a school which gives its pupils three years training in a hospital or giving them

> an equivalent training in a professional school and hospital or in one or more hospitals shall be eligible for membership.[29]

The representation of these affiliate organizations was also changed. Alumnae associations were entitled to one delegate for every fifty members and state nurses' associations were entitled to one delegate in addition to the president.

Although the organization redirected its efforts to unifying state societies, alumnae associations still retained the key responsibility for determining individual membership.

Official recognition of the different types of group membership necessitated a change in the association's name. Suggestions ranged from the American Graduate Nurses' Association to the American Federation of Nurses. However, delegates to the 1911 convention decided upon the "American Nurses' Association" as the title most reflective of the organization's composition. In November, 1911, permission was granted by District Court in New York to change the name of the association.[31]

At the same time that the Nurses' Associated Alumnae was re-evaluating the relationship of its constituent societies, it was also exploring relationships with other nursing organizations.

American Federation of Nurses

The first example of affiliation of the Nurses' Associated Alumnae with another organization occurred when the American Federation of Nurses was organized in 1901.

In 1898, the National Council of Women of the United States invited the various nursing groups across the country to unite for the purpose of obtaining membership in the Council. Since the Nurses' Associated Alumnae was newly formed, the executive committee chose to delay action on the invitation until the association was incorporated and more thoroughly organized.

In 1900, the Nurses' Associated Alumnae adopted a resolution to affiliate with the American Society of Superintendents of Training Schools for Nurses for the purpose of applying for membership in the National Council of Women.[32] The federation of the two groups was deemed worthwhile for several reasons:

1) Through the forum of the national council, the nursing profession could make its work and needs known as well as receive the help and support of a united force,

2) Through membership in the National Council of Women, nurses could be associated with the activities of the most outstanding women's organization in the United States,[33] and

3) Affiliation with the national council could lead to affiliation with the International Council of Women which had a section set apart for consideration of questions of special interest to nurses.

In 1901, the federation made formal application and was accepted for membership in the National Council of Women, composed of representatives of eighteen national organizations. Affiliation with the national council was viewed by the Nurses' Associated Alumnae as a means for completing the chain of organization for nurses. On the local level the graduate nurse could affiliate with her alumnae association which, together with other alumnae associations, constituted the Nurses' Associated Alumnae, the representative body at the national level. With the acceptance of the American Federation of Nurses in the National Council of Women, members of the Nurses' Associated Alumnae and the American Society of Superintendents of Training Schools for Nurses were entitled to representation at the international level through the International Council of Women.

Between 1901 and 1904, the federation functioned informally without constitution and bylaws. In 1904, the American Federation of Nurses, the National Council of Nurses of England, and the German Nurses' Association were invited to join the International Council of Nurses.[34] As a result of this invitation, the federation held a meeting on May 3, 1905, at which time: a constitution and bylaws were adopted; membership was withdrawn from the National Council of Women; and the invitation of ICN membership was accepted.[35] Mary Adelaide Nutting became the first president of the federation and remained its president until it was dissolved in 1913 and the American Nurses' Association (Nurses' Associated Alumnae of the United States) became the official representative to the International Council of Nurses.

By the end of 1911, fourteen years after the establishment of the national organization of training school alumnae associations, the American Nurses' Association emerged as the representative body of American nurses. Through the vehicle of the constituent association and representation on the International Council of Nurses, the American Nurses' Association was able to assume the role of national and international spokesman for the nursing profession of the United States.

THE CORPORATE SEAL OF THE AMERICAN NURSES' ASSOCIATION

Between 1911 and 1912, consideration was given to the creation of a corporate seal for the American Nurses' Association. Records show that the seal which was finally adopted was in the form of a circle designed about the figure of "America's first trained nurse," Linda Richards, around which were the words "Service, Humanity, Efficiency," and bearing the date "1873." 1873 is outstanding in the history of nursing in the United States as the year in which the first three schools of nursing were established in this country according to the Nightingale Plan.

REFERENCES

1. Miss Damer served as president of the Nurses' Associated Alumnae from 1901 to 1902 and again from 1905 to 1909.
2. Annie Damer, "President's Address," Proceedings of the Sixth Annual Convention (June 10-12, 1903), *American Journal of Nursing,* Vol. III (August, 1903), 843.
3. Eventually, she resigned her Army Nurse Corps position to become full-time director of the Department of Nursing of the American Red Cross.
4. The program in hospital economics was opened in 1899.
5. "Alumnae Associations and Members Belonging to the National Association," *Proceedings of the First Annual Convention (April 28-29, 1898) of the Associated Alumnae of Trained Nurses* (New York: O'Donnell Bros., 1898), 45-76.
6. Proceedings of the Thirteenth Annual Convention (May 18-21, 1910) of the Nurses' Associated Alumnae of the United States, *American Journal of Nursing,* Vol. X (August, 1910), 803.
7. Lavinia L. Dock, "Some Urgent Social Claims," Proceedings of the Tenth Annual Convention (May 14-16, 1907) of the Nurses' Associated Alumnae of the United States, *American Journal of Nursing,* Vol. VII (August, 1907), 898.
8. Isabel Hampton Robb, "President's Address," *Proceedings of the Third Annual Convention (May 3-5, 1900) of the Associated Alumnae of Trained Nurses* (Cleveland: J. B. Savage Print, 1900), 46.
9. Annie Damer, "President's Address," Minutes of the Proceedings of the Fifth Annual Convention (May 1-3, 1902) of the Nurses' Associated Alumnae, *American Journal of Nursing,* Vol. II (July, 1902), 752.
10. "Eligibility," Article III, *Constitution and By-Laws of the Nurses' Associated Alumnae of the U.S. and Canada,* 1897, 5.
11. The membership issue was not resolved until ANA's House of Delegates voted, at the thirty-fifth (1944) convention, that association membership was not dependent upon membership in an alumnae association.
12. "State and Provincial Associations," Article V, *Constitution and By-Laws of the Nurses' Associated Alumnae of U.S. and Canada,* 1897, 6.
13. *Proceedings of the Second Annual Convention (May 1-2, 1899) of the Associated Alumnae of Trained Nurses* (Cleveland: J. B. Savage, 1899), 18.
14. Objection was raised to the reference to the society. The observation was made that it was inappropriate to use the society of teachers as a gauge for eligibility for membership in a society of trained nurses.
15. *Proceedings of the Third Annual Convention (May 3-5, 1900) of the Associated Alumnae of Trained Nurses* (Cleveland: J. B. Savage Print, 1900), 28-29.
16. Isabel Hampton Robb, *Proceedings of the Third Annual Convention (May 3-5, 1900) of the Associated Alumnae of Trained Nurses* (Cleveland: J. B. Savage Print, 1900), 33.
17. *Ibid.,* 44.
18. Annie Damer, "President's Address," Proceedings of the Fifth Annual Convention (May 1-3, 1902) of the Nurses' Associated Alumnae, *American Journal of Nursing,* Vol. II (June, 1902), 751.
19. Proceedings of the Fifth Annual Convention (May 1-3, 1902) of the Nurses' Associated Alumnae, *American Journal of Nursing,* Vol. II (July, 1902), 766.
20. *Ibid.,* 791.
21. Prior to the fourth annual convention, in April, 1901, the association was

incorporated as a membership society. Consequently, those articles of the constitution which were included in the incorporation papers could no longer be changed without an act of the New York State Legislature. Delegates to the 1902 convention accepted the articles of the constitution as embodied in the incorporation, but delayed action on the bylaws.

22. "Alumnae associations whose members are graduates from general hospitals giving not less than three full years of training in the hospital, which training may be obtained in one or more hospitals, or include a term in a recognized technical school, shall be eligible for membership in this association by sending thereto accredited delegates and paying annual dues." ("Eligibility," By-Law I, *Constitution and By-Laws of the Nurses Associated Alumnae of the U.S.* in Proceedings of the Seventh Annual Convention (May 12-14, 1904) of the Nurses Associated Alumnae of the U.S., *American Journal of Nursing,* Vol. IV (July, 1904), 812.)
23. The Articles of Incorporation include the objects of the association, the corporate name of the asssociation, the territory of operation of the association, and the number of directors of the association.
24. Mary Adelaide Nutting, "State Reciprocity," Proceedings of the Seventh Annual Convention (May 12-14, 1904) of the U.S., *American Journal of Nursing,* Vol. IV (July, 1904), 779-785.
25. The organization was not able to provide the Inter-State Secretary with a salary until 1910.
26. Miss Jamieson, Proceedings of the Tenth Annual Convention (May 14-16, 1907) of the Nurses' Associated Alumnae of the U.S., *American Journal of Nursing,* Vol. VII (August, 1907), 894.
27. Annie Damer, Proceedings of the Twelfth Annual Convention (June 9-11, 1909), *American Journal of Nursing,* Vol. IX (September, 1909), 962.
28. Other issues included frequency of national meetings, establishment of an advisory council and dues increase, to name only a few.
29. "Membership," Article I, Section 1, *By-Laws of the American Nurses' Association,* 1911, 3-4.
30. This title was first suggested in 1889 as the appropriate name of a national nurses' organization.
31 In 1914, it was discovered that the 1911 amendment regarding the name of the organization had been improperly filed as the "American Association of Graduate Nurses." Under the state law of New York, the "American Nurses' Association" was not recognized as the organization's corporate title until 1914.
32. It was necessary for the two nursing organizations to create one national body, inasmuch as only one representative nursing group from each nation could participate in the International Council of Women.
33. During the fourth annual convention of the Nurses' Associated Alumnae in 1901, Mrs. Ethel Gordon Fenwick noted that a national women's organization could not effectively represent women of the United States, if the nursing profession was not affiliated with the group.
34. In July, 1900, a committee adopted a constitution and elected officers for the International Council of Nurses. Establishment of the international nursing organization was a by-product of an 1899 meeting of the International Congress of Women in London.
35. No further meetings of the American Federation of Nurses were held.

1912-1922

Signs of Growth

During ANA's nineteenth annual convention in 1916, Annie W. Goodrich observed that "another year has rolled by and we have met to discuss again our problems that do not seem to lessen, but rather increase with time, nor would we have it otherwise, for problems and progress go hand in hand."[1] She added, "The most casual observer of our program could not fail to note the rapid growth and expansion of our profession."[2]

In the decade between 1912 and 1922, nurses were faced with some sobering circumstances. The American Nurses' Association had experienced extensive expansion in a relatively short span of time. In attempting to keep pace with the needs of a young and growing profession, ANA had exceeded its legal limits as a membership corporation. At the same time that the nurses' association was faced with the problems of devising a more effective plan of organization, the profession was faced with a health crisis caused by a world war. Efforts were divided between provision of adequate nursing services to civilian and military populations and revision of the structure of the association.

National Public Health Nursing Organization

Between 1900 and 1910, there was a marked increase in the work of visiting nurses in cities and rural communities. Nurses

Between 1900 and 1910 there was a marked increase in the work of visiting nurses in cities and rural communities. Circa 1900.—Courtesy Nursing Archives, Mugar Memorial Library, Boston University.

were identified as the group of workers best equipped to disseminate knowledge and provide services aimed at health maintenance and disease prevention. In order to meet the demands for nurses to engage in public health movements, a number of societies were hastily established to organize visiting nurses. Unfortunately, these groups made no attempt to create uniform requirements for visiting nurses. By 1912, nursing leaders recognized the need to establish standards for visiting nurses in the United States. Both the American Nurses' Association and the National League of Nursing Education (formerly the American Society of Superintendents of Training Schools for Nurses) agreed that the standardization of visiting nurses would be most effectively achieved through the organization of a national visiting nurses association.[3]

In January, 1912, the two organizations commissioned a joint committee, chaired by Lillian D. Wald, to consider standardization of visiting nurses. This committee sent out 1,092 letters to organizations engaged in visiting and public health nursing. The letter requested that delegates be sent to ANA's annual convention in June to consider formation of a national public health organization. In the presence of 69 delegates, representing a portion of these organizations, the committee made two recommendations:

1) That a national visiting nurse association be formed and become a member of the American Nurses' Association, and

2) That certain standards be recommended to all organizations employing visiting nurses:

   a. That the nurse be twenty-five years of age and a graduate of a recognized general hospital of not less than fifty beds, providing a course of training of not less than two years, with obstetrics, and
   b. That a nurse applying from a state where state registration pertains be a graduate of a hospital acceptable to the state board of registration.

The committee encouraged the delegates to establish an association composed of a federation of organizations with provisions for individual membership. On June 7, 1912, the National Organization for Public Health Nursing[5] was formed

> to stimulate the general public and the visiting nurse associations to the extension and support of public health nursing service, to facilitate harmonious cooperation among the workers and supporters, to develop a standard of ethics and technique, and to act as a clearinghouse for information for those interested in such work.[6]

Affiliation of Nursing Organizations

The year 1912 not only marked the formation of a third national nurses' organization, but also the formal affiliation of the three organizations—the American Nurses' Association, the National League of Nursing Education, and the National Organization for Public Health Nursing.

During the last session of ANA's fifteenth annual convention, delegates were asked to consider an amendment to the ANA Bylaws which would increase the number of members on the board of directors. The purpose of the amendment was to create ex officio positions on the executive committee and board of directors for the presidents of NLNE and NOPHN. The proposal was adopted without discussion.

In 1913, the three organizations began holding joint conventions.[7] In 1916, membership in the American Nurses' Association became a prerequisite for active membership in the National League of Nursing Education. Inasmuch as the National Organization for Public Health Nursing included lay members, ANA membership could not be an eligibility requirement in the NOPHN.

Legal Issues

Eleven years after the American Nurses' Association (Nurses' Associated Alumnae) was incorporated under the laws of New

York State, it was apparent that the incorporation charter was too restrictive. Both the membership and the programs of the association had greatly expanded. A number of questions arose:

—Was it lawful to establish a central headquarters or hold annual meetings outside of New York?

—Was the board of directors liable for the debts of the *American Journal of Nursing?*

—Was it lawful to continue to administer the Nurses' Relief Fund and various scholarship programs under existing corporate status?

—Was it lawful to allow the presidents of NLNE and NOPHN to retain ex officio positions (minus voting rights) on ANA's Board of Directors?

—Was it lawful to designate state associations as the organization's basic membership unit (as opposed to individual members)?

In 1914, a special committee sought the advice of legal counsel, Walter R. Herrick. He informed ANA leadership that the structure and programs of the organization, as set forth in the bylaws, exceeded the limits of its legal charter. Upon his advice, a committee on bylaw revision proposed several amendments to the bylaws during the eighteenth annual convention in 1915. Delegates voted to eliminate the executive committee of the board of directors inasmuch as it represented a body of purely nominal power and authority. In compliance with the membership corporation law which dictated the use of the delegate convention system, delegates acted to substitute the words "annual convention" for "annual meeting" throughout the bylaws. After determining that the Nurses' Relief Fund, established by ANA in 1911, was not a mutual benefit fund which would require separate incorporation, delegates adopted a motion to extend the purposes of the existing Articles of Incorporation to include the administration of the fund.

Unfortunately, these amendments did not resolve the most serious problems facing ANA: the legality of the presidents of

NLNE and NOPHN serving as ex officio members of the board of directors and the legality of maintaining a variety of types of membership in the association.

According to Walter R. Herrick, no legal reason existed to prohibit the presidents of the two nursing organizations from occupying seats on ANA's Board of Directors, *provided they were elected according to law and they exercised the right to vote.* To maintain a bylaw provision that these officers automatically become ex officio members of the board was in direct contradiction to the membership's right to elect directors of their own choosing.

Delegates to the 1915 convention recommended that the Committee on Revision work cooperatively with committees of the other two national organizations on a plan to assure representation of their presidents on ANA's Board of Directors without an annual election by convention delegates.[8]

District Plan for Membership

An even more immediate problem of the association was resolution of the confusion which stemmed from duplication of membership. Between 1897 and 1901, the membership structure of the Nurses' Associated Alumnae was relatively uncomplicated.

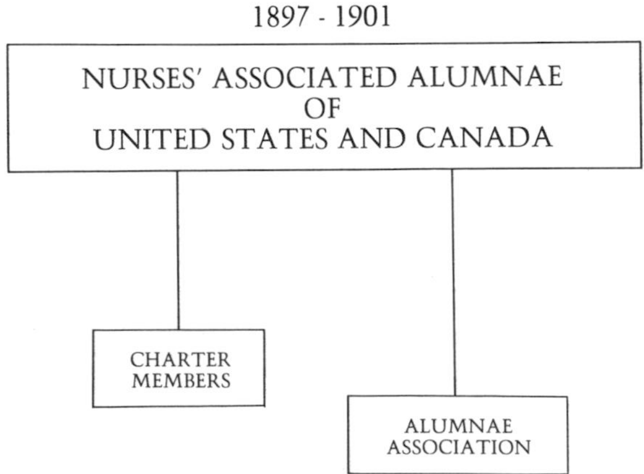

By 1915, the diversity of membership options presented problems of duplication of dues and representation at annual meetings. For example, one nurse might be counted on the membership rolls of the alumnae association as well as on the rolls of city, county, and state associations.

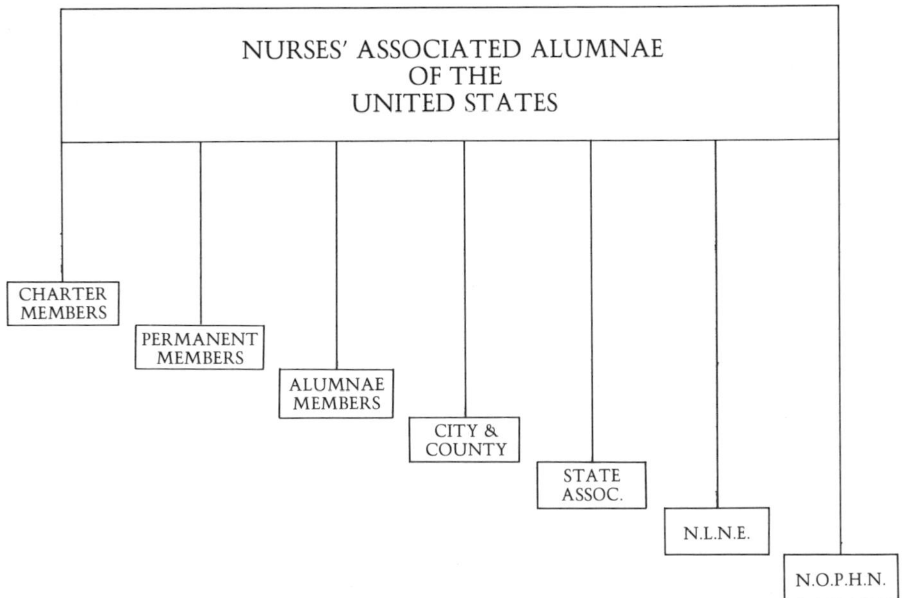

Provisions within the New York Membership Corporation Law also necessitated the restructuring of ANA membership. Under New York law, unincorporated associations and membership corporations were prohibited from maintaining membership in any other membership corporation. Moreover, delegates to annual gatherings convened by membership corporations were required to represent individual members, not constituent associations. In light of these stipulations, the articles of the bylaws referring to membership and representation were declared unlawful, because membership organizations were designated as the basic unit of the American Nurses' Association.

At the 1915 convention, delegates instructed the board of directors to appoint a committee to prepare a substitute article on membership as well as any other amendments deemed necessary.

At the suggestion of legal counsel, the Committee on Revision adopted a plan of districting the membership into state associations which would serve as the basic organizational units through which all membership would enter the national association. In drawing up the amendment, care was taken to stipulate that the basic unit of the American Nurses' Association would be the individual nurse. The following diagram reflects the plan of reorganization.

DISTRICT PLAN OF MEMBERSHIP

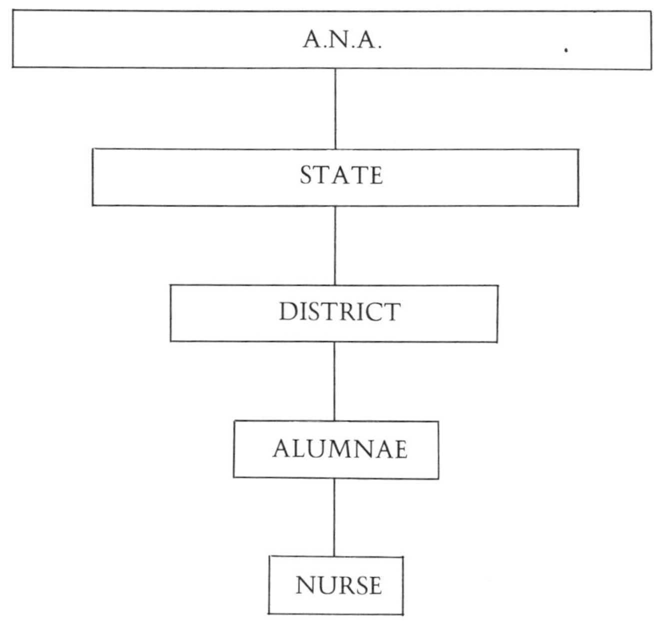

Through the district plan of membership, an individual nurse could become a member of the American Nurses' Association in one of two ways:

1) An individual nurse, maintaining membership in an alum-

nae association and residing in the proximity of the alumnae, could become a member of ANA through *district and state associations* or

2) An individual nurse, who was a non-resident of her alumnae association, could make application for membership in the *district association* within her state of residency.

The nineteenth annual convention, held in 1916, proved to be a momentous occasion in the association's history. Delegates accepted the proposed plan for the reorganization of the membership structure. In order to operationalize the plan, it was necessary to establish membership eligibility requirements which were consistent with state licensure laws. Delegates adopted an eligibility clause which differed markedly from the article on eligibility found in the original constitution and bylaws:

> Membership in this association shall consist of the members in good standing in the state associations;[9] such members of the state associations, being graduates of training schools connected with general hospitals giving a continuous training in a hospital of not less than two years or giving an equivalent training in one or more hospitals. This training must include practical experience in caring for men, women and children, together with theoretical and practical instruction in medical, surgical, obstetrical and children's nursing. The daily average number of patients shall be that established by the state nurses' association in the state from which the applicant comes, for admission to membership. In those states where nurse practice laws have been secured, registration shall be an additional qualification.[10]

Incorporation

Although ANA leadership was able to devise a plan of reorganization, it was readily apparent that a number of problems could not be resolved as long as ANA remained incorporated under the New York laws. The Committee on Revision commissioned a legal counsel to investigate a number of incorporation proposals, including secural of a national charter and incorporation under the laws of Delaware or the District of Columbia. Delegates to the 1916 convention were advised to adopt a motion to annul the New York charter and to incorporate under a national charter.

On August 5, 1916, "An Act to Incorporate the American Nurses' Association" was presented and passed by the United States Senate. This bill was introduced in the House of Representatives on September 1, 1916, at which time it was referred to committee for evaluation. Unfortunately, the critical issues posed by World War I overshadowed the charter request, which was eventually discarded.

Delegates to the 1917 ANA convention were asked to rescind the motion to secure a national charter in favor of incorporation under the laws of the District of Columbia.[11] This was accomplished without debate. Before the twentieth annual convention adjourned, the American Nurses' Association had secured a certificate of incorporation in the District of Columbia.

Certificate of Incorporation of American Nurses' Association

We, the undersigned, a majority of whom are residents of the District of Columbia, desiring to avail ourselves of the provisions of Sec. 599, *et sequitur*, of the Code of Laws of the District of Columbia, do hereby certify as follows:

1. The name or title by which this Society shall be known is American Nurses' Association.

2. The term for which it is organized shall be perpetual.

3. The purposes of this corporation are and shall be to promote the professional and educational advancement of nurses in every proper way; to elevate the standard of nursing education; to establish and maintain a code of ethics among nurses; to distribute relief among such

nurses as may become ill, disabled or destitute; to disseminate information on the subject of nursing by publications in official periodicals or otherwise; to bring into communication with each other various nurses and associations and federations of nurses throughout the United States of America; and to succeed to all rights and property held by the American Nurses' Association as a corporation duly incorporated under and by virtue of the laws of the State of New York.

4. The number of its trustees for the first year of its existence shall be thirteen.

IN WITNESS WHEREOF the undersigned Jane A. Delano, a resident of the District of Columbia, and Georgia M. Nevins, a resident of the District of Columbia, and Clara D. Noyes, a resident of the District of Columbia, and Annie W. Goodrich, a resident of the City of New York, and Sarah E. Sly, a resident of Birmingham, Michigan, have hereto set our hands and seals this 28th day of April, 1917.

JANE A. DELANO (Seal)
GEORGIA M. NEVINS (Seal)
CLARA D. NOYES (Seal)
ANNIE W. GOODRICH (Seal)
SARAH E. SLY (Seal)

Transition Period

Between 1916 and 1922, extensive reorganization took place as the state nurses' association replaced the alumnae association as the basic working unit of the national organization. In addition, ANA delegates authorized the organization of special interest sections on private duty nursing, mental hygiene, and legislation to satisfy individual nurse concerns. Through an amendment to the ANA Bylaws, a House of Delegates was created as the governing body of the association. Genevieve Cooke pointed out that the term House of Delegates "conveys an impression of a unified group, concentrating on matters of national interest and importance to our profession."[12]

ANA also discontinued its annual conventions in order to support state association conventions in alternate years. ANA's first biennial convention was held in Atlanta in 1920.

At the close of the twenty-first annual convention in 1918, the district plan of membership became effective. At that time, only twenty-four states had reorganized. Between 1918 and 1920, ANA's Committee on Revision developed a model constitution and bylaws to assist state, district, and alumnae associations in conforming to the revised membership requirements.

By 1920, membership totalled almost 35,000 nurses, an increase of 10,000 members in two years. Of the forty-seven state associations and the one territorial association (Hawaii), thirty-two had reorganized into districts. Moreover, under the reorganization plan, thirty-eight state associations had adopted a provision making the *American Journal of Nursing* their official organ.

In reading the report of the Committee on Revision to delegates of the 1920 convention, chairman Sarah E. Sly had a word of advice for the state associations:

> In building a house, one has to live in it to really know whether or not it is adapted to the needs of the family occupying it. This is equally true of the state associations which have been building new structures for their members. Readjustments have to be made, and each state must act as a clearing house in making these adjustments. This can only be done by having efficient state officers and by their hearty cooperation with the national officers.[13]

Convention delegates adopted a motion that the time limit for state associations to complete reorganization be February 1, 1921.

In 1922, the association's secretary reported that all county and alumnae associations except one had either resigned or had been dropped for nonpayment of dues.[14] Of the forty-eight state associations and the one territorial association which were organized, thirty-three had the district form of membership and seventeen had the alumnae form of membership. Fifteen of the alumnae associations had not fully completed revision of their bylaws and classified their membership according to national requirements. Consequently, the time limit for reorganization was extended to January 1, 1923, for those alumnae associations which had not completed their work.

The American Nurses' Association spent the first twenty-five years of its existence developing the most effective and efficient plan of organization. As ANA President Clara D. Noyes pointed out in 1922:

> Organization . . . is essential to the growth and development of our profession. The purpose of organization is to promote professional and educational advancement, to elevate the standards of nursing education and ultimately to improve the character of nursing care of the sick, whether it be in the field, through public health nurses; in the home, through private nurses; or in the institution, through the student and graduate nurse. Every profession has felt the necessity for organization not only for the purposes indicated above, but for protection as well.[15]

According to Annie W. Goodrich, president of the American Nurses' Association in 1918, ANA's reorganization proved to be extremely timely in light of national and international events. As she observed:

> Little did those whose vision brought these great associations of ours into such early existence, providing them with an official organ, dream of the public service they would be called upon to render and through these means, only, could effectively render. Through ever closer and closer cooperation with all sister organizations must the woman power of the country, so increasingly great, be brought to strengthen our hands so overfull and still so pitifully weak.[16]

The decade between 1912 and 1922 proved to be a milestone both in the organization of the ANA and in the growth and development of the nursing profession. As in the past, the drive for women's suffrage and the emergencies of war shed new light on the services of the nursing profession.

Nursing Services During World War I

The national emergencies which arose after the outbreak of World War I provided impetus for the women's movement. An old saying took a new twist: "A woman's place is in the war." Not only were women encouraged to enter industry and agriculture, they were offered positions in the armed forces. For the first time in history, some 216,000 women were admitted to the Army, Navy, Marines, and Coast Guard. Moreover, for the first time in history, a group of carefully selected nurses were available for military service. As ANA President Annie W. Goodrich pointed out in 1918, "For the first time in the history of our country included in the military establishment is a division of women in almost definite ratio to the number of men, one million men, ten thousand nurses. . . ."[17]

Between 1917 and 1918, nurses not only cared for patients suffering from shock, hemorrhage, and infection, they treated the victims of world-wide epidemics of influenza and pneumonia. In 1916 the War Department had estimated that 10,000 nurses (one nurse to ten hospital beds) would be needed for wartime service. By 1917, it was necessary to increase this figure to 22,000.

Over twenty-five percent (24,000) of the graduate nurses in the United States served during the "Great War." With the aid of the American Red Cross and the Committee on Nursing of the Council of National Defense, the nursing profession was able to maintain adequate nursing services for both the civilian and military populations. Historians assert that World War I, more than any previous war, helped to make Americans fully cognizant of their reliance on nursing. As Clara D. Noyes, ANA President, pointed out in 1922, "The World's War settled (if it needed settling) the question of position for the nursing profession."[18]

Twenty days after President Woodrow Wilson signed a declaration of war with Germany and its allies, ANA convened its twentieth convention in Philadelphia. Delegates, as a representative body of American nurses, took two steps. First, they unanimously adopted a motion against war:

"The American Nurses' Association, thirty-five thousand members, in convention assembled at Philadelphia, Pa., April 26 to May 2, heartily endorses war prohibition as suggested by Honorable Eugene M. Foss, of Boston, Massachusetts."[19]

Secondly, they encouraged military authorities to delineate nursing's role and define nursing's authority in military hospitals:

> This American Nurses' Association, in convention in Philadelphia, on this first day of May, 1917, would offer the following resolution:
>
> WHEREAS, it is true that nurses who are responsible for the actual nursing of the patients in the military hospitals have no authority to regulate hygienic conditions therein; and
>
> WHEREAS, this situation tends to discourage nurses from undertaking the work; and
>
> WHEREAS, this is a danger to the hospitals' population; and
>
> WHEREAS, it has been found essential in representative civil hospitals to place upon the nurses the responsibility of the care of the patients, the wards, and operating room and the cleanliness and order pertaining thereto:
>
> *Therefore, be it resolved:* that it is the sense of this meeting that the proper military authorities should be requested to specifically define the status of the nurse and confer upon her the authority necessary to control the situation, to the end that the general welfare of the sick may be promoted and a very grave danger to the well, averted.[20]

Before the close of the 1917 ANA convention, the War Department instructed the chief nurses of three base hospitals to immediately mobilize their units.[21]

The availability of trained nurses for military service did not present a problem during World War I. The problem which did exist was one of determining the most effective utilization of nursing manpower as well as identification of measures to increase nursing resources. The overriding concern of the profession was to insure adequate development of nursing resources by careful selection of students and utilization of the most effective educational techniques.

ANA's Survey of Nursing Resources—1918

In May, M. Adelaide Nutting organized the National Emergency Committee on Nursing. Shortly thereafter, the committee became the Committee on Nursing of the General Medical Board of the Council of National Defense. The efforts of the committee focused on preservation of educational standards. Committee purposes included determination of existing nurse resources, identification of plans for effective utilization of nursing manpower, and recruitment and training of student nurses.

The committee called upon Annie W. Goodrich, ANA President, to make surveys of national nursing resources and nursing in military hospitals. The American Nurses' Association delegated the task of a national survey of nursing manpower to state nurses' associations. According to Annie W. Goodrich, the value of the census was "the revelation of a very large number of nurses, not yet enrolled for war service either through the Red Cross or by direct enlistment in the Army or the Navy."[22] The survey, completed in March, 1918, revealed:

Graduate Nurses		
Registered	66,017	
Not registered	17,758	
Total graduates		83,775

Graduates in 1918		
From the 1,579 accredited schools	13,288	
From the 414 non-accredited schools	1,099	
Total graduating in 1918		14,387
Graduate nurses available at the end of 1918		98,162
Student Nurses		
In accredited schools	38,238	
In non-accredited schools	3,633	
Total student nurses in all schools		41,871[23]

Although the data was not statistically precise, the information provided a basis for wartime and postwar planning.[24]

Army School of Nursing

When Miss Goodrich began a survey of nursing in military hospitals in Spring, 1918, she requested that action be delayed on the Surgeon General's plan to employ American Red Cross aides in military hospitals. Upon completion of her survey, Miss Goodrich recommended the establishment of an army school of nursing instead of initiation of the ARC nurses' aide plan.

At the time of the joint convention of the three national nursing organizations in 1918, the War Department was examining the matter of recruitment and training of military nursing personnel. Delegates were presented with two options for boosting nurse manpower in military hospitals: 1) the ANA President's recommendation that an army school of nursing be established and 2) the recommendation of the director for the nursing department of the American Red Cross, Jane Delano, that Red Cross aides be prepared to serve in the armed services.[25] After much heated and emotional argument, convention delegates chose to support the proposal for an army school of nursing.

The Army School of Nursing was authorized by the War Department on May 25, 1918. It is suggested that establishment of this school, which was discontinued in August, 1931, played a key role in the development of American nursing. It served as an example of an institution which effectively employed principles of management and teaching.

American Nurses' Memorial

When the armistice was signed on November 11, 1918, two hundred ninety-six American nurses had died in World War I. One hundred one of them were buried in France. There was a keen desire on the part of American nurses to establish a fitting tribute to these women. With the help of the National League of Nursing Education and the National Organization for Public Health Nursing, ANA spearheaded a drive to secure the Florence Nightingale School of Nursing at Bordeaux, France, as a memorial to American nurses. United States nurses contributed approximately $51,000 in order to complete the school according to the original plans (a main building and two wings). The school's cornerstone was laid on June 5, 1921. Unfortunately, the postwar costs of construction prohibited completion of the school. In 1928, a second campaign was organized by the American Nurses' Memorial Committee to raise an additional $25,000. The committee was able to collect more than $32,000. In June, 1931, the entire school building was dedicated.

In 1920, at the twenty-second convention, Clara D. Noyes, president of the American Nurses' Association, observed that "while the pressure of actual war conditions has been lifted, the period of reconstruction brings pressure of quite a different type."[26] Following the signing of the armistice, ANA concentrated on aiding nurses in their adjustment from military to civilian life. In cooperation with the American Red Cross, ANA, NLNE, and NOPHN established a Bureau of Information in 1919 to counsel nurses returning from overseas. Between 1920 and 1922, 1,357 nurses applied for positions through the Bureau. The Bureau was able to place 1,275 nurses. Over 1,544 vacancies in hospitals and allied organizations were directly or indirectly filled through the efforts of the Bureau of Information.[27]

With the operation of the Bureau of Information, the American

Nurses' Association established physical roots for the first time.

ANA considered the issue of a central headquarters as early as 1914. A report was submitted to the board of directors in 1915 which recommended that a central place be established as 1) a meeting place for officers of the three nursing organizations, 2) a depository for valuable papers, seals, etc., of the three nursing organizations, 3) an information center for nursing, and 4) a headquarters office for the Interstate Secretary.[28]

It was not until January, 1919, that the three national nursing organizations appointed a joint committee to explore the possibilities of establishing a national headquarters. In the same year, ANA and NLNE set up operations for the Bureau of Information in the American Red Cross offices at 44 East 23rd Street in New York City.

National Headquarters

During ANA's biennial convention in 1920, delegates voted to establish a national office in New York City, using the resources and personnel of the Red Cross Bureau of Information as the operational nucleus. This action was taken in order that ANA could function on "modern organization methods and principles."[29] A national office was also deemed necessary if the organization was going to launch a plan for recruiting student nurses.

In September, 1920, the "Headquarters, National Nursing Associations" was established at 156 Fifth Avenue, adjacent to the office of the National Organization for Public Health Nursing. Headquarters operations were subsidized by the American Red Cross until July 1, 1921.

In 1921, the association was offered an opportunity to enter into an alliance with several national health organizations negotiating for joint accommodations in the Penn Terminal Building at 370 Seventh Avenue. Such an arrangement, it was believed, would enhance closer affiliation and cooperation among these organizations.

In April, 1921, the national office of the American Nurses' Association and the National League of Nursing Education was moved to the Penn Terminal Building where the National Organization for Public Health Nursing, American Social Hygiene Association, American Mental Hygiene Association and the National Tuberculosis Association occupied space. As a result of action of the 1922 House of Delegates, ANA dues were increased to undertake the financial responsibilities of maintaining a national headquarters. With the securement of adequate financial resources, ANA was able to appoint the first paid executive secretary at the headquarters in 1923.[30]

Between 1912 and 1922, the nursing profession and the American Nurses' Association experienced tremendous growth and development. The nursing profession gained stature in the health care field and won the respect of both military and civilian populations in this country and abroad. As the result of reorganization and the establishment of a central headquarters, ANA was better equipped to represent nurses who were characterized in 1920 as "a vast army of professional women . . . pledged to service."[31]

REFERENCES

1. Annie W. Goodrich, "President's Address," Proceedings of the Nineteenth Annual Convention (April 27-May 3) of the American Nurses' Association, *American Journal of Nursing*, Vol. XVI (June, 1916), 815.
2. *Ibid.*
3. Lillian D. Wald, "Report of the Joint Committee Appointed for Consideration of the Standardization of Visiting Nursing," Proceedings of the Fifteenth Annual Convention (June 5-7, 1912) of the American Nurses' Association, *American Journal of Nursing*, Vol. XII (August, 1912), 894-895.
4. *Ibid.*, 896-897.
5. The name of the organization was influenced by the fact that "visiting nursing," in some instances, referred to all forms of work involving home visits and, in other instances, "visiting nursing" was a restricted term not inclusive of such work as school, factory or social service work.
6. Lillian D. Wald, "Report of the Joint Committee Appointed for Consideration of the Standardization of Visiting Nursing," Proceedings of the Fifteenth Annual Convention (June 5-7, 1912) of the American Nurses' Association, *American Journal of Nursing*, Vol. XII (August, 1912), 897.

7. In 1910, the Nurses' Associated Alumnae and the American Society of Superintendents of Training Schools for Nurses began holding their annual conventions simultaneously. Beginning in 1913, ANA, NLNE and NOPHN held joint conventions annually until 1918, then biennially through 1952.
8. Following reorganization of ANA (1919), the two nursing organizations relinquished their affiliate memberships. However, the presidents retained their ex officio positions on ANA's Board of Directors until 1952.
9. Under the revised sections on membership, permanent and charter memberships would be eliminated by 1918, when the bylaws went into effect.
10. Proceedings of the Nineteenth Annual Convention (April 27-May 3, 1916) of the American Nurses' Association, *American Journal of Nursing,* Vol. XVI (June, 1916), 945.
11. The laws of Delaware would not permit the presidents of NLNE and NOPHN to retain ex officio positions on ANA's Board of Directors.
12. Genevieve Cooke, "President's Address," Proceedings of the Seventeenth Annual Convention (April 23-29, 1914) of the American Nurses' Association, *American Journal of Nursing,* Vol. XIV (July, 1914), 796.
13. Sarah E. Sly, "Report of the Committee on Revision," Proceedings of the Twenty-Second Convention (April 12-17, 1920) of the American Nurses' Association, *American Journal of Nursing,* Vol. XX (July, 1920), 778.
14. The one exception was Freedman's Hospital Alumnae Association which was allowed to maintain direct membership into the national association because the District of Columbia Nurses' Association would not accept colored nurses in their membership.
15. Clara D. Noyes, "President's Address," Proceedings of the Twenty-Third Convention (June 26-July 1, 1922) of the American Nurses' Association, *American Journal of Nursing,* Vol. XX (September, 1922), 992.
16. Annie W. Goodrich, "President's Address," Proceedings of the Twenty-First Annual Convention (May 7-11, 1918) of the American Nurses' Association, *American Journal of Nursing,* Vol. XVIII (August, 1918), 971.
17. *Ibid.*
18. Clara D. Noyes, "President's Address," Proceedings of the Twenty-Third Convention (June 26-July 1, 1922) of the American Nurses' Association, *American Journal of Nursing,* Vol. XX (September, 1922), 994.
19. Proceedings of the Twentieth Annual Convention (April 26-May 2, 1917) of the American Nurses' Association, *American Journal of Nursing,* Vol. XVII (July, 1917), 867.
20. *Ibid.,* 1009.
21. When World War I began in 1914, the American Red Cross sent medical and nursing units to help six European countries.
22. Annie W. Goodrich, "Report of the Survey of the Nursing Resources of the Country," Proceedings of the Twenty-First Annual Convention (May 7-11, 1918) of the American Nurses' Association, *American Journal of Nursing,* Vol. XVIII (August, 1918), 960.
23. *Ibid.,* 1078.
24. No survey was conducted in Arizona, Nevada, and New Mexico because state associations had not been established in these areas.
25. Jane Delano served as ANA President between 1909 and 1911.

26. Clara D. Noyes, "President's Address," Proceedings of the Twenty-Second Convention (April 12-14, 1920) of the American Nurses' Association, *American Journal of Nursing,* Vol. XX (July, 1920), 781.
27. R. Inde Allsaugh, "Business Report of National Headquarters," Proceedings of the Twenty-Third Convention (June 26-July 1, 1922) of the American Nurses' Association, *American Journal of Nursing,* Vol. XXII (September, 1922), 1044.
28. Agnes G. Deans, *ANA Historical Sketch* (New York: American Nurses' Association, 1925), 6-7.
29. R. Inde Allsaugh, "Business Report of National Headquarters," Proceedings of the Twenty-Third Convention (June 26-July 1, 1922) of the American Nurses' Association, *American Journal of Nursing,* Vol. XXII (September, 1922), 1043.
30. Since 1923, the association has had six executive secretaries (directors). Consult Appendix III for information on these individuals.
31. Clara D. Noyes, "President's Address," Proceedings of the Twenty-Second Convention (April 12-17, 1920) of the American Nurses' Association, *American Journal of Nursing,* Vol. XX (July, 1920), 781.

1924-1934

Professional Assessment

The period between 1924 and 1934 proved to be a volatile era in modern history. During the 1920s, the American style of living was greatly affected by a vast industrial revolution which brought about a temporary state of prosperity. According to historians, no other generation was so affected by industrial invention as those individuals living in the first two decades of the twentieth century.

The "gasoline-powered buggy" proved to be the most noteworthy invention of the times. The demand for motor vehicles gave rise to a vast automobile industry which provided jobs for nearly six million individuals. As a result of assembly-line methods and other mass production techniques, Henry Ford was able to construct a Ford Roadster every ten seconds. By 1929, 26,000,000 motor vehicles were registered in the United States.[1]

During this same period, another type of gasoline-powered vehicle made an impact on modern industry. In 1927, Charles A. Lindbergh flew his single-engined plane, "The Spirit of St. Louis," from New York to Paris in thirty-three and one half hours. This feat aroused interest in commercial aviation and created a huge new transportation industry.

Culturally, the American public was stimulated by radio and motion picture productions. In November, 1920, a Pittsburgh radio station was able to broadcast the national results of the presidential election. By 1926, color films were being produced. In 1927, the first talking picture, "The Jazz Singer," starring Al Jolson was heralded by moviegoers. Socially speaking, Americans began to look to the "filmland" to set standards for style and, even, morals.

Educationally, Americans gained new insight from newsreels, travelogues and literary broadcasts. However, the greatest educational advancement was made in the nation's school system. Not only were many states requiring students to remain in school until the age of sixteen, but also more extensive provisions were being made for vocational training. The most profound impact on education was made by John Dewey, a professor at Columbia University from 1904 to 1930. Dewey revolutionized educational theory by setting forth principles of progressive education which focused on "education for life." Moreover, during this same period, questions were raised regarding what could or could not be taught in the classroom. In 1925, a high school biology teacher in Tennessee was indicted for teaching evolution. The Scopes or "Monkey Trial" received national attention.

Although the decade of the 1920s was heralded as "the Gasoline Age," a period of vast industrial revolution, it was also labeled "the Jazz Age" and "the Roaring Twenties," a period of moral decay. The "flapper," bootleg whiskey, and gangsters were symbols of the times. It was an age of cynicism. Idealism gave way to materialism. Prohibition spurred a period of gangsterism and organized crime became one of the nation's leading businesses.

At the height of industrial advancement and moral degradation, the nation's economy experienced a staggering setback. In October, 1929, the stock market collapsed, causing a business depression. Between 1929 and 1932, over five thousand banks collapsed. By the end of 1930 approximately seven million workers were unemployed. By 1932, this figure had doubled.[2] In three short years, Americans had literally gone from "riches to rags." Breadlines and soup kitchens became the symbols of the

Great Depression of the 1930s, a bleak period for the nation.

According to economists, the depression was triggered by agricultural and industrial overproduction and technological unemployment. The nation's ability to produce commodities clearly surpassed the public's capacity to purchase and consume them. To some degree, overproduction was stimulated by the introduction of installment buying which caused many Americans to overestimate their purchasing power. Moreover, the introduction of new labor-saving machines eliminated the need for thousands of workers.[3]

During this period in American history, nurses were faced with more serious problems than any other body of workers. The profession struggled to gain conditions other professions were taking for granted; namely, reasonable hours, adequate income, health and retirement protection, and opportunity for growth.[4]

Characteristic of the times, there was an overproduction of trained nurses. Since 1900, the population of the United States had increased 62 percent while the number of trained nurses increased 2,374 percent.[5] Unfortunately, too many of these nurses were inadequately trained. Too few nurses were prepared to handle the changing needs of the public.

Between 1924 and 1934, increasing emphasis was placed on disease prevention and health maintenence. Physicians, in an attempt to provide instruction in personal hygiene, turned to the nursing profession for health teachers. The frequent contact of public health nurses with the populace made them the ideal workers to promote healthful living. Moreover, the public readily turned to the nursing profession for such instruction. As Eleanor Roosevelt observed, as she spoke to ANA convention delegates in 1934, the public not only expected the nurse to function in a caring role, but to act as a teacher along many lines.[6] This need for nurse-teachers created a demand for an enormous number of nurses specially skilled and trained to meet societal needs. Although there were numerous applicants for these positions, few nurses were actually qualified to assume the specific responsibilities. Consequently, unemployment posed problems for the nursing profession long before the onset of the economic depression.

During this period, it was the responsibility of the American Nurses' Association to minister to the problems of its membership which grew from 47,160 in 1924 to over 100,000 in 1934. As ANA President S. Lillian Clayton explained:

> ANA has grown out of the needs of the individual nurse . . . Its objectives consider the individual needs as they exist, and look forward in anticipation to future needs. The American Nurses' Association has taken into account the condition of the age, and has been forward-looking, so that the needs of the individual, and of the group have been thought of, and planned before the need became a conscious one to the group mind.[7]

The primary objective of the American Nurses' Association between 1924 and 1934 was to secure (in the minds of the public and the laws of the country) a professional status for the nursing profession. The Association concentrated its efforts in three areas:

1) Selection and preparation of students in schools of nursing,
2) Distribution of nursing services, and
3) Status and employment conditions of nurses.

Two events during the early part of the 1920s caused the nursing profession to carefully examine its educational system.

Reclassification Bill

As the result of the action of the Sixty-Seventh Congress, a Personnel Classification Board was established to categorize professional and nonprofessional personnel in government service. According to the provisions of the Reclassification Bill, the status of a given service would be determined by the educational preparation of the individual practitioner. The educational requirements deemed necessary to conduct a professional service included professional, scientific, or technical training equivalent to that presented by graduation from a college or university recognized by a duly authorized accreditation body.

In 1924, a committee of representatives of the three national organizations appealed to the Personnel Classification Board that nurses engaged in government service be granted professional status. Unfortunately, the committee was notified that the board intended to relegate nurses to a subprofessional category of workers.[8] The board's decision was influenced by the educational inequities among nurse practitioners. Inasmuch as the educational background of registered nurses varied from an eighth grade preparation to a university degree, authorities did not consider it appropriate to grant professional status to all nursing personnel. Representatives of ANA, NLNE, and NOPHN were advised that schools of nursing should be graded according to entrance requirements and curriculum. These representatives were also apprised of the need to distinguish between the various levels of nurse training in order to single out those nurses worthy of professional status.

Committee for the Study of Nursing and Nursing Education in the United States

A second event which aroused the concern of the nursing population was the 1923 publication of a study of nursing and nursing education in the United States. Popularly referred to as the Winslow-Goldmark Report, the study pointed out the shortcomings of nursing education and public health nursing.

In December, 1918, the Rockefeller Foundation sponsored a conference for individuals interested in the advancement of public health nursing in the United States. At the conclusion of the conference, delegates made a strong appeal for more extensive training programs for public health workers. In light of the conference findings, a committee was established to study nursing and nursing education. Such leaders as Annie W. Goodrich, S. Lillian Clayton, M. Adelaide Nutting, and Lillian Wald served on the twenty-member committee.

In 1919, the committee was commissioned with three responsibilities: 1) to survey the work executed by nurses and related types of workers, 2) to form a conceptual framework of nursing tasks and corresponding qualifications, and 3) to establish minimum education standards for each type of nursing service.

The committee published its findings, *Nursing and Nursing Education in the United States,* in 1923. It was the committee's observation that:

1) Unlike most professions which had established independent institutions of learning, nursing still maintained apprentice-type training programs which were operated as adjuncts to the management of hospitals.

AND

2) The extraordinary increase in hospitals within the brief span of time had created a tremendous demand for nursing students, who were regarded by hospital authorities as an inexpensive source of efficient labor. The need to secure more nursing students precipitated the lowering of admission requirements.

From the survey of nursing education and nursing practice, the committee drew ten conclusions, including:

1) All superintendents, supervisors, instructors, and public health nurses should receive special training beyond the basic nursing program. Moreover, all public and private agencies employing public health nurses should require postgraduate preparation.[9]

2) University schools of nursing should be developed and strengthened and no attempt should be made to lower standards of educational attainment.[10]

3) Steps should be taken to establish a training program to prepare subsidiary workers and to develop legislation for the definition and licensure of subsidiary levels of nursing practice.[11]

Committee on the Grading of Nursing Schools

In response to the issues raised by the committee surveying nursing education, a plan was formulated to create a national body to study ways of insuring an ample supply of adequately trained nursing personnel who could render quality care at a reasonable price. Established in 1925, the Committee on the Grading of Nursing Schools was composed of two representatives each from the American College of Surgeons, the American Hospital Association, the American Medical Association,[12] the American Nurses' Association, the American Public Health Association, the National League of Nursing Education, and the National Organization for Public Health Nursing as well as seven members elected at large.

The committee was commissioned to conduct an eight-year program,[13] which included an investigation of the supply and demand for nursing services, a job analysis of nursing and nurse-teaching, and the grading of nursing schools. Funds for the project, totaling $283,500, were contributed by the seven parent organizations, the Rockefeller Foundation, the Commonwealth Fund, and individual nurses across the country. The primary goal of the committee was better education for nurses which would insure better nursing care for patients. The committee operated on the premise that the establishment of nursing education standards was dependent upon a thorough understanding of the factors underlying nursing employment. Consequently, the first phase of the committee's work focused on a study of nursing economics.

The first reports of the committee, which included the book, *Nurses, Patients and Pocketbooks,* and the abstract, "Nurses—Production, Education, Distribution and Pay," were published in 1928. *Nurses, Patients and Pocketbooks* was heralded as "an important milestone in nursing progress."[14]

According to the findings of the committee, there were more graduate nurses available than employment opportunities. Yet many nursing positions remained unfilled because of a lack of qualified applicants. The committee concluded that there was a nursing shortage—a shortage in quality, not quantity.[15] This shortage of adequately trained nurses was the direct result of failure to adhere to a definite policy of educational preparation.

In the absence of uniform standards for nursing education, hospital training programs mushroomed between 1900 and 1926. In 1900, there were 432 nursing schools compared to 160 medical schools which the medical profession operated according to rigid standards. By 1926, there were only 79 medical schools, compared to 2,155 schools of nursing.[16] The committee speculated that the abundance of nursing programs producing poorly trained practitioners resulted from the singular desire of the hospital to secure cheap labor. Regarding nursing students as economic assets, hospitals established schools of nursing in order to secure student labor for their own patients, not to produce graduate nurses for public service.[17]

The Committee on the Grading of Nursing Schools concluded that the establishment of nursing schools should be based solely upon the type of educational opportunities afforded by the hospital.[18] Moreover, the committee emphasized the fact that nursing education should be a public responsibility. A hospital should not be expected to finance nursing education from funds collected for hospital services.

In addressing delegates to the 1928 ANA convention, May Ayres Burgess, director for the study on nursing economics, pointed out that *Nurses, Patients and Pocketbooks* revealed four main problems which were the "inevitable responsibility of the nursing profession for the immediate future:" 1) to reduce and improve the supply of nurses, 2) to replace nursing students with graduate nurses, 3) to help hospitals meet the costs of graduate nursing services, and 4) to secure public support for nursing education.[19]

Between 1930 and 1931, the Committee on the Grading of Nursing Schools conducted the first grading study. The results of the nationwide survey of nursing schools were presented in a series of three confidential reports: "The Student Body," "What Nurses Learn," and "Who Controls the Schools." In 1932, this comparative study of nursing schools was followed up by a second grading. Under the supervision of the committee, the nursing schools undertook a self-evaluation to determine the degree of improvement in standards of instruction.

The committee published two reports in 1934. *An Activity Analysis of Nursing,* compiled by Ethel Johns and Blanche Pfefferkorn, contained the findings of the studies made by nurse educators on a job analysis of nursing and nurse teaching. The purpose of the project was to identify all the activities related to nursing care. Included in the report were an explanation of what constitutes good nursing care, a description of basic conditions calling for the services of a nurse, and a list of the types of activities included in hospital, public health, and private duty nursing.

The final report of the Committee on the Grading of Nursing Schools was *Nursing Schools—Today and Tomorrow.* This volume provided a basic overview of the findings of the eight-year project, including discussions of the knowledge and skills of the professional nurse, the essential elements of a professional school of nursing, and courses for graduate nurses.

Posing the question "What should a professional nurse know and be able to do," Ethel Johns[20] proposed the following characteristics:

1) Nurses should be able to observe and interpret the physical and social symptoms of the patient and administer expert bedside care.

2) Nurses should be able to deal effectively with the special needs associated with the care of men, women, and children suffering from common types of diseases.

3) Nurses should be able to apply mental hygiene principles to the care of all patients.

4) Nurses should be able to contribute to the maintenance of health and prevention of disease by teaching elementary principles of hygiene and healthful ways of living.[21]

The grading committee, believing it was impractical to compile a comprehensive list of standards for an ideal school of nursing, set forth certain conditions deemed essential for the proper growth and functioning of any professional school. These conditions included the following:

1) A professional school of nursing should be controlled by an educational board composed of members of hospital, medical, and nursing groups, as well as individuals representing the interests of the whole community.

2) A professional school of nursing should draw its funds in part from tuition fees and in part from endowments, gifts, or subsidies.

3) The majority of the faculty in a school of nursing should be registered nurses with specialized training in a particular field of nursing.[22]

In order to deal with the problem of overproduction of trained nurses, the grading committee proposed measures for vocational readjustment, including provisions for courses for graduate nurses. The purposes of such courses were to make up deficiencies in basic nurse training and to provide additional specialized training.[23]

It was the committee's observation that the most serious problems in schools of nursing were the absence of qualified teachers and the lack of emphasis on the attributes of good nursing. The committee recommended that measures be taken to close many of the schools of nursing established as adjuncts to the management of hospitals, to transform other undergraduate schools into professional schools of nursing, and to open courses for graduate nurses.[24]

The disclosures of the committees studying nurse training programs and the grading of nursing schools prompted the three national nursing organizations to establish a Joint Committee on the Distribution of Nursing Services in 1928. Creation of this committee represented the attempt of organized nursing to formulate a plan which would place the qualified nurse "in contact with those situations in which nursing services are needed and in which nursing services will be available to all patients, under conditions which will allow for satisfaction in workmanship for the nurse."[25]

In 1932, the boards of directors of the three nursing organizations agreed to allow the American Nurses' Association to assume responsibility for the work of the committee.[26] ANA undertook a two-year project to develop standards of hourly and group nursing and to organize councils to study the nursing needs of communities. This work was accomplished by subcommittees on general staff nursing, community nursing councils, hourly nursing service, nurse registries, and rural nursing practice.

Community Nursing Councils

Between 1932 and 1934, the committee developed materials which explained how to form community nursing councils, how to change from student to graduate nursing staffs, how to establish hourly nursing services, and why organized nursing should establish nursing services in poverty-stricken rural and urban areas. Moreover, the committee formulated employment standards regarding hours, salaries, health services, and vacations for private duty nurses working in institutional settings. However, the most noteworthy accomplishment of this body was its efforts to improve and standardize nurse registries. The committee encouraged the nursing profession to view the registry as an instrument to provide the community with needed nursing services. The development of registries as a community service was a means of insuring adequate distribution of nurses. As Elnora E. Thomson, acting ANA president, pointed out in 1930:

> The registry has been regarded as merely an employment bureau for nurses rather than as a distributing center for nursing service in the community. It has been found through trial in several places that it can be such a distributing center, so that this larger view of the registry is not only sound from the standpoint of service to the patient in extending nursing service to all those who need nursing care, but also from the standpoint of the nurse. For in the light of our knowledge of economic conditions in the United States, it is obvious that the

> time has come when it is essential that the distribution of the services of nurses must be done in line with modern practices.[27]

In 1934, the Committee on Distribution of Nursing Services submitted its final report which included the recommendation that the committee be discontinued. The committee members recommended that problems regarding nurse distribution be referred to an ANA committee which had undertaken a study of the organization of professionally sponsored registries.

While special national committees surveyed schools of nursing and the distribution of nursing services, structural units of the American Nurses' Association focused their attention on the status of nursing and the general welfare of nurses. Between 1921 and 1934, the American Nurses' Association concentrated its efforts on the creation of a code of ethics for nurses, preparation of a brief and specifications for civilian nursing service in the federal government, and development of a statement on professional nursing and the professional nurse.

Ethical Standards of Nursing

Inasmuch as most business and industrial groups had developed a written statement on principles of ethical conduct, the nursing profession began to turn its attention to the identification of a code of ethics. In 1921, the National League of Nursing Education recommended that a committee, consisting of representatives of the three national nursing organizations, be appointed to prepare a statement on ethical principles of nursing practice. Eventually, the committee became an ad hoc body of the American Nurses' Association which had planned to compile a code of ethics as part of its work.

Between 1923 and 1924, ANA's Committee on Ethical Standards decided to develop a statement on the ideals of the nursing profession, rather than outlining elementary principles of good conduct. Upon selecting the topics of service, loyalty, educational development, and understanding of human needs, the committee asked Mary M. Riddle to compile the statement in the form of a pledge. However, it was eventually decided to prepare both a code of ethics and a pledge of conduct.

During the 1926 convention of the American Nurses' Association, the following code of ethics was presented for consideration and, subsequently, adopted by ANA delegates:

The Relation of the Nurse to the Patient

The nurse should bring to the care of the patient all of the knowledge, skill and devotion which she may possess. To do this, she must appreciate the relationship of the patient to his family and to his community.

Therefore the nurse must broaden her thoughtful consideration of the patient so that it will include his whole family and his friends, for only in surroundings harmonious and peaceful for the patient can the nurse give her utmost of skill, devotion and knowledge, which shall include the safeguarding of the health of those about the patient and the protection of property.

The Relation of the Nurse to the Medical Profession

The term "medicine" should be understood to refer to *scientific* medicine and the desirable relationship between the two should be one of mutual respect. The nurse should be fully informed on the provisions of the medical practice act of her own state in order that she may not unconsciously support quackery and actual infringement of the law. The key to the situation lies in the mutuality of aim of medicine and nursing; the aims, to cure and prevent disease and promote positive health, are identical, the technics of the two are different and neither profession can secure complete results without the other. The nurse should respect the physician as the person legally and professionally responsible for the medical and surgical treatment of the sick. She should endeavor to give such intelligent and skilled nursing service that she will be looked upon as a co-worker of the doctor in the whole field of health.

Under no circumstances, except in emergency, is the nurse justified in instituting treatment.

The Relation of the Nurse to the Allied Professions

The health of the public has come to demand many services other than nursing. Without the closest interrelation of workers and appreciation of the ethical standards of all groups, and a clear understanding of the limitations of her own group, the best results in building positive health in the community cannot be obtained.

Relation of Nurse to Nurse

The "Golden Rule" embodies all that could be written in many pages on the relation of nurse to nurse. This should be one of fine loyalty, of appreciation for work conscientiously done, and of respect for positions of authority. On the other hand, loyalty to the motive which inspires nursing should make the nurse fearless to bring to light any serious violation to the ideals herein expressed; the larger loyalty is that to the community, for loyalty to an ideal is higher than any personal loyalty.

Relation of the Nurse to Her Profession

The nurse has a definite responsibility to her profession as a whole. The contribution of individual service is not enough. She should, in addition, give a reasonable portion of her time to the furtherance of such advancements of the profession as are only possible through action of the group as a whole. This involves attendance

> at meetings and the acquisition of information, at least sufficient for intelligent participation in such matters as organization and legislation.
>
> The supreme responsibility of the nurse in relation to her profession is to keep alight that spiritual flame which has illumined the work of the great nurses of all time.[28]

The purpose of the code was not to provide rules of conduct covering specific types of nursing practice situations, but to create an awareness of ethical considerations. At the committee's suggestion, the code was printed in the *American Journal of Nursing* and copies distributed to constituent associations with the understanding that the code was subject to alteration as deemed necessary.

According to the Committee on Ethical Standards, reporting to the 1934 ANA House of Delegates, the concerns of nurses fell into three categories: 1) questions of etiquette which were mistaken for ethical considerations, 2) ethical problems, and 3) issues with both ethical and legal implications. Nurses raised questions concerning uniform requirements, the nurse participating in commercial advertisement, the nurse functioning as an anesthetist, the nurse working in the office of a chiropractor or osteopath, and the nurse outlining diabetic diets in the absence of the attending physician.[29]

Definition of Professional Nursing

As early as 1922, delegates to the ANA convention questioned the utilization of such terms as "professional" and "technical" to identify the level or degree of nursing preparation. According to delegates, the absence of criteria by which to determine the appropriate skills and knowledge for certain nursing responsibilities created confusion and, even, lead to misrepresentation. Between 1924 and 1934, the American Nurses' Association took specific steps to delineate the characteristics of professional nursing.

In 1930, the Personnel Classification Board announced its plan to categorize nurses engaged in government services as subprofessional workers. In response to this announcement, the American Nurses' Association prepared a "Brief and Specifications for Civilian Nursing Service in the Federal Government."

Utilizing the criteria for a profession developed by Dr. Abraham Flexner,[30] the association developed the thesis that nursing is a profession and that nurses are professional workers. This brief served as a public record of nursing's case for professional recognition. Nursing leadership regarded the document as one of the most outstanding achievements of the American Nurses' Association relative to the promotion of professional nursing.[31]

In 1931, ANA's Board of Directors appointed a committee to prepare a formal statement on the terms "professional nursing" and "professional nurse." Inasmuch as most nurse practice acts did not define nursing, the American Nurses' Association believed it was essential that the nursing profession formulate a definition of nursing which outlined the fundamental requirements for both professional recognition and legal sanction.

In April, 1932, the board of directors approved the following statements submitted by the Committee on the Definition of Nursing:

> **Professional Nursing.** Professional nursing is a blend of intellectual attainments, attitudes and manual skills based on the principles of scientific medicine, acquired by means of a prescribed course in a school of nursing affiliated with a hospital, recognized for such purposes by the state and practiced in conjunction with curative or preventive medicine, by an individual licensed to do so by the state.
>
> **Professional Nurse.** Therefore, a professional nurse is one who has met all the legal requirements for registration in a state and who practices or holds a position by virtue of her professional knowledge and legal status.[32]

The adoption of a concise definition of professional nursing as well as publication of the specifications for civilian nursing service helped to alleviate some of the confusion regarding nursing titles. Moreover, in 1934, ANA convention delegates voted to discourage the use of the term "practical nurse." In the form of a resolution, delegates encouraged ANA members to "give some thought to the selection and use of a more suitable term for this type of worker, which will define her functions without confusing them with those of the trained, graduate, registered nurse."[33]

Federal Enactments

Upon his presidential inauguration in 1933, Franklin D. Roosevelt initiated a "New Deal" program of relief, recovery, and reform from the depression. During the first one hundred days of the Roosevelt Administration, Congress enacted a number of measures which provided job opportunities for millions of unemployed Americans. In light of these federal enactments, the American Nurses' Association concentrated its efforts on pointing out the dangers to the community if nursing services were entrusted to nonprofessional personnel. ANA took specific steps to insure that federally sponsored projects provided for the employment of graduate registered nurses engaged in all types of nursing work. As Alma H. Scott, director of ANA headquarters, pointed out, "Possibly the most important of all the activities of the three national nursing organizations in connection with federal enactments has been the effort . . . to insure that . . . the professional status of nursing would be recognized and maintained."[34]

Although a number of "New Deal" acts provided temporary and part-time employment for nurses, two legislative measures had a significant impact on the nursing profession. In August, 1933, Congress authorized the National Recovery Act to expedite recovery and reform in labor and industry. One important feature of the act was the establishment of a code of fair competition, including minimum wage levels and a ceiling on maximum hours of labor. The aim of the National Recovery Act was to reduce the hours of labor in order that employment opportunities could be shared by more individuals. Since the federal government was encouraging the establishment of shorter working hours for all laborers, the American Nurses' Association took the opportunity to seek better working conditions for professional nurses. Shortly after the passage of the National Recovery Act, ANA's Board of Directors prepared the following statement on "The National Recovery Act and Nursing:"

> An arbitary limitation of hours controlled by law violates the whole spirit of nursing, as the comfort of the patient is the nurse's first consideration. Again, no nurse could be expected to hold to a specific hour schedule when engaged in emergency or disaster relief.
>
> However, an attempt should be made to approach reasonable working conditions by encouraging, where possible, in the interest of the patient as well as the nurse, an eight-hour day for those employed on a daily basis, and a 48-hour week for those employed on a weekly or monthly schedule. It is undoubtedly desirable to shorten the hours of duty so that the individual nurse may have a reasonable working day and also that there may be a spreading of work.[35]

Another important feature of the National Recovery Act was the guarantee of the laborer's right to organize and bargain collectively through representatives of the laborer's choosing. Unfortunately, in 1935, the Supreme Court ruled that Congress did not have the authority to delegate legislative powers to the Executive Branch, and the NRA was abolished. Inasmuch as the act made provisions for collective bargaining, the Supreme Court reasserted labor's right to engage in collective bargaining and self-organization in the Wagner or National Labor Relations Act of 1935.

Late in 1933, the Civil Works Administration, a branch of the Federal Emergency Relief Administration, was established to provide temporary employment opportunities. As a result of this program, approximately 10,000 nurses were able to secure employment.[36] According to ANA staff, the Civil Works Service program brought "the entire organization into one great working unit for a national cause" and strengthened working relationships between ANA and its constituent associations.[37]

At the close of 1934, there were 110,478 ANA members, the largest membership in the history of the association. The significant increase in membership was attributed to the association's efforts to safeguard the interests of nursing during the Great Depression. In 1936, the director of ANA headquarters reflected upon the problems of the decade and ANA's role:

> The pressure of immediate economic problems within any profession tends to distort the vision of a number of its members and to result in temporary blindness to larger professional issues and ideals. In such a situation, commercial interests are focused into sharp relief and assume an importance out of all proportion to their intrinsic and ultimate worth. Only an informed, cooperative, effectively organized and professionally minded membership, such as that of the ANA . . . could have weathered to any degree of success the storm of financial insecurity through which we have been passing.
>
> At no time . . . has faith in fundamental professional ideals wavered; this is true in spite of the fact that practically every member of the nursing profession has borne not only her own personal burdens, but has endeavored to assist with the problems of her colleagues. There has been universal realization that any trouble can be endured if it can be shared—any problem can be solved if organized effort is directed toward its solution—that any goal can be attained, provided it has real merit, and is deemed to be of sufficient importance to inspire the personal sacrifices which are necessary for its achievement.[38]

REFERENCES

1. Thomas A. Bailey, *The American Pageant* (Boston: D. C. Heath and Company, 1966), 811-813.
2. *Ibid.*, 819.
3. *Ibid.*, 818-820.
4. May Ayres Burgess (Director), *Nurses, Patients and Pocketbooks*, Report of a study of economics of nursing conducted by the Committee on the Grading of Nursing Schools (New York: Committee on the Grading of Nursing Schools, 1928), 496.
5. *Nursing Schools Today and Tomorrow*, Final Report of the Committee on the Grading of Nursing Schools (New York: Committee on the Grading of Nursing Schools, 1934), 45.
6. Eleanor Roosevelt, "What Does the Public Expect from Nursing?" *Proceedings of the Twenty-Ninth Convention (April 22-27, 1934) of the American Nurses' Association* (New York: American Nurses' Association, 1934), 59.
7. S. Lillian Clayton, "President's Address," *Proceedings of the Twenty-Sixth Convention (June 4-8, 1928) of the American Nurses' Association* (New York: American Nurses' Association, 1928), 6.
8. Upon learning that the Personnel Classification Board intended to place nurses in a subprofessional category, ANA (supported by nongovernment health organizations) waged a lengthy campaign against the action. Moreover, on April 7, 1924, the association secured membership in the Women's Joint Congressional Committee, a clearinghouse for the Congressional legislative work of the national organizations engaged in promoting federal measures of special interest to women.
9. C. E. A. Winslow and Josephine Goldmark, *Nursing and Nursing Education in the United States* (New York: The Macmillan Company, 1923), 11, 24.
10. *Ibid.*, 14, 26.
11. *Ibid.*, 16, 28.
12. The American Medical Association withdrew from the committee in 1928.
13. Originally, the proposal only called for a five-year program.
14. A unique feature of this study was the inclusion of estimates of the nursing population from 1920 to 1965. According to committee estimates, the graduating class of 1965 would number 60,000 members and a census in 1965 would find approximately 717,000 nurses actively engaged in practice. [May Ayres Burgess (Director), *Nurses, Patients and Pocketbooks*, Report of a Study of Economics of Nursing Conducted by the Committee on the Grading of Nursing Schools (New York: Committee on the Grading of Nursing Schools, 1928), 65.] During the 1964-65 school year, there were actually 34,686 nursing school graduates and 621,000 registered nurses in practice during 1965. [Department of Health, Education and Welfare, Public Health Service, *Health Resources Statistics, Health Manpower and Health Facilities, 1968* (Washington, D. C.: National Center for Health Statistics, 1968), 138, 140.]
15. May Ayres Burgess (Director), *Nurses, Patients and Pocketbooks*, Report of a Study of Economics of Nursing Conducted by the Committee on the Grading of Nursing Schools (New York: Committee on the Grading of Nursing Schools, 1928), 433.
16. *Ibid.*, 46.
17. *Ibid.*, 448.
18. *Ibid.*, 450.

19. May Ayres Burgess, "High Points of the Supply and Demand Study," *Proceedings of the Twenty-Sixth Convention (June 4-8, 1928) of the American Nurses' Association* (New York: American Nurses' Association, 1928), 42-43.
20. This information originally appeared as part of the report on *An Activity Analysis of Nursing.*
21. *Nursing Schools—Today and Tomorrow,* Final Report of the Committee on the Grading of Nursing Schools (New York: Committee on the Grading of Nursing Schools, 1934), 80-81.
22. *Ibid.,* 146-147.
23. *Ibid.,* 229.
24. *Ibid.,* 246.
25. Ella Best, *Brief Historical Review and Information About Current Activities of the American Nurses' Association* (New York: American Nurses' Association, 1940), 48.
26. Although the committee was placed under the directorship of ANA, representatives of all three nursing organizations remained on the committee.
27. Elnora E. Thomson, "President's Address," *Proceedings of the Twenty-Seventh Convention (June 9-14, 1930) of the American Nurses' Association* (New York: American Nurses' Association, 1930), 8.
28. "Code of Ethics Presented for the Consideration of the American Nurses' Association," *Proceedings of the Twenty-Fifth Convention (May 17-22, 1926) of the American Nurses' Association* (New York: American Nurses' Association, 1926), 26-27.
29. Sister John Gabriel, "Report of Committee on Ethical Standards," *Proceedings of the Twenty-Ninth Convention (April 22-27, 1934) of the American Nurses' Association* (New York: American Nurses' Association, 1934), 183.
30. According to Dr. Flexner, elements of a profession included a high degree of individual responsibility, a body of specialized knowledge and skills, a practical and definite service, and self-organization.
31. ANA was eventually successful in obtaining professional status classification for nurses from the U.S. Civil Service Commission. In 1946, nurses were granted professional status by the commission.
32. Ella Best, *Brief Historical Review and Information About Current Activities of the American Nurses' Association* (New York: American Nurses' Association, 1940), 67.
33. Resolutions Committee, *Proceedings of the Twenty-Ninth Convention (April 22-27, 1934) of the American Nurses' Association* (New York: American Nurses' Association, 1934), 492.
34. Ella Best, *Brief Historical Review and Information About Current Activities of the American Nurses' Association* (New York: American Nurses' Association, 1940), 70.
35. *Ibid.,* 69.
36. American Nurses' Association, *Handbook* (New York: American Nurses' Association, 1935), 36.
37. *Ibid.,* 37.
38. Alma H. Scott, "Report of Director of Headquarters—1934-1936," *Proceedings of the Thirtieth Convention (June 21-26, 1936) of the American Nurses' Association* (New York: American Nurses' Association, 1936), 117-118.

1936–1946

Unprecedented Demands

The period between 1936 and 1946 was a decade of "health consciousness." Speaking before ANA's Advisory Council in 1940, Pearl McIver, second vice president, observed:

> At no time in the history of the United States has so much thought been centered around the subjects of health work and medical care. The Associated Press today considers any information on health and medical care as front page news.[1]

Both the general public and the federal government displayed increased interest in provisions for health care services. Special emphasis was placed on developing programs which would expand hospital facilities, extend public and maternal-child welfare services, provide medical care for the needy, and establish insurance against loss of wages during illness.

During this period two events greatly affected the demand for nursing services: the enactment of the Social Security Act of 1935 and the United States' involvement in World War II from 1941 to 1945.

Between 1935 and 1950, Americans witnessed the passage of more social legislation than at any other period in the nation's history. Initiation of social and economic welfare programs was prompted by an extensive survey of medical practice in the

United States from 1927 to 1932. According to the Committee on the Costs of Medical Care, a significant portion of the population did not have access to essential medical and nursing services. The committee concluded that provision of adequate health care at reasonable costs could best be achieved through a program of group insurance. The committee recommended that government agencies assume responsibility for provision of medical services for all citizens, regardless of their ability to pay.

This recommendation gained great public support. In 1935, Congress enacted the Social Security Act, the first piece of social legislation to have a significant impact on the utilization of nurses.[2] The act was devised to alleviate economic distress during periods of illness. Its purpose was to provide for the public's welfare by establishing a federal system of old-age benefits as well as initiating measures which would enable state governments to make more adequate provision for aged and blind persons, dependent and crippled children, maternal and child welfare, public health, and the administration of unemployment compensation laws.[3]

According to social scientists, this legislation prompted the greatest expansion of public health facilities in American history. This expansion triggered a proportionate increase in the demand for the services of doctors, nurses, and other public health workers. In fact, those provisions of the Social Security Act concerning maternal and child welfare could not be operationalized without a significantly larger body of public health nurses.

While the federal government took steps to establish the basis for a national health program, private agencies created prepayment and group medical plans. As more and more Americans participated in these plans, the number of patients in hospitals greatly increased, creating the need for more doctors and nurses.

As the result of the creation of both public and private health programs, considerable emphasis was placed on the even distribution of medical and nursing services. In 1939, a national health conference was held in Washington, D. C., to explore measures aimed at health maintenance. Representatives of the three national nursing organizations, hospital and social service groups, and the American Medical Association were in attendance. Conference delegates recommended that health workers assume responsibility for the coordination and distribution of health care services within the community.

The adequate provision of community nursing services posed significant problems for the nursing profession. Studies revealed that nurses were unevenly distributed throughout the country. According to a 1938 report, there was a need for three to four times as many nurses in rural areas and at least twice as many nurses in the cities to provide needed maternal and child health services.[4] Moreover, a significant portion of the population was unable to secure needed nursing services because of their inability to pay. Consequently, the job of the nursing profession was twofold: 1) to train and distribute adequate numbers of nursing personnel and 2) to work for the inclusion of payment of nursing services in health insurance programs.

The problems of the nursing profession were further complicated by the involvement of the United States in World War II. Although extraordinary advances had been made in medical treatment, the number of war casualties and the high incidence of disease among military personnel created a great demand for health care workers. Moreover, the onslaught of World War II brought about a renewed state of prosperity as factories speeded up the production of wartime materials. The "war industry" brought about a significant expansion in industrial nursing. Industrial nurses not only rendered nursing care to ill and injured factory workers, they also conducted programs on accident prevention and safety education. The increasing demands for nurses in the armed services and industrial nurses for wartime industry severely depleted the supply of nursing manpower.

During the decade 1936 to 1946, the American Nurses' Association concentrated on safeguarding professional nursing services in the community. As Alma H. Scott, director of ANA headquarters, explained to convention delegates, "From a professional standpoint, the ANA has definite responsibility toward each community in the United States which is either adequately or inadequately supplied with nursing."[5]

Joint Committee on Community Nursing Service

Initial investigation of community nursing needs revealed that the problems regarding provision of adequate nursing services were the concern of medical, hospital, and lay groups, as well as the national nursing organizations. Therefore, the American Nurses' Association made a concerted effort to strengthen and expand relationships with other professional organizations, governmental agencies, and lay groups. As ANA President Susan C. Francis pointed out:

> A professional association, such as ours, comes together in the beginning because its members have common interests, problems, and ideals. It exists to serve its members and through them the community. If it honestly tries to make this service effective, it soon finds it necessary to establish new and ever widening relationships with other groups.[6]

Between 1936 and 1946, the aim of the association was to work with various groups in determining community nursing needs and establishing community nursing services. For no problem facing the nursing organization had greater implications for the profession than the preparation and distribution of nurses.

In January, 1935, the joint boards of directors of the three national nursing organizations adopted a recommendation that the Committee on Community Nursing of the National Organization for Public Health Nursing become the Joint Committee on Community Nursing Service. This joint committee was composed of lay and nurse representatives appointed by each of the three national nursing organizations. Other representatives from the medical, hospital, and public health fields, as well as consumer groups, were invited to act in a consultant capacity.

The aim of the committee was to help communities, upon request, plan a more complete nursing service.[7] The three national nursing organizations perceived the purposes of the committee to be twofold: first, to analyze existing needs for more satisfactory nursing services, and, second, to consider (through study and possible experimentation) new means for meeting nursing needs.

One of the early acts of the committee was to set forth the following general principles upon which any community nursing service should be based:

1) In planning for a community nursing service, the chief objective should be to furnish the best possible nursing service to the community.

2) A responsible group representing the nursing profession, the medical profession, and the lay public should work out the plans in each community for a nursing service.

3) The group charged with planning a community nursing service should have access to up-to-date information on nursing needs and resources.

4) A community nursing service should provide for all types of nursing. However, the demands for each type of nursing service will vary in different communities.

5) Efforts should be made to minimize the number of agencies distributing nursing services.[8]

According to the Joint Committee on Community Nursing Service, community participation in planning nursing services was essential. The committee encouraged the development of a council on community nursing,[9] composed of nurses, representatives of agencies distributing nursing services within the community, members of allied professions, and laymen. The purpose of this council was to serve as a connecting link between the agencies that provided the service, the nurse who rendered the service, and the public who were the consumers of the service.[10]

Between 1935 and the outbreak of World War II,[11] the Joint Committee on Community Nursing Service concentrated on analyzing data relative to nursing needs and resources and devising mechanisms to insure distribution of needed nursing services. Committee members found nurse registries to be of invaluable assistance in achieving their objectives. Registries were repositories for data on the types of nursing services requested, the frequency of the demands for nursing services, and the kinds of workers employed to render nursing care. Moreover, registries were one of the most important community agencies concerned with the actual distribution of nursing services. As Genevieve M. Clifford, chairman of ANA's Committee on Registries, pointed out:

> The professional registry is no longer only a cooperative employment agency for nurses. In many places the professional registry has enlarged its activities and is working closely with other nursing and health agencies in meeting the nursing needs of the community.[12]

Nurses' Professional Registries

The development of nurse registries dates back to the late 1800s. Registries were established by many early training schools as a means of helping their graduates obtain employment and as a source of manpower for the institution.

At an early date, registries sprang up which were operated solely for profit. Employment agencies, taking advantage of the public's lack of knowledge about skilled nursing, offered the services of unskilled nursemaids and practical nurses in place of the graduate nurse. Moreover, in the 1880s a number of medical societies established nurse registries. Inasmuch as these societies were not interested in the standardization and upgrading of nursing, they made no distinction between graduate and nongraduate nurses.

One of the early tasks of trained nurses was to establish registries controlled and operated by the profession. Between 1900 and 1909, the American Nurses' Association carefully examined the need for nurse registries. It was the belief of the association that a central registry could serve as a bureau of nursing services for the community as well as an employment agency for nurses.

Papers were presented to convention delegates which set forth the pros and cons of operating a central registry for nurses. Those opposed to the establishment of registries argued that nurses would lose their identity. Those in favor of such agencies contended that central registries would "insure promptness in securing nurses best fitted to give the required nursing care to the patient."[13]

An examination of statistics on the development of central registries suggests that the advantages of a professionally-sponsored agency outweighed the disadvantages. By 1929, there were more than thirty-five central nurses' registries in various parts of the country.

In order to avoid confusion between the professionally-sponsored registry and the commercial employment agency, the term "official" was used to designate those early registries sponsored by a nursing group. In 1932, the board of directors of the American Nurses' Association adopted the following definition for the "nurses' professional registry:"

> The nurses' professional registry in a given community is that registry which has been so designated by the local district nurses' association and has been approved as such by the state nurses' association. Where there is no district nurses' association, the state nurses' association is to designate and approve the nurses' professional registry.[14]

Between 1932 and 1934, ANA's Committee of Distribution of Community Nursing Services studied ways to improve and standardize nurse registries. The committee encouraged the nursing profession to view the registry as an instrument to provide the community with needed nursing services. In 1934, the House of Delegates of the American Nurses' Association adopted the following recommendation:

> First, That as rapidly as possible we work toward the end that registries be organized as community agencies with a nurse executive, with a board composed of the

> consuming public, and with an advisory committee of representatives from the nursing and medical professions.
>
> Second, That we work toward the end that all nursing activities be worked out in terms of an adequate community program and that this program have community but not political control.[15]

By 1936, the association had undertaken an investigation of community nursing needs and registry development. According to the director of ANA headquarters, it was believed that data on these subjects would be:

> of inestimable value in the inauguration of programs which will attract to the profession the type of young woman who will be an asset to nursing; assist members of the nursing profession to secure salaries commensurate with those of other professional workers; assist with prevention of exploitation of members of the nursing profession, and result in more adequate distribution of nursing and a superior type of nursing service for the community.[16]

Data collected from various nurses' professional registries provided significant information about the types of services requested and the kinds of health workers engaged to render nursing services. This information provided insight into the educational preparation necessary to meet the consumer's needs for nursing services. It also revealed the need for a public relations program and a nurses' placement and counseling service.

According to data collected from monthly registry reports, the highest percentage (52 percent) of requests was for surgical nursing service. Requests for medical nursing service and obstetrical nursing service ranked second and third in the range of demands for nursing care. ANA encouraged schools of nursing to utilize this information in planning their curriculums. As Alma H. Scott, director of ANA headquarters, pointed out, "These data are of significance in determining whether or not students in schools of nursing are being prepared from an educational standpoint to meet immediate nursing needs of the community . . . ."[17]

One of the more startling facts revealed by ANA's study was the utilization of the untrained worker for nursing care of medically and acutely ill patients in their homes in the cities.[18] Although the employment of the nonprofessional registrant appeared to be associated with the economic status of the patient, the association believed that much could be accomplished through an intensive and continuous program of education of the community regarding the use of the registered nurse. Consequently, ANA, in conjunction with the other national nursing organizations, established the Nursing Information Bureau. The purpose of the Nursing Information Bureau, which was operated as an independent functional unit by the American Journal of Nursing Company, was "to disseminate through the appropriate channels to the profession and the public such factual material as may enable both the profession and the public to work cooperatively in providing individuals and communities with the amounts and kinds of nursing service they may require.[19]

The bureau's program was based on the assumption that many nurses and most lay persons were uninformed or misinformed about the scope and quality of nursing service and type of nursing education required to provide adequate nursing care. Two basic activities were the annual production of the handbook *Facts About Nursing* and the preparation, at intervals, of the bulletin *Professional Nursing* which was intended to provide nurses and other persons in key positions with factual material.

One of the most significant facts revealed by ANA's study of community nursing needs and registry development was the definite need to provide nurses with information regarding existing nursing opportunities in the different fields. Data collected from various parts of the country suggested that the so-called shortage of nurses was actually a shortage of facilities for making nurses available at a particular time for a specific job. In

1936, ANA's Advisory Council expressed an interest in the development of a placement service. As one delegate explained:

> With specialization becoming more and more the distinguishing characteristic of modern nursing, some sort of national clearinghouse promises to be of enormous importance. . . . We believe that national placement would not only provide greater opportunities for nurses, but would enable agencies and institutions which employ nurses to procure more varied nursing skills.[20]

Professional Counseling and Placement Service

During ANA's convention in 1936, attention was focused on the association's role in the establishment of a guidance and placement service for nurses. Headquarters Director Alma H. Scott pointed out to the convention delegates that "as the demands for nursing service in any community indicate the number of nurses who are needed and the types of services which they should be prepared to give, placement is of vital importance to members of the nursing profession.[21]

Committees were established to explore the feasibility of establishing a national professional guidance and placement service which would operate through the state nurses' associations. In January, 1943, the board of directors adopted a recommendation that ANA conduct a functional experiment at the Nurse Placement Service in Chicago in 1944.[22] The year-long study provided data for use in formulating a national plan of professional counseling and placement service which was approved by the ANA Board of Directors and referred to state nurses' associations for consideration and adoption in January, 1945.

By May, 1945, a majority of state nurses' associations had approved the plan for the ANA "PC&PS" program. On May 25, 1945, the Professional Counseling and Placement Service, Inc., of the American Nurses' Association was officially organized and incorporated in the State of New York as a subsidiary corporation, wholly-owned by the American Nurses' Association. The purposes of the service were outlined as follows:

> To conduct the business of a professional placement and employment agency and employment information office for graduate registered nurses in any state, territory, or possession of the United States or in the District of Columbia; to collect and disseminate data concerning the needs for nurses and affiliated workers in the care of the sick in specialized types of service, to be used as the basis of geographic distribution; to collect and refer credentials of qualified nurses and auxiliary workers in the care of the sick.[23]

Although the Professional Counseling and Placement Service was a nonprofit organization, ANA was advised to obtain a license as an employment agency in order to protect the corporation, the nurse, and the employer. Association efforts to secure such licensure met with protests from groups claiming that ANA, if granted a license, would monopolize the business of nurse registries.[24] Moreover, New York's Commissioner of Licenses refused to issue a license and also refused to rule that ANA's PC&PS was not required to secure such a license. Consequently, ANA was forced to commence legal proceedings in the Supreme Court of the State of New York in order to determine the official status of the service. In 1946, the Court ruled that there was no basis for the conclusion that the ANA Professional Counseling and Placement Service, Inc., was required to obtain a license as an employment agency.[25]

On September 1, 1945, the American Nurses' Association acquired and reorganized the Nurse Placement Service, Midwest Bureau, as the Chicago branch office for its Professional Counseling and Placement Service. This office served as a repository for records of nurses. The records of more than 13,000 professional nurses, compiled by the Nurse Placement Service, were donated to ANA. The office also functioned as a placement agency for applicants residing in states which had not yet established their own placement and counseling services.

Soon after the establishment of the PC&PS program, the Veterans Administration entered into an agreement with the American Nurses' Association for the rendering of services in the counseling of men and women veterans who had served as nurses in a military or naval service or who were interested in nurse training. It was stated that ANA's Professional Counseling and Placement Service, Inc., was the only organization of professional personnel known to the Veterans Administration to have a nationwide distribution of its own counseling centers.

In cooperation with the Florence Nightingale Foundation, the Professional Counseling and Placement Service also assumed responsibility for planning programs and itineraries for foreign nurses visiting the United States. By 1946, increasing numbers of foreign nurses expressed the desire to study, visit, or work in the United States for varying lengths of time. The American Nurses' Association compiled lists of schools of nursing which were willing to enroll foreign nurses in courses of study and agencies which were willing to employ them in certain capacities.

Efforts to establish nurses' professional registries and professional counseling and placement services were regarded as measures aimed at making skilled nursing available to all individuals who needed such care in their homes and hospitals, regardless of their economic status. As these agencies were able to clearly identify consumer needs, it became apparent that a well-prepared body of subsidiary or auxiliary workers was also needed to assume housekeeping duties and/or the care of well children and mildly ill, convalescent, handicapped, and aged persons who did not require the expert care of a registered professional nurse. As the chairman of a joint committee studying the utilization of subsidiary workers in caring roles pointed out:

> The nursing profession fully realizes that the professional nurse does not and will not provide for all the care that is needed. It seems appropriate as well as important for the three national nursing organizations to inform

themselves of the need for and the use of the subsidiary worker, whether she be called attendant, nursing aide, hospital aide, hospital helper, nurse's aide, practical nurse or domestic nurse.[26]

Subsidiary or Auxiliary Workers

Since the beginning of organized nursing in this country, the role of subsidiary workers has been a key issue. The improper utilization of these individuals in skilled nursing roles created significant problems for professional nurses. As early as 1898, convention delegates of the Nurses' Associated Alumnae discussed measures to control the activities of the untrained nursemaid.

By 1930, there were 153,443 untrained personnel practicing nursing in the United States.[27] According to information collected by the Committee on the Grading of Nursing Schools, only ten states had established legal provisions for the registration of subsidiary workers and these laws were only loosely enforced. In 1936, a committee of the National League of Nursing Education and the Division on Nursing of the Council of the American Hospital Association published a *Manual of the Essentials of Good Hospital Nursing Service*. Included in the manual was the warning statement that the use of subsidiary workers was fraught with danger to the welfare of the patient "unless carefully supervised and controlled."[28]

In light of their desire to ensure quality nursing care, the three national nursing organizations established, in 1936, a joint committee to outline principles and policies for the control of subsidiary workers in the care of the sick.[29] This joint committee concentrated on three questions.

1) Should the nursing profession assume the responsibility for the nursing care of all sick persons?

2) Do the three national nursing organizations recognize a need for subsidiary workers in any nursing services?

3) Should the three national nursing organizations define the

duties of subsidiary workers, assume responsibility for their preparation through properly conducted courses, and make provisions for state licensing in nurse practice acts?[30]

Between 1936 and 1947, the committee prepared and periodically revised statements on the subsidiary worker in the care of the sick. It was the conclusion of the committee that:

1) As a profession, nursing is responsible for safeguarding the public in the use of both registered professional nurses and nonprofessional workers in the care of the sick.

2) There is a need for two levels of workers in the care of the sick—one which relates to registered professional nurses and a second which relates to vocationally-prepared workers with "circumscribed nursing responsibilities."[31]

3) It is the responsibility of the nursing profession to outline principles and policies for the control of nonprofessional workers in the care of the sick.

4) All who nurse for hire should be licensed.

5) Until such time as a method for the control of the practice of nonprofessional workers is devised, the establishment of formal courses should not be encouraged.

6) Formal courses for nonprofessional workers should not be established in the same institution which conducts a state accredited school for professional nurses.

7) Ward helpers and orderlies should be prepared on the job for the specific tasks they are to perform within the institution employing them.

In the early forties, the title used to identify the nonprofessional worker engaged in nursing-related activities was carefully scrutinized. In 1942, the word "auxiliary" replaced the term "subsidiary" to identify

> "all persons, other than graduate registered nurses, who are employed in the care of the sick, such as so-called practical nurses, attendants, trained attendants, licensed attendants, licensed undergraduate nurses, licensed practical nurses, ward helpers and orderlies, nurses' aides, nursing aides, etc."[32]

In 1942, the National Association for Practical Nurse Education was organized to develop courses for vocational workers. By 1946, the title "practical nurse" was more generally used by the nursing and medical professions and the lay public than any other term. Consequently, in 1947, the Joint Committee on Auxiliary Nursing Service[33] identified two categories of workers assisting registered professional nurses: practical nurses and auxiliary workers.

According to the committee, auxiliary workers were "persons carrying out duties necessary for the support of nursing service, including those duties which involve minor services for patients performed under the direct supervision of professional or practical nurses."[34] These workers were not required to be licensed inasmuch as their activities did not constitute nursing practice.

The committee defined practical nurses as individuals "prepared to care for subacute, convalescent, and chronic patients and to assist the registered professional nurse in the care of others."[35] Inasmuch as these workers nursed for hire, the national nursing organizations favored mandatory licensure of practical nurses and accreditation of schools of practical nursing.

By the end of 1947, the efforts of the three national nursing organizations had resulted in the establishment of over fifty recognized schools of practical nursing and a degree of legal control of practical nurses in twenty states.

National Nursing Council for War Service

Between 1936 and 1946, the efforts of the American Nurses' Association were not only directed toward satisfying community nursing needs, they were also aimed at fulfilling the demands for nursing services created by a national emergency. As ANA President Julia Stimson pointed out, "The American Nurses' Association has provided certain organization machinery and working channels whereby the defense and war programs for nursing throughout this country are being carried on."[36]

The experiences of the Spanish American War and World War I alerted the nursing profession and the nursing organizations to health care problems in times of international crisis. During World War II, American nurses began to prepare for their involvement in nursing the sick and wounded long before the bombing of Pearl Harbor. In 1939, the *American Journal of Nursing* began to call upon nurses to increase the reserve in the Red Cross Nursing Service. In May, 1940, delegates to the thirty-second convention of the American Nurses' Association adopted the following resolution:

> Whereas, This is a time of unusual anxiety and concern to this nation and of great responsibility for the President of the United States,
>
> Be it resolved, That we, the delegates of the American Nurses' Association and members of the National League of Nursing Education now assembled in convention in Philadelphia, wish to offer the support and strength of our organizations in any nursing activity in which we can be of service to the country.[37]

In July, 1940, the leadership of the American Nurses' Association called a meeting of representatives of five national nursing organizations, the American Red Cross Nursing Service, and the federal agencies most immediately concerned with the utilization and extension of nursing resources. The purpose of the meeting was to discuss the actual role of nursing in national defense. These deliberations resulted in the formation of the National Nursing Council for War Service,[38] which was established to 1) promote a national inventory of registered nurses, 2) expand facilities of existing accredited schools of nursing, and 3) supply supplementary nursing services to hospitals and public health agencies.[39] As demands for civilian and military nursing services increased, the council concentrated on two projects: 1) a survey of national nursing resources and 2) a plan to secure federal funds to expand educational opportunities for nurses.

In 1940, for the first time, registered nurses were classified as professional workers by the U. S. Census Bureau. Unfortunately, the census data was of little value to those agencies planning the distribution of military and civilian nursing services. Inasmuch as the Census Bureau failed to differentiate between graduate nurses and nursing students, the data did not project an accurate picture of existing nursing resources.

The first act of the National Nursing Council for War Service was to initiate a national inventory of nurses in 1941.[40] From the responses of over 300,000 registered nurses, the council was able to identify approximately 100,000 nurses who were eligible for military duty, provided they could pass the physical examination.[41] A similar study was made in 1943 by the U. S. Public Health Service. By that time more than 36,000 nurses were actively engaged in military service.

In light of the need to increase both the numbers of graduate nurses and nursing students to meet wartime demands, the council also conducted surveys of nursing school resources. Discovering that most schools were not equipped to expand their instructional and housing facilities, the council requested the appropriation of federal funds for nursing education. The efforts of the council, as well as other groups, resulted in the enactment of a multi-million dollar federal aid program to 1) increase enrollment in nursing schools, 2) prepare additional teachers and other nurse personnel for positions requiring advanced education, and 3) provide refresher courses for inactive nurses willing to return to active practice. Moreover, in 1943, Congress enacted the Bolton Bill, which authorized the U. S. Public Health Service to establish the United States Cadet Nurse Corps. The purpose of this program was to extend financial aid, in the form of scholarships, to persons wishing to enroll in schools of nursing.

Four months after the establishment of the National Nursing Council for War service, the Subcommittee on Nursing of the government's Health and Medical Committee was organized. The purpose of the subcommittee was to analyze both military and civilian needs for professional and auxiliary nursing services, devise methods for meeting these needs, and cooperate with the nursing services of allied nations.

The National Nursing Council for War Service was primarily a planning agency for voluntary organizations, while the government's Subcommittee on Nursing functioned in investigative and advisory roles for federal projects. Together, these two national agencies coordinated federal and voluntary nursing programs and worked cooperatively to develop the most effective methods for utilizing and expanding the nation's nursing resources.

Voluntary Recruitment of Nursing Manpower

In June, 1944, delegates to ANA's "wartime convention" received a letter from President Franklin D. Roosevelt congratulating ANA members on the grand spirit they were showing during a time of international crisis.[42] President Roosevelt added:

> One of the most necessary things to keep up the morale of our fighting men is the knowledge that competent nursing care is always at hand for those injured in battle. The record made by the . . . nurses who are serving with the Army and the Navy is one in which every American citizen can take pride. We will need more nurses in the Army and the Navy and I know you will not fail in providing them.[43]

By September, 1944, a total of 33,000 sick and wounded individuals were being returned from combat zones each month.[44] Although one out of every four active nurses was engaged in military nursing service, there was a need for even more nursing manpower in the armed forces.

The need for civilian nursing services was equally as great. The expansion of manufacturing plants to accommodate defense and war industries created a greater demand for industrial nurses to help safeguard the health of workers. Industrial casualties from December, 1941, to January, 1944, amounted to 37,600 American workers. This figure exceeded the number of military casualties during the same period by 7,500 individuals. Between December, 1941, and January, 1944, over 200,000 workers were permanently disabled and 4,500,000 persons were temporarily disabled.[45]

The growth of prepayment hospitalization plans resulted in a higher rate of occupancy of hospital beds. According to a survey of health care facilities across the country, hospital admissions increased over thirty percent between 1940 and 1944. This created demands for larger numbers of general staff nurses.

Between 1941 and 1945, the American Nurses' Association, cooperating with the National Nursing Council for War Service and the Subcommittee on Nursing, encouraged the voluntary enlistment of nurses in the armed forces. At the same time, they worked to insure an adequate force of civilian nurses.

In 1942, the National Nursing Council for War Service established a national Committee on Supply and Distribution of Nurses to work with state committees in providing nurses for military and civilian nursing services. Due to insufficient financial support, the council was forced to turn the project over to the Procurement and Assignment Service for Physicians, Dentists, Veterinarians, Sanitary Engineers, and Nurses of the War Commission. The Procurement and Assignment Service was a federal agency which had been delegated responsibility for the uniform distribution of professional personnel in accordance with military and civilian needs. By 1943, the agency had devised procedures for classifying nurses according to their availability for military service or essentiality in civilian service. The agency had also formulated plans for a national registration of nurses in February, 1944. However, in January, 1944, the War Department announced curtailment of appointments to the Army Nurse Corps. Consequently, the Procurement and Assignment Service abandoned the proposed program of nurse registration.

In May, 1944, the War Commission unexpectedly raised the total ceiling for the Army Nurse Corps from 40,000 to 50,000 nurses. In cooperation with the Procurement and Assignment Service, the American Nurses' Association took several measures to insure provision of an additional 10,000 trained nurses for military duty.

ANA communicated the need for more nurses in the armed

forces through the *American Journal of Nursing,* which had a circulation of 78,000, and the monthly bulletin, *Professional Nursing,* which was distributed to 30,000 medical, hospital, and nursing administrators. In addition, the Nursing Information Bureau of the American Nurses' Association circulated thousands of leaflcts explaining the procurement and assignment of nurses.

Working with the National League of Nursing Education, ANA's Clearing Bureau of State Boards of Nurse Examiners endeavored to make the maximum number of registered nurses available for military and civilian services as rapidly as possible. This was accomplished by administering licensure examinations more often and by promoting state reciprocity in order to simplify licensure procedures.

Between December, 1941, and December, 1944, 81,145, registered nurses volunteered for duty in the Army and Navy Nurse Corps. During this same period, a total of 53,267 assignments were reported to the Red Cross by the Army and Navy. By January 1, 1945, 235,000 nurses had been classified according to their availability for military or civilian service.[46]

Nurse Draft Legislation

Although national nursing agencies were successful in recruiting a large voluntary nursing force, on January 6, 1945, President Roosevelt urged Congress to amend the Selective Service Act to provide for the induction of nurses into the armed forces. He warned that one of the most urgent requirements of the armed forces was the provision of more nurses. Nursing historians speculate that the President's proposal was triggered by the rise in demands for civilian nursing services and the subsequent reluctance of health care institutions to concede priority to military needs.[47]

Three days after President Roosevelt proposed the enactment of nurse draft legislation, a bill, H.R. 1284, was introduced in the House of Representatives which would amend the Selective

Training and Service Act of 1940 to provide for registration and induction of every registered nurse between the ages of eighteen and forty-five years of age into the land and naval forces of the United States.

In light of the implications of the proposed legislation, ANA convened a special session of its Advisory Council to discuss the meaning of a national service act, selective service act for all women, and selective service act for nurses. As a result of the meeting, ANA's Board of Directors issued the following statement:

> In view of the emergency declared by the President, the American Nurses' Association endorses the principle of a draft of nurses as a first step but only a first step to selective service for all women.[48]

The board of directors also went on record as offering its services in drafting additional legislation and voted "to do everything in its power to continue to accelerate the prompt and voluntary recruitment of nurses to meet the present emergency."[49]

Between January 19, 1945, and February 14, 1945, the House Committee on Military Affairs conducted hearings on H.R. 1284. Representatives of numerous agencies concerned with the distribution of nursing services submitted testimony. Katharine Densford, president of the American Nurses' Association, presented testimony on two occasions. Speaking for the 178,000 ANA members, she pointed out that Americans were actually faced with a fourfold problem:

1) The needs of the military,
2) The needs of veterans,
3) The needs of civilians, and
4) The need for two types of educational and training programs—basic programs to maintain a continuous supply of new graduate nurses and advanced programs to secure teachers, supervisors, and administrators.[50]

President Densford explained:

> These phases of the problem are not separate, but are interrelated and interdependent. They do not affect nurses alone, but are vital to physicians, hospitals, industry, public health agencies, and indeed to the entire American people. We believe, therefore, that to be acceptable, legislation must treat the problem comprehensively. The two legislative measures now under consideration by the committee, standing alone, are designed to care for only one part of the problem, and are therefore incomplete.[51]

She went on to outline the position of the American Nurses' Association:

> The American Nurses' Association has been vitally concerned with nursing care for our armed forces since it was organized . . . .
>
> It is the belief of the American Nurses' Association that the problem now presented may be dealt with by some federal agency, adequately implemented with funds, personnel and authority, and a federally-financed recruitment program promptly instituted—this program to be at least comparable in scope to those employed in the recruitment of WACS and WAVES. The War Manpower Commission has in the past, together with the Red Cross Nursing Service, provided an effective mechanism for the selection of nurses for the armed forces on a voluntary basis and for the stabilization of civilian nursing services, and we think it can do so in the future if properly strengthened.
>
> If the committee does not agree that the plan I have just outlined can be put into immediate effect, then the only other suggested method of attacking the problem is through the medium of a draft. The association would accept a draft of nurses as a first step, but only as a first step, in a Selective Service Act for all women. This should be supplemented by a General Service Act in

order that our drastically reduced civilian nursing service may be augmented by help from other groups of women.

Draft legislation should, as a minimum, provide for:

1. Commissioning of nurses;
2. Proper safeguards for nursing standards, including the restriction of induction to graduate registered professional nurses and to graduates of state accredited schools of nursing who are eligible for state examinations;
3. Prohibition against discrimination with respect to race, color, creed or sex;
4. Administration either wholly or in part through some Federal agency, such as the Procurement and Assignment Service of the War Manpower Commission, with proper provision for essential civilian requirements and the educational necessities of the profession, including deferments for teachers, supervisors, certain classes of graduate students and those in essential key positions;
5. Proper credit to the states for voluntary recruitments;
6. Power to grant deferments based on family relationship, with permission granted for voluntary enlistment;
7. A commissioned nurse corps for the Veterans Administration, with the same provisions applicable to this corps as are applied to the military;
8. Limited service for all women.[52]

Following the hearings, the House Committee on Military Affairs made a number of alterations to the original bill. An amendment was presented which embodied ANA's proposal to provide expansion and implementation of the existing programs for voluntary recruitment of nurses. Unfortunately, the amendment was defeated.

The final version of the bill was reintroduced as H.R. 2277. It was passed by the House on March 7 and referred to the Senate on March 8. Known as the Nurses Selective Service Act of 1945, this bill provided that graduate registered nurses and graduates of state-accredited schools of nursing who were eligible for examination for registration and who were between the ages of twenty and forty-five be subject to registration and selection for induction into the land and naval forces of the United States.

Provisions of the act did not apply to women with dependent children or to women married before March 15, 1945. It stated that members of certain religious groups might not be classified.

Between March 19, 1945, and March 26, 1945, the Senate Committee on Military Affairs held hearings on the proposed nurse draft legislation. On March 23, 1945, Katharine Densford, ANA President, reinterated the stand of the American Nurses' Association. She testified:

> There is a limit beyond which nurses cannot be mobilized under any plan. This is particularly true because the duties of nurses in this war-time emergency have been extended far beyond their recognized field. In fact, they have become the "shock absorbers" for any and all unmet needs, both in military and civilian hospitals. In combat areas as well as on the civilian front, medical care necessarily is spread so thin that nurses are doing minor surgery, giving infusions, putting patients up in traction, etc. Conversely, they are for the same reason being used as auxiliary workers. Because we do not have a sufficient number of nurses aides and ward attendants, highly skilled nurses are performing such duties as making beds, preparing trays, and guarding the linen closets. This again applies both to the military and civilian situation and is a serious drain on the available nurse power. Nurses in some military areas are badly overworked, and are greatly in need of relief. The situation in civilian hospitals, gentlemen, is, frankly,

almost as acute. Many nurses are working far beyond their strength, which will eventually mean beyond their efficiency. This situation can be corrected only when nurses not now active in the profession come forward and when women outside the profession assume non-professional routine duties in civilian hospitals. Unless the voluntary plan can be immediately implemented as I have suggested and vigorously pursued, the only alternative is through the medium of a draft. The Association has gone on record as being willing to accept a draft of nurses as a first step, but only as a first step, in a Selective Service Act for all women. This should be supplemented by a General Service Act in order that our drastically reduced civilian nursing service may be augmented by help from other groups of women. The American Nurses' Association offered a series of amendments to the House bill. In the main the present Bill H.R. 2277 incorporates these amendments and is satisfactory to the ANA—if we must abandon the voluntary plan—with these further suggestions:

1. Annual national registration of all graduate registered professional nurses under 65 years of age for the duration of the war.
2. Restriction of induction to graduate registered professional nurses, eliminating graduate nurses who are not registered.
3. Establishment of definite monthly quotas by the military, with the understanding that only nurses classified as 1A would be commissioned and that actual draft machinery would not be used as long as these enlistments met the quotas. To facilitate this, the Nursing Division of the Procurement and Assignment Service of the War Manpower Commission should be further implemented and strengthened.[53]

Although H.R. 2277 was altered before it was reported out of committee, the bill underwent further amendment on the floor of the Senate. A provision was added that anyone who had volunteered for religious service or was taking theological or religious training in order to consecrate her life to religious service would be exempt from draft. The provision for the exemption of women whose marriage occurred prior to March 15, 1945, was deleted.[54]

The bill was discussed on the floor of the Senate on April 9 and May 21. It was "passed over" on both occasions. Finally, on May 24, 1945, the Acting Secretary of War stated that the rapidly changing events in the war had made it appropriate to reconsider the necessity for further action on pending legislation for the draft of nurses.[56] At his suggestion, Congress took no action on H.R. 2277. Although the legislation to draft nurses was eventually abandoned, the events surrounding the proposal of such legislation are considered a focal point in nursing history.[57]

Postwar Planning

According to Katharine Densford Dreves, nursing in the postwar period stood "at the cross roads."[58] The continued growth of the nursing profession was dependent upon a carefully planned program of development and realignment.

Recognizing the need for co-ordinated action, the leaders of the nursing organizations set up the National Nursing Planning Committee in April, 1944, to outline a five-year program for nationwide action in the field of nursing. The committee was composed of the presidents, executive secretaries, and planning committee chairmen of five national nursing organizations; representatives from the American Association of Industrial Nurses and the National Association for Practical Nurse Education; directors of the nursing divisions of the American Red Cross and certain federal agencies; and the chairman and executive secretary of the National Nursing Council for War Service.

The committee defined five areas in which programs for study and action should be developed:

1) Maintenance and development of nursing services,

2) A program of nursing education (professional and practical),

3) Channels and means for distribution of nursing services,

4) Implementation of standards to protect the best interests of the public and the nursing profession, and

5) Information and public relations program.

Following World War II, this committee exerted much effort to implement a nursing program which would enable the profession to provide and maintain a high level of nursing service wherever it was needed.

During the decade 1936 to 1946, the American Nurses' Association came to realize the importance of cooperation and collaboration in the provision of nursing services, both in times of peace and war. As ANA President Susan C. Francis pointed out:

> Today we, the largest organized body of professional nurses in the United States, have reached a period of concentration of effort; a period of working together for the good of our patients as well as for our own individual welfare; a period when we realize that we must work not only with each other but with the members of the communities which we serve, if that service is to leave the nurse and the patient the richer for their reciprocal experience.[59]

REFERENCES

1. Pearl McIver, "Subsidiary Workers in the Care of the Sick," *Advisory Council Reports of the Thirty-Second Convention (May 12-17, 1940) of the American Nurses' Association* (New York: American Nurses' Association, 1940), 16.
2. Many historians assert that, following the passage of the Social Security Act of 1935, the federal government exerted increasing influence on the development and expansion of nursing.
3. Public Law No. 271, Seventy-Fourth Congress, H.R. 7260.
4. Interdepartmental Committee to Coordinate Health and Welfare Activities, *Report of the Technical Committee on Medical Care* (Washington, D.C., 1938), 30-31.
5. Alma H. Scott, "Report of the Headquarters Director," *Proceedings of the Thirtieth Convention (June 21-26, 1936) of the American Nurses' Association and Institute*

for Registrars (June 27-28, 1936) (New York: American Nurses' Association, 1936), 117.

6. Susan C. Francis, "President's Address," *Proceedings of the Thirtieth Convention,* 103.
7. The forerunner of this committee was a Joint Committee on Distribution of Nursing Services established in 1928, which later became ANA's Committee on Distribution of Nursing Services.
8. Elsbeth H. Vaughan, "Joint Committee on Community Nursing Service Report," *Proceedings of the Thirty-First Convention (April 24-29, 1938) of the American Nurses' Association* (New York: American Nurses' Association, 1938), 397.
9. The development of councils on community nursing were first recommended by ANA's Committee on the Distribution of Nursing Services in the early 1930s.
10. Vaughan, 396.
11. In December, 1941, it was agreed that the program of the Joint Committee would rest in abeyance. Efforts were directed toward creation of state nursing councils for war service.
12. Genevieve M. Clifford, "Committee on Registries Report," *Proceedings of the Thirty-First Convention (April 24-29, 1938) of the American Nurses' Association* (New York: American Nurses' Association, 1938), 346.
13. Ella Best, "How Are The Goals of Tomorrow's Community Nursing Service to Be Reached?" *Proceedings of the Thirtieth Convention (June 21-26, 1936) of the American Nurses' Association and Institute for Registrars (June 27-28, 1936)* (New York: American Nurses' Association, 1936), 562.
14. Genevieve M. Clifford, "Nurses' Professional Registries," *Proceedings of the Thirty-First Convention (April 24-29, 1938) of the American Nurses' Association* (New York: American Nurses' Association, 1938), 50.
15. Ella Best, "How Are The Goals of Tomorrow's Community Nursing Service to Be Reached?" *Proceedings of the Thirtieth Convention (June 21-26, 1936) of the American Nurses' Association and Institute for Registrars (June 27-28, 1936)* (New York: American Nurses' Association, 1936), 564.
16. Alma H. Scott, "Report of Director of Headquarters—1934-1936," *Proceedings of the Thirtieth Convention (June 21-26, 1936) of the American Nurses' Association and Institute for Registrars (June 27-28, 1936)* (New York: American Nurses' Association, 1936), 134.
17. Alma H. Scott, "Report of Director of Headquarters," *Proceedings of the Thirty-First Convention (April 24-29, 1938) of the American Nurses' Association* (New York: American Nurses' Association, 1938), 154.
18. Alma H. Scott, "Report of Director of Headquarters—1934-1936," *Proceedings of the Thirtieth Convention (June 21-26, 1936) of the American Nurses' Association and Institute for Registrars (June 27-28, 1936)* (New York: American Nurses' Association, 1936), 130.
19. Stella Goostray, "Nursing Information Bureau Committee Report," *Proceedings of the Thirtieth Convention (June 21-26, 1936) of the American Nurses' Association and Institute for Registrars (June 27-28, 1936)* (New York: American Nurses' Association, 1936), 314-315.
20. Elizabeth S. Soule, "Question of American Nurses' Association Assuming Responsibility for Placement Service," *Proceedings of the Thirtieth Convention (June 21-26, 1936) of the American Nurses' Association and Institute for Registrars (June 27-28, 1936)* (New York: American Nurses' Association, 1936), 31-32.

21. Alma H. Scott, "Report of Director of Headquarters—1934-1936," *Proceedings of the Thirtieth Convention (June 21-26, 1936) of the American Nurses' Association and Institute for Registrars (June 27-28, 1936)* (New York: American Nurses' Association, 1936), 145.
22. The Board of Directors realized that the collection of statistical data regarding placement and counseling during the period of national emergency would be of comparative value only. However, they did believe that some fundamental principles and policies concerning the operation of a nurse placement service could be developed through such a study.
23. Helen M. Roser, "Nursing Information Bureau Report," *Proceedings of the Thirty-Fifth Biennial Convention (September 22-27, 1947) of the American Nurses' Association,* Volume I: *House of Delegates* (New York: American Nurses' Association, 1946), 164.
24. Nurse registries were considered the most strategic centers for the development of placement and professional counseling services.
25. Helen M. Roser, "Nursing Information Bureau Report," *Proceedings of the Thirty-Fifth Biennial Convention (September 22-27, 1947) of the American Nurses' Association,* Volume I: *House of Delegates* (New York: American Nurses' Association, 1946), 165.
26. Ella Hasenjaeger, "Joint Committee to Outline Principles and Policies for the Control of Subsidiary Workers in the Care of the Sick," *Proceedings of the Thirty-First Convention (April 24-29, 1938) of the American Nurses' Association* (New York: American Nurses' Association, 1938), 400.
27. "The Subsidiary Worker," *American Journal of Nursing,* Vol. XXXVII (March, 1937), 1 (reprint).
28. Division on Nursing of the Council of the American Hospital Association and a Committee of the National League of Nursing Education, *Manual of the Essentials of Good Hospital Nursing Service* (New York: National League of Nursing Education, 1936).
29. This committee replaced an NLNE committee, established in 1933.
30. Ella Hasenjaeger, "Joint Committee to Outline Principles and Policies for the Control of Subsidiary Workers in the Care of the Sick," *Proceedings of the Thirty-First Convention (April 24-29, 1938) of the American Nurses' Association* (New York: American Nurses' Association, 1938), 400.
31. Ellen Creamer, "Joint Committee on Auxiliary Nursing Service of ANA, NLNE, and NOPHN Report," *House of Delegates Reports of the Thirty-Fourth Convention (June 4-7, 1944) of the American Nurses' Association* (New York: American Nurses' Association, 1944), 83.
32. Joint Committee of ANA, NLNE, and NOPHN, *Subsidiary Workers in the Care of the Sick* (New York: American Nurses' Association, 1941), 4.
33. The committee was composed of representatives of the American Nurses' Association, National League of Nursing Education, National Organization for Public Health Nursing, National Association of Colored Graduate Nurses, Association of Collegiate Schools of Nursing, and National Association for Practical Nurse Education.
34. Joint Committee on Auxiliary Nursing Service, *Practical Nurses and Auxiliary Workers for the Care of the Sick* (New York: American Nurses' Association, 1947), 11.

35. *Ibid.*, 7.
36. Julia Stimson, "President's Address," *Excerpts from Proceedings of the Thirty-Third Convention (May 17-22, 1942) of the American Nurses' Association* (New York: American Nurses' Association, 1942), 41.
37. "Report of Committee on Resolutions," *Report of the Thirty-Second Convention (May 12-17, 1940) of the American Nurses' Association* (New York: American Nurses' Association, 1940), 80.
38. The Council was originally named the National Nursing Council for War Service.
39. The groups originally represented on the Council were: the American Nurses' Association, National League of Nursing Education, National Organization for Public Health Nursing, Association of Collegiate Schools of Nursing, National Association of Colored Graduate Nurses, American Red Cross Nursing Service, Federal Children's Bureau, U.S. Army Nurse Corps, U.S. Navy Nurse Corps, U.S. Public Health Service, Nursing Service of the U.S. Veterans Administration, and Nursing Service of the Department of Indian Affairs.
40. With the financial help of the American Red Cross, the U. S. Public Health Service sponsored this survey. The American Nurses' Association, National League of Nursing Education, and National Organization for Public Health Nursing served as co-sponsors.
41. Pearl McIver, "Registered Nurses in the U.S.A.," *American Journal of Nursing*, Vol. XLII (July , 1942), 769.
42. Julia C. Stimson, "President's Report," *Proceedings of the Thirty-Fourth Convention (June 4-7, 1944) of the American Nurses' Association* (New York: American Nurses' Association, 1944), 33.
43. *Ibid.*
44. Mary M. Roberts, *American Nursing: History and Interpretation* (New York: The Macmillan Company, 1954), 375.
45. Katharine J. Densford, "ANA Testimony Regarding H.R. 1284," presented to the Military Affairs Committee of the U. S. House of Representatives, 8.
46. *Ibid.*, 5-7
47. Mary M. Roberts, *American Nursing: History and Interpretation* (New York: The Macmillan Company, 1954), 380.
48. Katharine J. Densford, "Report of the President," *Proceedings of the Thirty-Fifth Biennial Convention (September 22-27, 1946) of the American Nurses' Association*, Volume I: *House of Delegates* (New York: American Nurses' Association, 1946), 17.
49. *Ibid.*
50. Katharine J. Densford, "ANA Testimony Regarding H.R. 1284," presented to the Military Affairs Committee of the U. S. House of Representatives, 9-10.
51. *Ibid.*, 10.
52. *Ibid.*, 8-10.
53. Katharine J. Densford, "ANA Testimony Regarding H.R. 2277," presented to the Military Affairs Committee of the U. S. Senate, 7-8.
54. Katharine J. Densford, "Report of the President," *Proceedings of the Thirty-Fifth Biennial Convention (September 22-27, 1946) of the American Nurses' Association*, Volume I: *House of Delegates* (New York: American Nurses' Association, 1946), 20.
55. On May 8, 1945, Germany had surrendered unconditionally.
56. Katharine J. Densford, "Report of the President," *Proceedings of the Thirty-Fifth*

Biennial Convention (September 22-27, 1946) of the American Nurses' Association, Volume I: *House of Delegates* (New York: American Nurses' Association, 1946), 20.

57. In 1952, ANA's House of Delegates authorized the Board of Directors to approve legislation for Selective Service for nurses in the event such legislation should be introduced in a time of national emergency.
58. National Nursing Planning Committee, *A Comprehensive Program for Nation-Wide Action in the Field of Nursing* (New York: National Nursing Council for War Service, Inc., 1945), 4.
59. Susan C. Francis, "President's Address," *Proceedings of the Thirty-First Convention (April 24-29, 1938) of the American Nurses' Association* (New York: American Nurses' Association, 1938), 102.

1948-1958

Blueprint for Action

Throughout the history of modern nursing in America, the demand for nursing services during wartime has acted as a catalyst in the growth and development of the profession of nursing. Each major war in which the United States was involved between 1861 and 1945 presented distinct challenges for nursing.

When the Civil War began in 1861, there were virtually no trained nurses in the country. Some 2,000 men and women from the North and South volunteered for nursing assignments in field hospitals and on hospital transports. Although these individuals performed a valuable service, the experiences of the Civil War focused attention on the weaknesses of the volunteer system of nursing and created an interest in reform.

During the Civil War, discerning women discovered that "motherly instinct" and good intentions did not adequately equip individuals to nurse the sick and wounded. Many historians assert that the establishment of trained nurses in the United States came as a direct result of the pioneering work done by women during the Civil War.

During the Spanish American War, a large nursing force was desperately needed because of the epidemics of typhoid fever, malaria, and yellow fever which afflicted thousands of American soldiers. Although over 400 nurse training schools were in existence and more than 2,000 trained nurses were available, there was no organized army nurse corps, as we know it today, at the outset of the 1898 war. The difficulties encountered in the recruitment and supervision of an adequate force of trained nurses called attention to the need for a systematic method of organizing nurses for health services during wartime. Nursing leaders were motivated to fight for legislation to establish a permanent army nursing service under the direction of a qualified nurse. With the enactment of the Army Reorganization Act of 1901, an army nurse corps was established under nursing directorship. This represented one of the earliest attempts of the nursing profession to promote legislation which established nursing standards and ensured supervision of nurses by nurses.

According to historians, World War I, more than any previous war, helped to make Americans fully cognizant of their reliance on nurses. Between 1917 and 1918, some 24,000 graduate nurses cared for battle casualties and victims of world-wide epidemics of influenza and pneumonia. It was the first time in the history of the United States that provision was made in the armed forces for a division of nurses in definite ratio to the number of soldiers.

The availability of trained nurses for military service did not pose a problem during World War I. The problem which did exist was one of determining the most effective utilization of nursing manpower as well as identification of measures to increase nursing resources. The desire of the nursing profession to insure the adequate development of nursing resources led to the recommendation that an army school of nursing be established. The Army School of Nursing was authorized by the War Department in 1918. It has been suggested that the establishment of this school played a key role in the development of American nursing, for it served as an example of an institution which effectively employed principles of management and teaching.

Although the experiences of the Spanish American War and World War I alerted nurses to health care problems in times of international crises, the United States' involvement in World

War II placed extraordinary and unexpected demands upon the profession. By September, 1944, 33,000 sick and wounded soldiers were being returned from combat zones each month. Although one out of every four active nurses was engaged in military nursing service, there was a need for even more nursing manpower in the armed forces.

The problems associated with the recruitment of an adequate voluntary nursing force were compounded by increased demands for civilian nursing services. The expansion of manufacturing plants to accommodate defense and war industries created a greater demand for industrial nurses to help safeguard the health of workers. Industrial casualties from December, 1941, to January, 1944, exceeded the number of military casualties during the same period by 7,500 individuals. For the first time in American history, the nursing profession was faced with the possibility of legislative action to draft nurses.

The wartime demands for nursing services triggered the development of the Government Subcommittee on Nursing and the National Nursing Council for War Service.[1] These two agencies successfully coordinated federal and voluntary nursing programs and worked cooperatively to develop the most effective methods for utilizing and expanding the nation's nursing resources. As the war progressed, it became increasingly apparent that coordinated action in nursing would be as important in the postwar period as it had proven to be during the war. As one observer pointed out, the circumstances of World War II demonstrated the fact that the nursing profession could not function effectively without an extensive plan for organized action.

According to nursing leaders, it was essential that organized nursing concentrate on three objectives in the postwar era:

1) Development and implementation of standards for the educational preparation and practice of the nursing profession and nursing's auxiliary force,

2) Promotion and protection of the economic and general welfare of qualified nurse practitioners, and

3) Provision of quality nursing services to all individuals at reasonable costs.

Consequently, a five-year "Comprehensive Program for Nationwide Action in the Field of Nursing" was developed in 1945. It was generally agreed that the national nursing organizations which were members of the national council would assume responsibility for war service coordination of the various phases of the program. As a preliminary measure, an extensive study was undertaken between 1945 and 1952 to determine what structural revisions would be necessary in the nursing organizations to enable them to best achieve the desired objectives.

By 1945, seven national nursing organizations had been established: the National League of Nursing Education (1893), the American Nurses' Association (1897), the National Association of Colored Graduate Nurses (1908), the National Organization for Public Health Nursing (1912), the American Association of Nurse Anesthetists (1931), the Association of Collegiate Schools of Nursing (1932), and the American Association of Industrial Nurses (1942). Although each body was originally formed to meet a specific need and represent interests not covered by any other organization, duplication of nursing activities and programming occurred frequently.

As early as 1924, the American Nurses' Association, the National League of Nursing Education, and the National Organization for Public Health Nursing explored the practicability of consolidation. An investigation was initiated to examine the relationships of the three organizations to each other, to the nursing profession, and to the community. At that point in time, a recommendation was adopted that each organization retain its autonomy.

Some fifteen years later, the board of directors of the American Nurses' Association suggested that another committee be formed to consider the question of the formation of one national nursing organization. When the United States became involved in World War II, the work of this special committee on consolidation was discontinued. The issue of a structural study of nursing organizations was not resolved until January, 1944, when the Committee on Domestic Postwar Planning of the National Nursing Council for War Service recommended:

> That in order to implement the postwar nursing program there should be a review of the organization structure of the member agencies of the council to determine whether their organization is such as will make for effective handling of postwar problems.[2]

After appointing a small committee to study this matter, the board of directors of the American Nurses' Association adopted the following recommendation:

> That national professional nursing organizations undertake a joint survey of their organization structure, administration, functions, and facilities to determine whether a more effective means can be found for professional nursing and nurses.
>
> That an advisory committee made up of board members of the national professional nursing organizations act in an advisory capacity for this study.
>
> That the study be made by an impartial expert or group such as the Brookings Institution.
>
> That this undertaking be financed jointly by the organizations concerned in such proportion as determined by the finance committee of the participating organizations.[3]

Initially, the Promoting Committee for the Study of the Structure of National Nursing Organizations was composed of representatives[4] of the American Nurses' Association, the National League of Nursing Education, and the National Organization for Public Health Nursing. In late 1944 and early 1945, the National Association of Colored Graduate Nurses, the Association of Collegiate Schools of Nursing, and the American Association of Industrial Nurses were asked to participate on the committee.[5]

Viewing the project as a cooperative enterprise, these organizations spent almost two years drawing up the initial plans for the study. As Pearl McIver, ANA First Vice President, pointed out:

> It was felt that we should not have a study made of our present structure until we had a well-defined program. It seemed best that the profession should set forth the program which it hoped to accomplish and then a research organization be asked to evaluate our present machinery to see whether those objectives could be attained therewith.[6]

In April, 1946, the promotion committee selected Raymond Rich Associates to conduct the detailed study of the six organizations. The actual study was made during the spring and summer of 1946. Addressing delegates attending ANA's thirty-fifth convention, Miss McIver observed:

> It took some time to find a satisfactory research group to make this study. Raymond Rich Associates was selected because that company had made similar studies and surveys of national organizations. Those of us who attended that final structure meeting, I think, were convinced that we had not made a mistake. They made an exhaustive study and collected something like six filing cases of cross-indexed information on nursing, nursing needs, organization, what their programs are, and what they hope to accomplish. After finishing this they began to interview people. While it was impossible to visit every state and to interview all nurses, I think they got a good cross-section of different types of nurses in different types of nursing positions.[7]

The Raymond Rich Report

Initially, the overall goal of the study conducted by Rich Associates was to identify structural principles essential for the efficient and effective operation of the existing nursing organizations. Upon completion of a two-month study, the investigative agency concluded that all general and specialist nursing organizations should be consolidated into one united body.

According to Rich Associates, the American Nurses' Association, the National League of Nursing Education, the National Organization for Public Health Nursing, the Association of Collegiate Schools of Nursing, the National Association of Colored Graduate Nurses, and the American Association of Industrial Nurses[8] were divided on three key points: non-nurse membership, devotion to special interests, and program emphasis.[9] Raymond Rich observed that the times necessitated that "nursing be able to speak authoritatively with one strong voice and to act quickly when necessary as a united force."[10] Therefore, he recommended that all professional nurses be united in one national nursing organization structured to: 1) include autonomous special interest groups, 2) employ appropriate mechanisms to effectuate maximum service to the profession and the public, 3) maximize direct participation of membership in decision-making concerning major nursing issues, 4) provide suitable leadership training programs, and 5) facilitate cooperation and assistance from allied professions and the general public.

In a lengthy report to the six organizations sponsoring the study, Rich Associates set forth a number of recommendations regarding the essential elements of a new nursing organization.[11]

With regard to membership composition, Rich Associates recommended that 1) all professional nurse members of the six national nursing organizations and those registered nurses applying before the end of a designated period of time be eligible, without further classification, for professional nurse membership in the new association, and 2) after a reasonable transition period, this membership category be open only to nurses who graduate from schools of nursing accredited by the new nursing association[12] or who pass a special examination prescribed by the association.

The investigative agency recommended against consideration of the incorporation of nursing auxiliary membership until the functions and standards of professional nurses, practical nurses, and other auxiliary workers were more clearly defined. However, inclusion of non-nurse membership was presented as a viable option.

In light of study findings, Rich Associates recommended that a system of reconstituted district associations[13] be established as the constituent bodies of the national association. In addition, they recommended that these newly structured district associations form reconstituted state associations to deal with common intrastate problems. Under the proposal offered by Rich Associates, the governing body, the House of Delegates, would be composed of a proportionate number of representatives from the members of each reconstituted district. This body would be responsible for the election of a fifteen-member board of directors (one-third to be chosen annually for three year terms). The board would be given full power to act as the interim governing body. They would also be empowered to elect the president of the association from the board membership.

Rich Associates proposed that the structural scheme of the organization include the following units: specialist sections, commissions, a national academy of nurses, and a national nursing center.

As diagrammed in Chart I, they recommended the establishment of a series of sections, representing each of the nursing specialties, which would be empowered to carry on activities necessary to further special interests. Every member of the new association would elect membership in one of the specialist sections for voting purposes.

They recommended the establishment of a series of commissions (Chart II) to deal with those basic problems affecting all nurses, regardless of their nursing specialties. Each commission would be charged to study a general problem-area in nursing, report its findings and recommendations to the House of Delegates for action, and carry on other activities authorized by the House of Delegates. The purposes of the Commissions on Ethics

RAYMOND RICH ASSOCIATES' PROPOSALS FOR STRUCTURAL UNITS

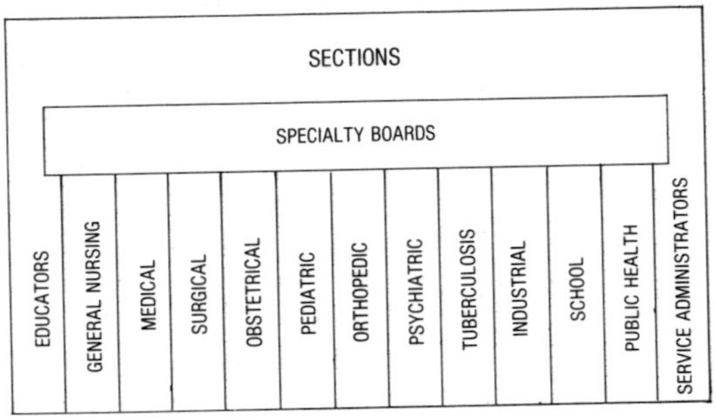

SECTIONS												
	SPECIALTY BOARDS											
EDUCATORS	GENERAL NURSING	MEDICAL	SURGICAL	OBSTETRICAL	PEDIATRIC	ORTHOPEDIC	PSYCHIATRIC	TUBERCULOSIS	INDUSTRIAL	SCHOOL	PUBLIC HEALTH	SERVICE ADMINISTRATORS

Chart I

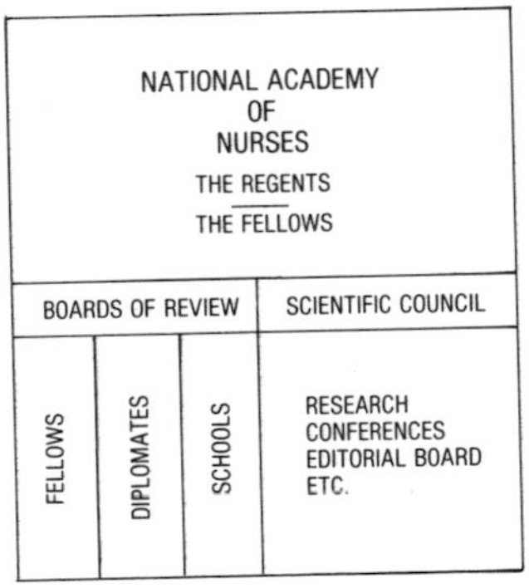

NATIONAL ACADEMY OF NURSES THE REGENTS THE FELLOWS			
BOARDS OF REVIEW			SCIENTIFIC COUNCIL
FELLOWS	DIPLOMATES	SCHOOLS	RESEARCH CONFERENCES EDITORIAL BOARD ETC.

Chart III

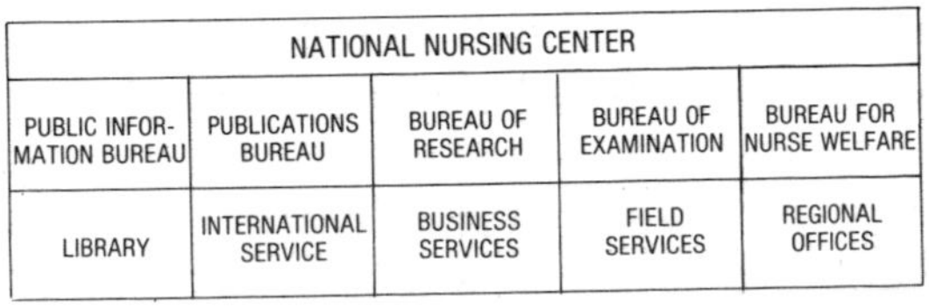

NATIONAL NURSING CENTER				
PUBLIC INFOR-MATION BUREAU	PUBLICATIONS BUREAU	BUREAU OF RESEARCH	BUREAU OF EXAMINATION	BUREAU FOR NURSE WELFARE
LIBRARY	INTERNATIONAL SERVICE	BUSINESS SERVICES	FIELD SERVICES	REGIONAL OFFICES

Chart IV

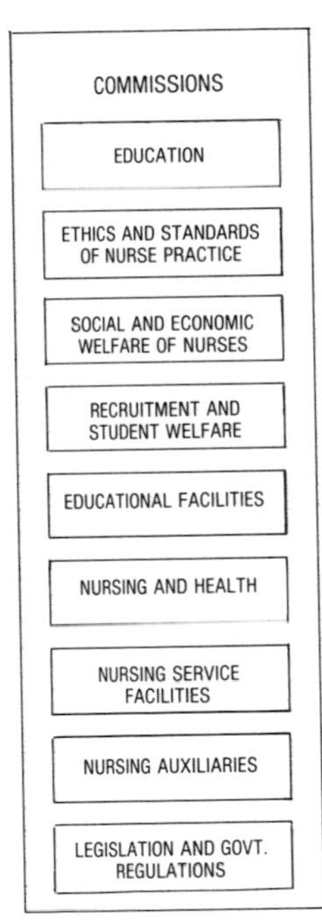

Chart II

and Standards of Nurse Practice, Social and Economic Welfare of Nurses, Nursing Auxiliaries, Legislation, and Government Regulations were self-explanatory. Rich Associates characterized the other five commissions as follows. The Commission on Recruitment and Student Welfare would be concerned with measures for recruiting the needed number of candidates for schools of nursing, graduate programs, and practical nurse training schools accredited by the new nursing association. The Commission on Education would focus on issues concerning educational counseling, curricula for basic and graduate nursing programs, testing, and accreditation. The Commissions on Educational Facilities and Nursing Service Facilities would examine problems of organization, administration, finance, and distribution of educational establishments and nursing service facilities. The Commission on Nursing and Health would investigate ways and means of making adequate nursing services available to all who needed it.

In order to insure the highest quality of nursing in the future, Rich Associates recommended that a National Academy of Nurses be set up, which would derive its authority from the House of Delegates. The academy would seek endowments and other sources of financial support to promote research in nursing. Fellows of the academy would be professional nurse members of the new association who passed specialty examinations in nursing. The governing council (regents) would be elected by the fellows of the academy. Incorporated in the structure of the National Academy of Nurses (Chart III) would be three distinct review boards as well as a scientific council which would sponsor nursing research projects, scientific programing, and nursing research publications. Rich Associates also recommended that the academy be empowered to act as sponsor for two allied, but independent organizations: a Conference of State Boards of Nurse Examiners (a clearinghouse for state board problems) and a Conference of Accredited Schools of Nursing (a clearinghouse for common problems of schools accredited by the new nursing association).

To implement the basic activities of the national nursing organization, assist in the work of the commissions, specialty sections, and National Academy of Nurses, and to serve the needs of the nursing profession and the public, Rich Associates proposed the establishment of a National Nursing Center which would be responsible to the board of directors of the new nursing association. As identified in Chart IV, the center would be composed of various bureaus and services.

Recognizing the need to provide the existing nursing associations with more than one option, Rich Associates presented two plans of organization which employed the structural recommendations explained above.

Plan I proposed the establishment of a single organization, the American Nursing Association, to represent the entire nursing field. This plan, which called for the immediate establishment of five membership categories (professional nurses, public, allied professions, nursing schools and service agencies, and non-nurse organizations), would provide for complete incorporation and maximum participation of non-nurse members.

Plan II proposed the development of two separate organizations linked together by a unifying center unit. One organization, operating under the title American Nurses' Association, would be reserved for professional nurse membership. The purpose of this newly-formed organization would be to provide services to the nursing profession. The other organizaton, the National Organization for Nursing Service, would be composed of seven categories of membership: professional nurses, public, allied professions, schools of nursing, nursing service agencies, non-nursing organizations, and local councils for nursing service. This body would focus on issues and problems related to the distribution of nursing services to the community. It was the recommendation of Rich Associates that these two organizations establish a nonprofit corporation (the National Nursing Center). According to Rich Associates, this corporation would operate "the pooled and combined major services of the two organizations, for purposes of increasing their usefulness" to the nursing profession and the public.[14]

The chief difference between Plan I and Plan II was the degree to which non-nurse members were incorporated and permitted to participate in association activities. Plan I provided for virtually equal participation of both nurse and non-nurse members in the activities of the single national nursing organization. Plan II restricted the opportunities for non-nurse participation by establishing two separate organizations—one reserved for professional nurse membership, the other composed of both nurse and non-nurse members.

At the conclusion of their report on the structure of organized nursing, Rich Associates suggested that as a "next step," six representatives from each organization be elected and authorized to act as the Joint Committee on the Structure of National Nursing Organizations: 1) to recommend possible structural changes to the six organizations, 2) to develop a plan to explain the program for joint reorganization, and 3) to establish the necessary reorganization machinery.

The governing bodies of the National League of Nursing Education, the National Organization for Public Health Nursing, the National Association of Colored Graduate Nurses, the Association of Collegiate Schools of Nursing, and the American Association of Industrial Nurses accepted this recommendation. After lengthy discussion and debate during the 1946 convention, ANA's House of Delegates adopted the following recommendations:

1) That the American Nurses' Association, through its constituent associations, complete a detailed analysis of the Rich Report and the feasibility of its proposals,

2) That the American Nurses' Association be represented by twelve members because of the organization's large membership,[15] these representatives to include proportionate representation from private duty, federal government, institutional, industrial, and men nurses sections of the association,

3) That the authority granted ANA's twelve representatives be restricted to receiving the report as analyzed and interpreted to the members of the joint structure committee, and

4) That, before ANA approval shall be given in regard to the general structure report, it must be approved by the House of Delegates at a special session to be called no later than October 1, 1947.[16]

The adoption of these recommendations was based on the belief that the American Nurses' Association should study and evaluate the report of Rich Associates in relation to its own organization and interpret it to its own membership. This course of action departed from the procedure suggested by Rich Associates and adopted by the other five nursing organizations, that all six organizations undertake a joint study of the proposals. Moreover, in comparison to the authority granted to representatives of the other nursing organizations, ANA committee members functioned merely as auditors. As a result of the action of the House of Delegates, representatives of the American Nurses' Association could not

> take part in discussions, make motions, or vote in meetings of the joint committee, with regard to: 1) explaining and interpreting the report to national, state, and local nursing organizations and their individual members, and developing exchange of opinion and suggestions, 2) adjusting a future plan for a new structure in accordance with opinions and suggestions obtained, for later submission, or 3) raising the necessary funds to carry on 1) and 2).[17]

Consequently, the American Nurses' Association was unable to participate in the formulation of the committee's proposals which were submitted to all six organizations in August, 1947. These proposals included the following recommendations:

1) A joint subcommittee be appointed to study the possibility of combining the programs of the National League of Nursing Education, the National Organization for Public Health Nursing,

and the Association of Collegiate Schools of Nursing as "a practical beginning toward a comprehensive organized effort for better nursing service,"[18]

2) A joint subcommittee be appointed to study and plan ways in which the American Nurses' Association could absorb the functions of the National Association of Colored Graduate Nurses,[19]

3) A joint subcommittee be formed to analyze the functions of the existing nursing organizations as they relate to industrial nursing and to formulate recommendations aimed at unification of these interests, and

4) A new or revised organization structure include provision for non-nurse members who would be restricted from participation in decision-making activities regarding strictly professional matters.

Special Session of the House of Delegates

Confronted with the proposals of Rich Associates and the recommendations of the Joint Committee on the Structure of National Nursing Organizations, the American Nurses' Association convened the first special session of the House of Delegates. On September 13 and 14, 1947, some 1,500 ANA members assembled to consider future directions of the organization. As one individual observed, "Never in the history of the nursing profession . . . have so many nurses taken time to study seriously the where, why, and how of their organization's activities."[20]

After two full days of deliberations, delegates chose to adopt neither Plan I nor Plan II presented by Rich Associates. In the closing business session, ANA President Katharine Densford summarized the tenor of the discussions:

> You agree you want a UNITED FRONT ORGANIZATION FOR NURSING. You want a strong, vital organization representing all of the nurses. You want to eliminate duplication, overlapping. You want an organization that will eliminate power politics, many different

> associations in the marketplace crying their wares. From the public standpoint, you recognize the public will favor nursing more if you are a UNITED FRONT, and not a series of separate organizations competing for public interest . . . .[21]

However, Miss Densford concluded, "Stripped of everything but essentials, your discussions indicate that there is a difference of opinion on the method to bring about unity—a unified organization."[22]

According to the ANA President, delegates to the special session were faced with two alternatives:

1) Should the American Nurses' Association assume responsibility as the central united front organization, integrating within itself the constituent associations as well as other nursing organizations?

OR

2) Should a new organizational structure be built through the cooperative efforts of the six existing nursing organizations?

With these alternatives in mind, the ANA Board of Directors recommended to the House of Delegates that:

> it be the sense of the House of Delegates that, in any activities aimed at bringing about unity in nursing organizations, the American Nurses' Association take the leadership in the endeavor; and that it be the further sense of the house that in any such activities the American Nurses' Association be preserved in its essential structure as to district, state, and national associations; and that it be the further sense of the house that in relations between the American Nurses' Association and the other nursing organizations for the purpose of achieving unity, the American Nurses' Association must remain the national organization representing all graduate professional nurses and that it retain its status in an expanded form in any unified action which may be undertaken. Since there are many methods of

> achieving unity, all requiring further study, it be the sense of the house that the matter be diligently pursued by its authorized representatives.[23]

However, delegates chose to postpone any action on this resolution until the 1948 biennial convention.[24]

The immediate question facing the delegates was: Should the American Nurses' Association continue to conduct its own structure study independent of the Joint Committee on the Structure of National Nursing Organizations or should all six organizations conduct the study jointly and democratically? In response to this question, ANA's House of Delegates voted to support the activities of the joint structure committee and empowered ANA representatives to participate and vote in the deliberations and studies which the joint structure committee might conduct. While such action did not commit ANA to any particular structural proposal, it did convey the desire of the association that all six organizations work cooperatively. The House of Delegates also voted that:

> the ANA Board of Directors request a joint meeting of the boards of directors of the six national professional nursing organizations not later than November 15, 1947, to consider ways and means of implementing a program of united action, which meeting would consider the areas of activities and interests peculiar to each organization and the areas of activities and interests common to more than one of the organizations.[25]

A Tentative Plan for One National Nursing Organization

In the months following the special session of the House of Delegates, the Joint Committee on the Structure of National Nursing Organizations developed a proposal to serve as a "basis for discussion and further development."[26] This presentation, "A Tentative Plan for One National Nursing Organization," was based on four major premises:

1) "Effort should be made to find ways to perform the necessary

functions of organized nursing within the single organization framework."[27]

2) "The structure problem should be approached from the standpoint of functions . . . that is, the total program of nursing both from the point of view of service and of the individual nurse, rather than from the standpoint of present organizations or present activities."[28]

3) Initial consideration should be given to the functions of the local organization in relation to nurses working in the community. "State and national organizations must be built upon this all-essential local unit and must be shaped so as best to meet needs of the local unit."[29]

4) The local-to-state-to-national form of organization, exemplified in the ANA, should not be changed unless local needs warrant new emphasis. "It should be the continuous aim of both state and national organizations to strengthen and broaden the work of the local unit."[30]

Since so many nurses had expressed the desire for a single organization, the joint structure committee suggested a plan in which the nurse membership could act upon strictly professional matters and both nurse and non-nurse membership could work together on community nursing problems. As Hortense Hilbert, chairman of the joint structure committee, pointed out:

> The plan is an effort to find one roof for the dual task of organized nursing. That dual task as defined by the committee on structure is: first, providing better nursing service to the people of the United States; and second, promoting and protecting the interests of members of the nursing profession.[31]

The outstanding features of the single national organization (Chart V), the American Nursing Association, were the specialty sections which would be comprised of professional nurse members only and the divisions of nursing service and nursing education which would be comprised of nurses as well as non-nurses, schools of nursing, and nursing service agencies.

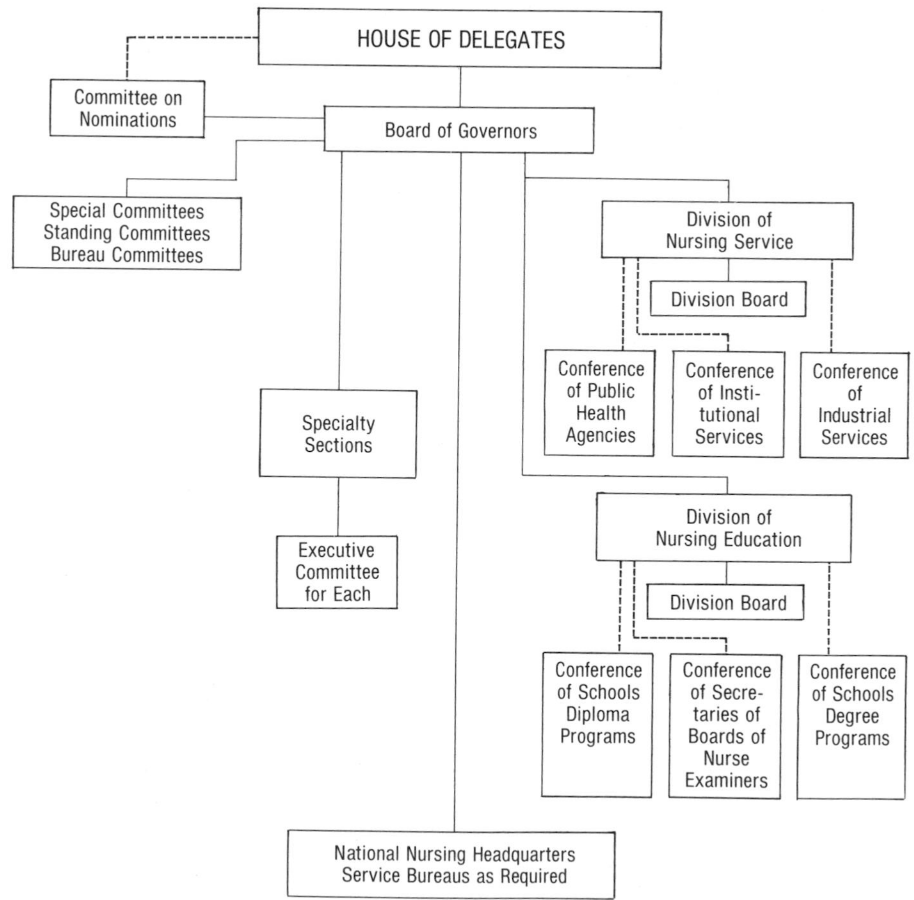
1948 TENTATIVE PLAN FOR
ONE NATIONAL NURSING ORGANIZATION
AMERICAN NURSING ASSOCIATION
HOUSE OF DELEGATES
Committee on Nominations
Board of Governors
Special Committees
Standing Committees
Bureau Committees
Division of Nursing Service
Division Board
Conference of Public Health Agencies
Conference of Institutional Services
Conference of Industrial Services
Specialty Sections
Executive Committee for Each
Division of Nursing Education
Division Board
Conference of Schools Diploma Programs
Conference of Secretaries of Boards of Nurse Examiners
Conference of Schools Degree Programs
National Nursing Headquarters
Service Bureaus as Required

Chart V

The functions of the specialty sections would be to develop programs in accord with the needs of the group and promote the special interests of the group in relation to the broad overall nursing program. The functions of the division of nursing service would be to determine current nursing resources; estimate current and future nursing needs; study content, organization, and administration of nursing services; maintain and develop needed facilities for nursing services in the community; and form policies on counseling and placement in relation to nursing service. The functions of the division of nursing education would be to study, evaluate, and continuously develop curricula (basic, advanced, and practical) for schools of nursing; maintain and develop needed facilities for basic, advanced, and practical nurse education; develop policies and standards for accreditation; form policies on counseling and placement relating to nursing education; and recruit and aid students of nursing.

Adhering to the premise that a new association should retain the "local-to-state-to-national organization," the joint structure committee incorporated these units in each level of the association.

By May, 1948, some 20,000 copies of the tentative plan had been distributed to nurses across the country. While the plan was looked upon as "a definite milepost toward a decision regarding the future structure"[32] of organized nursing, nurses recognized the need for further study and development. Speaking to delegates attending the thirty-sixth biennial convention in June, 1948, ANA President Katharine Densford pointed out, "There seem to be certain basic principles which must be agreed upon if the next two years are to be fruitful in developing a plan to which the professional organizations can look forward."[33]

During the 1948 convention, delegates focused their attention on four basic questions:

1) Does the ANA House of Delegates agree that the new organization should include non-nurse members?

2) If so, should the non-nurse members have full

equality of membership, including the right to vote and hold office?

3) Does the House of Delegates wish one national nursing organization in place of the present national professional organizations?

4) If so, should the new organization be composed of local, state, and national units?[34]

Delegates were not asked to vote on any particular plan, rather they were asked to state whether or not they wanted one organization in place of the six existing organizations. Therefore, the issue regarding the future structure of nursing organizations was readily resolved. Delegates adopted motions supporting the concept of one national nursing organization, composed of local, state, and national units, to replace the existing structures.

Inasmuch as they had adopted a motion to maintain a single nursing organization, delegates also approved the basic concept of non-nurse participation. However, resolution of the issue of non-nurse membership rights proved to be more difficult.

The question of non-nurse membership had been explored by the association on a number of occasions. In 1936, the board appointed a committee to consider this issue. One year later, the committee went on record as being opposed to any extension of ANA membership. Committee members pointed out that responsibility for ANA programming could not be delegated to non-nurse groups. However, they did encourage non-nurse participation in nursing-related activities. In 1940, the issue was re-examined. Blanche A. Blackman, chairman of a special committee to consider the membership issue, reported the findings of a survey of state associations. She observed that the nursing profession itself needed to know more about its present status and the problems it faced before expanding membership.[35]

In 1948, convention delegates raised two significant questions:

1) Would non-nurse membership in the national nursing organization jeopardize membership in the International Council of Nurses?[36]

2) Would non-nurse membership affect an economic security program for nurses?

Lack of information regarding the implications of non-nurse membership on matters of a strictly professional nature prompted delegates to adopt a motion to refer the issue to the joint structure committee for further study. Moreover, the general sentiment of ANA delegates was that, if the one organization plan proved to be impractical, the joint structure committee should prepare an alternate plan.

The ICN Membership Question

Extensive investigation revealed that it would be impossible to continue membership in the International Council of Nurses under the 1948 tentative plan for one national nursing organization. Consequently, at the November, 1948, meeting of the joint structure committee, the ANA delegation recommended the elimination of the divisions of nursing service and nursing education as presented in the 1948 plan for one organization. ANA proposed the establishment of one nursing organization which would offer membership in forums to non-nurses, nursing service agencies, and schools of nursing. These forums would serve only as advisory bodies. ANA's recommendation was not acceptable to the representatives of the other five nursing organizations who argued that such a proposal would hinder the execution of vital nursing-related activities requiring full participation of non-nurse groups. Consequently, the joint structure committee voted to propose to the boards of directors of the six nursing organizations two alternate plans:[37]

1) A revised one-organization plan offering association membership to nurses only and forum membership to non-nurses, nursing service agencies, and schools of nursing, and

2) A two-organization plan establishing one association for nurses only and one association for nurses, non-nurses, nursing service agencies, and schools of nursing.

Both plans were adaptations of the 1948 plan. Both plans offered an organization for nurses that would be admissible to membership in the International Council of Nurses. Both plans offered mechanisms to facilitate the establishment of collective bargaining units for nurses. Both plans offered the same groupings (occupational sections and specialist councils) within the profession.

The 1949 Two-Organization Plan

Like the "Tentative Plan for One National Nursing Organization," presented in 1948, the 1949 proposal for two organizations (Chart VI) was based on the premise that state and national organizations must be built upon the local unit and "must be shaped so as best to meet the needs of the local unit."[38]

Under the two-organization plan,[39] a new American Nurses' Association would be responsible for:

1) Promotion of professional and educational advancement of registered nurses,
2) Promotion and protection of the social and economic welfare of registered nurses,
3) Definition and implementation of ethical and professional standards of nursing practice,
4) Involvement in the creation of legislation concerning qualifications for nursing practice as well as other legislation affecting nursing education and nursing practice, and
5) Representation of American nurses in the International Council of Nurses.

It was proposed that the membership of the constituent state associations be composed of nurses who had graduated from schools of nursing accredited by a legally authorized agency and who were registered in one or more states. American nurses who met the professional requirements and who were residing in a foreign country, or nurses who met the professional requirements and who were restricted from membership in a state association because of race or color, would be eligible for direct national

1949 PLAN FOR TWO ORGANIZATIONS

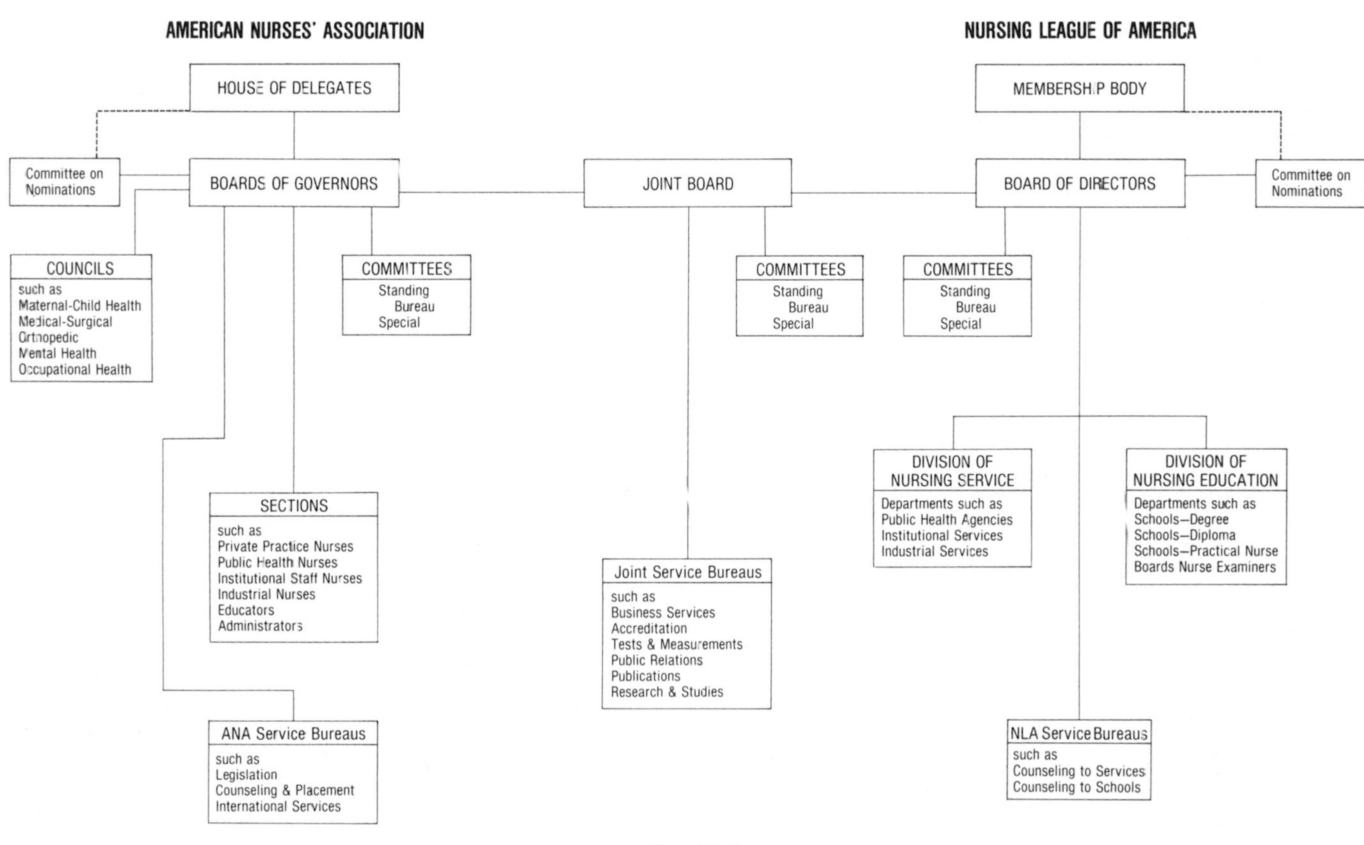

AMERICAN NURSES' ASSOCIATION
NURSING LEAGUE OF AMERICA
HOUSE OF DELEGATES
MEMBERSHIP BODY
Committee on Nominations
BOARDS OF GOVERNORS
JOINT BOARD
BOARD OF DIRECTORS
Committee on Nominations
COUNCILS
such as
Maternal-Child Health
Medical-Surgical
Orthopedic
Mental Health
Occupational Health
COMMITTEES
Standing
Bureau
Special
COMMITTEES
Standing
Bureau
Special
COMMITTEES
Standing
Bureau
Special
DIVISION OF NURSING SERVICE
Departments such as
Public Health Agencies
Institutional Services
Industrial Services
DIVISION OF NURSING EDUCATION
Departments such as
Schools—Degree
Schools—Diploma
Schools—Practical Nurse
Boards Nurse Examiners
SECTIONS
such as
Private Practice Nurses
Public Health Nurses
Institutional Staff Nurses
Industrial Nurses
Educators
Administrators
Joint Service Bureaus
such as
Business Services
Accreditation
Tests & Measurements
Public Relations
Publications
Research & Studies
ANA Service Bureaus
such as
Legislation
Counseling & Placement
International Services
NLA Service Bureaus
such as
Counseling to Services
Counseling to Schools

Chart VI

membership. The initial member population would be comprised of the nurse members in good standing of the six existing nursing organizations.

It was proposed that each member, according to his or her occupation or interest, declare membership in one section of the association for voting purposes. Sections would be established for private practice nurses, public health nurses, institutional staff nurses, industrial nurses, nurse educators, and nurse administrators.

The House of Delegates, the association's governing body, would be composed of:

1) One delegate for each state association section representing at least fifty members or a combination of sections totaling at least fifty members; two delegates from a section of over 200 members; three delegates from a section of over 400 members, etc.,

2) One delegate for every fifty direct members in any one state; two delegates for every 200 direct members in any one state, etc., and

3) The chairman and secretary of each national section.

A Board of Governors, consisting of association officers [president, president-elect (first vice president), second vice president, third vice president, secretary, and treasurer], one governor elected by members of each national section, and eleven governors elected at large by the association membership, would be empowered to transact general business in the interim between biennial conventions.

It was proposed that a series of councils be established to develop standards and procedures and define criteria for qualified specialists in maternal-child health nursing, medical-surgical nursing, mental health nursing, orthopedic nursing, and occupational health nursing. Eligibility for council membership would be based on completion of a program of advanced study in the designated area of nursing and/or at least three years experience in the designated area of nursing.

The responsibilities of the second organization, the Nursing

League of America, would be:

1) To determine existing and potential nursing needs in all fields of nursing service,

2) To identify resources to satisfy needs in both nursing education and nursing service,

3) To assist in defining, interpreting, promoting, and maintaining nursing service and educational facilities,

4) To study content, organization, and administration of nursing service and nursing education, and

5) To counsel member agencies concerning the maintenance of standards.

It was proposed that the Nursing League of America offer three membership categories: nurse, non-nurse, and agency and school. A person who was a graduate of a duly accredited school of nursing, a registered nurse in one or more states, and a member of the American Nurses' Association or, if a resident in a foreign country, a member of a professional nurses' association recognized by the International Council of Nurses would be eligible for nurse membership. A person who displayed a general interest in promoting standards of nursing service and nursing education or who was or had been affiliated with a hospital, public health agency, school of nursing, nursing service coordinating agency, or a study important to nursing service and nursing education would be eligible for non-nurse membership. Organizations conducting, promoting, or coordinating community nursing services, duly accredited schools of nursing, and departments or divisions of nursing education within accredited colleges and universities would be eligible for agency and school membership. Initially, the membership would be composed of individual members in good standing of the National League of Nursing Education, the National Organization for Public Health Nursing, and the American Association of Industrial Nurses and agency members in good standing of the National Organization for Public Health Nursing and the Association of Collegiate Schools of Nursing. Members of the American Nurses' Association and the

National Association of Colored Graduate Nurses would be admitted upon application for membership.

It was proposed that two divisions be established: a division on nursing service, composed of departments for health services, institutional services, and industrial services, and a division on nursing education, composed of departments of schools offering a diploma program, schools offering a degree program, and schools offering a practical nurse program, and secretaries of nurse examiners. Each individual member and agency member would elect membership in one department for voting purposes.

Those members attending the biennial convention would constitute the voting body to conduct general business. The twenty-one member board of directors [comprised of the president, president-elect (first vice president), second vice president, third vice president, secretary, treasurer, one director elected by each department, two directors elected at large by each division and directors elected at large by the league membership, including two non-nurse individual members and two agency members] would be empowered to act as the governing body and transact general business in the interim between conventions.

It was proposed that officers of the Nursing League of America and presidents of the state nursing leagues form a council in order to keep the national organization informed of the progress of nursing service and nursing education in the states and to promote the work of the national organization.

It was proposed that a joint board be established composed of the president and six members of the ANA's Board of Governors and the president and six members of the NLA's Board of Directors as well as a treasurer to be elected by the fourteen designated board members. It would be the responsibility of this joint board to operate cooperative projects and create central bureaus for business service, accreditation, test and measurements, publications, research and studies, and public relations.

The 1949 One-Organization Plan

A second plan (Chart VII) of the Joint Committee on the

1949 PLAN FOR ONE ORGANIZATION

AMERICAN NURSING ASSOCIATION

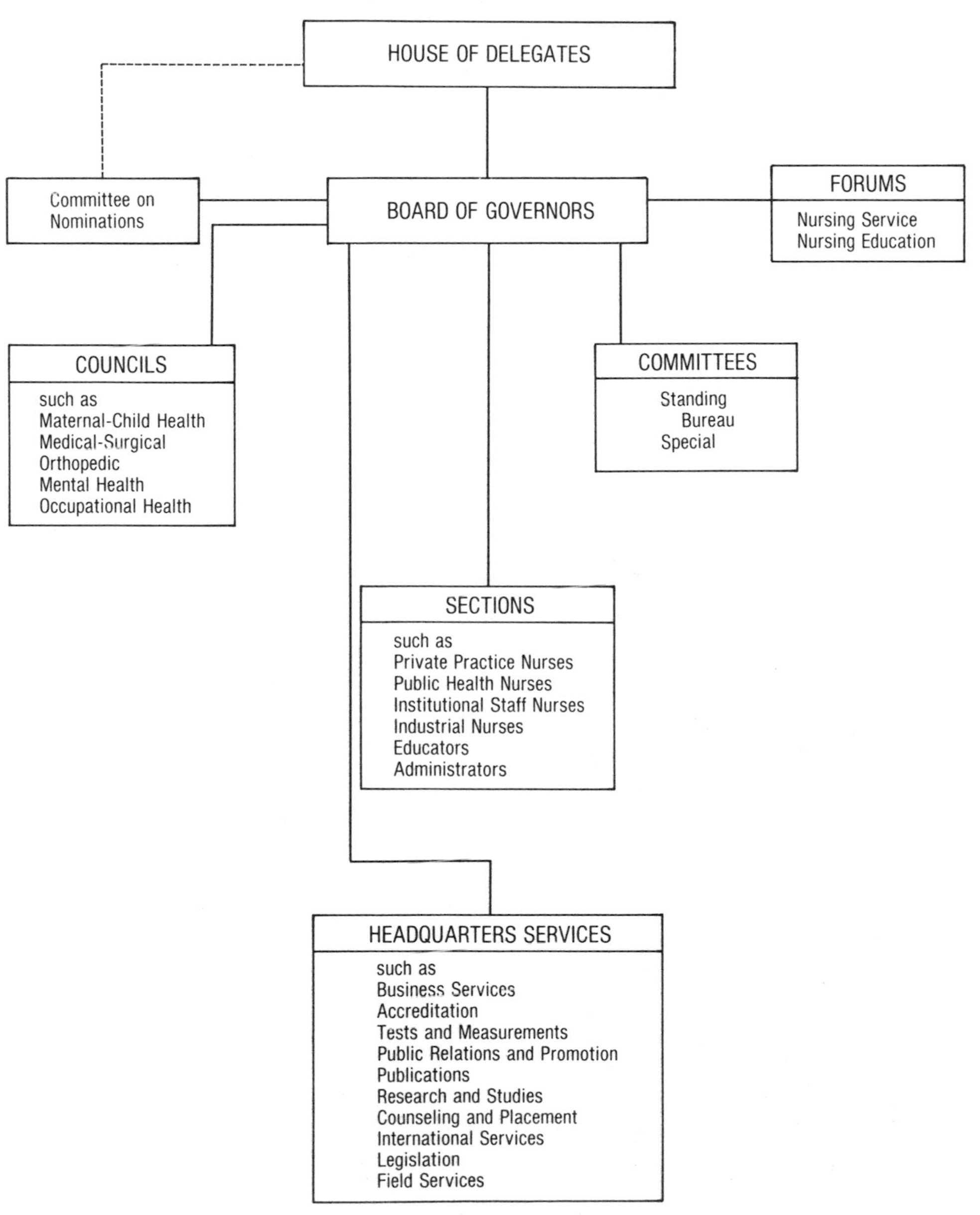

Chart VII

Structure of National Nursing Organizations provided for a single organization,[40] the American Nursing Association, which would:

1) Meet the nursing needs of the public,

2) Develop the best possible nursing services,

3) Improve nursing education,

4) Carry on a program of public relations,

5) Maintain cooperative relations with other organizations in the health field,

6) Deal with international nursing problems concerning nursing education and nursing service and represent the United States in the International Council of Nurses,

7) Promote professional and educational advancement of registered nurses,

8) Promote and protect the social and economic welfare of registered nurses,

9) Define and implement ethical and professional standards of nursing practice, and

10) Deal with legislation concerning qualifications for nursing practice and other legislation affecting the education of nurses and the practice of nursing.

According to the joint structure committee, requirements for membership and provisions for structural units for the American Nursing Association would be essentially the same as those listed in the two-organization plan for the American Nurses' Association. The key difference would be the provision for forums with non-nurse membership in the one-organization plan. The establishment of forums on nursing service and nursing education would provide a common meeting ground for discussions of mutual problems by nurses, allied professional groups, consumers of nursing, schools of nursing, and nursing service agencies—all of whom would be members of the forums.

Any nurse member in good standing of the six nursing organizations would be eligible for forum membership. All members in good standing of the National Organization for Public

Health Nursing would be eligible for membership in the Forum on Nursing Service and members in good standing of the National League of Nursing Education and the Association of Collegiate Schools of Nursing would be eligible for membership in the Forum on Nursing Education.

The basic objective of the Forum on Nursing Service would be to recommend ways to provide the best possible nursing service. The basic objective of the Forum on Nursing Education would be to recommend means for developing standards and facilities for a nursing education system which would adequately prepare personnel to render all types of nursing service.

Over 25,000 copies of the 1949 alternate plans were circulated to nurses and interested parties across the nation. According to an opinionnaire, seventy-four percent of approximately 7,000 nurses surveyed favored the two-organization plan while only twenty-four percent favored the one-organization plan. Eighty-seven percent of those nurses favoring the two-organization plan approved of the joint board as presented and eighty-three percent thought that nurse members of the Nursing League of America should be required to hold membership in the new American Nurses' Association.[41]

Upon careful examination of the 1949 alternate plans, delegates to the 1950 convention of the American Nurses' Association endorsed the concept of a two-organization plan with the inclusion of three provisios recommended by ANA's Board of Directors:

> 1) That the existing American Nurses' Association corporation be retained and the proposed new functions and sections as approved by all six national nursing organizations be provided for by amendments to, or revisions of, the present ANA bylaws,
>
> 2) That the joint board become a subsidiary corporation, jointly owned by the ANA and NLA, and its name be changed to more clearly indicate the functions which it will assume, and

3) That the creation of councils be delayed for the present and, so far as possible during the interim, council functions be assumed by the appropriate sections.[42]

The other five nursing organizations followed suit by endorsing a two-organization plan provided that the ANA retain its corporation and that any changes in ANA functions be accomplished through revision or amendment to the ANA Bylaws. Upon the advice of legal counsel, the six nursing organizations also agreed that the second association should be built upon the charter of one of the existing organizations. The boards of directors of those nursing organizations which were planning to dissolve concluded that the national nursing association composed of both nurse and non-nurse membership should be established by amendment to the charter of the National League of Nursing Education.

The boards of directors of the six national nursing organizations appointed committees on structure and agreed that the chairman of each structure committee, together with the president and executive secretary of each organization, would function as a joint coordinating committee. Between late 1950 and summer, 1951, the Joint Coordinating Committee on Structure "reviewed and harmonized the proposals from each organization"[43] regarding final plans for the two national nursing organizations, the American Nurses' Association and the National League for Nursing. According to Chairman Pearl McIver, the joint coordinating committee attempted to assign "those functions which should be the sole responsibility of the members of a profession" to the American Nurses' Association and "those functions which the members of any profession should share with the consumers of their product and allied professional workers" to the National League for Nursing.[44]

During the thirty-eighth convention in 1952, ANA delegates approved the general plans for the American Nurses' Association and the National League for Nursing (Chart VIII) and adopted detailed revisions to the bylaws of the association.

Under the new organizational plan, the American Nurses' Association and the National League for Nursing were charged with distinct functions and activities. The American Nurses' Association would:

1) Define and promote the implementation of the functions, standards, and qualifications of nursing practitioners in the various occupational and clinical fields.

2) Promote the economic and general welfare of nurses which directly affect the recruitment and efficiency of nursing personnel.

3) Work to provide like opportunities in nursing for men and women of all racial and religious groups.

4) Provide professional counseling and placement referral service to individual nurses and to employers in regard to employment opportunities and available personnel.

4) Promote legislation and speak for nurses regarding legislative action for general health and welfare programs.

5) Work closely with the various state boards of nursing in the interpretation of nursing practice acts and the facilitation of interstate licensure by endorsement.

6) Survey periodically the nurse resources of the nation and finance research in nursing functions.

7) Represent and serve as national spokesman for nurses with allied professional and governmental groups and with the public.

8) Implement the international exchange of nurses program and assist other nurses who immigrate to the United States.

9) Serve as official representative of American nurses in the International Council of Nurses.

The National League for Nursing would:

MEMBERSHIP ORGANIZATION CHARTS

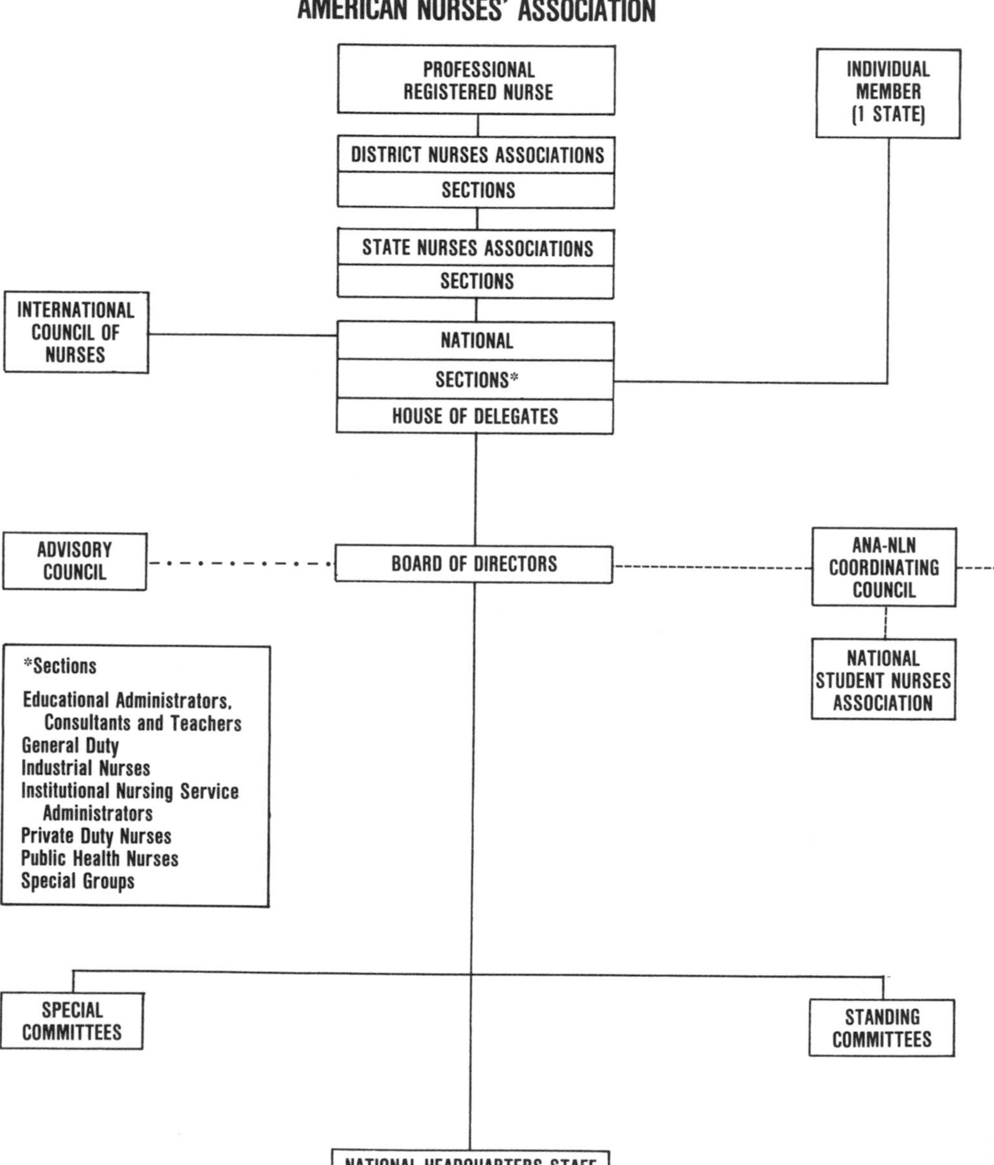

Chart VIII

NATIONAL LEAGUE FOR NURSING

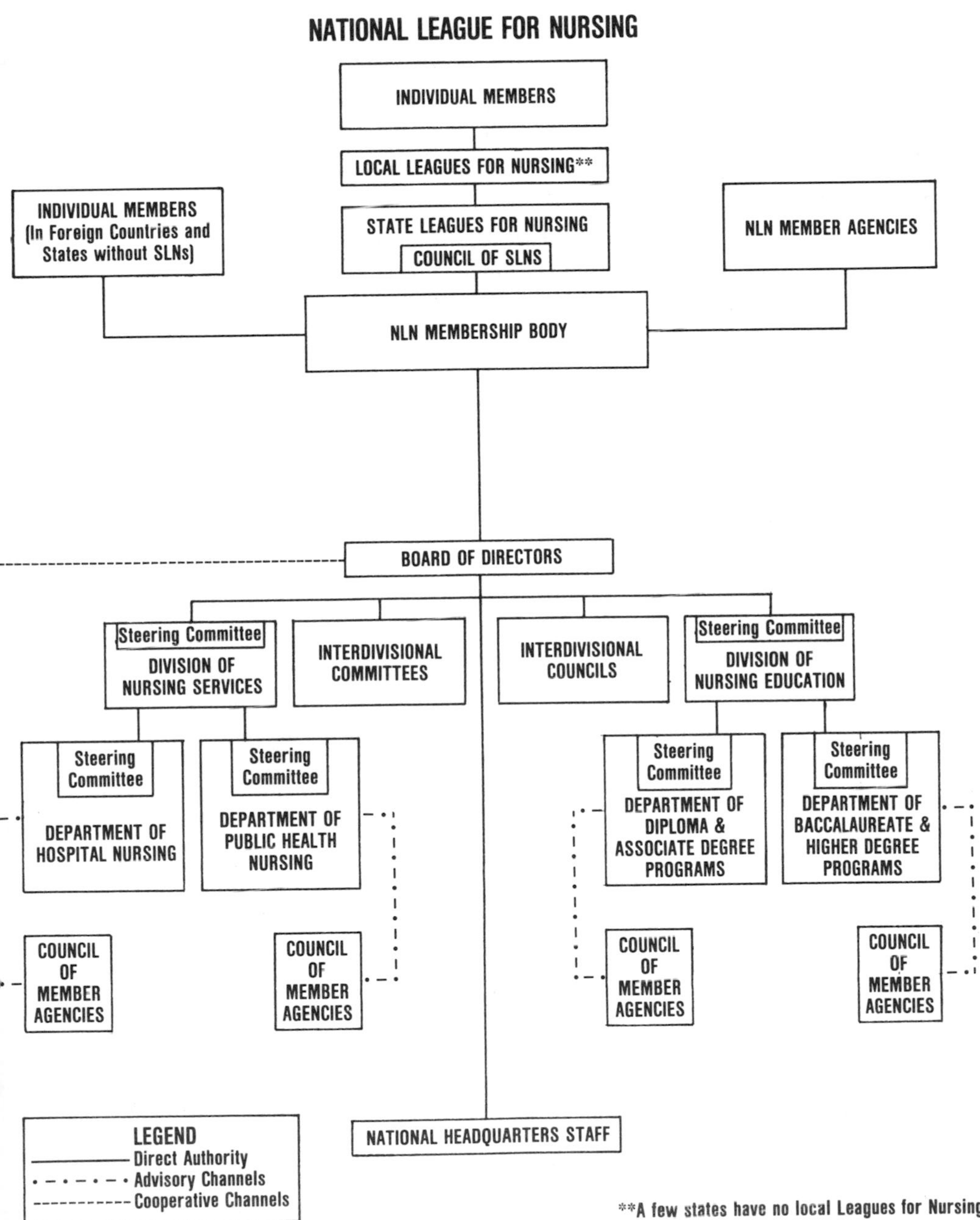

**A few states have no local Leagues for Nursing.

1) Define standards for organized nursing services and education.

2) Stimulate communities, nursing services, and educational institutions to achieve the standards defined.

3) Provide consultation, publications, cost analysis methods, data, and other services to individuals, nursing services, schools, and communities.

4) Offer comprehensive testing and guidance services to institutions with practical, basic, or advanced nursing education programs.

5) Offer consultation to institutions for nursing education upon request and accredit nursing programs.

6) Carry out and promote continual study and research about nursing services and educational curricula as related to changing needs. Encourage similar studies and research by nursing services, schools, and communities and provide assistance in these studies.

7) Provide, in cooperation with state licensing authorities, examinations and related services for use in licensing professional and practical nurses.

8) Conduct a national student nurse recruitment program co-sponsored by ANA, NLN, AHA, and AMA.

9) Represent nursing services and nursing education units with allied professional, governmental, and international groups and with the public.

The actions of the ANA delegates at the 1952 convention represented the final steps in the six-year structure study. Labeled "one of the most significant experiments in democratic action," the study of the structures of the national nursing organizations represented a concentrated effort on the part of the nursing profession to seek appropriate ways and means to insure provision of quality nursing services and to promote the economic and general welfare of nurses.

Realizing that a thorough study of the national nursing organizations would take several years, ANA's House of Delegates, in

1946, approved a recommendation that the association's program be carried forward without regard to future organizational changes. At the same convention, delegates adopted the first association platform. Between 1948 and 1958, the association concentrated on the three broad objectives outlined in the platform: 1) to provide health protection for the American people, 2) to aid nurses to become more effective and more secure members of their profession, and 3) to promote better health care for the peoples of the world. Consequently, during the period of study and reorganization, the American Nurses' Association continued to make significant strides. The following is a brief summary of the association's achievements.

International Relations

Between 1948 and 1958, association activities included the expansion of international relations through active participation in the International Council of Nurses and through support of the United Nations program. The American Nurses' Association arranged opportunities for nurses from other countries to observe, study, and practice nursing in the United States and assisted American nurses seeking vocational opportunities abroad. In order to stay in tune with world health needs, ANA took an active interest in the activities of the United Nations. According to Ella Best, executive secretary of the American Nurses' Association, ANA's support of the United Nations "expressed a determination to assist in bringing about better understanding of the international community of nations which exists solely for the furtherance of peaceful, wholesome, and healthful conditions for all."[45]

Nursing in National Defense

During the decade of the 1950s, national defense was a key concern. The Korean War and the advent of atomic weapons triggered the development of a civil defense program to prepare Americans for the eventualities of atomic, chemical, and bacteriological warfare.

In 1950, the American Nurses' Association created a Committee on Nursing Resources to Meet Civilian and Military Needs. Due to the changes in the world situation, the name of the committee was changed in 1953 to the ANA Committee on Nursing in National Defense.

The establishment of the committee was based on the supposition that nurses, by virtue of their skills and professional and social obligations, would assume a major role in the care of both civilians and military personnel in the event of full-scale war. Composed of representatives of the armed forces, American Red Cross, Federal Civil Defense Administration, and Public Health Service, the committee concentrated on the preparation of nursing resources for national disasters. The efforts of this committee resulted in the preparation of a comprehensive document on those phases of nursing essential to national defense.

Government Relations

In working toward the objectives set forth in the association's platform, ANA placed greater emphasis on legislative activities. In 1951, the association opened a government relations office in Washington, D.C. Staff were responsible for the review of Congressional and state bills affecting nurses, nursing, and health care; preparation and distribution of informative materials on legislation, legislative problems, and the government relations program of the American Nurses' Association; and preparation of Congressional testimony reflecting nurses' interests and concerns. During the decade of the 1950s, the government relations program promoted:

1) State laws which would provide for mandatory licensure for the practice of professional nursing and practical nursing,

2) Desirable social legislation including those labor measures which would benefit nurses,

3) Legislation which would provide public funds for research, scholarships, and continued improvement in nursing education, and

4) Inclusion of nursing benefits in prepaid hospital and medical care plans.

Nursing Practice

Recognizing the need to improve nursing practice and nursing service, the American Nurses' Association launched a series of controlled studies.

In 1950, the board of directors initiated a five-year study of nursing functions which was financially supported by voluntary membership contributions. The purpose of the study was to determine "what should be the functions and relationship of institutional nursing personnel of all types (professional nurses, practical nurses, and auxiliary nursing workers) in order to improve nursing care and to utilize nursing personnel most economically and effectively."[46]

In 1954, when the seven sections, representing occupational groups of professional nurses, were established, the association charged each group with the responsibility of 1) defining the functions, standards, and qualifications for nursing practice, 2) initiating studies or experiments for the improvement of nursing practice, 3) studying the general welfare and economic needs of nurses, and 4) developing desirable standards of employment.[47]

ANA's studies of nursing functions, standards, and qualifications provided guidelines and criteria for a definition of nursing practice, preparation of nursing curricula, and construction of specifications and qualifications for various nursing roles.

Nursing Research

In 1954, ANA President Elizabeth K. Porter pointed out:

> Heretofore, our progress in nursing has been due in large part to unselfish, far-seeing nurses who contributed freely of their time and talent to volunteer research. But a profession such as ours, touching every phase of life, can no longer depend wholly upon occasional or interrupted research. Although such research will always

> make a contribution, we must have, in addition, a very definite program of full-time nursing research.[48]

In addition to expanding the association's research and statistical service, the 1954 House of Delegates authorized the incoming board of directors "to develop a foundation or trust for receiving tax-free funds for desirable charitable, scientific, literary, or educational projects in line with the aims of the American Nurses' Association."[49] In responding to the directive of the House of Delegates, the new board approved the creation of the American Nurses' Foundation. On January 27, 1955, the organization of the foundation, a membership corporation, was completed. According to the Certificate of Incorporation, the aims and purposes of the foundation included the following:

> To increase the public knowledge and understanding of professional and practical nursing and of the science and art upon which the health of the American people depends by engaging in studies, surveys, and research. . . .[50]

Intergroup Relations

In *An American Challenge,* published by the American Nurses' Association in 1951, the observation was made that American nurses faced two crucial questions: 1) How can the barriers which still existed between nurse groups of different origins be abolished? and 2) How can intergroup relations be improved throughout the profession?

One of the most significant aims of the American Nurses' Association, between 1946 and 1958, was to promote the inclusion and full participation of minority groups in association activities and to eliminate discrimination in job opportunities, salaries, and other working conditions. In 1948, ANA's House of Delegates adopted measures to provide direct individual membership for Negro nurses restricted from membership in the state nurses' association. In 1949, ANA's Board of Directors authorized the establishment of a special committee to study the functions of the National Association of Colored Graduate Nurses as they related to the total program of the American Nurses' Association. Between 1950 and 1951, the functions and responsibilities of the National Association of Colored Graduate Nurses were absorbed by the American Nurses' Association which initiated an intergroup relations program to work for the full integration of nurses of all racial groups in all aspects of nursing.

Reflecting on the significance of these events, Elizabeth K. Porter, president of the American Nurses' Association, observed:

> Probably no single program of ANA has received such widespread and favorable acclaim outside of our own profession as had the intergroup relations program which had its genesis in 1946. This program is concerned with the tensions, rifts, and cleavages between nurse groups of different origin, stemming from different peoples or races.
>
> The bold and forthright action of 1946 recommending that all state and district nurses' associations eliminate racial bars to membership, and the subsequent record of progress, has earned for nursing the proud right of enlightened leadership among the professions. Indeed, our action has been a real contribution to the entire nation in our present world-wide struggle for ideologies. And might I add, not only is the integration of colored graduate nurses into the association a deserved recognition but, the American Nurses' Association will, as the years pass, continue to be enriched by their contribution.[51]

ANA's Economic Security Program

In addressing delegates to the thirty-fifth convention in 1946, ANA President Katharine Densford concluded, "If the nursing profession is ready to take decisive action on hours, economic advancement, enlargement of nursing resources while maintaining standards, and the possible reconstruction of its own organizational structure, we shall this week make nursing history."[52]

Nurses did make history the week of September 22-27, 1946. Members of the American Nurses' Association not only endorsed a study of the national nursing organizations, they unanimously adopted an economic security program which included collective bargaining.[53]

Four of the ten planks of the association's first platform, which was adopted at the 1946 convention, reflected ANA's interest in promoting the economic and general welfare of nurses:

> 1) Improvement in hours and living conditions for nurses, including wider acceptance of the 40-hour week with no decrease in salary and minimum salaries adequate to attract and hold nurses of quality and to enable them to maintain standards of living comparable to other professions.
>
> 2) Increased participation by nurses in the actual planning and in the administration of nursing services in all types of employment situations.
>
> 3) Greater development of nurses' professional associations as exclusive spokesmen for nurses in all questions affecting their employment and economic security.
>
> 4) Removal of barriers that prevent the full employment and professional development of nurses belonging to minority racial groups.[54]

Moreover, delegates adopted the following position statement:

> The American Nurses' Association believes that the several state and district associations are qualified to act and should act as the exclusive agents of their respective memberships in the important fields of economic security and collective bargaining. The association commends the excellent progress already made and urges all state and district nurses' associations to push such a program vigorously and expeditiously.
>
> Since it is the established policy of other groups, including unions, to permit membership in only one collective bargaining group, the association believes

such policy to be sound for the state and district nurses' associations.[55]

What prompted the American Nurses' Association to initiate an extensive economic security program?

One of the original purposes of the American Nurses' Association was "to promote the usefulness and honor, the financial and other interests of the nursing profession." Therefore, the adoption of the economic security program in 1946 did not represent a new objective for the association. It did represent a new means of achieving the goal of economic security.

For more than forty years, the American Nurses' Association had issued recommendations on policies governing nursing personnel and the distribution of nursing services. Although the association's 1934 campaign for the eight-hour work day for nurses was very effective, most measures met with only modest success. Nurses had little or no opportunity to participate in the determination of their working conditions. They were beginning to realize that quality nursing care could not be provided without some improvement in the employment conditions of nurses rendering the care. Studies had shown that capable young women were not entering the nursing field because of unsatisfactory working conditions and that graduate nurses were leaving the field for the same reason. The nursing profession was learning that insistence on satisfactory working conditions was compatible with the "spirit of service."

By the late 1930s, it had become obvious to the national association that nurses needed to employ more effective methods to insure quality nursing service and to promote the economic and general welfare of the nurse. Collective bargaining appeared to be the most appropriate means.

Collective bargaining has been described as "a system of industrial jurisprudence"—a code of rules, regulations, and precedents to govern employer-employee relations. In 1926, railroad companies joined with their employee organizations to support the passage of the Railway Labor Act of 1926 which established collective bargaining as the normal mode of industrial relations in the railroad industry. In 1932, the Norris-La Guardia Act restricted the power of the federal court to grant injunctive relief in labor disputes. In essence, the act fostered the principles of collective bargaining throughout American industry. The policies set forth in the Norris-La Guardia Act were implemented in 1933 with the enactment of the National Industrial Recovery Act. In 1936, the National Labor Relations Act (Wagner Act) promoted and protected the right of employees to organize freely and bargain collectively through representatives of their own choosing with their employer.[56] During the 1930s and 1940s, the increased use of collective bargaining was triggered by the failure of salaried groups to secure satisfactory living standards in the midst of inflation and by the growth of labor unions. By 1946, several million workers were covered by collective bargaining agreements. Collective bargaining had become the accepted mode of employer-employee relations with respect to wages, hours, and conditions of work.

During the late 1930s, the nursing profession struggled with two important questions:

1) Is collective bargaining consistent with professional ethics?

AND

2) Should collective bargaining be controlled by professional societies or by unions?

It was the contention of the American Nurses' Association that:

> 1) Nurses have the right and responsibility to promote and protect their economic security . . . .
>
> 2) Nurses have the right of full freedom of association and liberty of contract accorded to all employees by contemporary legal and social sanctions, and to maintain this right by unified action through organization.
>
> 3) Nurses have the right and responsibility to participate actively in determining the conditions of employment which directly affect them and to see that

such conditions of employment are put into effect.[57]

It was also the contention of the American Nurses' Association that collective bargaining for nurses should be conducted by the professional nurses' association. Responding to the question of nurse membership in unions, ANA's Board of Directors issued the following statement on January 24, 1938:

> Before allying herself with any recently organized groups, the individual nurse should ask what these new organizations can do for her and for the profession of nursing as compared with the services which her professional organizations have rendered, continue to render, and which they will be on the alert to develop for nursing and for the nurse as need for them arises in the future.
>
> The American Nurses' Association stands for the fulfillment of all professional obligations.
>
> The American Nurses' Association does not at this time recommend nurse membership in unions.
>
> WHEREAS, The ANA stands for the fulfillment of all professional obligations, and does not recommend nurse membership in any organization which can interfere with her professional or personal obligations to the patient, and
>
> WHEREAS, The ANA is obligated, through its units, to make available to individual nurses information which will indicate to them the services which their professional organizations can give them in comparison with those rendered by other organizations;
>
> BE IT RECOMMENDED: That, through the state nurses' associations, the district nurses' associations be made more cognizant of their strength and assume their responsibility for certain problems in their communities. Such problems are standards of nursing care and employment conditions for nurses, particularly as the latter relate to hours of duty and fee schedules.[58]

Prior to World War II, the American Nurses' Association conducted an economic security program which stopped short of collective bargaining. In 1941, California nurses began to work actively for better salaries and improved working conditions. The California Nurses' Association, acting as the duly authorized agent, represented their members before the War Labor Board. After securing a fifteen percent increase in salaries, the state nurses' association proceeded to implement a total economic security program. The success of the California Nurses' Association prompted the American Nurses' Association to adopt a more extensive national program for nurses in 1946.

The purpose of the ANA Economic Security Program was "to secure for nurses, through their professional associations, reasonable and satisfactory conditions of employment which, in turn, will enable the public to secure top quality nursing service in sufficient quantity to meet the demands for such services."[59] It was the association's intention to campaign for:

1) Wider acceptance of the 40-hour week with no decrease of salary,

2) Minimum salaries adequate to attract and hold qualified nurses and to enable them to maintain standards of living in keeping with their professional status, and

3) Increased participation by nurses in the actual planning and administration of nursing services in hospitals and other agencies.[60]

In 1948, the ANA House of Delegates voted that the ANA Committee on Employment Conditions of Registered Nurses be authorized to draw up criteria for the evaluation of the economic security programs of the state nurses' associations. According to ANA's Economic Security Unit, these criteria represented "a coming of age of the ANA Economic Security Program as a major professional activity and as a major contribution of the profession to contemporary society."[61]

Between 1948 and 1958, the House of Delegates adopted a number of resolutions regarding labor relations laws and policies governing nurses' relationships with non-nurse personnel. One of the most significant actions of ANA's governing body was the endorsement of a no-strike policy in 1950:

> In recognition of the fact that the nursing profession and employers of nurses share responsibility for provision of adequate nursing service to the public, the American Nurses' Association, in conducting its Economic Security Program, 1) reaffirms professional nurses' voluntary relinquishment of the exercise of the right to strike and of the use of any other measures wherever they may be inconsistent with the professional nurses' responsibilities to patients; and 2) reaffirms its conviction that this voluntary relinquishment of measures ordinarily available to employees in their efforts to improve working conditions imposes on employers an increased obligation to recognize and deal justly with nurses through their authorized representatives in all matters affecting their employment conditions.[62]

By 1958, ANA's Economic Security Program had been labeled a success. According to observers, the nursing profession had achieved new status in employer-employee relations. As Elizabeth K. Porter, president of the American Nurses' Association, explained, "The economic security program means that the nursing profession is saying to all groups concerned that the only way to get superior nursing service is to *recognize it, emphasize it, honor it,* and *reward it.*"[63]

When delegates assembled for the 1958 convention, attention was focused on the revision of *The Code for Professional Nurses* to include statements on economic security. As ANA President Pearl McIver pointed out, "The development of democratic relationships and work satisfaction are invaluable assets in the attainment of true professional status.[64]

Delegates voted to incorporate the following principles and concepts in nursing's code of ethics:

1) Every professional nurse has an ethical and profes-

> sional duty, not only to give the best nursing care possible, but also to maintain the standards of the profession so that others elsewhere and in the future may also have adequate nursing care.
>
> 2) The future of the nursing profession depends on maintenance of high professional standards which include economic standards as well as standards of professional practice; and these can be competently defined only by the professional organization of nurses. Acting through their professional organization, nurses should participate responsibly in the establishment of terms and conditions of their employment as a partial fulfillment of the ethical duty to maintain professional standards.[65]

The phrase "a united front" best describes the efforts of the nursing profession to reorganize the national nursing organizations and to promote an economic security program for nurses. Between 1948 and 1958, the nursing profession learned the true value of group endeavor. As Agnes Ohlson, president of the American Nurses' Association, observed:

> Perhaps, one of the most significant trends today, of which we must be cognizant, is the growing importance and influence of organized groups in our society. One can accomplish little alone these days. Community action, group action, are the order of the day. There is a growing tendency for groups to speak for and represent individuals. This is a trend which gathers momentum obviously. For as soon as one group acts in this way, other persons find they cannot stand against the pressures exerted unless they, too, are organized. The objective of any group is to change the status quo. We, ourselves, are an example of this. When nursing first organized, one of the major objectives was to change the situation regarding the licensure of nurses. Underlying all our programs is the aim to improve patient care. This

denotes change. Today, many of our programs are designed to change present situations. It goes without saying that there are bound to be organized groups whose objectives do not match ours, whose aims may be contrary to ours. To cope with such situations we must be united and firm.[66]

REFERENCES

1. The groups originally represented on the Council were: the American Nurses' Association, National League of Nursing Education, National Organization for Public Health Nursing, Association of Collegiate Schools of Nursing, National Association of Colored Graduate Nurses, American Red Cross Nursing Service, Federal Children's Bureau, U.S. Army Nurse Corps, U.S. Navy Nurse Corps, U.S. Public Health Service, Nursing Service of the U.S. Veterans Administration, and Nursing Service of the Department of Indian Affairs.
2. Minutes of the ANA Board of Directors, Janurary 26, 1944, 57.
3. Minutes of the ANA Board of Directors, January 28, 1944, 97-98.
4. Each organization was represented by three members and the executive secretary.
5. Organizations represented on the National Nursing Council for War Service (ANA, NLNE, NOPHN, ACSN, and NACGN) plus the American Association of Industrial Nurses, established in 1942, served as subjects for the structure study.
6. Pearl McIver, *Proceedings of the Thirty-Fifth Biennial Convention (September 22-27, 1946) of the American Nurses' Association,* Volume II: *Advisory Council—Section Meetings, Joint and Special Sessions* (New York: American Nurses' Association, 1946), 250.
7. *Ibid.,* 251.
8. Consult Appendix IV for the basic characteristics of each organization.
9. Raymond Rich, "Report on the Structure of Organized Nursing," *Proceedings of the Thirty-Fifth Biennial Convention (September 22-27, 1946) of the American Nurses' Association,* Volume I: *House of Delegates* (New York: American Nurses' Association, 1946), 198.
10. *Ibid.,* 197.
11. The recommendations which follow appeared in the "Report on the Structure of Organized Nursing by Raymond Rich Associates," *Proceedings of the Thirty-Fifth Biennial Convention (September 22-27, 1946) of the American Nurses' Association,* Volume I: *House of Delegates* (New York: American Nurses' Association, 1946), 193-224.
12. Rich Associates recommended that the national nursing organization assume responsibility for the accreditation of basic nursing schools, graduate programs, and auxiliary training programs.
13. According to Rich Associates, the district should be constituted of not less than 500 nor more than 2,000 members.
14. Raymond Rich, "Report on the Structure of Organized Nursing," *Proceedings of the Thirty-Fifth Biennial Convention (September 22-27, 1946) of the American Nurses' Association,* Volume I: *House of Delegates* (New York: American Nurses' Association, 1946), 214.

15. The other five organizations agreed to allow ANA to retain twelve members on the joint committee.
16. *Proceedings of the Thirty-Fifth Biennial Convention (September 22-27, 1946) of the American Nurses' Association,* Volume I: *House of Delegates* (New York: American Nurses' Association, 1946), 224-226.
17. Unpublished letter from the ANA to the chairman of the Joint Committee on the Structure of National Nursing Organizations, January 25, 1947.
18. Hortense Hilbert, "Joint Committee on the Structure of National Nursing Organizations Report," *Proceedings of the Special Sessions of the Advisory Council (1947-1948) and the House of Delegates (1947) of the American Nurses' Association* (New York: American Nurses' Association, 1948), 118.
19. In January, 1947, the National Association of Colored Graduate Nurses recommended to the ANA Board of Directors that the association take the necessary steps to absorb the functions now carried by the NACGN.
20. Hortense Hilbert, "Joint Committee on the Structure of National Nursing Organizations Report," *Proceedings of the Special Sessions of the Advisory Council (1947-1948) and the House of Delegates (1947) of the American Nurses' Association* (New York: American Nurses' Association, 1948), 108.
21. Katharine Densford, *Proceedings of the Special Sessions of the Advisory Council (1947-1948) and the House of Delegates (1947) of the American Nurses' Association* (New York: American Nurses' Association, 1948), 159.
22. *Ibid.*
23. *Proceedings of the Special Sessions of the Advisory Council (1947-1948) and the House of Delegates (1947) of the American Nurses' Association* (New York: American Nurses' Association, 1948), 161.
24. In 1948, the resolution was referred to the joint structure committee for further consideration. In 1949, the concept projected in the recommendation provided the basis for a two-organization plan which was adopted by the six organizations in 1952.
25. Katharine E. F. Miller, "Committee on the Structure Study Report," *Proceedings of the Special Sessions of the Advisory Council (1947-1948) and the House of Delegates (1947) of the American Nurses' Association* (New York: American Nurses' Association, 1948), 100.
26. Committee on the Structure of National Nursing Organizations, "A Tentative Plan for One National Nursing Organization," *Proceedings of the Thirty-Sixth Biennial Convention (May 31-June 4, 1948) of the American Nurses' Association,* Volume I: *House of Delegates* (New York: American Nurses' Association, 1948), 289.
27. *Ibid.*
28. *Ibid.*, 290.
29. *Ibid.*
30. *Ibid.*
31. Hortense Hilbert, *Proceedings of the Thirty-Sixth Biennial Convention (May 31-June 4, 1948) of the American Nurses' Association,* Volume I: *House of Delegates* (New York: American Nurses' Association, 1948), 157.
32. *Ibid.*, 163.
33. Katharine Densford, *Proceedings of the Thirty-Sixth Biennial Convention (May 31-June 4, 1948) of the American Nurses' Association,* Volume I: *House of Delegates* (New York: American Nurses' Association, 1948), 154.
34. *Ibid.*

35. Blanche A. Blackman, *Report of the Thirty-Second Convention (May 12-17, 1940) of the American Nurses' Association* (New York: American Nurses' Association, 1940), 89.
36. The ICN Constitution stated clearly that members "shall be one national association from each country, composed of nurses or a national federation of nurses."
37. Upon presentation of the two alternate plans, the Joint Committee on the Structure of National Nursing Organizations went out of existence. It was replaced by a structure steering committee which attempted to provide supplemental information on the reorganization proposals.
38. Committee on the Structure of National Nursing Organizations, "A Tentative Plan for One National Nursing Organization," *Proceedings of the Thirty-Sixth Biennial Convention (May 31-June 4, 1948) of the American Nurses' Association,* Volume I: *House of Delegates* (New York: American Nurses' Association, 1948), 290.
39. The complete explanation of this plan appears in the *1949 Handbook on the Structure of Organized Nursing* prepared by the Committee on the Structure of National Nursing Organizations published in March, 1949.
40. *Ibid.*
41. *Proceedings of the Special Session of the Advisory Council—1950* (New York: American Nurses' Association, 1950), 26.
42. Pearl McIver, *Proceedings of the Thirty-Seventh Convention (May 7-12, 1950) of the American Nurses' Association,* Volume I: *House of Delegates* (New York: American Nurses' Association, 1950), 185.
43. Pearl McIver, *Proceedings of the Thirty-Sixth Convention (June 16-20, 1952) of the American Nurses' Association,* Volume I: *House of Delegates* (New York: American Nurses' Association, 1952), 84.
44. *Ibid.*, 85.
45. Ella Best, "Report of the Executive Secretary," *Proceedings of the Thirty-Ninth Convention (April 26-30, 1954) of the American Nurses' Association,* Volume I: *House of Delegates* (New York: American Nurses' Association, 1954), 52.
46. Elizabeth LaPerle, *Proceedings of the Thirty-Seventh Convention (May 7-12, 1950) of the American Nurses' Association,* Volume I: *House of Delegates* (New York: American Nurses' Association, 1950), 196.
47. Dorothy E. Glynn, *Proceedings of the Thirty-Eighth Convention (June 16-20, 1952) of the American Nurses' Association,* Volume II: *Section Meetings, Joint-Special-Student Meetings* (New York: American Nurses' Association, 1952), 18.
48. Elizabeth K. Porter, "President's Address," *Proceedings of the Thirty-Ninth Convention (April 26-30, 1954) of the American Nurses' Association,* Volume I: *House of Delegates* (New York: American Nurses' Association, 1954), 17.
49. Clara A. Hardin, "American Nurses' Foundation, Inc.," *House of Delegates Sections Reports, 1954-1956* (New York: American Nurses' Association, 1956), 161.
50. *Ibid.*, 161-162.
51. Elizabeth K. Porter, "President's Address," *Proceedings of the Thirty-Eighth Convention (June 16-20, 1952) of the American Nurses' Association,* Volume I: *House of Delegates* (New York: American Nurses' Association, 1952), 17.
52. Katharine Densford, "President's Address," *Proceedings of the Thirty-Fifth Biennial Convention (September 22-27, 1946) of the American Nurses' Association,* Volume I: *House of Delegates* (New York: American Nurses' Association, 1946), 13.

53. In 1944, the ANA House of Delegates made the economic security program one of the official programs of the association. However, the program stopped short of collective bargaining activities.
54. Katharine Densford, "President's Address," *Proceedings of the Thirty-Fifth Biennial Convention (September 22-27, 1946) of the American Nurses' Association,* Volume I: *House of Delegates* (New York: American Nurses' Association, 1946), 12-13.
55. *Ibid.*
56. In 1947, some modifications were made in the Wagner Act, however, the Labor-Management Relations Act (Taft-Hartley Act) retained provisions for collective bargaining.
57. Economic Security Unit, *A Manual for an Economic Security Program: A Guide for State Nurses' Associations* (New York: American Nurses' Association, 1952), 16.
58. ANA Board of Directors, unpublished memo to state nurses' associations dated January 24, 1938.
59. Nursing Information Bureau, *Fact Sheet on the Economic Security Program of the American Nurses' Association* (New York: American Nurses' Association, 1947), 3.
60. *Ibid.*
61. "Criteria for the Evaluation of State Programs in Relation to Official National Policy," *American Journal of Nursing,* Vol. XLIX (October, 1949), 1 (reprint).
62. Economic Security Unit, *Major Official Policies Relating to the Economic Security Program* (New York: American Nurses' Association, 1965), 3.
63. Elizabeth K. Porter, "The Meaning of the Economic Security Program to the Profession of Nursing," *Proceedings of the Thirty-Sixth Biennial Convention (May 31-June 4, 1948) of the American Nurses' Association,* Volume II: *Advisory Council—Section Meetings, Joint and Special Meetings* (New York: American Nurses' Association, 1948), 748.
64. Pearl McIver, "President's Address," *Proceedings of the Thirty-Seventh Convention (May 7-12, 1950) of the American Nurses' Association,* Volume I: *House of Delegates* (New York: American Nurses' Association, 1950), 14.
65. Economic Security Unit, *Major Official Policies Relating to the Economic Security Program* (New York: American Nurses' Association, 1965), 2.
66. Agnes Ohlson, "President's Address," *Proceedings of the Fortieth Convention (May 14-18, 1956) of the American Nurses' Association* (New York: American Nurses' Association, 1956), 11-12.

1960-1970

Four Major Concerns

The fifteen years spanning 1960 to 1975 will be remembered in nursing history as a period in which the American Nurses' Association made crucial decisions affecting the nature of nursing practice and the future of nursing education. The actions taken by ANA's House of Delegates between 1960 and 1974 are significant not only to nurses but to other health care providers and consumers of health care services who are concerned with the preparation of an adequate force of qualified professional nurses and the provision of quality nursing care to large numbers of people.

Long-Term Planning

In saluting the American Nurses' Association on its seventy-fifth anniversary in 1971, the *American Journal of Nursing* highlighted the activities of the association during "the cautious 50s" and "the confident 60s." For the association, the period of 1948 to 1958 was a time of careful deliberation regarding the most effective organizational structure(s) for the nursing profession. By 1960, the nursing organizations had been restructured and ANA, as the official representative of nurses, had undertaken a study of the association's current and long-term goals.

By action of ANA's House of Delegates in 1954, a Committee on Current and Long-Term Goals was created to 1) propose an association platform, 2) develop a statement on the long-term goals of the association, indicating extension or modification of current programs, and 3) make recommendations regarding association services. In September, 1955, the ANA Board of Directors enlarged the scope and function of the committee to provide for the preparation of a report which would consist of "an inventory of the major problems and goals of the American Nurses' Association and its constituent parts."[1] The board of directors also charged the committee with the responsibility of arranging the inventory in "some rough order of importance or priority, recognizing that this is difficult and will not necessarily meet with unanimous approval."[2]

Upon assuming its responsibilities, the committee developed a plan of action for developing the inventory of major problems and association goals:

First—major sociological trends and changes would be identified and listed;

Second—developments of major concern to nurses which were occurring or could be anticipated in the future, as a result of sociological trends, would be enumerated and explored fully;

Third—ANA programs and activities which were or could be implicated by these developments would be identified; and

Fourth—criteria or principles for prioritizing the problems and goals of the association would be developed.[3]

By May, 1956, the Committee on Current and Long-Term Goals had identified those major sociological and economic trends which, the committee believed, would have an impact on the nursing profession and the activities of the American Nurses' Association during the next ten to twenty years. The committee's list included:

1) Growth of government concern in meeting needs of citizenry;

2) Growing significance and influence of organized groups in this country;

3) Emergence of unions as a political, social, and economic force;

4) The widespread trend toward professionalism in society at large;

5) Trend for higher education in the general population;

6) Increasing productivity of workers, rising standards of living, and technological changes and advances;

7) Changes in disease patterns, advances in medical science, changing practice, increasing costs of medical care, and changes in hospital administration and business management;

8) Population shifts and changes in mobility of people.[4]

Between 1956 and 1958, the committee made considerable progress in formulating long-range goals for the nursing profession and the association. In a report to ANA delegates attending the forty-first convention in June, 1958, the committee identified those responsibilities which it believed the profession must assume: "constant improvement of standards of competence, motivation and recognition of superior performance, promotion of educational standards of true professional calibre, and secural of economic rewards commensurate with the professional nature of nursing practice."[5] In light of these responsibilities, the committee recommended that the 1958 House of Delegates endorse two goals.

Goal One proposed that the association "stimulate efforts by nurses and other specialists to identify and enlarge the scientific principles upon which nursing rests, and to encourage research by them in the application of these principles to nursing practice."[6] The committee provided the following rationale:

> Nursing has experienced almost revolutionary changes in the scope of its practice. In part, the change is

> a result of the delegation of many tasks, techniques, and responsibilities from other professional groups. Professional nursing has, in turn, prepared new personnel to perform selected aspects of health care.
>
> Some changes in nursing will always take place due to reallocation of the components of health care. However, nursing like other professions, should develop a clear concept of its province which would provide the guidelines for the selection of these reallocations.
>
> The major source of changes and improvements in practice of a profession should, however, result from enlargement of the body of knowledge on which that practice rests. Each profession has a responsibility to constantly engage in research in order to enlarge and perfect that knowledge. Nursing is more than a complex of skills and techniques. It is a scientific practice and a healing art based on a specific body of knowledge. Research concerning the scientific foundations of nursing should be a major source for the refinement, change, and perfection of nursing practice.
>
> Nursing must, therefore, develop nurses skilled in research who are expert both in nursing and in those branches of science upon which nursing knowledge rests. These research nurses could undertake basic research in nursing. They could attempt to discover the relationships between nursing care and the health process. They could both identify and enrich nursing knowledge, and utilize for nursing the findings of investigators in other sciences.[7]

Goal Two proposed that the association "establish ways within the ANA to provide formal recognition of personal achievement and superior performance in nursing."[8] The committee suggested that, during the next ten to twenty years, the association establish a program to formally recognize ANA members who "demonstrate exceptional accomplishment in the practice of nursing, contribute to the development of the profession, advance nursing knowledge and understanding of nursing, and serve both society and their profession by their special contribution."[9] In support of this goal, the committee provided the following rationale:

> Nursing, as a profession, has the responsibility for providing the public with the best possible care. It has sought and secured those concrete protections which result from the establishment of minimum legal standards of practice.
>
> The ANA has adopted a code which establishes the ethical standards for nursing practice. The sections have developed statements of functions, standards, and qualifications for practice in the various areas of nursing, and are working toward their widespread implementation. These activities demonstrate the nursing profession's continuing organized efforts to improve the standards of competency of all of its members to the end that the standard of nursing practice far exceeds the minimum required by law.
>
> Concomitantly, many professional nurses have, as individuals, raised the standards of nursing by perfecting their own arts and skills, through additional formal preparation, and by contributing to the advancement of nursing knowledge and the profession. It is a proper function of the professional organization to confer on such individuals formal recognition for their contribution, achievement, and the excellence of their practice.[10]

Both of these goals were adopted.

In 1960, the Committee on Current and Long-Term Goals recommended that the House of Delegates endorse a third goal:

> To insure that, within the next 20 to 30 years, the education basic to the professional practice of nursing, for those who then enter the profession, shall be secured in a program that provides the intellectual, technical, and cultural components of both a professional and

> liberal education. Toward this end, the ANA shall promote the baccalaureate program so that in due course it becomes the basic educational foundation for professional nursing.[11]

The committee supplied the following rationale for this goal:

> The past two decades have been a period of explosive growth in the knowledge of the health professions. There have been major theoretical discoveries, a technological revolution in care, and development of radical new therapies. Medicine and nursing have been able to incorporate this new knowledge into practice through intensive self-education by practitioners and through a reallocation of professional responsibilities.
>
> Basic changes in professional nursing emerged with the increased need for a practitioner who could perform critical, independent therapeutic functions for patients. Effective performance of these functions requires the ability to independently assess, evaluate, and interpret health needs and to follow these judgments with appropriate actions. Therefore, the professional nurse must master a complex, rapidly growing body of knowledge. The nursing profession always has recognized the inseparable relationship between the quality of practice and the quality of education. When the functions of nursing were dependent and primarily required a high degree of technical skill, the major focus for raising standards of education was the improvement of diploma schools of nursing. As the practice of nursing moved into new fields and positions emerged where independent judgment and rigorous academic preparation were required, professional programs were developed in colleges and universities. Here, students had ready access to instruction in the basic sciences, the professional body of knowledge, and the liberal arts. They studied in an intellectually stimulating and challenging environment.

> This collegiate preparation initially was established to prepare nurses for specialized roles in such fields as education, public health, and administration.
>
> But, because of the changing, more demanding character of all positions in nursing, baccalaureate programs are now devoted to providing basic education for professional practice. Specialized preparation is acquired on the graduate level. An increasing proportion of students are securing basic professional education in baccalaureate programs while more than ten thousand graduate nurses annually enroll in supplementary programs which confer baccalaureate degrees.
>
> A profession must build for the future. Nursing can expect more profound changes in its practice with the continued research on chronic and degenerative diseases, the growing proportion of the population in the older age groups, and the continued high birth rate. The profession of nursing, through the American Nurses' Association, must establish standards for the education necessary for such practice. The baccalaureate programs, with their ready access to instruction in all fields, with their emphasis on intellectual discipline, and with their only purpose that of education can best prepare professional nurses.[12]

In 1960, the goal was accepted as a basis for continued discussion. It was not until 1964 that the House of Delegates approved a recommendation that the American Nurses' Association work toward baccalaureate education as the educational foundation for professional nursing.

As the American Nurses' Association identifed the major issues confronting the nursing profession and proposed a long-range plan of action, questions were raised regarding the division of labor between the American Nurses' Association, considered the organization for *nurses*, and the National League for Nursing, considered the organization for *nursing*. The key issue appeared to be—Who should make policy in what aspects of the programs of organized nursing?

The three long-term goals presented to ANA's House of Delegates between 1958 and 1960 touched on all aspects of nursing. In adopting these goals, ANA members acted on the belief that the American Nurses' Association must serve the profession as a whole if it is to carry out the functions traditionally performed by professional associations in society.

In order to implement these goals effectively, the American Nurses' Association undertook a study of association functions and structure. Inherent in a study of the functions of the American Nurses' Association was a re-evaluation of the relationship between the American Nurses' Association and the National League for Nursing.

One Organization

As early as 1955, the state and local constituencies of the American Nurses' Association and the National League for Nursing expressed dissatisfaction with the two-organizational plan. Inasmuch as the plan had been in effect only three years, the boards of directors of both organizations agreed that it would be inadvisable to experiment with reorganization. However, one year later a state nurses' association and a state league for nursing jointly recommended to the ANA-NLN Coordinating Council "that an effort should be made for the amalgamation of the two nursing organizations as soon as practical."[13] Although ANA and NLN were at odds on the appropriate course of action, both organizations agreed that more specific information regarding the problems encountered under the current structure should be collected. Subsequently, a small committee composed of board members of the American Nurses' Association and the National League for Nursing developed a questionnaire designed to identify problems in the relationships between the state nurses' associations and state leagues for nursing.

At the January, 1957, meeting of the ANA-NLN Coordinating

Council, the committee recommended a plan for a five-year investigation of the functioning of state and local units. A general lack of interest in this project prompted the board of directors of the National League for Nursing to recommend that the committee studying interorganizational functions be dissolved. In addition, in January, 1958, NLN issued the following statement:

> 1) The nursing needs of society can be met only through the concerted efforts of a membership body composed of nurses, allied professional members, and interested citizens working together to develop and carry out the decisions of the group.
>
> 2) The NLN provides services and carries on programs which are distinctive to its goals and which complement, not duplicate, those of any other organization.
>
> 3) Only through efforts of members working together in local and state groups as well as nationally can the nursing service and education needs be met in any community, and
>
> 4) Only NLN's membership can determine its present and future goals.[14]

This statement was reaffirmed by NLN's Committee on State and Local Constituents prior to ANA's forty-first convention in June, 1958.

ANA delegates to the 1958 convention were unwilling to disregard the complaints of state nurses' associations regarding the structure of organized nursing. For the first time since 1952, the House of Delegates officially discussed the desirability of one organization for nurses and nursing. The primary concern of the delegates was that the responsibilities of the nursing profession be effectively discharged. By an overwhelming vote, delegates adopted the following resolution:

> *Recognizing,* That ANA cannot legislate action that affects the NLN,
>
> *Resolved,* That this House of Delegates go on record as believing that one national organization can best meet

> the needs of nurses and nursing in the United States,
>
> *Resolved,* That the Board of Directors of the ANA invite the Board of Directors of the NLN to cooperate in appointing a joint committee to study the question of how best to bring about one organization for nurses and nursing, and
>
> *Resolved,* That the ANA Board of Directors invite the NLN to be co-sponsors of a meeting of the state leagues for nursing and the state nurses' associations immediately before the 1959 NLN convention for a progress report on this joint committee.[15]

At the same meeting, the House of Delegates adopted a platform which included the following plank: "improve the structure and functioning of national nursing organizations to facilitate effective action in nursing . . ."[16]

At its post-convention meeting, ANA's Board of Directors transmitted the action of the House of Delegates to the board of directors of the National League for Nursing with an invitation to cooperate in appointing the joint committee as proposed in the resolution. In November, 1958, the board of directors of the American Nurses' Association was informed that the National League for Nursing had declined its invitation on the basis of the statement of position issued by NLN's Board of Directors in January, 1958, and reaffirmed by the presidents and executive secretaries of state leagues for nursing in September, 1958. NLN recommended that ANA's Advisory Council meet with its board of directors, the Council of State Leagues for Nursing, and SLN executive secretaries for the purpose of clarifying the respective functions of the two organizations prior to the 1959 NLN convention.

Upon considering a number of alternatives, ANA's Board of Directors took the following action:

1) A communication was sent to the NLN Board of Directors expressing regret that the National League for Nursing was unable to accept the invitation to appoint a joint committee to study the

question of how best to bring about one organization for nurses and nursing. In response to NLN's meeting proposal, the NLN Board of Directors was informed that the ANA was unable to participate in such a meeting at that time.

2) A May, 1959, meeting of the presidents and executive secretaries of the state nurses' associations and the ANA Board of Directors was called to discuss the issues and problems involved in implementation of the House of Delegates' action on the matter of one organization for nurses and nursing.

In light of the discussion of issues by SNA presidents and executive secretaries in May, 1959, ANA's Board of Directors composed the following letter to the president of the National League for Nursing:

> The board of directors of the American Nurses' Association, meeting in September, 1959, considered the advice of the presidents and executive secretaries of the state nurses' associations on steps to be taken to carry out the resolution on one organization adopted by the 1958 ANA House of Delegates. As reported in a letter of February 10, 1959, the ANA Board of Directors called these representatives of our constituent associations together in May, 1959, to advise regarding the next steps in implementation of this resolution in light of the decision by the National League for Nursing that it could not accept the proposal of the ANA House of Delegates.
>
> Acting upon this advice, the ANA invites the National League for Nursing to join in a review and evaluation of the objectives of the two organizations in terms of how well they function to fulfill the nursing profession's responsibility to the public, and how well they function to meet the needs of the nursing profession.
>
> On its part the American Nurses' Association is now establishing a Study Committee on the Functions of ANA. This committee will work to develop a plan for

presentation to the 1960 ANA House of Delegates which will involve the membership in a study directed towards working out any organizational rearrangements deemed necessary if the profession is to meet its responsibilities more fully. The plan is to be based upon a preliminary examination of how the present organizations serve the public and the profession. An essential first step towards the preliminary examination and drafting of the plan will be development of criteria to aid in a determination of the functions which ANA, as the professional association, must carry if it is to discharge its responsibilities to the public and to the nursing profession.

Before formulating their advice to the ANA Board, the SNA representatives discussed the action of the 1958 House of Delegates in great detail. *They came to the conclusion that, in adopting the resolution, the delegates had as their primary concern the taking of steps to ensure that the ANA will live up to its responsibilities, as a professional association, by performing those functions essential to fulfilling its basic obligations to the public and to members of the profession.* The SNA representatives also expressed the definite opinion that further movement in this direction was expected before the next meeting of the ANA House of Delegates. It was their hope that NLN would agree with the ANA that a review and evaluation of the objectives of our two organizations should be undertaken at this time.

We look forward to your favorable consideration of this proposal and to receiving your suggestions regarding appropriate arrangements for making such a review and evaluation of how well ANA and NLN function to fulfill the responsibilities of the profession to the public and to its members.[17]

After several months' deliberation, the National League for Nursing adopted the following resolution:

> Be it resolved, That the board of directors of the NLN establish a study committee similar to that in the ANA as a mechanism for review of its objectives and programs.
>
> That the board of directors of NLN affirm its belief in the value of joint meetings of the two committees in the interests of constructive accomplishment and of complementing other methods of communication between NLN and ANA, and
>
> That the board of directors of NLN assure the ANA of its wholehearted eagerness to review objectives and evaluate programs to the end that the ANA and NLN effectively may continue to pursue their purposes in the promotion of the best possible nursing care for the American people.[18]

By May, 1960, ANA's Study Committee on the Functions of the ANA was able to report that it had developed criteria to determine the functions of the American Nurses' Association as a professional organization. Early in its deliberations, the committee decided to accept the purposes of the professional association as set forth by Dr. Robert K. Merton, a noted sociologist, as appropriate functions for the American Nurses' Association. Briefly stated, these functions were divided into three categories:

1) Functions for Individual Practitioners

—To give the individual practitioner social and moral support in his or her job as a professional.

—To help the individual practitioner achieve more effective performance (life-long professional education).

2) Functions for the Profession as a Whole

—To set and continually upgrade the standards for the quality of personnel to be recruited into the profession.

—To set and continually upgrade the standards for the training and education of recruits.

—To set and continually upgrade the standards of professional practice.

—To set and continually upgrade the standards for research designed to enlarge the knowledge on which the work of the profession rests.

—To advance research and disseminate the results of research.

—To be the voice of the profession.

3) Functions for the Society

—To mediate between the practitioner and the profession and between the profession and its social environment.

—To help prepare the practitioner to achieve more effective performance.

—To propose and monitor legislation that bears on the work and goals of the profession.[19]

Between 1960 and 1962, the ANA and NLN study committees met on several occasions and frequently exchanged information. An analysis of each organization's objectives as set forth in the articles of incorporation and enumerated in the bylaws revealed some confusion as to the two organizations' responsibilities for matters related to nursing service and nursing education and their respective roles as official spokesmen for nurses and nursing.

In April, 1961, NLN's Board of Directors issued a working statement entitled "This Is The National League For Nursing." In this document, the board explained that the National League for Nursing mobilized the community's resources in nursing services and nursing education by 1) defining and assessing needs and demands in these two areas, 2) establishing goals designed to meet these needs and demands, and 3) promoting the attainment of these goals. According to the board of directors, the essential criterion for an NLN activity was that the activity be directly or indirectly related to the community's nursing needs and that it meet one or more of the following criteria:

1) Responsibility is shared by more than one segment of the community.

2) Planning and programming are accomplished by the concerted action of participants from more than one segment of the community.

3) Performance requires human and financial resources in excess of those that can be supplied by any one occupational group.[20]

In response to NLN's statement, the American Nurses' Association posed the question, "What aspects of nursing would be excluded from the scope of NLN activities by applying the criteria?" NLN's study committee provided the following examples:

1) Development of a professional code of ethics and its application, including the discipline of members,

2) Definition of nursing and its practice, both legal and professional,

3) Development of functions, standards, and qualifications for practitioners and promotion of these in improvement of the practice of nursing,

4) Promotion of welfare of nurses, and

5) Spokesman for professional nursing.[21]

ANA's Board of Directors pointed out that the association could not execute such responsibilities as the development and implementation of functions, standards, and qualifications for nurse practitioners without dealing with crucial issues related to nursing service. In 1960, a special ANA committee on nursing practice had pointed out:

> The majority of nurses now practice in organized services which are essential components of health care facilities. Standards for such services are inherent in the statements of functions, standards and qualifications, the approved legal definition of practice, and other policy statements of ANA. The essential elements in a nursing service that would meet the standards of the nursing profession should be identified in order that there be guidelines to the establishment of conditions under which nurses may perform their professional functions to the satisfaction of themselves and the public they serve.[22]

As the ANA study committee explained "while the professional association may choose to delegate to another organization some measures of responsibility for carrying out its purposes, the profession should retain for itself the prerogative of enunciating the standards for service it provides.[23]

Moreover, ANA's Board of Directors pointed out that the association could not promote nursing practice without dealing with crucial issues related to nursing education. Recognizing that the improvement of nursing practice is dependent on the advancement of nursing education, ANA's House of Delegates, in 1960, adopted a platform which included a plank to elevate the standards of nursing education by formulating basic principles of education essential for effective nursing practice.

ANA's Board of Directors observed that a major shortcoming of the existing two-organization plan was that "neither organization sets forth in the language of its bylaws any particular responsibility to the other in the area of standard setting and implementation of standards."[24]

By 1962, the Study Committee on the Functions of ANA had examined the activities of the organization in terms of the traditional functions of a professional association. It had attempted to identify obstacles to fulfillment of these functions both in structural organization and programs of the American Nurses' Association and in the allocation of responsibilities between the American Nurses' Association and the National League for Nursing. The committee concluded that the principal problems could be dealt with only if ANA, the professional association for nurses, "moves with dispatch to put its own house in order to assume responsibility for the functions it should carry, to make whatever arrangements are necessary to meet the real needs of nurses."[25]

Believing that the statement of functions of the association should be sufficiently general to permit flexibility, the committee recommended the adoption of the following list of functions:

1) To establish functions, standards, and qualifica-

tions for nursing practice.

2) To enunciate standards of nursing education and implement them through appropriate channels.

3) To enunciate standards of nursing service and implement them through appropriate channels.

4) To establish a code of ethical conduct for practitioners.

5) To stimulate and promote research designed to enlarge the knowledge on which the practice of nursing is based.

6) To promote legislation and to speak for nurses in regard to legislative action.

7) To promote and protect the economic and general welfare of nurses.

8) To provide professional counseling and placement service for nurses and employers of nurses.

9) To provide for the continuing professional development of practitioners.

10) To represent nurses and serve as their spokesman with allied national and international organizations, governmental bodies, and the public.

11) To serve as the official representative of the United States nurses as a member of the International Council of Nurses.

12) To promote the general health and welfare of the public through all association programs, relationships, and activities.[26]

In addition, the committee recommended that:

The purposes of the American Nurses' Association shall be to foster high standards of nursing practice, promote the professional and educational advancement of nurses, and promote the welfare of nurses to the end that all people may have better nursing care. These purposes shall be unrestricted by consideration of nationality, race, creed, or color.[27]

These two proposals were incorporated in the ANA Bylaws during the 1962 convention.

The committee also recommended fundamental changes in the organizational arrangements within ANA. According to the committee, the existing arrangements did not facilitate the development of the clinical interests of members or provide opportunities to establish relationships with common interest groups.

During the 1962 convention, the Study Committee on the Functions of ANA provided membership with a proposal for a national association organized at three levels—district, state, and national—in ways which would facilitate the distinctive functions of each. The plan for rearrangement (which was later modified) included provisions for a commission on economic and general welfare, a commission on nursing education, and a commission on nursing service on the national level and a commission on nursing practice at the state level of the organization. It was proposed that clinical content be the basis of component units on the national level and occupational concerns be the basis of section membership on the state level.[28]

The basic philosophy expressed in the 1962 report called for the American Nurses' Association to recognize the growing interest and knowledge in areas of clinical nursing practice. ANA's responsibility for protecting and promoting the interests of nurses in their respective occupational areas was identified. Emphasis was placed on the role of the professional association in nursing education and nursing service.

In developing this design, the committee had sought a plan which would "facilitate the efforts of the organized profession to carry its responsibilities for setting standards in the areas of practice, service, education, and economic welfare."[29]

The committee's presentation was viewed by 1962 convention delegates as "a report of significance for the profession of nursing, for the public served by nursing, and the professional association of nurses."[30] The House of Delegates voted that:

The ANA press forward for intensive study by membership at all levels of the association throughout the country, so that the basic philosophy expressed in this report can be translated into effective, forward movement of the association and the membership, after appropriate study, be prepared to move into the next historic phase of the ANA as the professional association of American nurses.[31]

In the two years following the forty-third convention, members were given the opportunity to study proposed plans for the functions and responsibilities of the American Nurses' Association as the professional association of nurses. During this same period, ANA's study committee developed a more definite outline (Chart I) for a structural rearrangement designed to carry out the purposes and functions of the association as adopted by ANA's House of Delegates in 1962. Upon review of the committee's 1964 report, the House of Delegates adopted the following resolution:

WHEREAS, the Study Committee on the Functions of ANA, or its predecessor, has been studying our organization and its role ever since the adoption by the House of Delegates in 1958 of a resolution setting us on that path, and

WHEREAS, the committee has through the intervening years kept the membership and organizational constituents fully informed of developments as well as assiduously cultivating the opinions and soliciting the questions of individuals and groups at all levels and in all areas of the organization, and

WHEREAS, the House of Delegates considered and adopted overwhelmingly at its meeting in 1962 the new and revised set of functions for the ANA as recommended by the Committee, and

WHEREAS, the additional proposals regarding structural rearrangement of the ANA as presented by the

1964 Proposal
The Professional Association for Nursing: The American Nurses' Association

The purposes of the American Nurses' Association shall be to foster high standards of nursing practice, promote the professional and educational advancement of nurses, and promote the welfare of nurses to the end that all people may have better nursing care. These purposes shall be unrestricted by considerations of nationality, race, creed or color.

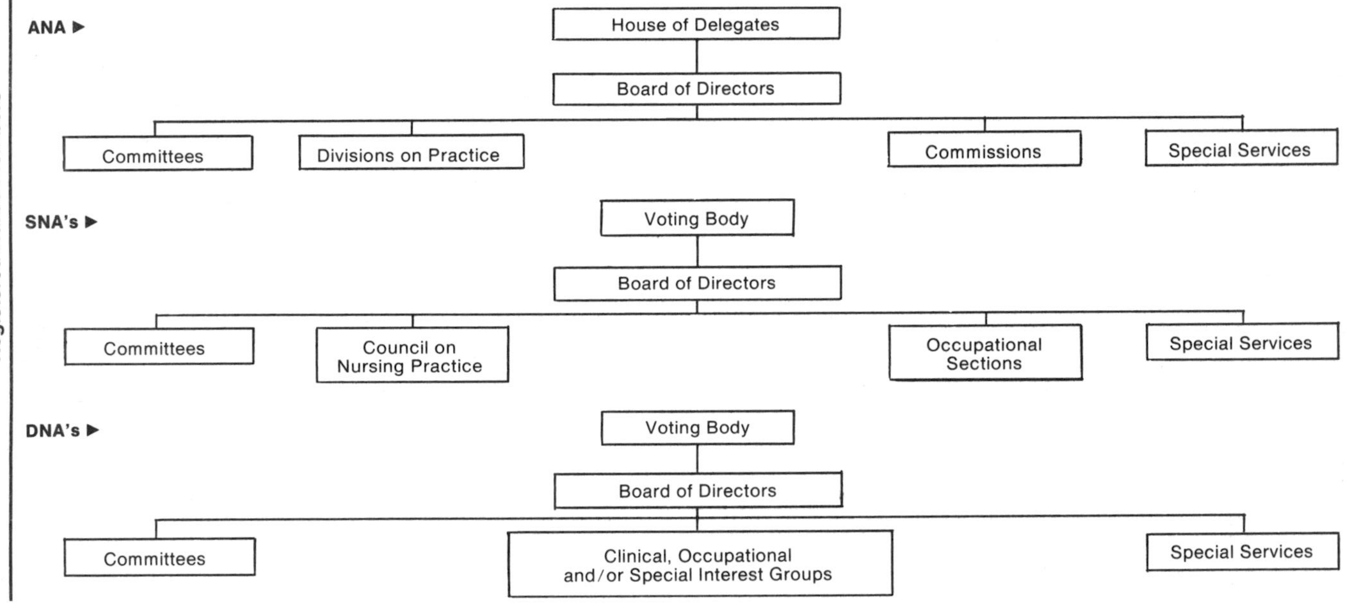

Chart I

committee at that same meeting were designed to meet the needs of nurses and the nursing profession while serving the public and these additional proposals have now been before the entire membership of the ANA for the last biennium for study and comment, and

WHEREAS, the refinement and polishing of the recommendations resulting from this study and comment has produced the committee's recommendations, as embodied in the report presented today, and because these recommendations approach the development of the ANA on a sound basis, therefore be it

Resolved, that this House of Delegates commend the work of the committee by endorsing the principles and recommendations of their report as the basis for the future development and structure of the ANA, and be it further

Resolved, that the bylaws committee be instructed to draft as rapidly as possible the bylaws, new or revised, needed to embody these principles and recommendations in the ANA structure, and be it finally

Resolved, that in order to take definite action at the House of Delegates meeting in 1966 the following should occur during the coming biennium:

1) Continued active study of the present proposals and materials at all levels of the organization,

2) Preparation and distribution of tentative proposals for bylaw changes as rapidly as possible so that they can be a part of the ongoing study, and

3) Continued work by the committee for further clarification, definition, and refinement of proposed structural changes and the inherent functional relationships.[32]

Between 1964 and 1966, the Study Committee on the Functions of ANA and the Committee on Bylaws drafted the necessary revisions to the ANA Bylaws. While the American Nurses'

Association restructured its own organization, the National League for Nursing undertook a study of its functions and structure. In January, 1963, NLN's Board of Directors appointed a Task Force on Organizational Structure. The task force's assignment was "to take steps to provide the most effective structure to carry out the purposes of the league."[33] In presenting a progress report to delegates at the 1965 NLN convention, the task force pointed out the need to review the article on functions of the NLN Bylaws in order to clarify the league's responsibility for "defining standards as differentiated from the responsibility of a professional membership association such as ANA."[34] The task force observed that "NLN has a distinctive relationship with ANA over and above other professional and health organizations" because both organizations focus on a single health discipline.[35]

As it became apparent to the American Nurses' Association and the National League for Nursing that both organizations would require periodic evaluation and possible restructuring, they developed a statement on their working relationships. Approved by both boards in January, 1966, the statement contained the following observations:

> The American Nurses' Association and the National League for Nursing as cooperating organizations in the field of nursing have the need to examine periodically the fundamental premises on which they will work together and serve society. While they are totally different organizations in both responsibilities and structure, they are complementary in purpose and function.
>
> The needs of the profession and the needs of the public for nursing service are different in 1966 from those of 1952 when a design for function and structure of both organizations was adopted. Change in the demands upon both organizations has caused each to examine its own functions and structure, and its relationships with the other. It is essential that ANA and NLN work cooperatively in areas of common concern as

each builds its program in full recognition of the role of the other.[36]

Delegates to ANA's forty-fifth convention in June, 1966, adopted bylaw revisions in order to operationalize the necessary structural rearrangements. According to Judith Whitaker, ANA Executive Director,

> Action taken on the ANA structure was the climax of seven years of study which encompassed intermediate decisions in 1962 and 1964 by ANA delegates to design a more effective professional association for registered nurses . . . Structural changes adopted by the House of Delegates in 1966 make it possible to focus on four primary areas of concern—nursing practice, nursing education, nursing services, and the economic and general welfare of nurses.[37]

ANA's new structure (Chart II) was referred to as "a blueprint to build on." Outstanding features of the reorganization included provisions for commissions, divisions on practice, a council of division chairmen, and occupational forums. The following descriptions of these units were developed for inclusion in the ANA Bylaws.

Commissions

There shall be three commissions, each responsible for developing and implementing a program of activity designed to carry out its functions and obtain recognition and acceptance of the extent of the association's concern, action, and influence in its respective area of responsibility. Each commission shall be composed of members who are experts in fields related to the commission's functions.

The Commission on Nursing Education shall:

1) Evaluate relevant scientific and educational developments, changes in health needs and practices, with reference to their implications for nursing education.

2) Establish the scope of the association's responsibil-

Structural Arrangement as Adopted in June, 1966
American Nurses' Association
NATIONAL LEVEL

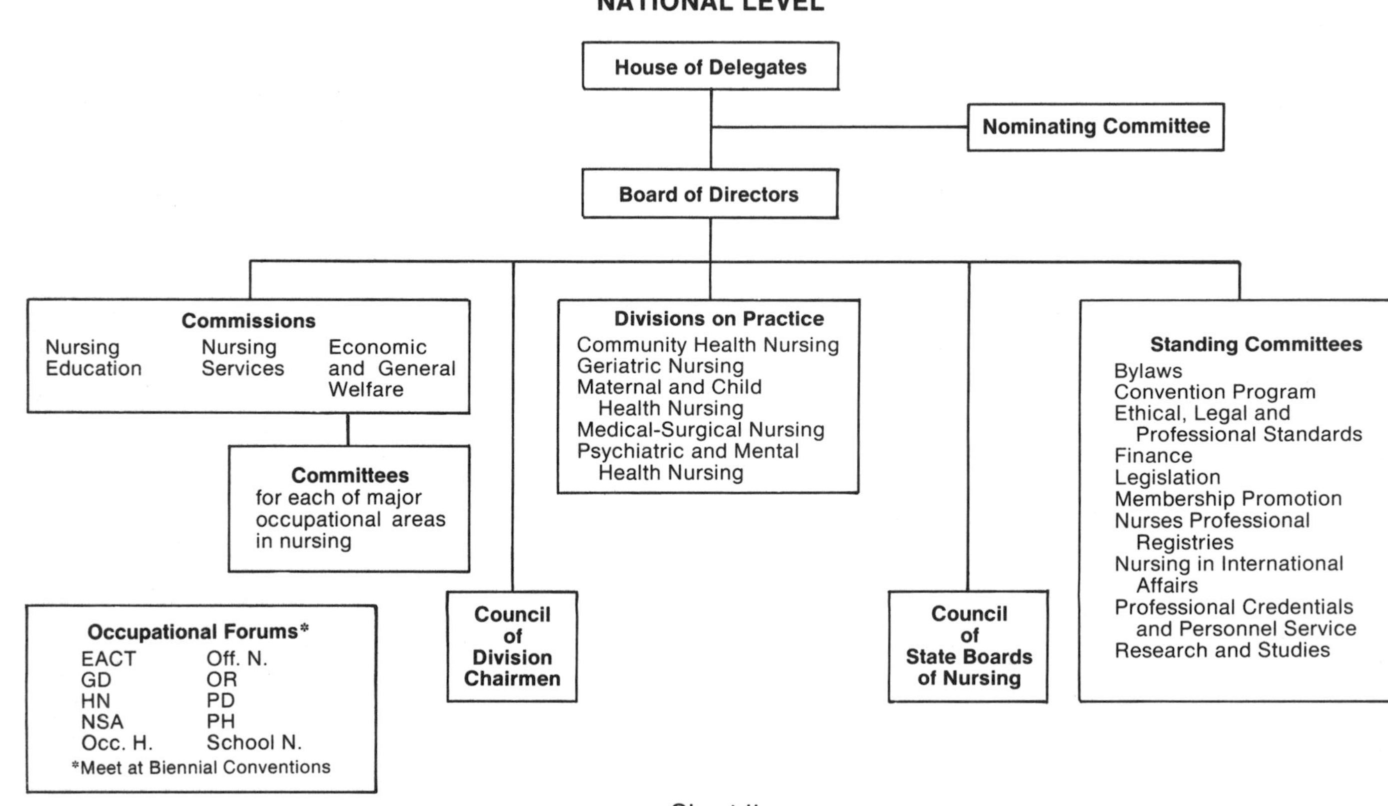

Chart II

ity for nursing education.

3) Develop standards of nursing education and devise methods for gaining their acceptance and implementation through appropriate channels.

4) Encourage and stimulate research in all areas of nursing education.

5) Formulate policy and recommend action concerning federal and state legislation in the field of education.

The Commission on Nursing Service shall:

1) Establish the scope of the association's responsibility for nursing services.

2) Develop standards of organized nursing services and devise methods for gaining their acceptance and implementation through appropriate channels.

3) Encourage and stimulate research and studies on the organization and management of nursing services.

4) Evaluate relevant scientific and educational developments, changes in health needs and practices, with reference to their implications for nursing services.

5) Develop and disseminate guides and otherwise assist with improvements in the organization and management of nursing services.

6) Study changes in health needs and care and estimate requirements for nursing manpower and resources.

7) Formulate policy and recommend action concerning federal and state legislation related to health manpower and nursing services.

The Commission on Economic and General Welfare shall:

1) Establish the scope of the association's responsibility for the welfare of nurses.

2) Develop general economic standards for the profession and devise methods for gaining their acceptance and implementation through appropriate channels.

3) Establish committees for each of the major occu-

pational areas in nursing. These committees shall identify, study, and advise on the concerns of nurses in their respective occupational settings.

4) Develop basic principles of desirable employment conditions of nurses and promote the use thereof in places of employment.

5) Study and evaluate the economics of health care.

6) Study and evaluate the economics of nursing in the various occupational settings.

7) Initiate research and studies related to the economic position of the nursing profession.

8) Develop and implement a program of economic education.

9) Formulate policy and recommend action related to federal and state legislation in the field of economics and general welfare of nurses.

10) Advise and assist constituent associations in the development of their programs in economic and general welfare.

11) Evaluate developments and trends in health care practices and the general economy for their social and economic implications for nurses.

Divisions on Practice

There shall be divisions on practice responsible for advancing the practice of nursing and composed of the members and associates who select such affiliation. Divisions on practice shall be established by the board of directors upon evidence that a substantial number of nurses are practicing in a field with a well-defined and unique body of nursing knowledge and skills and/or upon evidence that a significant health problem exists in which nursing is involved.

There shall be divisions on practice for each of the following:

1) Community Health Nursing
2) Geriatric Nursing

3) Maternal and Child Health Nursing
4) Medical-Surgical Nursing
5) Psychiatric and Mental Health Nursing

The functions of each division on practice shall include:

1) Establishing standards for nursing practice in the area of the division's concern.

2) Making recommendations as appropriate to the Commissions.

3) Providing for the recognition of professional achievement and excellence in its area of concern.

4) Conducting clinical and scientific sessions at conventions, institutes and other meetings of the association.

5) Stimulating research, studies and experiments in its area, providing forums for reporting and discussion of significant findings, and otherwise disseminating information to improve practice.

6) Providing for the dissemination of relevant information in its area of concern to its members.

7) Developing and maintaining working arrangements with other units of the association and with related professional and community groups as appropriate to the defined responsibilities of the division.

8) Maintaining communication with Councils on Practice of the constituent associations and/or with appropriate state and district groups as required to carry out the defined responsibilities of the division.

There shall be a certification board of each division composed of qualified division members. The certification board shall:

1) Develop the division's specialized criteria for certification.

2) Review credentials of division members for certification.

3) Recognize qualified division members as board-certified practitioners.

4) Endorse board-certified practitioners for appointments as fellows in the academy of nursing.

Council of Division Chairmen

There shall be a Council of ANA Division Chairmen composed of the chairmen of the divisions on practice to provide coordination of the work of the divisions and insure a reasonable uniformity in their defined responsibilities.

The functions of the council shall include:

1) Developing guidelines for the formulation of standards of nursing practice.

2) Developing necessary definitions, basic standards, and guidelines for clinical sessions and publications.

3) Developing the basic standards and guidelines for formulation of criteria by which professional achievement and excellence in nursing practice are recognized, and for certification of members within the divisions on practice.

4) Providing for the initial formulation of basic standards and guidelines for the appointment of fellows in the academy of nursing.

5) Endorsing candidates for fellows in the academy.

Occupational Forums

At each biennial convention of the association there shall be forums for representatives of each of the following occupational areas of nursing:

1) Educational Administrators, Consultants and Teachers

2) General Duty Nurses

3) Head Nurses

4) Nursing Service Administrators

5) Occupational Health Nurses

6) Office Nurses

7) Operating Room Nurses

8) Private Duty Nurses
9) Public Health Nurses
10) School Health Nurses.

The purpose and function of the forums shall be to provide:

1) For discussion of questions of organization and program of state sections.

2) For discussion of questions of concern to employed nurses such as roles and conditions of work.

3) One of the means of communication on matters of mutual concern with the Commission on Nursing Education, the Commission on Nursing Services and the Commission on Economic and General Welfare.

Although major structural revisions were instituted in late 1966, the association continued to study the organizational scheme. During the 1966-1968 biennium, members expressed concern that the newly adopted structure failed to provide a mechanism (similar to the commissions) to consolidate and coordinate nursing practice activities. Believing that nursing practice should be the central focus of a professional nurses' organization, members requested modification of ANA's structure to create a component which would reflect the organization's concern for nursing practice. Consequently, during the 1968 convention, delegates were presented the appropriate revisions to the bylaws.

Congress for Nursing Practice

The House of Delegates adopted provisions for a Congress for Nursing Practice responsible for defining, developing and implementing a program for the improvement of the practice of nursing.[38] The functions of the Congress for Nursing Practice were identified as follows:

1) To establish the scope of nursing practice.

2) To evaluate relevant scientific and educational developments and trends in health care practices for implications for nursing practice.

3) To encourage and stimulate research on the practice of nursing.

4) To formulate policy and recommend action concerning federal and state legislation related to nursing practice.

5) To formulate, interpret, and revise the code for registered nurses.

6) To study and advise upon the ethical and legal aspects of nursing practice.

7) To plan and promote educational programs and guides for implementation of principles related to ethical and legal aspects of nursing practice.

8) To provide continuing guidance to committees or councils on practice of state and district associations.

9) To provide coordination of the work of the divisions to insure a reasonable uniformity in approaches to their defined responsibilities.

Commission on Nursing Research

Consistent with the basic concept that all professions have three components—education, service, and research—ANA's Committee on Research and Studies recommended that the board of directors establish a Commission on Nursing Research which would be equal in status and responsibilities to the existing three commissions.

The American Nurses' Association had encouraged nursing research for a number of years. In 1962, the association had developed the "ANA Blueprint for Research in Nursing" to serve as a guide for shaping research programs in nursing. In 1968, the association had published guidelines on ethical values for nurses in research. Although ANA maintained an active interest in nursing research, the Committee on Research and Studies believed it was "essential to the viability and productivity of both the association and the profession that ANA provide a member grouping for nurse researchers" as soon as possible.[39]

In January, 1970, the board of directors endorsed a proposal calling for the dissolution of the Committee on Research and Studies and the establishment of a Commission on Nursing Research. The board directed the bylaws committee to draft the appropriate bylaw provisions for the House of Delegates' consideration at the 1970 convention.

During the convention, there was some discussion regarding the relationship of an ANA Commission on Nursing Research and the American Nurses' Foundation. It was pointed out that the American Nurses' Foundation had been founded to give financial support to research projects and to disseminate research findings. The commission would be established to formulate policy in such areas as human subject rights.[40] Confident that the functions of the two bodies would not overlap, delegates adopted the provision for a Commission on Nursing Research. The commission was charged with the following functions:

> 1) To evaluate social, scientific, and educational changes in health needs and practices with reference to their implication for nursing and for research.
>
> 2) To formulate policy concerning research and recommend action for the implementation of these policies.
>
> 3) To recommend priorities for the profession's research concerns.
>
> 4) To encourage and stimulate research in all areas of nursing.
>
> 5) To participate in the establishment of standards of nursing research and assist in devising methods for gaining their acceptance and implementation through appropriate channels.
>
> 6) To establish the scope of the association's responsibility for nursing research.
>
> 7) To develop research-related documents as needed by the association and guide their dissemination.
>
> 8) To provide for the conduct of nursing research

forums, workshops, and scientific sessions at conventions, conferences, institutes, and other meetings of the association.

9) To develop and implement a program to assist in the dissemination of research findings.

10) To assist each of the organizational units of the association in identifying research and studies needed to expand the body of nursing knowledge.

11) To review and advise, as needed, on research proposals of other organizational units of the association.

12) To advise and assist constituent associations in the development of their programs in nursing research.

13) To develop and maintain liaison relationships with other organizational units of the association, with the American Nurses' Foundation, and with other professional and community groups as appropriate to the responsibilities of this commission.

Councils

A basic concept underlying the restructuring of the association in 1966 was the view that the American Nurses' Association must be the representative voice of as large a number of nurses as possible. To accomplish this, the association had to be organized to deal effectively with the current and continuing needs of many nurses, recognizing the many different interests in the field and affording them an opportunity to participate in the association.

By 1971, ANA members had expressed special interest in the development of councils composed of nurse researchers, nurse educators, and advanced practitioners in specialized areas of nursing. Upon approving the establishment of the Council of Nurse Researchers and the Council on Continuing Education in 1971, ANA's Board of Directors decided that it would be appropriate to develop general guidelines to be used in the formation of other councils.

On January 31, 1973, the board of directors requested that the Congress for Nursing Practice and chairmen of the commissions hold a meeting to discuss guidelines for the establishment of practice councils. On the basis of input from these groups, ANA's Board of Directors developed a statement on the establishment of councils. "Council" was defined as "a specific group of individuals called together for specific and clearly defined purposes which may be administrative, advisory, or legislative.[41] The board identified the following basic functions to be served by a council:

1) To develop standards where no standards currently exist within the association.

2) To provide opportunity for dissemination of information in a field through scientific sessions, regional meetings, etc.

3) To provide an opportunity for the exploration of common issues and concerns.

4) To develop mechanisms for recognizing excellence in practice in the areas of nursing research, nursing education, and nursing service.[42]

With regard to the structure of the councils, the board of directors observed that a council should exist to meet a specific need for a specific group and should be dissolved when that need no longer exists. Consequently, organizational arrangements should be flexible and as simple as possible.

Between 1973 and 1974, five councils were created: a Council of Pediatric Nurse Practitioners, a Council of Advanced Practitioners in Psychiatric and Mental Health Nursing, a Council of Advanced Practitioners in Medical-Surgical Nursing, a Council of Family Nurse Practitioners and Clinicians, and a Council of Nursing Service Facilitators.

American Academy of Nursing

At the same time the association was modifying the structure to provide for the Congress for Nursing Practice, the Commission on Nursing Research, and the councils, a committee was investigating the feasibility of the establishment of an academy of nursing, composed of ANA members who had made significant contributions to the nursing profession. Interest in the creation of such a group stemmed from the House of Delegates' adoption of a long-term goal to establish ways within the American Nurses' Association to provide formal recognition of personal achievement and superior performance in nursing. As the result of a study conducted between 1964 and 1966, the revisions to the ANA Bylaws, presented at the forty-fifth convention, included a provision for an academy of nursing "for the advancement of knowledge, education, and nursing practice."[43] In presenting the proposal for an academy, the chairman of the Study Committee on the Functions of ANA stated:

> Established for the purpose of advancing knowledge, with election as a fellow therein being a high honor in recognition of substantial achievement and contribution to nursing, the academy envisioned by the study committee would enhance in great measure the authority and effectiveness of the ANA. In other fields such bodies are often formed outside the professional association. The study committee proposes that ANA encompass the academy for the nursing profession within itself.[44]

Delegates to the forty-fifth convention endorsed the idea of an academy of nursing and adopted bylaw provisions which designated academy members (fellows) as individuals selected by the academy's governing council "from among those members of the association who have been certified and endorsed by division certification boards and otherwise deemed qualified by the academy."[45]

The development of a certification program to recognize professional excellence was a long-term goal of the association. Each division on practice was charged with the responsibility of developing formal recognition of professional achievement and excellence in its area of concern. As the divisions proceeded to carry out their defined responsibilities, question arose about the nature and purpose of certification. In light of unresolved issues, ANA's Board of Directors, at its January, 1970, meeting, voted to temporarily postpone the work on certification by the divisions on practice and the Congress for Nursing Practice.

Since 1968, individuals had expressed concern that many qualified ANA members could be excluded from the academy if the association enforced the membership requisite of certification by the divisions on practice. The board of directors' action to postpone work on certification in 1970 created even more serious concern about the membership criteria for the academy. As long as certification remained the basis for entry into the academy, there was no certainty as to when and how the academy would become a functioning reality. During the 1970 convention, an ad hoc committee, appointed in 1969 to study ways to enter the academy, reported:

> Certification could be seen as one measure of an individual's qualifications for fellowship in the academy. The committee, however, concluded that the development of criteria and procedures for entrance into the academy should be independent of the association's developing program for certification of clinical practitioners.[46]

Upon considering the issues, ANA's Board of Directors concurred in May, 1971, that:

> Fellowship in the academy should be conferred on those members of ANA who have made a significant contribution to knowledge, education, nursing practice, or to the nursing profession in general; and certification by an ANA division on practice should not be a requirement for entrance into the academy of nursing.[47]

Between 1971 and 1973, a committee, appointed by the ANA Board of Directors, planned the next steps towards establishment of the academy of nursing. The committee addressed itself to further clarification of the purposes and functions of the academy and to the development of criteria for selection of charter fellows.

The American Academy of Nursing was initiated on January 31, 1973, with the adoption of a resolution by the ANA Board of Directors which designated thirty-six charter fellows, named pro tem officers, and directed that specific action be taken to establish the academy. During the 1974 convention, ANA delegates adopted bylaw revisions which removed certain obstacles and clarified the purposes and objectives of the academy. According to the bylaws, academy fellows "shall be selected by the governing council of the academy from among those members of the association who have made a significant contribution to the advancement of knowledge, education, practice in nursing, or to the profession of nursing.[48] Criteria for selection of these individuals include: five years of professional experience beyond basic nursing education, evidence of outstanding contributions to nursing, and evidence of potential to continue contributions to nursing.

The academy is viewed as "a working body which would operate in a climate in which current systems, ideas, and practices may be challenged, new ideas in nursing and other fields explored, and experimentation and innovation in nursing encouraged."[49] The functions of the academy are:

1) To advance new concepts in nursing and health care.

2) To identify and explore issues in health, in the professions, and in society as they effect and are affected by nurses and nursing.

3) To examine the dynamics within nursing, the interrelationships among the segments within nursing, and examine the interaction among nurses as all these affect the development of the nursing profession.

4) To identify and propose resolutions to issues and problems confronting nursing and health, including alternative plans for implementation.

In closing its report to the 1962 House of Delegates, the Study

Committee on the Functions of ANA stated:

> Organizations must change to meet changing demands made upon them by their members and by the society. If the American Nurses' Association is to serve its basic purposes, if it is to provide a rapidly evolving and growing profession with the organization it needs to define and research its goals, it too must change.[50]

Between 1960 and 1974, the American Nurses' Association sought to develop structural units which could deal with the growing interests and concerns of the membership and the nursing profession. Chart III reflects the association's current internal arrangement.

The association's success in facilitating programs and activities to promote nursing's interests is the result of a continuous review of ANA's organizational scheme. Periodic structural modification has made it possible for the American Nurses' Association to achieve significant goals, even during a period of financial crisis. As Judith Whitaker, ANA Executive Director, observed:

> It is a fundamental of life itself that no association of people ever completely achieves every goal, every objective it sets for itself. This fundamental holds true in education, in government, in the corporate world, and in the professions. But I believe that ANA is moving closer and closer to achievement of its goal . . . . Despite distances, despite regional differences, despite the fact that communication becomes ever more difficult in a super-communication world, we appear to be able to move with decision and greater unanimity in all those matters that influence nursing progress.[51]

In the fifteen years spanning 1960 to 1975, the American Nurses' Association has been able to:

1) Develop and initiate the implementation of standards of nursing practice and nursing service.

2) Establish a certification program to recognize excellence in clinical practice.

AMERICAN NURSES' ASSOCIATION: STRUCTURAL UNITS, NATIONAL LEVEL—1975

2420 Pershing Road, Kansas City, Mo. 64108

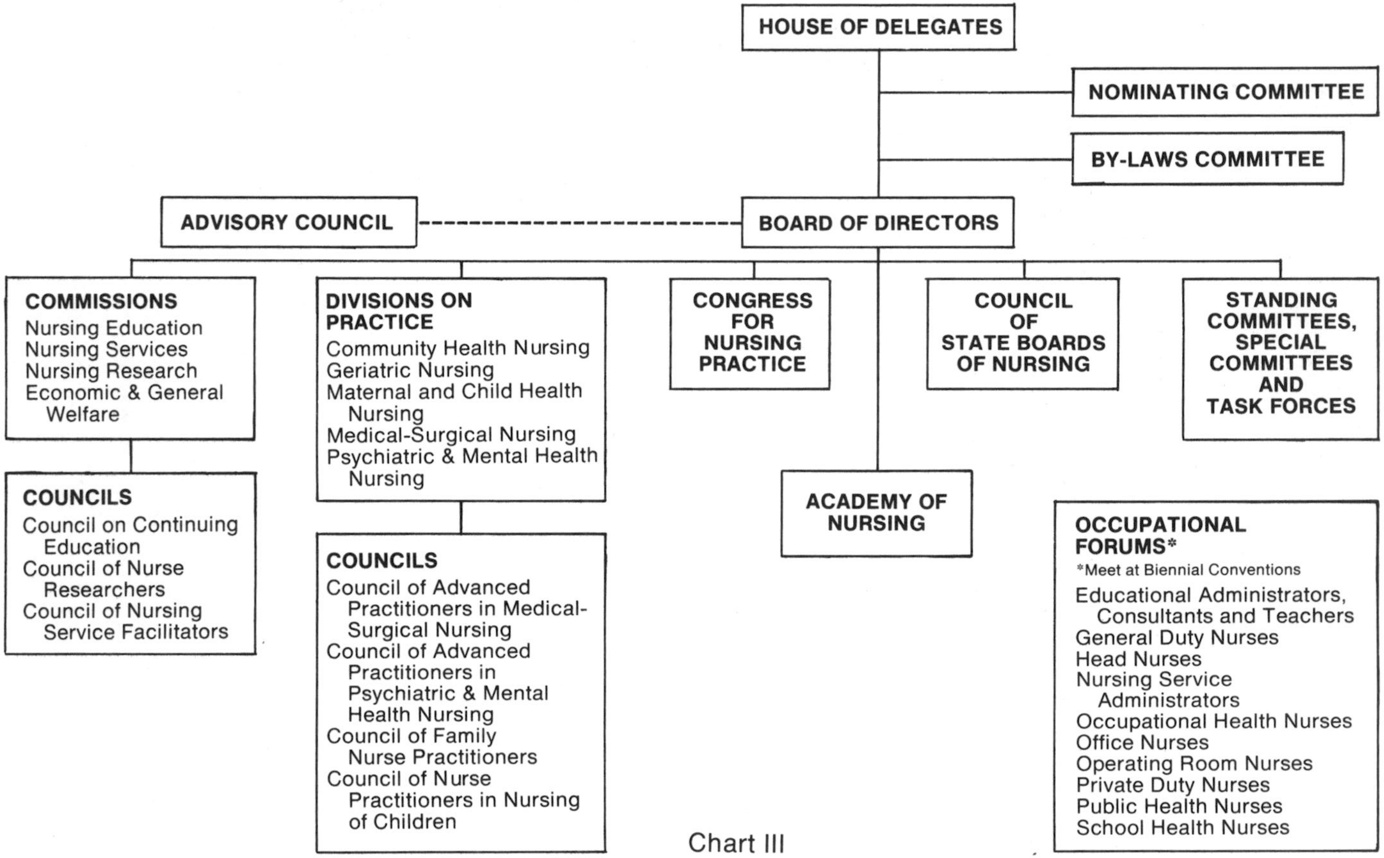

HOUSE OF DELEGATES

NOMINATING COMMITTEE

BY-LAWS COMMITTEE

ADVISORY COUNCIL

BOARD OF DIRECTORS

COMMISSIONS
Nursing Education
Nursing Services
Nursing Research
Economic & General Welfare

COUNCILS
Council on Continuing Education
Council of Nurse Researchers
Council of Nursing Service Facilitators

DIVISIONS ON PRACTICE
Community Health Nursing
Geriatric Nursing
Maternal and Child Health Nursing
Medical-Surgical Nursing
Psychiatric & Mental Health Nursing

COUNCILS
Council of Advanced Practitioners in Medical-Surgical Nursing
Council of Advanced Practitioners in Psychiatric & Mental Health Nursing
Council of Family Nurse Practitioners
Council of Nurse Practitioners in Nursing of Children

CONGRESS FOR NURSING PRACTICE

COUNCIL OF STATE BOARDS OF NURSING

STANDING COMMITTEES, SPECIAL COMMITTEES AND TASK FORCES

ACADEMY OF NURSING

OCCUPATIONAL FORUMS*
*Meet at Biennial Conventions
Educational Administrators, Consultants and Teachers
General Duty Nurses
Head Nurses
Nursing Service Administrators
Occupational Health Nurses
Office Nurses
Operating Room Nurses
Private Duty Nurses
Public Health Nurses
School Health Nurses

Chart III

3) Develop and initiate the implementation of standards of nursing education and promote continuing education programs.

4) Expand its economic and general welfare program for nurses.

Standards of Nursing Services and Nursing Practice

In 1958, ANA's Committee on Legislation developed the following resolution:

> WHEREAS, a profession assumes responsibility for the competence of its members, and
>
> WHEREAS, the American Nurses' Association as the professional organization of nurses has an obligation to protect the public and the nurse from the practice of unqualified persons, be it therefore
>
> *Resolved,* that each state nurses' association establish a committee of its members on unauthorized and improper practice of nursing, such committee to have the function of recommending appropriate action in instances of unauthorized or improper practice of nursing in the state.[52]

In submitting the resolution for consideration by ANA's House of Delegates, the committee stated:

> Of major concern to the committee during this biennium has been the degree to which the American Nurses' Association fulfills the profession's obligation to control the practice of nursing. It has attempted to assess the effectiveness of the organization's efforts to secure universal mandatory licensure for the practice of professional nursing as a means of protecting the public and nurses from incompetent and unsafe practitioners. The inevitable conclusion must be that while considerable progress has been made through the organized efforts of nurses themselves, the association faces grave responsibilities in the immediate future if it is to more firmly establish its place as an important professional organiza-

> tion in this country. All that has been accomplished in terms of licensing legislation will have little real meaning without concerted effort to insure compliance with the laws and without concerted effort to continually improve the practice of nursing.
>
> The profession has a clear and distinct responsibility to protect its members and the public they serve from unqualified practitioners in nursing. If this responsibility is to be met, the American Nurses' Association and its constituent state associations must fully recognize this obligation and must devise and carry out specific measures to control the practice of nursing.[53]

Adoption of this resolution symbolized the association's intent to improve nursing practice. The broad and far-reaching implications for nursing and the American Nurses' Association were obvious. Through its action, the House of Delegates had provided the means by which nurses, acting through their professional organization, could develop standards of nursing practice.

When the House of Delegates adopted the resolution in 1958, the American Nurses' Association was campaigning for mandatory licensure for the practice of professional nursing. In 1954, the association's occupational sections had been charged with the responsibility of defining the functions, standards, and qualifications for nursing practice. These statements provided guidelines and criteria for a legal definition of nursing practice. By 1958, some twenty states had enacted laws calling for the mandatory licensure of nurses. However, licensure requirements were viewed as the minimal standards of competency necessary to ensure that the public's health, safety, and welfare would be reasonably well protected. The American Nurses' Association, in seeking to improve nursing practice, set out to develop higher standards of nursing practice. As one observer pointed out, "In nursing, licensure is our minimal standard. The norms of practice enforced by the professional association should be more stringent than the legal control by licensure."[54]

From a definitive standpoint, the term "standard" may be explained in a number of ways. A standard is an authoritative statement describing certain specifications by which an assessment can be made. A standard is an authoritative statement denoting a rule, principle, or measure by which outcomes can be determined. A standard is a criterion by which an accepted unit of performance can be judged and evaluated. From a perceptive point of view, a standard provides a double-edged tool. For the individual practitioner, it provides a yardstick for day-to-day evaluation. For the association, it provides one criterion for recognition of excellence. The American Nurses' Association chose to define the term in the following manner: A standard is an "authoritative statement by which the quality of practice, service, or education can be judged."[55]

In order to implement the resolution on nursing practice, the ANA Board of Directors assembled an ad hoc committee to develop an appropriate course of action. In 1960, the committee observed that the absence of professional standards for nursing service was a deterrent to the efforts of the state nurses' associations to improve nursing practice. The committee reported:

> The essential elements in a nursing service that would meet the standards of the nursing profession should be identified in order that there be guidelines to the establishment of conditions under which nurses may perform their professional functions to the satisfaction of themselves and the public they serve.[56]

In June, 1961, the board of directors authorized the formation of a Committee on Nursing Services 1) to develop standards for nursing services for use in hospitals, public health agencies, nursing homes, industries, and clinics and 2) to devise and recommend methods for implementation of these standards.

As the result of the work of this committee, the American Nurses' Association was able to publish *Standards for Organized Nursing Services* in 1965.[57] The purpose of these standards was to delineate guidelines for the development of a nursing care system relevant to contemporary health care needs. These standards were based on the following assumptions:

1) The services of all nursing personnel are focused on clinical practice.

2) Nursing personnel are committed to identify innovative patterns of practice in increasingly varied settings.

3) Nursing personnel are used in administrative positions to activate an environment beneficial to clinical practice.

4) Standards for clinical practice are established as a result of collaboration among nursing personnel, other health care workers, and the consumers.

5) Nursing personnel are prepared to give relevant service.

6) Nursing personnel assume primary responsibility for their competence through self development and continuing education.

7) Nursing administration promotes the discovery of new knowledge by placing increasing emphasis on research to bring about changes in clinical practice.

8) Nursing is responsive to changing societal needs.[58]

When the Joint Commission on Accreditation of Hospitals upgraded its regulations in 1968, ANA's standards for nursing service were incorporated in the commission's specifications.

In 1966, when the association was reorganized, emphasis was placed on nursing practice and top priority was assigned to the development of standards for nursing practice. This task was viewed by many as a pioneering venture. As Judith Whitaker, ANA Executive Director, pointed out,

> There are many precedents to be set in carrying out the spirit and intention of the ANA reorganization plan to make nursing practice the central focus of the organization. Some of the responsibilities assigned to the divisions on practice—in particular, those of setting

> standards for practice—have never been fulfilled by any other profession.[59]

At the June, 1966, ANA convention, the 1,063 voting delegates overwhelmingly approved the amendment to the bylaws which created five divisions on practice. The significance of this action was explained in *A Blueprint To Build On—A Report To Members, 1966-1968:*

> In an age marked by specialization and expertise, in a time when the consultant, the expert, or the specialist often has the final word, the House of Delegates in one of the most significant actions of the 1966 convention acted to encourage increasing specialization in nursing practice.[60]

In view of the trend toward specialization, the American Nurses' Association charged each division on practice with the responsibility of establishing standards of nursing practice in the area of the division's concern. ANA believed that, by assigning responsibility for defining and upgrading standards of practice to each division, the nature of nursing in a given clinical field would be explored and means found for improving nursing practice.

In October, 1967, the Council of Division Chairmen (which was replaced by the Congress for Nursing Practice in 1968) formulated guidelines to be used by the standards committees. The council stressed that the standards should reflect "reasonable forward trends in nursing practice, in keeping with the association's leadership role, and serve the purpose of upgrading practice."[61] In light of this concern, the council suggested that each division include in its standards: 1) an opening descriptive statement of its practice reflecting the dynamic nature of the practice in the societal framework, 2) a rationale for the development of standards, and 3) an identification of the significant factors in its clinical practice that make it distinct.[62]

In February, 1968, the first meeting of the standards committees was held. As each of the five committees met separately, they accepted the guidelines as proposed by the council. The individual standards committees established their own timetable and convened at various times during the fall of 1968 and during 1969. As each committee focused on standards for its division, concerns were expressed regarding the number of sets of standards to be developed and the measurability of the standards.

Between 1968 and 1970, significant progress was made in drafting the standards. In 1969, the committees devised the format for the standards—a *statement* of the standard, the *rationale* for including the standard, and the *assessment factors* or nurse behaviors by which a judgment could be made concerning the practitioner's use of the standard. The development of assessment factors for each standard was viewed as an initial step toward measurability. By May, 1970, tentative standards of maternal and child health nursing, medical-surgical nursing, and psychiatric and mental health nursing had been distributed. In September, 1970, tentative standards of geriatric nursing were published in the *American Journal of Nursing* and in the Fall issue of *ANA in Action,* the association's newspaper.

Unfortunately, in 1970, the ANA Board of Directors was forced to recommend that all further work on standards be postponed. This action was the result of two factors: ANA's financial crisis and the unresolved issues regarding the number of sets of standards and the measurability of the standards. The board requested that ANA staff undertake a study of the issues and refer the results of the study to an ad hoc committee for action.

The staff committee conducted a year-long study of the problems encountered in the development of standards. The key issue appeared to be the number of sets of standards. Four proposals had been introduced:

1) One set of standards for each of the five areas of practice should be developed.

2) One set of general standards, representing nursing practice across the board, should be developed.

3) One set of general standards and one set of standards for each of the five divisions of practice should be developed.

4) Two sets of general standards, one set each for the episodic and distributive concepts of nursing care, should be developed.

In January, 1971, the staff committee submitted its report to the ad hoc committee of the board of directors. The report contained the recommendation that the American Nurses' Association develop one set of generic (general) standards initially and investigate the possibility of developing specialty standards at a later date.

In February, 1971, the ad hoc committee, composed of the Congress for Nursing Practice and the chairman or representative of each standards committee, met to consider the issues regarding standards of nursing practice. This board-appointed committee concluded:

1) Standards should be written about the practice of nursing, not the practitioner of nursing.

2) Representatives of the standards committees and two members of the Congress for Nursing Practice should develop one set of generic standards of nursing practice.

3) The preliminary work on standards should be used in developing the one set of generic standards of nursing practice.

4) Work should be initiated or resumed on the specialized sets of standards once the generic standards are published.[63]

By the end of 1971, eight generic standards for nursing practice had been identified:

> 1) The collection of data about the health status of the client/patient is systematic and continuous. The data are accessible, communicated, and recorded.
>
> 2) Nursing diagnoses are derived from the data about the health status of the client/patient.
>
> 3) The plan of nursing care includes goals derived from the nursing diagnoses.
>
> 4) The plan of nursing care includes priorities and the prescribed nursing approaches or measures to achieve the goals.
>
> 5) Nursing actions provide for client/patient partici-

pation in health promotion, maintenance, and restoration.

6) Nursing actions assist the client/patient to maximize his health capabilities.

7) The client's/patient's progress or lack of progress toward goal achievement is determined by the patient/client and the nurse.

8) The client's/patient's progress or lack of progress toward goal achievement directs reassessment, reordering of priorities, new goal setting and revision of the plan of nursing care.[64]

In 1972, the standards committees drafted standards of community health nursing practice, maternal and child health nursing practice, medical-surgical nursing practice, and psychiatric and mental health nursing practice, using the generic standards as a guideline. Inasmuch as the standards of geriatric nursing practice had already been printed in the *American Journal of Nursing* in September, 1970, and had been well received, the Division on Geriatric Nursing Practice chose to leave their standards intact.

All six sets of the standards were presented in a working paper at the 1972 biennial convention. The working paper represented the first step toward fulfilling a plank of the association's platform which had been adopted by the House of Delegates in May, 1968—"Advance the practice of nursing by establishing standards of practice for the major clinical areas . . . ."[65]

Following the convention, and in light of member reactions, revisions were made to the standards. At the April, 1973, meeting of the Congress for Nursing Practice it was decided that the standards would be published. At that time, the standards were not envisioned to be completed works, but rather working documents. Consequently, the following statement appears in the introduction of each standards brochure:

> In recognition of the importance of standards of professional practice and the need to guarantee quality

> service, the various divisions on nursing practice have each formulated a set of standards. The American Nurses' Association recognizes that as standards are implemented in practice settings and, as the scope of nursing practice enlarges and the theoretical basis upon which this practice rests becomes more sharply delineated, ongoing revision of the standards of professional practice will be warranted.[66]

In August, 1973, standards of community health nursing practice, geriatric nursing practice, maternal and child health nursing practice, and psychiatric and mental health nursing practice as well as the generic standards of nursing practice appeared in print. Standards of medical-surgical nursing practice were published in February, 1974. In 1975, the Division on Medical-Surgical Nursing Practice collaborated with specialty nursing organizations on standards of nursing practice in the operating room, standards of orthopedic nursing practice, standards of cardiovascular nursing practice, and standards of emergency nursing practice.

Inasmuch as nursing practice standards were based on the premise that the individual practitioner is responsible and accountable for the quality of nursing care, ANA took certain steps to insure the implementation of these standards by each nurse. In 1968, ANA's House of Delegates charged all nurses to accept responsibility for their own involvement in the decisions that affect quality care. In 1970, the House of Delegates urged the ANA to define and support methods through which nurses could have a definite and effective voice in their practice. When the working draft of the standards was presented to delegates at the 1972 convention, the Congress for Nursing Practice and the Commission on Economic and General Welfare co-sponsored a resolution on the implementation of standards of nursing practice within the employment setting. These two groups pointed out that "collective participation by nurses in shaping decisions that affect conditions of employment and practice is inseparable from and contributes to the goal of implementing high standards of nursing practice."[67] In adopting the resolution, delegates urged the American Nurses' Association to continue to support and work with state nurses' associations in implementing and expanding their economic and general welfare programs "to the end that high standards of nursing practice will be achieved and maintained."[68]

During this same convention, delegates voted that in every health care facility there be provision for continuing peer review as one means of maintaining standards of nursing practice. Peer review is the process by which registered nurses, actively engaged in the practice of nursing, appraise the quality of nursing care in a given situation in accordance with established standards of practice.[69] In order to implement this resolution, the Congress for Nursing Practice appointed an ad hoc committee, composed of representatives of the congress, commissions, divisions on practice, and the National Student Nurses' Association, to develop guidelines for peer review, local joint practice, and nursing audit. In November, 1973, the committee completed guidelines for the formation of peer review committees. In its final report, the committee stressed the fact that the purposes of peer review should be:

> 1) To evaluate the quality and quantity of nursing care as it is delivered by the individual practitioner and/or group of practitioners, the purpose being to identify the extent of consistency to established standards of practice.
>
> 2) To determine the strengths and weaknesses of nursing care.
>
> 3) To provide evidence to utilize as the basis of recommendations for new or altered policies and procedures to improve nursing care.
>
> 4) To identify those areas where practice patterns indicate more knowledge is needed.[70]

During the 1972-1974 biennium, the Congress for Nursing Practice, the Commission on Economic and General Welfare, and the Commission on Nursing Services met jointly to discuss the roles of the divisions on practice, the Congress for Nursing Practice, and the two commissions in implementing standards of nursing practice. It was agreed that:

1) The Congress for Nursing Practice and the divisions on practice must assume responsibility for the enunciation, interpretation, and implementation of standards of practice and must be the primary agents for implementing them.

2) Other structural units of the association are facilitators for the implementation of standards of practice.

3) The responsibility and accountability for the quality of nursing care is an integral part of each nurses' practice.

4) The Congress for Nursing Practice and the divisions on practice should investigate methods of massive distribution of the standards of practice to include one free copy to every ANA member.

5) Collective bargaining is one method to be used in facilitating the implementation of standards of practice by negotiation for the appropriate milieu in which quality practice can be achieved.

6) The Commission on Nursing Service should speak to the role of directors of nursing services in facilitating the implementation of standards of practice.

Finally, delegates attending ANA's forty-ninth convention in June, 1974, voted that the implementation of ANA's standards of nursing practice be given major priority. Since that time, the association has published *A Plan for Implementation of the Standards of Nursing Practice* which includes a model for quality assurance. In developing this plan, the Congress for Nursing Practice identified the potential impact for nursing:

> 1) Nurses involved in assuring the quality of nursing care will use the model for quality assurance presented in this report in order to assess and guide their activities in evaluating the quality of nursing care.
>
> 2) Nurses will commit themselves to involving consumers in the implementation of standards.

> 3) Nurses will actively participate with other members of the health care team in quality assurance review.
>
> 4) Nurses will collaborate with other health disciplines in multi-disciplinary quality appraisals of the planning, development, and implementation of the national priority for quality assurance in health care.[71]

Certification for Excellence in Practice

In 1958, when the American Nurses' Association assumed responsibility for the development and implementation of nursing practice standards, the ANA Committee on Current and Long-Term Goals proposed that the association also provide formal recognition of personal achievement and superior performance in nursing. The committee affirmed the fact that it was the responsibility of the nursing profession to upgrade the standards of competence of all its members to the end that "an increasing number of nurses meet maximum, not minimum standards."[72] According to the committee,

> To accomplish this, the professional organization must do more than motivate and exhort individual practitioners to improve their abilities and knowledge, it must recognize and reward these individuals for the activities they undertake and the service they render.[73]

At the encouragement of the Committee on Current and Long-Term Goals, the House of Delegates endorsed a recommendation that the American Nurses' Association establish ways to formally recognize members who demonstrated exceptional accomplishment in the practice of nursing, contributed to the development of the profession, advanced nursing knowledge, and served both society and the profession by their special contributions.[74]

The responsibility for implementation of this goal was delegated to the Intersection Committee on Recognition of Superior Performance, composed of representatives of the Committees on Functions, Standards, and Qualifications for Practice created in

1954 by the eight occupational sections of the association. This committee concurred that:

1) The basic intent of this goal is the advancement of nursing.

2) This is to be accomplished by identifying what constitutes excellence

a. Superior performance in nursing,

b. Outstanding contributions to the develop ment of the profession and to society, and

c. Advancement in nurses' knowledge and the body of nursing knowledge.

3) Criteria will be developed for each area of excellence in professional practice.

4) On the basis of these criteria members of the association will be identified and recognized for performance within any one area.[75]

In 1960, the committee proposed a twelve-year timetable and targets for the establishment of a recognition program.[76]

In a 1962 report to the House of Delegates, the Intersection Committee on Recognition of Superior Performance made three observations:

1) The committee has developed its work within the framework of the present occupational sections; however, it has been observed that clinical groups more readily lend themselves to identification of excellence in the practice of nursing.

2) It is evident to the committee that before an individual can be recognized for superior performance, baselines of competent performance or common cores of functions, standards, and qualifications for the practice of nursing must be identified.

3) Due to the interrelatedness of the work of this committee and the work of the Study Committee on the Functions of ANA, it is believed that any approach to the primary intent of the goal to establish ways within

> the American Nurses' Association to provide formal recognition . . . should await membership consideration and eventual decision on proposed rearrangements within the association.[77]

In 1966, the Study Committee on Functions of the ANA proposed that the association's responsibilities to set standards of practice and to recognize achievement in practice be delegated to the divisions on practice. In adopting the plan for reorganization, the House of Delegates endorsed the establishment of certification boards within each division which would be responsible for the development of the division's criteria for certification.

The association defined certification and explained the objective of its program in the following manner:

> Recognition of excellence in the practice of nursing is provided by the American Nurses' Association, the professional association for registered nurses, through the process of certification. The association issues a formal statement attesting that the recipient has met special criteria for individual achievement and superior performance in a particular area of nursing practice.
>
> The objective of ANA certification is to improve nursing practice and to assure the public, employers, and members of allied professions that efforts are being made to recognize excellence in the practice of nursing. The process of certification affords direction for clinical content in educational programs. It also provides incentive for nurses to expand their knowledge and to make application of knowledge in their practice.[78]

There are three forms of credentialing mechanisms for health care workers: licensure, accreditation, and certification or registration. Traditionally, certification has been utilized to recognize those who have attained specialized knowledge above and beyond that necessary to safely engage in practice. This process differs from licensure which has evolved as a means of setting a minimal standard for those persons entering the health care system as practitioners. Accreditation differs from both certification and licensure in the sense that accreditation recognizes the educational institution's ability to impart a certain level of knowledge to students. Accreditation of an educational institution does not directly reflect the student's ability to administer quality nursing care.

There are basically three types of certification:

1) Voluntary or mandatory certification which serves as entry into practice.

2) Voluntary or mandatory certification of competence which serves as validation of educational attainments and continuing education activities.

3) Certification which serves as recognition of professional achievement.

ANA certification does not represent credentialing for entry into practice or validation of educational attainments. It does represent recognition of excellence in the clinical practice of nursing.

In December, 1968, the five interim certification boards held their first meetings.[79] In January, 1969, a questionnaire was mailed to twenty-six professional organizations to obtain facts regarding the methods by which these organizations recognized members who exhibited excellence in practice, functioned at a high level of achievement in their field, or made outstanding contributions to their professions.

The objective of the survey was to collect information which could be utilized by the Congress for Nursing Practice in the identification of basic guidelines for certification which would be used by the interim certification boards in developing the division's criteria.

The organizations responding to the questionnaire identified the following objectives for recognition programs:

1) To advance the art and science of the profession.

2) To protect the public by specifying those members qualified to function in special areas, and

3) To recognize and award superior performance and leadership.

Of the twenty-three organizations which responded, fourteen had some type of formal structure for recognizing excellence, advanced achievement, and outstanding contributions and nine gave honorary awards.[80]

Early in 1969, the Congress for Nursing Practice finished drafting guidelines for the certification process. Fifteen tentative guidelines were submitted to the interim certification boards at their meetings in the spring of 1969.

Discussion centered on the congress' recommendation for two types of certification for excellence in nursing practice: one for professional practice and one for technical practice. For the purpose of certification, the Congress for Nursing Practice developed the following definitions of professional and technical practice:

> *Professional Nursing Practice* is the diagnosis and treatment of the nursing problems of clients. It involves all those actions essential to diagnosis, the prescriptions for nursing care, the implementation of those prescriptions requiring professional knowledge and skill, the delegation of those prescriptions not requiring professional knowledge and skill, and the evaluation of the outcome of nursing actions in client welfare and progress. It demands acceptance of personal responsibility and accountability by the professional nurse not only for the nurse's actions, but also for the actions of all those who follow the nurse's prescriptions. Such practice is marked by creativity in the innovation of needed diagnostic and treatment measures; perception of a wide range of cues in the patient's problematic situation; a high order of cognitive skill. It often requires the instruction and supervision of the technical nurse and nursing assistants.
>
> *Technical Nursing Practice* is the execution upon

> prescription by the professional nurse of those activities of nursing which have been standardized experientially, empirically, and through research. It requires skill in performance of these activities and judgment based on scientific knowledge in order to adjust these activities to ongoing changes in the client's situation and condition. It involves observation of expected symptomology and of the expected outcomes of nursing or medical prescriptions; the use of these observations to adjust these activities; the reporting of observations; and the seeking of professional direction when needed. It demands acceptance of personal responsibility and accountability for actions.[81]

In September, 1969, the Congress for Nursing Practice met again to revise the guidelines in response to reactions from the interim certification boards. At that time, the congress modified the guidelines to specify three types of certification: professional general practice, professional specialty practice, and technical general practice. Reacting to this proposal, the interim certification boards questioned whether the distinction between technical and professional nursing practice and the character of clinical specialty practice had been sufficiently defined to permit more than a single level or type of certification. The division executive committees concurred that this issue should be resolved before the interim certification boards could complete their work.

At its meeting in January, 1970, the board of directors concluded that further development of the procedures for ANA certification should be postponed pending a study of the issues by staff. On April 15, 1971, a staff committee submitted a thirty-seven page working paper on certification. In this report, the staff committee set forth several propositions, including:

1) The primary purpose of ANA certification should be the recognition of the practitioner who has demonstrated professional achievement and excellence in practice.

2) For the purposes of certification, the term "practice" should

refer to the areas of education, research, and administration as well as clinical practice.

3) A prerequisite for certification in any of the areas of nursing practice or their subgroups should be the development of a definition of the scope of practice and standards of practice applicable to that area.

4) Certification should be attainable to all nurses, regardless of type of basic educational preparation, whose practice is consistent with the scope of practice and standards for that area.

5) There should be *one* type of certification in each area and it should be for recognition of excellence in current practice. ANA certification should not be a vehicle for defining types of practice or career patterns.[82]

Taking into consideration the staff report on the essential characteristics of a certification program, the Congress for Nursing Practice, on October 15, 1971, distributed a revised set of guidelines for one level of certification—certification for excellence in clinical practice. These guidelines provided the answers to three basic questions about the procedure, eligibility requirements, and criteria for ANA certification.

What are the steps in the certification process?

1) Application
2) Determination of Eligibility
3) Testing: Assessment of Knowledge
4) Documentation: Evidence of Excellence in Nursing Practice
5) Evaluation of Evidence
6) Certification

Who is eligible for certification?

1) A currently licensed practitioner of nursing, regardless of the basic nursing program from which the individual was graduated, is eligible for certification.

2) Only clinical practitioners of nursing qualify for certification. A nurse is engaged in the clinical practice of nursing when the nurse's actions and reflections are focused on a particular client (individual, family, community) and when there is per-

sonal responsibility and accountability to the client for the outcome of such actions. Consultants, researchers, administrators, and educators are eligible to seek certification if they are also engaged in clinical practice and can meet the criteria as specified.

3) A candidate for certification must provide evidence of current licensure to practice, at least two years of practice as a registered nurse following completion of basic educational requirements, and current engagement in the clinical practice of nursing in which certification is sought.

4) ANA membership is not a requirement for certification by the American Nurses' Association.[83]

What are the criteria for certification?

ANA certification is based on assessment of knowledge, demonstration of competence in clincial practice, and endorsement by colleagues.

A candidate for certification must provide proof of clinical practice in the area of nursing in which certification is sought. Evidence of this practice includes a narrative description of the work setting and type of clinical practice. In addition, the candidate is asked to submit the names and addresses of individuals who can assess the candidate's nursing ability and working relationships within the health care facility.

A candidate for certification must successfully complete an examination in a specific area of nursing practice. The examination is designed to identify levels of knowledge and understanding which are within the competence of a professional nurse practitioner. A candidate who fails the examination will be provided guidance in dealing with the aspects of nursing in which his/her knowledge is deficient.

A candidate for certification must also demonstrate excellence in clinical practice by independently completing case studies, innovative projects, continuing education courses, and/or other specified exercises.

By February, 1972, three divisions on practice—psychiatric and mental health nursing, maternal and child health nursing, and geriatric nursing—had delineated guidelines for certification in their respective areas. These guidelines were endorsed by the board of directors in April, 1972, and shared with the membership at the ANA convention in May, 1972. During the convention, the House of Delegates identified the recognition of excellence and continued competence among practitioners of nursing as one priority of the American Nurses' Association.

Late in May, 1973, the American Nurses' Association formally announced the initiation of its nationwide certification program to recognize excellence in the clinical practice of nursing. This announcement was prompted by the signing of a contract with the Educational Testing Service of Princeton, New Jersey. The association engaged the talents of the Educational Testing Service to train item writers and provide the technical assistance for processing, scoring, and analyzing candidate data. The Educational Testing Service conducts more than 800 different testing programs and projects for a variety of sponsors, including the College Entrance Examination Board, the Graduate Record Examination Board, and a broad array of certification agencies across the occupational spectrum.

ANA's own experience provided valuable insight into the development of the certification examinations. Since the early 1940s, the American Nurses' Association has worked to develop a pool of licensing examinations for State Boards of Nursing and now owns the process by which the examinations are developed. Moreover, the association has had the experience of developing an ongoing program of evaluation for the test pool.

Unlike certification programs which merely acknowledge educational attainments, ANA certification is based on three factors: assessment of knowledge, demonstration of competence in clinical practice, and endorsement by colleagues.

Depending on the area of nursing practice, one of two types of testing is utilized to assess a candidate's competence: objective multiple choice or case simulations. These examinations are developed by expert nurse practitioners under the guidance of the

Educational Testing Service.

The objective multiple choice examination is intended to cover essential knowledge, understanding, and application of principles and values in a specific area of nursing practice.

The patient management simulations examination is intended to cover the basic concept in a given area of nursing and includes interpretation and application of principles and values. In this technique, standardized case studies are presented by revealing only part of the case information at different points in time. The candidate is required to make a decision each time more information about the patient is revealed. The candidate's choices provide the base of information used to make the next decision about the patient. The process of making sequential decisions and receiving information about the consequences of those decisions is continued to a logical stopping point.

Each applicant for ANA certification is requested to submit case studies and innovative projects which reflect the applicant's clinical practice. These projects are evaluated in light of ANA's *Standards of Nursing Practice.* The standards provide a means for determining the quality of nursing which a patient receives. Each standard is followed by a rationale and assessment factors. The assessment factors are used in determining achievement of the standard. They identify behaviors by which a judgment can be made concerning the practitioner's use of the standard.

The candidate's nursing ability and working relationships are evaluated by other members of the health care team. The Educational Testing Service has prepared special reference vouchers which consist of several rating scales covering various observable aspects of nursing.

In June, 1973, the Congress for Nursing Practice extended an invitation to the nurse specialty organizations to share with ANA and each other information concerning their activities in relation to certification and to explore together ways of cooperating to develop a system or systems that complement and support the activities of all nursing organizations.

With the administration of certification examinations in geriatric nursing and pediatric nursing in ambulatory health care in May, 1974, and a psychiatric and mental health nursing examination in September, 1974, ANA formally launched its recognition program. Formal ceremonies were held in January, 1975, to honor the first nurse practitioners to be certified for excellence in clinical practice by the American Nurses' Association. In 1975, certification examinations in community health nursing, geriatric nursing, and pediatric nursing in ambulatory health care were administered. By December, 1975, 304 nurse practitioners had been awarded ANA certification.

In 1975, ANA's Division on Maternal and Child Health Nursing Practice and the Nurses' Association of the American College of Obstetricians and Gynecologists formed a joint committee to establish a certification program in maternal-gynecological-neonatal nursing.

Between 1976 and 1977, candidates will be screened for ANA certification in the following areas: community health nursing, geriatric nursing, pediatric nursing in ambulatory health care, medical-surgical nursing, maternal-gynecological-neonatal nursing, adult and family nursing in ambulatory health care, and psychiatric and mental health nursing.

During the 1972-1974 biennium, the Congress for Nursing Practice appointed an ad hoc committee to study the matter of certification for the specialty practice of nursing. Two recommendations of the ad hoc committee have been given top priority: 1) certification for excellence in practice as a specialist is needed and 2) there should be documentation of proficiency in areas of specialty practice based on continuing education beyond the basic nursing education program.

Standards of Nursing Education

ANA's campaign to improve nursing practice through the development and implementation of standards of practice and the recognition of professional achievement necessarily involved considerations regarding nursing education. In adopting the resolution on nursing practice in 1958, the House of Delegates assumed responsibility for the improvement of standards of competence. As ANA's Committee on Current and Long-Term Goals pointed out, "assumption of responsibility for standards of competence cannot be divorced from a concern with the standards of education."[84] In light of this observation, the committee urged the American Nurses' Association to promote "educational standards of true professional calibre."[85] In May, 1960, the committee presented a proposal to the House of Delegates which was viewed by ANA membership and the nursing profession as a crucial issue facing the association. The committee recommended:

> To insure that, within the next 20 to 30 years, the education basic to the professional practice of nursing, for those who then enter the profession, shall be secured in a program that provides the intellectual, technical, and cultural components of both a professional and liberal education. Toward this end, the American Nurses' Association shall promote the baccalaureate program so that in due course it becomes the basic educational foundation for professional nursing.[86]

At that time, there were three types of basic educational programs preparing individuals for licensure as registered professional nurses: college and university programs leading to the baccalaureate degree, junior college programs leading to an associate degree, and hospital programs leading to a diploma.

The Committee on Current and Long-Term Goals devised twelve principles for nursing education from generally accepted theories of professional education:

> 1) The determination of standards for professional education is the responsibility of the nursing profession.
>
> 2) All graduates of professional educational programs in nursing shall have mastered that core of basic and applied knowledge essential for effective practice.

3) The requirements for curricula and methods of teaching shall be flexible in order to stimulate experimentation and to permit revision and expansion of subject matter.

4) Professional education should provide the student with an opportunity to develop the capacity for independent judgment in the application and advancement of nursing knowledge.

5) The educational program should include an opportunity for the student to expand intellectual and cultural horizons through acquiring a broad liberal education.

6) Responsibility for the total educational experience should rest with the faculty of the educational institution.

7) The standards governing the organization, faculty, and facilities of a nursing education program should be comparable to those of other professional programs within an educational institution.

8) The nursing faculty should have responsibility for developing and implementing the professional education program.

9) Responsibility for financing professional education rests with the entire society.

10) Adequate and stable financial resources should be provided for the programs of professional education.

11) The requirements for admission to programs in nursing education should be comparable to those of other professional programs within an educational institution.

12) Graduation from undergraduate professional programs in nursing should qualify students for entrance to graduate programs in nursing with, generally, no further academic preparation.[87]

The committee's proposal that basic nursing education be

placed in a baccalaureate degree program was not a new concept. In 1948, the National Nursing Council had issued a report on the future of nursing which contained the recommendation that the term "professional" when applied to nursing education should reflect the same basic concept as professional training in other fields. The council pointed out that, inasmuch as professional schools in most other fields were situated in degree-conferring institutions, possession of a degree was fast becoming a criteria to distinguish professional education from vocational training.

During the 1960 ANA convention, delegates adopted a plank to continue to elevate standards of nursing education by formulating principles of the education essential to effective practice. Between 1960 and 1964, the American Nurses' Association utilized the report on nursing education prepared by the Committee on Current and Long-Term Goals as the basis for continued study and discussion. In June, 1961, the board of directors approved the establishment of a committee on education. In January, 1962, the committee was charged with the following responsibilities:

> 1) To study and make recommendations for meeting the association's specific responsibilities in nursing education.
>
> 2) To formulate basic principles of the education essential for effective nursing practice.
>
> 3) To study the effect of federal and state legislation in terms of its effect on nursing education and make appropriate recommendations.[88]

In May, 1962, the House of Delegates identified "enunciation of standards of nursing education" as one of the association's primary functions.

Finally, in June, 1964, delegates to ANA's forty-fourth convention approved the recommendation that the American Nurses' Association work toward baccalaureate education as the educational foundation for professional nursing. In approving the recommendation, delegates confirmed the need to clarify the various levels of nursing practice and to identify the education needed for each level of practice.

The House of Delegates' action came in the midst of week-long activities focusing on "The Knowledge Explosion—Its Implications for Health Care." From the information presented during various convention sessions, it was apparent to ANA members that current and pending changes in the patterns of demand for health services, the structure of health care services, licensure, and the scope of nursing practice warranted practitioners who were more comprehensively prepared to assume greater responsibility and to adapt to fast-changing techniques and approaches to practice.

In May, 1965, the National League for Nursing passed a resolution advocating community planning to implement the orderly transition of nursing education into institutions of higher learning. In September, 1965, the board of directors of the American Nurses' Association endorsed the association's first definitive statement on nursing education—*Educational Preparation For Nurse Practitioners and Assistants to Nurses: A Position Paper.* The major assumption underlying the development of the position paper was that "education for those in the health professions must increase in depth and breadth as scientific knowledge expands."[89]

The American Nurses' Association contended that:

> 1) The education for all those who are licensed to practice nursing should take place in institutions of higher education.
>
> 2) Minimum preparation for beginning professional nursing practice at the present time should be baccalaureate degree education in nursing.
>
> 3) Minimum preparation for beginning technical nursing practice at the present time should be associate degree education in nursing.
>
> 4) Education for assistants in the health service occupations should be short, intensive preservice pro-

> grams in vocational education institutions rather than on-the-job training programs.[90]

Two events prompted the association to develop this statement: the 1963 report of the Surgeon General's Consultant Group on Nursing and the passage of the Nurse Training Act of 1964.

In 1963, the Consultant Group on Nursing, appointed by the Surgeon General of the Public Health Service in 1961, published a report entitled *Toward Quality in Nursing: Needs and Goals.* In considering future patterns for nursing education, the consultant group made the following observations:

> The present educational structure for the training of nurses lacks system, order, and coherence. There is no clear differentiation as to the levels of responsibility for which the graduates of each type of program are prepared. The consultant group is convinced that the baccalaureate program should be the minimal requirement for nurses who will assume leadership positions.[91]

The Surgeon General's Consultant Group recommended that a study be made immediately of the system of nursing education in relation to the responsibilities and skill levels required for high-quality patient care and that the study be funded by private and government sources.

ANA's Committee on Education proposed the establishment of an autonomous commission which would design and spearhead a comprehensive study and prepare a report for the profession and the public to consider. ANA's Committee on Education recommended that this commission be composed of professional nurses, educators, and people drawn from other health disciplines, economics, sociology, and communications. Both the American Nurses' Association and the National League for Nursing appropriated funds to establish a joint committee to investigate ways to conduct and finance the study. ANA's Board of Directors believed that the association's position paper on nursing education would serve as useful resource material to the commission.

On September 1, 1964, President Lyndon B. Johnson signed into law the Nurse Training Act of 1964. This legislation was the first federal law to give comprehensive assistance for nursing education. It authorized appropriations of $283,000,000 over a five-year period for construction grants to collegiate, associate degree, and diploma schools of nursing for new facilities or for rehabilitation or replacement of existing facilities; for teaching improvement grants to diploma, collegiate, and associate degree schools; for payment to diploma schools for traineeships for professional nurses; and for loans to student nurses.

The passage of the nurse training act and the establishment of federal programs providing funds for training various categories of health workers made it imperative that ANA provide sound guidelines regarding the preparation needed for nursing practice and for the work of ancilliary nursing personnel.[92] The position paper reflected the association's best judgment on the nature of nursing practice, the characteristics of the nurse practitioner, and the preparation needed to practice nursing and to assist nurses.

In presenting a report to the 1966 House of Delegates, the chairman of ANA's Committee on Education pointed out that implementation of the position paper called for immediate attention in two areas: "continued interpretation and clarification of the association's position and collaborative planning by all groups involved in health care."[93]

When the American Nurses' Association published its position on nursing education in December, 1965, approximately seventy-eight percent of the nurses in practice were graduates of hospital-based diploma programs. Concern was expressed regarding the impact of ANA's position paper on the status of these nurses. In 1967, the association published *A Date With The Future,* a brochure which interpreted the meaning of the position paper for graduates of hospital schools of nursing. According to ANA,

> The position paper addresses itself to the future of the nursing profession to insure that nursing will exercise its rightful voice and influence in the health care complex

> of tomorrow. As ANA plans for the future ANA members are assured that:
>
> 1) There is no change in legal status for the diploma nurse. Nurses graduated from and now enrolled in state-approved diploma programs are eligible upon graduation to become licensed as registered nurses.
>
> 2) The position paper does not in any way affect what nurses have already achieved, but rather it focuses on the impending and long overdue changes in the system of nursing education.[94]

By 1966, both the American Nurses' Association and the National League for Nursing had taken official positions on the future of nursing education. In June, 1966, the boards of directors approved a joint statement on community planning for nursing education:

> In recognition of the many changes taking place in the health field and the need for appropriate education for nursing personnel to meet present and future requirements, both in quantity and quality of nursing services, the American Nurses' Association and the National League for Nursing believe that sound community planning for nursing education is essential and should be begun or accelerated promptly.[95]

By the end of 1966, it was becoming apparent that nursing education was gradually becoming campus-based (as recommended in ANA's position paper) rather than being centered in the traditional hospital school. It had been predicted that the transition process would take years. However, in the one year spanning from 1966 to 1967, associate programs increased from 218 to 281, baccalaureate programs from 210 to 221, and diploma programs decreased 797 to 767.[96]

In March, 1967, ANA's Commission on Nursing Education was inaugurated. The functions of the commission were:

> 1) To evaluate relevant scientific and educational developments and changes in health needs and prac-

tices, with reference to their implications for nursing education.

2) To establish the scope of the association's responsibility for nursing education.

3) To develop standards of nursing education and devise methods for gaining their acceptance and implementation through appropriate channels.

4) To encourage and stimulate research in all areas of nursing education.

5) To formulate policy and recommend action concerning fuderal and state legislation in the field of education.[97]

In May, 1968, the Commission on Nursing Education reported, "The ANA's first position paper concerned basic nursing education. This extremely useful document has effected a great deal of change in the field of nursing. The commission now believes it appropriate and urgent to develop a position setting forth the focus of graduate education."[98]

During the summer of 1968, ANA's Nursing Education Department conducted a survey of the problems which existed in the various schools of nursing. It was reported that there was a tremendous need to intensify recruitment of qualified baccalaureate graduates into the existing accredited master's programs in nursing. It was also reported that there was a need for further formal education to increase the educational qualifications of faculty. Staff pointed out, "The most serious problem faced by nursing educational programs is the inability to recruit prepared faculty . . . Preparation of faculty can only be achieved by strengthening and expanding existing graduate programs in nursing."[99]

Statement on Graduate Education

In August, 1969, the American Nurses' Association issued a statement on graduate education in nursing. The statement was based on the following assumptions:

1) Graduate education is a more intensive and analytic extension of undergraduate education, enabling students to perceive and develop new relationships among the various factors and forces that affect nursing.

2) There is now available an increasingly large body of nursing knowledge which appropriately and logically belongs in graduate education.

3) Nursing must further develop and structure its body of knowledge, and add new knowledge that is relevant to both general and specialty practice.

4) Corporate responsibility for the education of nurse clinicians capable of advancing nursing theory and science rests with institutions of higher learning.

5) Nurses prepared at graduate levels can assume leadership assessing the role of nursing in relation to changing concepts of health care, delineating action to bring about change, selecting that action most feasible at any given time, implementing decisions, and evaluating results in order to achieve quality nursing care.[100]

On the basis of an examination of the traditional goals and values of graduate education and an analysis of the expanding responsibilities of nurses, the association declared, "The major purpose of graduate study in nursing should be the preparation of nurse clinicians capable of improving nursing care through the advancement of nursing theory and science."[101] The following rationale was provided:

Traditionally, graduate education in nursing has been considered as preparation for particular functions and positions—primarily, teaching and administration. This emphasis, unfortunately, has tended to devalue nursing care and practice, by suggesting that there is no more to nursing knowledge than can be encompassed in the initial, undergraduate preparation. In fact, the failure to conceive of nursing science as an appropriate subject for advanced study has implied that nursing does not meet

> two of the primary criteria of a profession:
>
> 1) The use in its practice of a well-defined and well-organized body of specialized knowledge on the intellectual level.
>
> 2) Constant enlargement of the body of knowledge it uses and constant improvement of its techniques of education and service, through systematic inquiry.
>
> Not until recently has serious attention in graduate study been directed toward enriching nursing's clinical competencies, structuring nursing's science, and identifying and expanding nursing's body of knowledge. Today, however, there is movement in this direction as nurse practitioners, investigators, and theorists become increasingly engaged in structuring and refining nursing knowledge, clarifying nursing's unique contribution to the welfare of mankind, and advancing practice to a high degree of sophistication.[102]

In February, 1970, upon completing its two and one half year investigation, the National Commission for the Study of Nursing and Nursing Education stated that nursing's educational system should be centered in collegiate institutions to insure enlarged social, economic, and educational opportunities. The report, *An Abstract for Action,* contained four recommendations:

1) Federal agencies and private foundations should appropriate grant funds and research contracts to investigate the impact of nursing practice on the effectiveness of the health care system.

2) Each state should create a planning committee to recommend specific guidelines to insure inclusion of nursing education within collegiate institutions.

3) A national joint practice commission, composed of representatives of physicians and nurses, should be established to discuss the congruent roles of the two professions.[103]

4) Federal, regional, state, and local governments should adopt measures for the increased support of nursing research as well as nursing education.[104]

In May, 1970, ANA's House of Delegates endorsed the report of the National Commission for the Study of Nursing and Nursing Education. Between 1970 and 1972, the association worked to implement the commission's recommendations. Special attention was placed on secural of federal aid for nursing education. During this period, there was an observable increase in numbers of baccalaureate and associate degree programs in nursing and a decrease in diploma programs. In the fall of 1972, there were 23 more baccalaureate programs and 97 more associate degree programs than in 1970. During the same period, there were 98 fewer diploma programs. In the fall of 1972, there were approximately 7,000 more admissions to associate degree programs than in 1971 and nearly 4,500 more graduations than in 1971. Admissions to baccalaureate programs increased by nearly 4,500 in 1972 over 1971, and graduations increased by over 1,000, an 11 percent increase. Admissions and graduations in diploma programs declined slightly in 1972 over 1971.[105]

Action of the ANA Board

Although there appeared to be an orderly transition from diploma to degree programs in nursing education, the bulk of the nursing care in the country was being delivered by graduates of diploma schools of nursing. Thus, in May, 1973, the ANA Board:

1) Urged every unit of ANA—commissions, congress, divisions, academy—to take into account the needs and interests of diploma school graduates when developing their plans for each biennium;

2) Asked the Commission on Nursing Education to identify means by which diploma school graduates can continue their education, to use its knowledge and influence to make educational opportunities available, and to promote the use and standardization of challenge mechanisms which would permit diploma graduates to have their skills and knowledge recognized and credited;

3) Asked all structural units and especially the Commission on Economic and General Welfare to explore other mechanisms which can be adopted to allow for horizontal and vertical mobility, and which recognize the individual's experience, competency, and demonstrated abilities, and

4) Voted to appoint a task force to examine the contemporary relevance of the terms "professional" and "technical" to distinguish basic preparation for nursing practice, and to recognize all registered nurses as professionals.[106]

In June, 1975, a key objective of the association was realized. The Commission on Nursing Education released *Standards for Nursing Education.* Contained in the association's publication are standards for programs leading to graduate, baccalaureate, and associate degrees and diplomas from hospital schools of nursing. Standards for continuing education in nursing are also included. In developing these standards, the Commission on Nursing Education set forth the following basic assumptions about the nursing profession's approach to education.

1) Nursing science is the structured body of verified knowledge essential to the practice of nursing. Scientists from several disciplines, including nursing, engage in teaching nursing students, with each discipline providing essential learning opportunities. In collaboration with students, nurse educators are responsible for identifying students' learning needs.

2) Faculty responsible for programs preparing health professionals provide opportunities for students to learn to function interdependently and, additionally, for nursing students to learn the interdependence of those within the total field of nursing.

3) The approach to professional education is primarily that of inquiry with regard to the applicability of existing knowledge to the resolution of problems and to

the discovery of new knowledge. The development of judgment in the use of nursing science and in the art of humane practice provides the focus for programs of professional study.

4) The approach to technical education is that of demonstrating the use of verified knowledge in the skillful execution of tasks, procedures, and functions. The knowledgeable development and application of nursing judgment and skills provide the focuses for programs of technical study.

5) Professional education for nurses is the responsibility of senior colleges and universities offering programs leading to undergraduate and graduate degrees with majors in nursing.

6) Advanced education for nurse specialists is the responsibility of universities offering programs leading to master's or doctoral degrees.

7) Selected university nursing schools (departments) offer nurse specialists the preparation to equip them for entering the practice of: 1) nursing education, 2) nursing (health care) administration, and 3) nursing research. Such programs lead to appropriate graduate degrees and/or appropriate credentials attesting to competence of graduates as educators, administrators, or investigators in the field of nursing.

8) Technical education for nurses is the responsibility of junior and community colleges offering programs leading to associate degrees with majors in nursing.

9) Career mobility exists for personnel in nursing who seek additional educational opportunities, including those prepared as nurses' aides and practical nurses, as well as those holding diplomas and associate, baccalaureate, master's, and doctoral degrees in nursing. Demonstration of competencies of students enrolled in all nursing education programs determines their placement

and rates of progress.

10) Financial support for nursing education and nursing research is derived from multiple sources.

11) The system of nursing education continues to be in transition, moving toward the goal that education for nursing shall be within the general system of education.[107]

The explosion of knowledge, resulting from technological and scientific advances, prompted the American Nurses' Association to identify a baccalaureate degree in nursing as the minimum preparation for professional nursing practice. It also prompted the association to launch a campaign to involve nurses in continuing education activities. Continuing education was viewed as one means by which nurses could maintain their competence and meet standards of nursing practice.

At the same time the association was formulating statements on basic and graduate education in nursing, work was underway to develop and promote continuing education opportunities. As stated in the Articles of Incorporation, the purpose of the American Nurses' Association is to promote the professional and educational advancement of nurses "in every proper manner . . . ." Since its inception in 1896, the association has given priority to the promotion of both basic and continuing education as the basis for nursing's professional growth and development.

Continuing education is defined as "planned learning experiences beyond a basic nursing educational program" which are designed to promote "the development of knowledge, skills, and attitudes for the enhancement of nursing practice."[108] There are various categories of continuing education programming, including long and short-term courses, refresher programs, inservice education, and self-directed learning.

The idea of continuing education in nursing dates back to the beginning of organized nursing. The earliest types of continuing education activities were sponsored by alumnae associations of schools of nursing. These organizations, established soon after the first students were graduated, served social and educational purposes. Since these associations provided educational programs for their members, they have been credited with providing the first continuing education for nurses.

The first formal continuing education designed for practicing nurses occurred in 1894, some twenty years after the first schools of nursing were founded in the United States. Colleges and universities did not become involved in the continuing education of nurses until the 1920s. By the late 1940s, increasing numbers of universities and colleges began to offer short-term courses, conferences, and workshops.

In the 1940s, the American Nurses' Association began to campaign for public funding for continuing education programs for nurses. However, the topic of continuing education for nurses was not officially discussed by the House of Delegates until 1962. Consideration of the issue was triggered by a report of the Committee on Nursing Practice. The report contained the following statements:

> . . . the clinical practitioner should continually develop her clinical knowledge and judgment and be truly involved in the full scope of her professional practice. This means that she must have depth and breadth in educational preparation and continuing opportunities to develop her unique contribution in collaboration with others within and without the profession.[109]

In that same year, the association proposed the presentation of clinical papers at ANA conferences. The purpose of the papers was to describe clinical issues and to offer suggestions for the improvement of nursing practice. These conferences were viewed as one means of briefing ANA members on the most up-to-date information affecting the delivery of nursing care.

In 1963, the American Nurses' Association expressed its intention to encourage and support the continuing professional education of the nurse. Between 1964 and 1966, the association attempted to define the type of educational preparation necessary to function effectively in professional and technical roles. In 1966, the Commission on Nursing Education was created to evaluate relevant scientific and educational developments and changes in health needs and practices, with reference to their implications for nursing education. In 1967, the association issued its first definitive statement on continuing education. Entitled *Avenues for Continued Learning*, this publication identified three categories of continuing education: 1) formal academic study leading to a baccalaureate or higher degree, 2) short-term courses offered by institutions of higher learning but not necessarily directed toward a degree, and 3) independent and informal study carried on by the practitioner, including inservice education and self-study. According to the association,

> In nursing, as in any other field concerned with the welfare of human beings, practice must be based on a continuously expanding and updated body of knowledge . . . . Education for nursing, therefore, must be a continuing process. No program of basic education, whatever its type or quality, could possibly encompass all that the practitioner will need to know for skilled practice throughout a lifetime career. More and more, completion of the basic program in any of the fields of human service is seen as fulfilling only the initial and minimum requirement for practice within that field. For continuing practice, increasing emphasis is placed upon the necessity for each practitioner—teacher, engineer, doctor, or nurse—to keep skills and competencies current with the growth of knowledge in each field.
>
> Acceptance of this fact imposes obligations upon both the nursing practitioner and the nursing profession . . . .[110]

By 1970, greater impetus was being placed on continuing education programs by professional associations, government agencies, and various groups investigating educational and/or health related issues. The growth in biomedical knowledge and medical techniques and the changes in the roles of health professionals warranted the development of more extensive continuing education opportunities for nurses. In May, 1970, a staff unit on continuing education was established to unify and strengthen the association's programming in that area.

By 1971, evidence of continuing education for licensure renewal had become an issue. In the summer of 1971, ANA's Board of Directors approved the establishment of a Task Force on Continuing Education to study the concepts of voluntary continuing education, as a professional responsibility, and mandatory continuing education, as a requirement for renewal of licensure.

In September, 1971, the American Nurses' Association was awarded a $42,000 grant for a project entitled "Identification of Need for Continuing Education for Nurses by the National Professional Organization." Completed in late 1972, the survey identified the diversity, subject matter, location, and sponsorship of existing continuing education programs, including short-term courses, conferences, seminars, workshops, clinical sessions, and other conference group meetings.

In September, 1971, ANA formally established the Council on Continuing Education to determine the scope of the association's role in continuing education and to develop standards and program guidelines for continuing education in nursing. The council determined that the role of the association was:

> 1) To assess the needs for, the availability of, and necessity of continuing education opportunities.
>
> 2) To encourage the development of quality continuing education activities throughout the state.
>
> 3) To assist in the planning and provision of offerings.
>
> 4) To participate in evaluation of programs in terms of changes in nursing practice.
>
> 5) To disseminate information about continuing education offerings.[111]

In 1972, the House of Delegates instructed the American Nurses' Association to communicate the expectation that all schools of nursing within educational institutions develop innovative approaches to continuing education. The House of Delegates also encouraged regional planning in order to provide a broad spectrum of continuing education opportunities and to minimize unnecessary duplication.

Between 1972 and 1974, the interim executive committee of the Council on Continuing Education developed standards for continuing education in nursing and continuing education guidelines for state nurses' associations. These standards and guidelines were developed in light of four major premises:

1) Continuing education is essential for maintaining competence in nursing practice.

2) Faculties in schools of nursing have a responsibility to assist students in conceptualizing nursing as a health career which requires life-long learning.

3) Continuing education is necessary for the personal growth and professional maturity of the individual.

4) Continuing education needs of nursing personnel are affected by many factors, including:

a) Greater acceptance of individual accountability and responsibility for practice.

b) Changes in licensure laws.

c) Legislative changes which influence health care.

d) Health and nursing research with associated advances in health and nursing science.

e) Changes in demographic characteristics (recipient population/provider population).

f) Increased consumer demands for health care.

g) Changes in health delivery systems with increased participation of nurses in those systems.

h) Increase in number and variety of health personnel.[112]

In 1974, the House of Delegates urged state nurses' associations to move forward to strengthen continuing education recognition programs. In addition, the House of Delegates moved that:

> The American Nurses' Association express its strong support for establishing participation in continuing education approved by state nurses' associations as one prerequisite for continuing registration of the license to practice the profession of nursing, and that the American Nurses' Association assist state nurses' associations in developing systems for implementing this requirement which will insure interstate mobility of licensed practitioners of nursing.[113]

After reviewing the verbatim transcripts of the House of Delegates proceedings, the Commission on Nursing Education interpreted this motion as follows:

> The intent of the motion was in support of states rights and is not a mandate for all states to move ahead to establish continuing education requirements for relicensure.
>
> The motion directs ANA to provide support to those states which choose to establish continuing education as one prerequisite for relicensure as well as those states which choose to encourage continuing education through a voluntary program. In either case the quality of the continuing education must be assured by the professional association.[114]

The 1974 House of Delegates charged the American Nurses' Association to assist state nurses' associations to establish a system which would facilitate interstate recognition of continuing education activities for nurses, regardless of the approach selected. It was believed that compatibility among state continuing education systems would:

1) Enable each state to accept continuing education programs/offerings which have been approved by other states;

2) Facilitate the transfer of individual continuing education activity records from state to state;

3) Facilitate evaluation of ANA Certification applica-

tions by providing a commonly understood record of continuing education activities;

4) Facilitate the review of records of individuals whose continuing education activities take place in more than one state;

5) Facilitate recognition of nurses who are licensed in one state but whose practice and continuing education activities are in other states or outside the United States (e.g. federal employees and members of the military);

6) Provide a basis for the collection of data about continuing education to be used in research;

7) Promote acceptance of continuing education as an individual process of lifelong learning by facilitating recognition of participation in continuing education activities in multiple states;

8) Provide a base for those states which may establish legislative requirements for continuing education.[115]

ANA's *Standards for Continuing Education in Nursing*, which were published in 1974, were applicable to both mandatory and voluntary systems. In 1975, an ad hoc committee of the Council on Continuing Education developed guidelines for state voluntary and mandatory systems of continuing education programs as well as guidelines for staff development.

In addition to the development of standards for basic, graduate, and continuing education in nursing and the establishment of guidelines for continuing education recognition programs and staff development, the American Nurses' Association assumed responsibility for the regulation and accreditation of these programs. In 1974, the House of Delegates directed the ANA Board of Directors "to move with all deliberate speed to establish a system of accreditation of basic, graduate, and continuing education programs in nursing."[116]

Between 1972 and 1974, there was a rapid proliferation of continuing education offerings for nurses. Because of the direct relationship between the quality of continuing education and the

ACCREDITATION OF CONTINUING EDUCATION IN NURSING

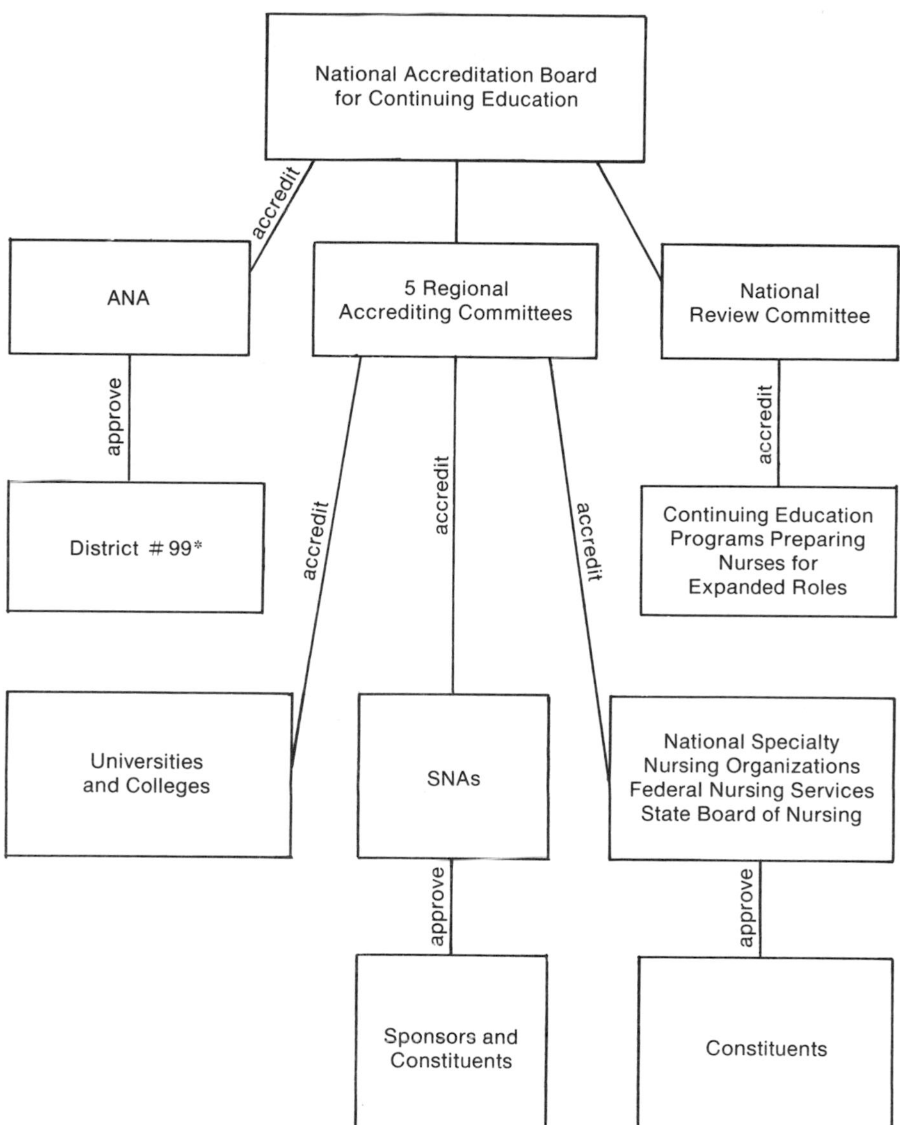

*District #99 refers to those ANA members who, because they reside in foreign countries or in United States territories or possessions where there is no constituent unit of the Association, have direct membership in the Association.

Chart IV

quality of nursing practice, the Council on Continuing Education appointed an ad hoc committee to develop an accreditation mechanism for continuing education in nursing. In 1975, the ad hoc committee completed work on a national system of accreditation of continuing education activities in nursing. As diagrammed in Chart IV, ANA's accreditation mechanism for continuing education in nursing encompasses local, state, regional, and national levels. The mechanism emphasizes self-regulation and collaboration between all levels of the American Nurses' Association and other national organizations and agencies which sponsor continuing education activities.

The overall authority and responsibility for reviewing and revising the accreditation and approval criteria and implementing, regulating, and evaluating the accrediting process is assigned to a 14-member National Accreditation Board for Continuing Education. The responsibility for reviewing and evaluating the process for accrediting nondegree granting continuing education programs preparing nurses for expanded roles is assigned to the 11-member National Review Committee. Both of these groups were appointed in 1975.

Credentialing Study Endorsed

In late 1974, the American Nurses' Association also began to investigate the feasibility of devising accreditation mechanisms for basic and graduate education programs. During 1975, representatives of agencies interested in accreditation of nursing programs, general education accrediting bodies, and other associations involved in accreditation of health programs met with members of ANA's Commission on Nursing Education to prepare a formal proposal for a study of the feasibility of accreditation of basic and graduate education for nursing by the association. In December, 1975, a proposal to study credentialing mechanisms in nursing was endorsed. The National League for Nursing was invited to co-sponsor the study. As of March, 1976, the league had declined this invitation.

As reported thus far, the activities of the American Nurses' Association between 1960 and 1975 focused on the improvement of nursing practice by the development of high standards of practice, the recognition of superior performance, and the promotion of educational standards of true professional calibre. In addition, the association sought to improve nursing practice by safeguarding the right of individual nurses to participate fully in the determination of all matters relevant to the nursing profession. As the ANA Commission on Economic and General Welfare pointed out, "The American Nurses' Association recognizes that the quality and quantity of nursing care requires the right of professional self-determination and full participation by nurses in shaping the decisions that affect the conditions under which they practice."[117]

New Approach to Economic and General Welfare

Between 1960 and 1975, ANA expanded its economic and general welfare program, which was launched in 1946, in order to accomplish two objectives:

1) To achieve an employment status for nurses commensurate with their preparation and qualifications and with the intellectual and technical nature of their services, and

2) To involve nurses actively in determining the conditions of employment under which they practice, through collective action.

In June, 1966, the Committee on Economic and General Welfare reported to the House of Delegates that "the nursing profession has very little control of how salaries are actually set and administered and only limited control over the level of preparation an individual must have before she is employed to carry a certain level of nursing functions and responsibility."[118]

At that time the average salary for nurses stood at $4,700 while secretaries were earning an average salary of $5,300 and classroom teachers an average salary of $6,700. The committee observed that nurses' salaries should reflect the values of their services to society, their investment in education, and their worth in relation to other professions and occupations. The committee's report prompted the House of Delegates to adopt the following national salary goal: "In 1966, a registered nurse should enter the profession at a salary of not less than $6,500."[119]

The Commission on Economic and General Welfare, created in 1966, viewed the salary pronouncement as a means to retain nurses on the job, to attract inactive nurses into practice, and to recruit qualified young people into the profession.

During the 1966-1968 biennium, substantial improvements in nurses' salaries were recorded across the country. By the fall of 1967, starting salaries in federal short-term hospitals were estimated to average $6,100. In early 1968, beginning salaries in private hospitals in New York City and San Francisco averaged $7,200. In other communities, salaries met or exceeded $6,500.[120]

In 1968, the House of Delegates approved a minimum entrance salary of $7,500 for those nurses with a diploma or associate degree in nursing. This was 15.5 percent above the 1966 minimum. It was viewed as the minimum salary required to place nursing in a competitive position with other professions.

Throughout 1967 and early 1968, the newly formed Commission on Economic and General Welfare conducted an extensive study of the association's approach to economic security for nurses. The commission concluded:

> A unique combination of circumstances had created a favorable climate for expansion of state nurses' association programs: the advent of Medicare, arousing a wide public interest in health care; the adoption of the national salary goal, focusing public attention on the economic needs of the profession; the dramatic salary increases won by nurses in New York City and San Francisco, demonstrating the effectiveness of group action to nurses throughout the country. As more and more nurses turned to their professional association for economic security assistance, the needs of state constit-

> uents for direct and immediate aid became increasingly apparent.[121]

The commission outlined a plan based on two essential considerations: 1) the need for a program of sufficient scope and concentration to achieve a significant change, within a relatively short period of time, in the number of nurses represented and 2) the need to provide state nurses' associations with direct assistance by qualified staff.

The Commission on Economic and General Welfare recommended "a new approach" to the association's economic security program. The commission proposed that additional staff be assigned to specific projects in various parts of the country where state nurses' associations requested assistance in implementing their economic and general welfare programs. It was proposed that the funding of these projects be shared by the American Nurses' Association and the state nurses' associations.

It was intended that the new approach augment the services provided ANA's Economic Security Department to the state nurses' associations by offering assistance in preparing briefs, developing educational programs, conducting workshops, giving advice on collective bargaining legislation, analyzing surveys, and recruiting membership.

In January, 1968, the ANA Board of Directors approved funding to support eighteen field representatives. The action of the board was endorsed by the House of Delegates in May, 1968, and the "new approach to economic security" was approved.

At both the 1968 and 1970 conventions, delegates took steps to modify association policies in order to achieve the major goal of the association's economic security program—to give nurses "a definite and effective voice in their profession."

In 1968, the House of Delegates voted to rescind ANA's 18-year-old no-strike policy. In so doing, the house adopted a motion that:

> The American Nurses' Association supports the efforts of the state nurses' associations acting as bargaining

> representatives for members in taking necessary steps to achieve improved conditions, including concerted economic pressures which are lawful and consistent with the nurse's professional responsibilities, and with the public's welfare.[122]

In 1970, the House of Delegates voted to rescind ANA's neutrality policy as adopted in 1950. This policy stated that "nurses . . . should maintain a scrupulously neutral position in regard to labor-management relations between their employers and nonnurse employees."[123]

> The Commission on Economic and General Welfare redefined the neutrality policy as a position on relations with other employee bargaining groups that urges nurses, in the event of a dispute between their employer and other employee groups, to continue to perform their distinct nursing duties, but to press for action in the interest of safe patient care, to reduce the patient census by curtailing admissions or by expediting discharge and transfer to other facilities, and to coordinate activities through their local unit organizations in the SNA.[124]

Between 1966 and January, 1971, there was a strong upsurge in the economic security activities of the state nurses' associations. At the end of 1966, 15 SNAs reported a total of 121 agreements in effect for 16,999 nurses and 245 employers. At the end of 1970, a total of 333 contracts negotiated by 32 SNAs were in force for 40,200 nurses and 471 employers.[125] By January, 1971, 45 of the state and territorial associations had established employment standards for salaries, hours, and other employment conditions for general duty, private duty, and head nurses. Similar standards had been set for nursing service administrators and public health nurses in 43 states; for educational administrators, consultants, and teachers in 42 states; for office nurses in 30 states; for occupational health nurses in 26 states; and for school nurses in 24 states.[126]

Unfortunately, staff and budgetary cutbacks required suspension of the economic security projects in the spring of 1970. Between 1970 and 1972, the level of staff services to the state nurses' association was sharply reduced.

In late 1971, the Commission on Economic and General Welfare proposed a modified program of specialized field service. The program was planned to provide a flexible range of ANA services to an increased number of state nurses' associations. In January, 1972, when the board of directors approved and funded the program, the Commission on Economic and General Welfare was asked to develop long-range, five-year projections for the field service program. In making preliminary projections for the next five years, the commission identified several significant trends:

1) Increased unionization of health care employees,
2) Proliferation of collective bargaining laws covering health care employees,
3) Increased organization of other professionals,
4) Increased awareness of nurses of the need for organized action,
5) Growing use of contracts to provide mechanisms for implementing nursing standards, and
6) A growing lack of ability of many SNAs to implement an economic and general welfare program.[127]

Between 1972 and 1974, emphasis was placed on educational training, conferences, and workshops for state nurses' association staff members and local unit members. In addition, ANA staff prepared information and testimony on legislation affecting nurses' employment conditions and assisted in the formulation of collective bargaining proposals.

In December, 1973, the American Nurses' Association announced that it would commit substantial financial resources to assist the 52 constituent nurses' associations to expand collective bargaining activities in health care facilities. In 1974, the association launched an aggressive campaign to assist state nurses' associations to organize the nation's 800,000 active registered nurses for the purpose of professional collective action. In light of the passage of the amendments to the National Labor Relations Act, which extended the right of collective bargaining to nurses in nonprofit hospitals, the American Nurses' Association, working through the state nurses' associations, has intensified its efforts:

1) To secure conditions of employment and a climate for practice that foster a lifetime career attachment to nursing.

2) To secure conditions of employment that will attract able persons to careers in nursing.

3) To involve nurses actively in determining the conditions of employment under which they practice, through collective action.

4) To represent nurses at their place of employment utilizing collective bargaining.

5) To attain wide understanding and recognition of the scientific and social contribution of nurses to the health and welfare of the community.

6) To achieve an employment status for nurses commensurate with their preparation and qualifications and with the intellectual and technical nature of their services.

7) To promote social, economic, and health legislation beneficial to the economic and general welfare of nurses.

In the past fifteen years, the American Nurses' Association has been able to:

1) Develop and initiate the implementation of standards of nursing practice and nursing services,

2) Establish a certification program to recognize excellence in clinical practice,

3) Develop and initiate the implementation of standards of nursing education,

4) Promote continuing education recognition programs, and

5) Expand its economic and general welfare program for nurses.

However, much work remains to be done "to foster high standards of nursing practice, promote the professional and educational advancement of nurses, and promote the welfare of nurses to the end that all people may have better nursing care." There are many unresolved issues which demand further study and analysis and many programs which require expansion or refinement. To remain a viable professional association for nurses, ANA must continue to expand its activities and to create new and innovative programs to advance the interests of the nursing profession.

REFERENCES

1. Olive M. Klump, "Report of the Committee on Current and Long-Term Goals of the ANA," *House of Delegates Sections Reports, 1954-1956* (New York: American Nurses' Association, 1956), 113.
2. *Ibid.*, 116.
3. *Ibid.*
4. Olive M. Klump, "Supplemental Report," *Proceedings of the Fortieth Convention (May 14-18, 1956) of the American Nurses' Association* (New York: American Nurses' Association, 1956), 36.
5. Mathilda Scheuer, "Supplemental Report," *Proceedings of the Forty-First Convention (June 9-13, 1958) of the American Nurses' Association* (New York: American Nurses' Association, 1958), 70.
6. *Ibid.*, 71.
7. *Ibid.*, 71-72.
8. *Ibid.*, 74.
9. *Ibid.*, 74.
10. *Ibid.*, 75.
11. Helen C. Hanson, "Supplemental Report," *Proceedings of the Forty-Second Convention (May 2-6, 1960) of the American Nurses' Association* (New York: American Nurses' Association, 1960), 54.
12. *Ibid.*, 56-57.
13. Frances L. A. Powell, "Report of the Committee to Implement Resolution on One Organization," *House of Delegates Reports, 1958-1960* (New York: American Nurses' Association, 1960), 175.
14. *Ibid.*, 177.
15. *Proceedings of the Forty-First Convention (June 9-13, 1958) of the American Nurses' Association* (New York: American Nurses' Association, 1958), 20.
16. *Ibid.*, 67.
17. Frances L. A. Powell, "Report of the Study Committee on the Functions of the ANA," *Proceedings of the Forty-Second Convention (May 2-6, 1960) of the American Nurses' Association* (New York: American Nurses' Association, 1960), 110-111.
18. *Ibid.*, 113.
19. Robert K. Merton, "The Functions of the Professional Association," *American Journal of Nursing*, Vol. LVIII (January, 1958), reprint.
20. Frances L. A. Powell, "Report of the Study Committee on the Functions of ANA," *House of Delegates Sections Reports, 1960-1962* (New York: American Nurses' Association, 1962), 91.

21. *Ibid.*, 95.
22. Bernice E. Anderson, "Supplemental Report," *Proceedings of the Forty-Second Convention (May 2-6, 1960) of the American Nurses' Association* (New York: American Nurses' Association, 1960), 119.
23. Frances L. A. Powell, "Report of the Study Committee on the Functions of ANA," *House of Delegates Sections Reports, 1960-1962* (New York: American Nurses' Association, 1962), 100.
24. *Ibid.*, 92.
25. *Ibid.*, 108.
26. Study Committee on the Functions of ANA, *Guide to Study of the Functions of ANA* (New York: American Nurses' Association, 1963), 5.
27. *Ibid.*
28. Frances L. A. Powell, "Report of the Study Committee on the Functions of ANA," *House of Delegates Sections Reports, 1960-1962* (New York: American Nurses' Association, 1962), 109-118.
29. *Ibid.*, 109.
30. Frances L. A. Powell, "Report of the Study Committee on the Functions of ANA," *Proceedings of the Forty-Third Convention (May 14-18, 1962) of the American Nurses' Association* (New York: American Nurses' Association, 1962), 31.
31. *Ibid.*
32. *Proceedings of the Forty-Fourth Convention (June 15-19, 1964) of the American Nurses' Association* (New York: American Nurses' Association, 1964), 32-33.
33. NLN's membership approved a structural reorganization in 1967.
34. Task Force on Organizational Structure, *A Progress Report* (New York: National League for Nursing, 1965), 7.
35. *Ibid.*
36. "Working Relationships Between ANA and NLN," approved by the ANA and NLN Board of Directors, January, 1966. The complete statement as well as a similar statement adopted in 1970 and reaffirmed in 1973 appear in Appendix V. In addition, ANA's Board of Directors adopted a statement on "The Professional Association and Its Relationships with Other Organizations" in January, 1975. The text of this statement appears in Chapter Nine.
37. Judith Whitaker, "Executive Director's Report," *House of Delegates Reports, 1966-1968* (New York: American Nurses' Association, 1968), 16.
38. The Congress for Nursing Practice replaced the Council of Division Chairmen.
39. Jeanne S. Berthold, "Report of the Committee on Research and Studies," *House of Delegates Reports, 1968-1970* (New York: American Nurses' Association, 1970), 101.
40. Jeanne S. Berthold, "Report of the Committee on Research and Studies," *Proceedings of the Forty-Seventh Convention (May 3-8, 1970) of the American Nurses' Association* (New York: American Nurses' Association, 1970), 40.
41. *ANA Guidelines for Establishment of Councils,* 1973, 2.
42. *Ibid.*
43. *ANA Bylaws,* as amended June, 1966, 29.
44. Frances L. A. Powell, "Report of Study Committee on the Functions of ANA," *Proceedings of the Forty-Fifth Convention (June 14-17, 1966) of the American Nurses' Association* (New York: American Nurses' Association, 1966), 28.
45. *ANA Bylaws,* as amended June, 1966, 29.
46. Katharine Greenough, "Report of the Ad Hoc Committee on Ways to Enter the

Academy," *House of Delegates Reports, 1968-1970* (New York: American Nurses' Association, 1970), 104.

47. Katharine Greenough, "Report of Committee to Plan for the Academy," *Proceedings of the Forty-Eighth Convention (April 30-May 5, 1972) of the American Nurses' Association* (New York: American Nurses' Association, 1972), 82.
48. *ANA Bylaws,* as amended June, 1974, 25.
49. Katharine Greenough, "Report of the Ad Hoc Committee on Ways to Enter the Academy," *House of Delegates Reports, 1968-1970* (New York: American Nurses' Association, 1970), 103.
50. American Nurses' Association, "Overall Structural Changes in ANA," December 7, 1966, 3.
51. Judith Whitaker, "Executive Directors' Report," *House of Delegates Reports, 1966-1968* (New York: American Nurses' Association, 1968), 45.
52. "Resolution on Unauthorized and Improper Practice of Nursing," *Proceedings of the Forty-First Convention (June 9-13, 1958) of the American Nurses' Association* (New York: American Nurses' Association, 1958), 96.
53. Lillian B. Reilly, "Report of the Committee on the Resolution on Nursing Practice," *House of Delegates Reports, 1958-1960* (New York: American Nurses' Association, 1960), 210-211.
54. Dorothy V. Moses, "Report of the Committee on Standards of Geriatric Nursing Practice," *Proceedings of the Forty-Sixth Convention (May 13-17, 1968) of the American Nurses' Association* (New York: American Nurses' Association, 1968), 72.
55. American Nurses' Association, "Glossary of Terms Relating to Organizational Arrangements and Functioning," January, 1975, 1.
56. Lillian B. Reilly, "Supplemental Report," *Proceedings of the Forty-Second Convention (May 2-6, 1960) of the American Nurses' Association* (New York: American Nurses' Association, 1960), 119.
57. These standards were revised in 1973.
58. Commission on Nursing Services, *Standards for Nursing Services* (Kansas City: American Nurses' Association, 1973), 2.
59. Judith Whitaker, "Executive Director's Report," *House of Delegates Reports, 1966-1968* (New York: American Nurses' Association, 1968), 20.
60. *A Blueprint To Build On—A Report To Members, 1966-1968* (New York: American Nurses' Association, 1968), 4.
61. American Nurses' Association, "Issues on Standards," January, 1971, 3.
62. *Ibid.*
63. The development of a set of generic standards was regarded as a means of insuring uniformity in the standards developed by each division.
64. Congress for Nursing Practice, *Standards of Nursing Practice* (Kansas City: American Nurses' Association, 1973), 1-4.
65. "Platform," *Proceedings of the Forty-Sixth Convention (May 13-17, 1968) of the American Nurses' Association* (New York: American Nurses' Association, 1968), 97.
66. Congress for Nursing Practice, *Standards of Nursing Practice* (Kansas City: American Nurses' Association, 1973), 1.
67. "Resolution on the Implementation of Standards of Nursing Practice within the Employment Setting," *Proceedings of the Forty-Eighth Convention (April 30-May 5, 1972) of the American Nurses' Association* (Kansas City: American Nurses' Association, 1974), 37.

68. *Ibid.*
69. Ad Hoc Committee on Implementation of Standards, *Peer Review: Guidelines for Establishment of Committees* (Kansas City: American Nurses' Association, 1973), 1.
70. *Ibid.*
71. Congress for Nursing Practice, *A Plan for Implementation of the Standards of Nursing Practice* (Kansas City: American Nurses' Association, 1975), 26.
72. Unpublished report of the Committee on Current and Long-Term Goals, February, 1969.
73. *Ibid.*
74. Mathilda Scheuer, "Supplemental Report," *Proceedings of the Forty-First Convention (June 9-13, 1958) of the American Nurses' Association* (New York: American Nurses' Association, 1958), 74.
75. Mary E. Beam, "Report of the Intersection Committee on Recognition of Superior Performance," *Proceedings of the Forty-Second Convention (May 2-6, 1960) of the American Nurses' Association* (New York: American Nurses' Association, 1960), 87-88.
76. This timetable was eventually abandoned.
77. Mary E. Beam, "Report of the Intersection Committee on Recognition of Superior Performance," *Proceedings of the Forty-Third Convention (May 14-18, 1962) of the American Nurses' Association* (New York: American Nurses' Association, 1962), 25-26.
78. ANA Nursing Practice Department, "The Meaning of Certification," January, 1968, 1.
79. Initially, ANA established "interim" certification boards. It was the association's belief that a certification board should be composed of certified nurses. The members involved in the initial work would, after the program had been in effect for a reasonable time, go out of office and certified nurse practitioners would be appointed to the boards.
80. ANA Nursing Practice Department, "Summary of Responses From Other Organizations Concerning Certification," April, 1969.
81. Congress for Nursing Practice, "Definitions of Professional and Technical Nursing Practice," April, 1969.
82. Audrey F. Spector (chairman of the ANA Staff Committee on Standards and Certification), "Report on Certification Issues," April 15, 1971.
83. On February 1, 1973, ANA's Board of Directors recommended that ANA membership should not be a requirement for certification by the association.
84. Lillian B. Reilly, "Report of the Committee on the Resolution on Nursing Practice," *House of Delegates Reports, 1958-1960* (New York: American Nurses' Association, 1960), 212.
85. Clara M. Brauer, "Report of the Committee on Current and Long-Term Goals of the ANA," *House of Delegates Reports, 1958-1960* (New York: American Nurses' Association, 1960), 113.
86. Helen C. Hanson, "Supplemental Report," *Proceedings of the Forty-Second Convention (May 2-6, 1960) of the American Nurses' Association* (New York: American Nurses' Association, 1960), 55.
87. *Ibid.*, 57-61.
88. Frances Reiter, "Report of the Committee on Education," *House of Delegates Sections Reports, 1962-1964* (New York: American Nurses' Association, 1964), 102.

89. American Nurses' Association, *Educational Preparation for Nurse Practitioners and Assistants of Nurses: A Position Paper* (New York: American Nurses' Association, 1965), 4.
90. *Ibid.*, 5-9.
91. Department of Health, Education, and Welfare, *Toward Quality in Nursing: Needs and Goals*, Report of the Surgeon General's Consultant Group on Nursing (Washington, D.C.: U.S. Government Printing Office, 1963), 33.
92. In 1966, President Johnson's National Advisory Commission recommended that formal education for all health professionals should be conducted under the supervision of colleges and universities.
93. Frances Ritter, "Report of the Committee on Education," *Proceedings of the Forty-Fifth Convention (June 14-17, 1966) of the American Nurses' Association* (New York: American Nurses' Association, 1966), 48.
94. American Nurses' Association, *A Date With The Future* (New York: American Nurses' Association, 1967), 3.
95. "The American Nurses' Association and the National League for Nursing Joint Statement on Community Planning for Nursing Education," June, 1966, 1.
96. American Nurses' Association, *A Blueprint To Build On: A Report To Members, 1966-1968* (New York: American Nurses' Association, 1968), 10.
97. Rozella M. Schlotfeldt, "Report of Commission on Nursing Education," *House of Delegates Reports, 1966-1968* (New York: American Nurses' Association, 1968), 87.
98. *Ibid.*, 90.
99. Hildegard E. Peplau, "Executive Director's Report," *House of Delegates Reports, 1968-1970* (New York: American Nurses' Association, 1970), 13.
100. American Nurses' Association, *Statement on Graduate Education in Nursing* (New York: American Nurses' Association, 1969), 2.
101. *Ibid.*
102. *Ibid.*, 3-4.
103. This joint practice commission was inaugurated in January, 1972.
104. Jerome P. Lysaught, *An Abstract for Action* (New York: McGraw-Hill Book Company, 1970), 156-161.
105. "Educational Preparation for Nursing—1972," *Nursing Outlook*, Vol. XXI (September, 1973), 587.
106. ANA Board of Directors, "Statement on Diploma Nurse Education," *The American Nurse*, June, 1973, 5.
107. American Nurses' Association, *Standards for Nursing Education* (Kansas City: American Nurses' Association, 1975), 4-5.
108. American Nurses' Association, *Standards for Continuing Education in Nursing* (Kansas City: American Nurses' Association, 1974), 2.
109. Henrietta Welsh, "Supplemental Report," *Proceedings of the Forty-Third Convention (May 14-18, 1962) of the American Nurses' Association* (New York: American Nurses' Association, 1962), 23.
110. American Nurses' Association, *Avenues for Continued Learning* (New York: American Nurses' Association, 1967), 2-3.
111. American Nurses' Association, *Standards for Continuing Education in Nursing* (Kansas City: American Nurses' Association, 1974), 3.
112. Commission on Nursing Education, *Standards for Nursing Education* (Kansas City: American Nurses' Association, 1975), 34.

113. *Summary Proceedings of the Forty-Ninth Convention (June 9-14, 1974) of the American Nurses' Association* (Kansas City: American Nurses' Association, 1975), 36.
114. American Nurses' Association, *Guidelines for State Voluntary and Mandatory Systems* (Kansas City: American Nurses' Association, 1976), 1.
115. *Ibid.*, 2.
116. *Summary Proceedings of the Forty-Ninth Convention (June 9-14, 1974) of the American Nurses' Association* (Kansas City: American Nurses' Association, 1975), 38.
117. Commission on Economic and General Welfare, *ANA's Economic and General Welfare Program: Philosophy, Goals, Policies, Positions* (Kansas City: American Nurses' Association, 1975), 2.
118. Valatrice S. Nordin, "Report of the Committee on Economic and General Welfare," *House of Delegates Sections Reports, 1964-1966* (New York: American Nurses' Association, 1966), 61.
119. *Proceedings of the Forty-Fifth Convention (June 14-17, 1966) of the American Nurses' Association* (New York: American Nurses' Association, 1966), 23.
120. Estimates made by ANA's Research and Statistics Department based on various studies and investigations.
121. Anne L. Zimmerman, "Report of the Commission on Economic and General Welfare," *House of Delegates Reports, 1966-1968* (New York: American Nurses' Association, 1968), 74.
122. *Proceedings of the Forty-Sixth Convention (May 13-17, 1968) of the American Nurses' Association* (New York: American Nurses' Association, 1968), 33.
123. Economic Security Unit, *Major Official Policies Relating to the Economic Security Program* (New York: American Nurses' Association, 1965), 3.
124. *Summary Proceedings of the Forty-Seventh Convention (May 3-8, 1970) of the American Nurses' Association* (New York: American Nurses' Association, 1970), 36.
125. Preliminary data based on reports from the state nurses' associations.
126. Eileen M. Jacobi, "Executive Director's Report," *House of Delegates Reports, 1970-1972* (New York: American Nurses' Association, 1972), 43-44.
127. Muriel A. Poulin, "Report of the Commission on Economic and General Welfare," *House of Delegates Reports, 1970-1972* (New York: American Nurses' Association, 1972), 77.

1972-1976

Tomorrow's Challenge

In 1956, the American Nurses' Association identified those major sociological and economic trends which it believed would have an impact on the health care system and the nursing profession between 1960 and 1980. This list of trends included: population growth (including increased mobility and dislocation of population patterns), changes in disease patterns, technological and scientific advances, increasing costs of medical care, higher education in the general population, emergence of unions as a political, social, and economic force, and the growth of government concern in meeting the public's health needs. Today, it is obvious that the health care system is undergoing dynamic alteration as the result of many of these trends.

Changes in Population

The population now exceeds 200 million and estimates for the year 2000 place the figure at 300 million. Population growth alone has resulted in greatly increased demands for more health facilities and additional personnel. This problem is accentuated by the fact that, because of changes in the population curve, a disproportionate percentage of the people in the United States are under 20 years of age or over 65 years of age, an increase in both ends of the continuum.

During the last thirty years, internal migration has increased at an almost unbelievable degree. In the face of dislocation of population patterns, orderly planning of health care and other services has become almost impossible.

As a result of the inequities in the present system, millions of Americans do not have access to needed health care services. Statistics show that between four to seven million persons in need of long-term care are living outside of health care institutions. Millions of American children have never seen a dentist, ten percent of the adult population suffers from undiagnosed hypertension, and an estimated 60,000 persons suffering from cancer will die needlessly because the disease was not diagnosed early enough to be treated.

Moreover, technological and scientific advances in the health care field have occurred at an accelerated rate. It is estimated that within the past fifteen years, there have been more advances in methods of diagnosing and treating physical illnesses, including chronic, long-term illnesses, than had been made in the preceding 1,500 years. As a result, there are more elderly, more chronically ill, and more patients on complex medical regimens requiring careful observation, health education, and supportive measures.

Inflation

Today, the high costs of essential services stand in the way of effective delivery of existing health care services to a significant portion of the population. In the last twenty years, health care expenditures have increased by almost 600 percent. Unfortunately, over fifty percent of this cost increase reflects price inflation rather than the addition of more comprehensive health care services.

Compounding the rise in health care costs is the factor of insufficient health care coverage. At least thirty million Americans have no health insurance whatsoever. Twenty percent of the population under the age of 65 are not covered against hospital and surgical services. One hundred million Americans have no health insurance for other than hospitalized care.

Moreover, there are limitations to coverage provided through voluntary and other social insurance and tax-funded medical programs. Claims by insurance programs imply that, in the event of a health crisis, the consumer will receive full service to the extent of his needs. Yet many insurance companies will not cover the period an individual is in an extended care facility for continuing treatment for an illness that required hospitalization. Furthermore, the insistence by third-party payors, both private and governmental insurance carriers, that no services can be covered or provided unless physician-prescribed, prohibit many persons from procuring a service which, while not requiring medical intervention from a disease-oriented standpoint, may be psychologically and socially necessary from a health supportive or disease preventive standpoint.

Social Revolution

The attitude of the American public toward health care services has been affected by two phenomena.

In the past few years this country has experienced a "social revolution." Civil rights, human rights, basic needs and their satisfaction, autonomy, self-identity, and self-respect have received increased attention as subjects requiring re-examination. This climate of concern for individual rights is being reflected in the current attitude among individuals that health be conceived not only as freedom from disease, but as a positive state of physical and mental well-being, and that health care be recognized as a basic right of all people.

Secondly, larger incomes and better education are now enjoyed by a much wider segment of the population. As a result, a greater number of individuals display an increased awareness of medical and scientific developments and the importance of preventing sickness through periodic examinations and early treatment. There is greater concern about the continuity of care and the possibility of assuring that there will be services and trained personnel available to provide assistance during a period of illness or increased stress.

Increasing attention is being paid to the plight of the mentally ill. There is growing concern about the mentally retarded, alcoholics, drug addicts, unwed mothers, and juvenile and adult delinquents. These groups are now recognized as individuals in need of health related services and new methods of care, treatment, and prevention. There is growing concern about the health of employed workers and the relationship between poor health and unemployment.

In short, there is growing concern that health care services be more comprehensive. More Americans than ever before are seeking preventive, health maintenance, diagnostic, treatment, restorative, and protective services at reasonable costs.

Expansion of Nursing Roles

In recent years, one of the most significant opportunities for improvement in the health care system has been the expansion of the scope of nursing practice.

In 1971, the Secretary of Health, Education, and Welfare commissioned a task force to study the feasibility of extending the scope of nursing practice. The committee, composed of nurses, physicians, and hospital administrators, concluded:

> One of the most important opportunities for change in the current system of health care involves altering the practice of nurses and physicians so that nurses assume considerably greater responsibility for delivering primary health care services.[1]
>
> As health care becomes increasingly valued in our society, nurses will be expected to take more responsibility for the delivery of primary health and nursing care, for coordinating preventive services, for initiating or participating in diagnostic screening, and for referring patients who require differential medical diagnoses and medical therapies.[2]

According to a follow-up study of this report in 1973, the implementation of the committee's recommendations has resulted in changes in nurse practice acts, improved quality nursing care, and increased accessibility of some health care services at more reasonable costs.

The nurse functioning in a primary care role is not a new concept. Nurses have provided supportive and preventive care services for many years. Although this role has received less public recognition than the role played in hospital nursing, there are valid examples of nursing's impact. The Frontier Nursing Service is one of the oldest and best examples of health care provided by nurses to people in remote or otherwise underserved areas. Founded in 1925 to provide care for mothers and babies, the service now consists of family nurse practitioners who provide care to entire families. Located in rural Appalachia in eastern Kentucky, the service has approximately 53,000 outpatient contacts each year.

Nurse midwives in outlying rural zones and visiting nurses in overpopulated, underserved urban areas have assumed responsibility for the clinical care of patients for a number of years. However, the concept of preparing specialized nurse practitioners capable of decisive, independent action in aspects of health care in colleagueship with a health care team is relatively new.

In the past several years, many nurses have assumed the role of independent nurse practitioner, a licensed professional nurse who contracts with an individual, group, agency, or corporation to provide primary nursing care in a variety of settings. The independent practitioner of nursing engages in independent decision-making about the nursing needs of consumers and collaborates with other health professionals in making decisions about other health care needs.

The independent nurse practitioner role was developed to increase the accessibility and availability of preventive and health maintenance services at reduced costs to the consumer. With physician fees increasing at a rate of more than sixteen percent annually, the nurse practitioner offers a more economical option in the health care system. The average fees range from $4 to $15 per office or home visit. Of the practices recently surveyed, all of the independent nurse practitioners were on twenty-four hour call and maintained office hours daily.

In recent years, the effective utilization of nursing resources has had a significant impact on the quality of care delivered to the two groups of consumers requiring the greatest amount of ambulatory care, namely, young children and aged adults.

Numerous studies and demonstration projects have indicated that educational preparation and professional orientation permit the nurse to provide a wide range of services in a family context. Pediatric nurse practitioners capably handle normal physical examinations, identify health problems, monitor growth and development, and counsel children and their parents. A controlled two-year study of the effectiveness of well-child care by pediatric nurse practitioners of 1,152 children aged 0-22 months was made at the Kaiser-Permanente Medical Centers in San Francisco and Oakland, California. In this setting, a large prepaid group practice health care plan, the pediatric nurse practitioners were found to be entirely competent in maintaining the health status of their patients and were generally accepted by the parents. Moreover, the costs of well-child care were reduced.[3] Pediatric nurse practitioners have demonstrated effectiveness in providing well-child care in pediatric clinics and in private practice.

Currently, a number of other investigations are underway to study nursing roles. Preliminary data from PRIMEX, experimental demonstration projects undertaken by the National Center for Health Services Research and Development, reveal that family nurse practitioners are making a valid contribution to the provision of quality health care services.

Nurses also appear particularly suited to handle the diversified health needs of the aged. The nurse practitioner is able to observe and to distinguish a broad range of problems of a physical and socio-psychological nature.

In addition, the increase in prevalence of chronic diseases has created a greater demand for long-term medical and supportive health care. Individuals with chronic illnesses require the guidance and supervision of health professionals in order to insure the level of health which will permit them to remain at home. The nurse practitioner is the appropriate health professional to provide these services. Nursing in the home, homemaker/home health aide, and social work services can maintain individuals in their homes, thus keeping families together and avoiding crises which might require the most expensive care in nursing homes and hospitals.

Unfortunately, the expansion of the scope of nursing practice has not resolved many of the problems which exist in the health care system. As a result of the unexpected population growth, the dislocation of population patterns, and the inflationary cost of services, the present provision of health care services, on a national basis, is fragmented, uncoordinated, and incomplete.

National Health Insurance

In light of the shortcomings of the present health care system, the federal government has taken increasing steps to set the terms and conditions under which health care services are provided.

Since 1972, a number of proposals for a national health insurance program have been introduced in Congress. In analyzing specific legislative proposals, the American Nurses' Association has paid particular attention to the criteria for a reimbursement system. The one factor which will most greatly affect the delivery of nursing care is the provision for reimbursement and/or fee-for-services. The demand for nursing services will only grow to the extent that a national health care program provides for nursing services. Experience has shown that the character of insurance benefits and the payment systems determine what services health care systems provide, to whom they provide services, and how and where services are delivered.

An examination of the traditional philosophy upon which most health insurance systems are based reveals a failure on the part of insurance companies to stay abreast of trends in health care delivery and to stay in tune with consumer needs. The idea of comprehensive health care has earned increasing acceptance by those who are responsible for planning health care services and facilities. Health planners have shifted their emphasis from the prevention and treatment of disease and illness to the maintenance of health. Yet insurance companies with their hospital and surgical coverage, physicians' expense insurance, and major medical expense insurance still focus their benefits on the treatment of the sick.

Under an improved system of health care, emphasis should shift from the use of expensive facilities to the imaginative use of ambulatory services, clinics, outpatient departments, and neighborhood health centers. Attention should be focused on the effective utilization of health manpower to provide preventive, diagnostic, health maintenance, and protective services as well as treatment and restorative measures.

For a number of years, the American Nurses' Association has been advocating inclusion of the benefits of nursing service in all prepaid medical and health insurance contracts. As early as 1916, the association appointed a committee on health insurance. In 1917, this committee recommended that: "nurses in each state keep a close watch on health insurance legislation in order that no unfortunate wording of the law may interfere with the nursing of the beneficiaries."[4] (A complete historical perspective of ANA's stand on national health insurance and related issues appears in Appendix VI.)

Close examination of the 1974 Resolution on National Health Insurance adopted by the ANA House of Delegates reveals the contentions upon which ANA bases its support of national health insurance and enumerates essential elements of an effective program.

Basically, ANA contends that:

1) Health, a state of physical, social and mental well-being, is a basic human right.

2) Government at all levels must act to insure that health care services are provided for all citizens.

3) There is a need for integrated systems to deliver comprehensive health care services that are accessible and acceptable to all people without regard to age, sex, race, social, or economic condition.

4) There is a need for a national program designed to correct serious inadequacies in present health care delivery systems.

5) Nursing care is an essential component of health care.

In order to achieve a more effective and efficient health care system, ANA proposes that:

1) The national health insurance program guarantee coverage of all people for the full range of comprehensive health services.

2) The scope of benefits be clearly defined so that they can be understood by beneficiaries and providers alike.

3) The national health program clearly recognize the distinctions between health care and medical care; and that the plan provide options in utilization of health care services that are not necessarily dependent on the physician.

4) Nursing care be a benefit of the national health program.

5) The data systems necessary for effective management of the national insurance program protect the rights and privacy of individuals.

6) The plan include provisions for peer review of services that will protect the right and the responsibility of each health care discipline to monitor the practice of its own practitioners.

7) There continue to be a system of individual licensure for the practice of nursing.

8) Provision be made for consumer participation in periodic evaluation of the national health insurance program.

9) The national health insurance program be financed through payroll taxes or payment of premiums by the self-employed, and purchase of health insurance coverage for the poor and unem-

ployed from general tax revenues.

ANA has been privileged to present the views of professional nurses related to the necessity of a national program of health insurance benefits before committees of the Congress on numerous occasions over the past thirty years. The role of the nursing profession and factors for consideration in the involvement of nurses in a national health insurance plan become apparent upon a review of the points stressed in ANA testimony over the past three years.

In testifying on the general concept of national health insurance and in analyzing specific legislative proposals, ANA has stressed the need for provisions which speak to nursing education, nursing practice, nursing research, nursing services, and the economic and general welfare of nurses. A number of points have been stressed:

1) Comprehensive health services should include preventive, health maintenance, diagnostic, treatment (including full community mental health services, alcohol and drug addiction programs, migrant health programs), restorative and protective services for all citizens. Emphasis must shift to the imaginative use of ambulatory services, clinics, outpatient departments, neighborhood health centers, the physician's office, and the home. Research must be undertaken to identify more effective and innovative utilization of nursing manpower in these situations.

2) If a national health insurance plan is to provide comprehensive health care services, more recognition must be given to the nurse's role in the delivery of primary care. Appropriate preparation and utilization of the nurse practitioner in the primary care role is one important way to extend health services and use health manpower more effectively. As nursing roles are modified, there will be need for continuing education and additional education opportunities to keep nurses abreast of changes in the health care of people.

3) Provisions must be made to permit payments for certain

health services in addition to those provided by physicians or arranged and directed by physicians. Payment mechanisms should be such as to facilitate effective and efficient use of the knowledge and skills of qualified professional nurses as providers of primary care services.

4) Benefits in national health insurance available to persons of all ages should be such as to promote the utilization of home care as an alternative to institutional care. Consequently, ample provision should be made for home health services under a national health program. Moreover, reimbursement for home health care services should not be contingent upon prior hospitalization or prior confinement in a nursing care facility.

5) No institution should be considered a hospital for the purposes of implementing national health insurance legislation unless there is an organized nursing service under the direction of a registered professional nurse and unless all nursing care is rendered and/or supervised by registered nurses 24 hours of each day.

6) There should be a registered professional nurse in every skilled nursing facility to direct nursing care services and to execute policies established to govern skilled nursing care and related health care services.

7) The federal government should make provisions for national standards governing health insurance coverage so that each citizen is assured equal benefits. The development of standards of nursing services and of nursing practice should be the responsibility of the nursing profession. Moreover, any utilization review committee should include registered professional nurses. Finally, in establishing systems of peer review, the nursing profession should have the right and carry the responsibility to monitor its own practitioners.

Forecasting Future Trends

In recent years, the nursing profession has taken concrete measures to counteract those trends which have had a significant impact on the health care system. Role adaption on the part of the professional nurse practitioner has been necessitated by at least two factors of change in society: 1) the technological and scientific advances which have introduced complex methods of dealing with specific problems as well as new approaches to the diagnosis and treatment of certain conditions and 2) changes in patterns of demand for health services which warrant provision of a more comprehensive continuum of care.

If nursing is to maximize its potential effectiveness in the future, the nursing profession must be able to identify and predict trends which may affect health care and nursing during the next thirty years. Answers must be sought to three basic questions:

1) What factors will have a significant effect on society in the next twenty to thirty years?

2) What is the potential impact of these factors on the health care system, in general, and the nursing profession, in particular?

3) In light of the above, what should be the role of the American Nurses' Association in relationship to society, to the profession, and to the individual nurse practitioner?

One method of predicting trends is to analyze past events in order to delineate those trends and forces which would appear to remain operative in the future.

According to experts, population growth, population shifts, and population mobility will continue to have a negative impact on the orderly planning of health care facilities and services. As these trends persist, authorities foresee greater governmental regulation and control of the health care system.

The drive for unionization of health professionals will continue to gain momentum. The health care field is the third largest in numbers of employees in the United States and the largest unorganized industry. Nurses comprise approximately one-third of the 1½ million health care personnel who will be affected by such unionization.

In the next thirty years, there will be continued proliferation of knowledge and increased use of technology. The acquisition of new knowledge and the more extensive use of technology will enhance the trend toward professional and occupational specialization. According to health care experts, an increasing dependence of health professionals on technology will tend to remove incentives for innovation, creativity, and personalization of health care services. It is predicted that, in an accelerated age of technology, health care providers may become mere "technicians" in "technological emporiums."

In the decades to come, many more lives will be prolonged as the result of the discovery of more curative methodologies, and "wonder drugs," greater utilization of transplants and organ substitutions, increased efficiency and effectiveness of surgical operations through medical electronics, and "new birth technology." According to scientific projections, in the next fifty years:

1) Human body resources will be more effectively mobilized to fight infectious diseases.

2) Cancer will be controlled.

3) There will be new methods of diagnosis and preventive measures for cardiovascular disease.

4) All organ transplants and organ replacements will become routine.

5)"Medical Electronics" will be more extensively utilized in diagnosis and surgery.

6) Genetic and congenital disorders in the fetus will be diagnosed and corrected prior to birth.

7) The concept of genetic engineering will receive greater attention and wider acceptance. More extensive research will be undertaken of processes such as cloning.[5]

As scientific and technological advances increase man's capabilities to control life, health professionals will be forced to cope with a growing number of moral, ethical, and legal questions. Does an individual have the right to determine where, how, and when death will occur? Whose permission should be sought when fetal research is undertaken? Is it possible for the philosophical, moral and legal definitions to coincide?

As the body of knowledge increases at an accelerated rate, traditional forms of education will be abandoned in favor of innovative approaches to learning. There will be more mass education and universities without walls, greater use of teaching technology, and increasing student participation in the teaching process. The key emphasis will be on the individual's ability to adapt to continual change. The trend toward a liberal arts education will gain momentum.

According to experts, the emphasis on technology, depersonalization, reformulation of work values, and changing roles of men and women will create new types of health problems, including increased stress leading to mental illness and emotional disturbances and greater occurrence of psychosomatic illnesses among the general population.

All of these factors have significant implications for the organization and administration of health care services and the nature and scope of practice of health professionals.

In the next thirty years, the emphasis will continue to be on change—change brought about by a vast array of socioeconomic, political, and scientific and technological trends. In order to maintain a viable position in the health care system, nursing must become a futuristically-based profession. The nursing profession must begin to forecast consumer needs. Forecasting involves three steps: 1) the critical appraisal of past and present developments in health care and nursing, 2) the determination of significant goals and priorities desired for nursing, and 3) the development and initiation of innovative nursing programs aimed at satisfying projected health care needs for the next three decades. This process of forecasting can best be achieved within the framework of the professional association, which has at its disposal appropriate mechanisms for systematic investigation.

According to Dr. Robert K. Merton, noted sociologist, the vital function of the professional association is to mediate between the practitioner and the profession and the practitioner and the social environment.[6] As a professional association, the American

Nurses' Association has a responsibility to insure the educational and professional advancement of the practitioner and to safeguard the public's right to quality nursing care.

There are basic premises on which the American Nurses' Association operates. These premises are consistent with the expectation of society that professional disciplines need to be unified and organized in order to carry out effectively their social responsibilities. These basic premises are:

1) The ANA is the professional association of American nurses.

2) The ANA is the official voice of nursing, speaks for nursing, and represents the profession in all relationships with the federal government, with national and international organizations, and with associations or agencies concerned with health.

3) The ANA enunciates and promulgates the profession's standards for education, practice, research, and organized nursing services.

4) The ANA, as a multipurpose organization, has a variety of functions which it must carry out in order to meet the needs of nurses and nursing and to fulfill its responsibilities for the advancement of the profession so as to discharge its obligations to society.

5) The ANA develops and implements an ethical code for nurses.

6) There are increasing demands on the association by the profession and the public to bring concerted influence to bear on all matters affecting the provision of health care of people, to recognize excellence in practice, to safeguard and improve individual licensure for the protection of the public, to perform appropriate surveillance on the system of both basic and continuing education and to develop means to evaluate and assure continued competence of practitioners.[7]

Based on these premises, the American Nurses' Association

assumes the ultimate responsibility for the advancement of the profession.

In the past, the American Nurses' Association has fostered nursing research, promoted nursing practice legislation, encouraged the development of advanced and continuing education programs, stimulated the establishment and implementation of standards of nursing practice, nursing service, and nursing education, and safeguarded the economic and general welfare of nurses. In the future, under the leadership of nurses who have the ability to chart future directions for the profession, the American Nurses' Association will continue to promote the educational and professional advancement of nurses to the end that the American public will receive quality nursing care.

REFERENCES

1. Committee to Study Extended Roles for Nurses, *Extending the Scope of Nursing Practice* (Washington, D.C., U. S. Government Printing Office, 1971), 8.
2. *Ibid.*, 9.
3. Burnip, Erickson, Barr, Shinefield, and Schoen, "Well-Child Care by Pediatric Nurse Practitioners in a Large Group Practice," Grant #HS00154 from the National Center for Health Services Research and Development, Department of Health, Education, and Welfare.
4. Martha M. Russell, "Report of the Committee on Health Insurance," Proceedings of the Twentieth Annual Convention (April 26-May 2, 1917) of the American Nurses' Association, *American Journal of Nursing*, Vol. XVII (July, 1917), 866.
5. Cloning is the process of growing from the nucleus of an adult cell a new organism with the same genetic characteristics as the individual contributing the cell nucleus.
6. Robert K. Merton, "The Functions of the Professional Association," *American Journal of Nursing*, Vol. LVIII (January, 1958), 53.
7. American Nurses' Association, "The Professional Association and Its Relationships with Other Organizations," January 31, 1975.

Section II

Witnesses to Nursing History

Introduction
Isabel Hampton Robb, 1897-1901
Annie Damer, 1901-1902, 1905-1909
Mary Riddle, 1902-1905
Jane Delano, 1909-1911
Sarah E. Sly, 1911-1913
Genevieve Cooke, 1913-1915
Annie W. Goodrich, 1915-1918
Clara D. Noyes, 1918-1922
Adda Eldredge, 1922-1926
S. Lillian Clayton, 1926-1930
Elnora E. Thomson, 1930-1934
Susan C. Francis, 1934-1938
Julia C. Stimson, 1938-1944
Katherine J. Densford, 1944-1948
Pearl McIver, 1948-1950
Elizabeth K. Porter, 1950-1954
Agnes Ohlson, 1954-1958
Mathilda Scheuer, 1958-1962
Margaret B. Dolan, 1962-1964
Jo Eleanor Elliott, 1964-1968
Dorothy A. Cornelius, 1968-1970
Hildegard E. Peplau, 1970-1972
Rosamond C. Gabrielson, 1972-1976

Introduction

In speaking to the early leaders of the American Nurses' Association, Isabel Hampton Robb declared, "We are the history makers of trained nurses. Let us see to it that we work so as to leave a fair record as the inheritance of the those who come after us, one which may be to them an inspiration to even better efforts." Throughout ANA's history, leaders have taken to heart the charge of the association's first president. Consequently, the record of the American Nurses' Association is an illustrious one.

For some seventy-eight years, during the national conventions, ANA Presidents have reviewed the activities of the organization, identified the problems confronting nurses, and proposed future directions for the association and the profession. Section Two is a collection of the convention addresses of the twenty-three presidents of the American Nurses' Association. Each of the forty-eight speeches provides insight into the workings of the association and the status of nursing during a particular period in history.

History is best understood when viewed through the eyes of those who observed and participated in significant events. As witnesses to nursing history, the presidents of the American Nurses' Association address the pressing issues facing the profession during their terms in office. Licensure, utilization of nursing resources, educational preparation, standards of practice, economic security, and professional growth are explored in light of technological and scientific advances, the world situation, the nation's economy, and the health needs of the public.

Although each president describes a distinct challenge facing the profession, the charge to ANA members, and nurses in general, is always the same. In the 1890s, it was called esprit de corps; in the 1940s, a united front; in the 1960s, a spirit of oneness; and in the 1970s, collaborative action. Each president stresses the importance of a strong unified organization of nurses, working to establish and implement professional standards and to protect the economic and general welfare of the profession. Be it 1926 or 1976, the theme of each address closely resembles the thought expressed by Edith Draper in 1893—"To advance we must unite."

1897-1976

ANA Presidents

Isabel Hampton Robb
1897-1901

Annie Damer
1901-1902, 1905-1909

Mary M. Riddle
1902-1905

Jane A. Delano
1909-1911

Sarah E. Sly
1911-1913

Genevieve Cooke, R.N.
1913-1915

Annie W. Goodrich, R.N.
1915-1918

Clara D. Noyes, R.N.
1918-1922

Adda Eldredge, R.N.
1922-1926

S. Lillian Clayton, R.N.
1926-1930

Elnora E. Thomson, R.N.
1930-1934

Susan G. Francis, R.N.
1934-1938

Julia C. Stimson, R.N.
1938-1944

Katharine J. Densford, R.N.
1944-1948

Pearl McIver, R.N.
1948-1950

Elizabeth K. Porter, Ed.D., R.N.
1950-1954

Agnes Ohlson, R.N.
1954-1958

Mathilda Scheuer, R.N.
1958-1962

Margaret B. Dolan, R.N.
1962-1964

Jo Eleanor Elliott, R.N.
1964-1968

Dorothy A. Cornelius, R.N.
1968-1970

Hildegard E. Peplau, Ed.D., R.N.
1970-1972

Rosamond C. Gabrielson, R.N.
1972-1976

1897-1901

Isabel Hampton Robb

The first president of the American Nurses' Association was a Canadian-born nurse who was an early graduate of the Training School for Nurses associated with Bellevue Hospital, New York City. Mrs. Robb served as superintendent of the Illinois Training School, in Chicago, where she planned and enforced the first graded curriculum of nursing study and instruction used in the United States and prohibited private nursing duty by nurses in training, a common practice of the time.

Mrs. Robb helped to organize the Training School at Johns Hopkins Hospital, in Baltimore, and was a founder of the Society of Superintendents of Training Schools. She also encouraged the development of a hospital economics course at Columbia and was one of America's earliest nurse authors. Her principle works include *Nursing, Its Principles and Practice* and *Nursing Ethics*, and she was one of the founders of the *American Journal of Nursing*.

Mrs. Robb died on April 15, 1910, in a streetcar accident.

The Spirit of the Associated Alumnae

By Isabel Hampton Robb, *president*
(First Annual Convention, New York City, April 28-29, 1898)

On one other occasion it has been my privilege to make the opening address at a gathering of trained nurses, and in the fact that in that first meeting was laid the foundation stone for this present organization lies the exceedingly great pleasure I now take in announcing the opening of the first annual meeting of the Nurses' Associated Alumnae of the United States and Canada. The occasions have a certain similarity, in that the former had the distinction of being the first occasion in the history of trained nursing in America on which nurses had met together to discuss affairs dealing with the various interests of their profession, while this second meeting heralds the beginning of organized work among nurses. But, from another point of view, the two meetings show a marked dissimilarity. The first presented an unorganized body of women with indefinite views and an uncertain future. To the present one we come as an organized, representative body with definite objects and ready to deal with some of the problems which, with the growth of the profession, have presented themselves for solution. Among the papers read and discussed at the Congress of Nurses in 1893 were two that had a direct bearing upon this present association. One, by Miss McIsaac, was on "The Benefits of Alumnae Associations"; the other, by Miss Draper, on "The Necessity of an American Nurses' Association." These two papers ably outlined the necessity for development in nursing work along the lines of organization. Under the stimulus of these papers, as well as that which was naturally evoked by the meeting together in a common interest, the hitherto unexpressed thought or feeling on the part of different superintendents that more co-operation and community of ideas in the general work would be helpful and a necessity, found vent, with the result that the American Society of Superintendents of Nurses was organized. This was the most vital and only really important result of that first meeting. The avowed objects of the Superintendents' Society are "To further the best interests of the nursing profession by establishing a universal standard of training and by promoting fellowship among its members by meetings, papers and discussions and by interchange of opinions." From the beginning it was very clear to the society that the broader outlook for nurses must first come through organized school alumnae associations of the graduates before anything could be done toward establishing a national association on anything like a permanent basis. It also recognized the advantage to the busy graduate nurses of having a body already organized to relieve them of the burden and responsibility of all the various details involved in the formation of an organization. And, appreciating this fact, what more natural than that these superintendents should declare themselves willing to undertake this work looking toward the higher and better interests of the nursing profession and of the graduates, many of whom these superintendents were responsible for making trained nurses. Papers and discussions were therefore prepared on "Training School Alumnae Associations" for each of the first two annual meetings. The second of these papers, by Miss Palmer, read February, 1895, with the purpose of showing the available material for a national association, gave a report of the number of alumnae associations in existence at that date. From a list of 164 training schools there were thirty-one organized alumnae associations or clubs; eighteen reported no organization, and fifty-five were not heard from. No attempt had been made, however, to classify these bodies with reference to their eligibility for membership in a national association. At the time of the meeting in Chicago there were possibly half a dozen alumnae associations organized. The fact that thirty-one were already in existence after the lapse of only two years was a gratifying evidence of the mind of the nurses on the subject.

Movement Toward a National Organization

At the third annual meeting of the Superintendents' Society a very comprehensive paper was read by Miss L. L. Dock on "A National Association for Nurses and Its Legal Organization." After the discussion that followed, it was moved that a committee of five be appointed by the Chair, to select seven others, who should form the nucleus of a convention to prepare a national constitution, and that they should secure an equal number of delegates from among the oldest alumnae societies, who should not be holding hospital positions, to unite with them in drawing up a constitution. This motion was carried, and it was also ordered that a report should be made at the next annual meeting. In accordance with this resolution the committee submitted its first, which was also its final, report, at the annual meeting, held in Baltimore in February, 1897.

Immediately following the third annual convention of the Society, a committee composed of L. L. Dock, Isabel McIsaac, Isabel Merrit, M. B. Brown, and Lucy L. Walker met to discuss plans for a convention to organize a national association. Adelaide Nutting, Edith Draper, M. A. Snively, Anna Maxwell, Sophia Palmer, Isabel Hampton Robb, and Florence Hutchinson were selected to join the committee. Twelve representative alumnae associations (Massachusetts General, New York Presbyterian, Bellevue, New York, New Haven, Orange Memorial, Johns Hopkins, University of Pennsylvania, Philadelphia, Brooklyn City, Illinois, and Farrand) were invited to send one delegate each to a convention at Manhattan Beach on September 2, 1896. A constitution and bylaws for a nurses' association of the U.S. and Canada were drafted and arrangements were made for a second meeting in conjunction with the Society's fourth annual convention. In February, 1897, in Baltimore, the constitution was adopted and officers were elected.*

The result of the second meeting in Baltimore we have heard from the Secretary.

Such in brief is the history of the beginnings of this national organization of alumnae associations of training schools. With the presentation of the report above also ends the responsibility of the Superintendents' Society, as a society, toward this organization.

It seems like a brief dream as to time since that June of 1895, but a dreaming true as to results. So splendid have these results been

* L. L. Dock, *Proceedings of the Fourth Annual Convention (Feb. 10-12, Baltimore) of the American Society of Superintendents of Training Schools for Nurses.* (Harrisburg, Pa.: Harrisburg Publishing Company, 1897).

thus far that I look forward into the future of the association alumnae with joy and with certainty that it will achieve greater and better things by nurses and for nurses than have ever yet come to pass. And with such a feeling and in such a spirit do I invite you to a consideration of the work before us at this meeting and of the future aims of the association.

This meeting is full of importance. We have first to consider our methods of work, arrangements of committees and constitutional amendments. The question of admitting the smaller schools into institutional membership and with what limitations is the most important one now before us. Recognizing the immense importance of very full discussions, it has been thought best that only one paper should be read at each session. These papers will deal with subjects that are of ethical and practical importance to us in beginning our work. We have one on "The Duty and Opportunity of the Alumnae." Another on "The Best Means of Co-ordinating the Work of the General Association and Its Branches," which will deal with State and local organizations. A third will deal with finance and investment, and I trust will help to lay a foundation toward a future practical method of encouraging our members in thrift and economy. Feeling sure, then, that all our discussions will be characterized by a dignified, wisely conservative and generous spirit, I will now very briefly direct your attention to some of the problems and possibilities that the future holds for us and which should furnish us with inspiration and encouragement to be loyal and true to the trust that is committed to each individual member of this association.

The objects as outlined in our constitution may seem simple and few in the reading; and yet concealed in each there lies folded up the seed of many a plan and purpose that can only come to maturity in the fulness of time, when the work shall be lifted from our hands, as we become incapacitated, and carried on to loftier ideals and higher aims by the strong young hands, hearts and brains of future nurses. And remembering this, it may be as well if we begin by making haste slowly, but steadily and surely.

For if we proceed on these lines from the first, we shall have less to regret and less to pull down later and shall end by accomplishing some little of real worth.

'Our Work Must Be Constructive'

Our work for the first few years must be constructive. A code of ethics is the first object mentioned in the constitution. But it cannot be among the first to be realized, for such a code should be the central point of thought of the association, reaching out in its influence and inspiration to our most remote branches and toward which each individual member may look vibrant with a sense of personal responsibility toward the association and toward the highest standard attainable by nurses. It should stand for deeds and actions, not words and form. Were we, therefore, to appoint a committee to forthwith formulate a code of ethics, we should get words, but not the spirit. Surely, it will be better to wait until we have taken sufficient and better form in the matter of numbers and closer organization, to learn the mind of the greater number on what shall constitute our national code of ethics. But I would like to say, in passing, that it should be founded, not on the lines of that of any existing association or society, but should be formulated to meet our own special needs in our own particular way.

The second clause reads, "To elevate the standard of nursing education." If ethics is our central thought, here indeed is our central problem, embodying, as it will in its solution, the combined and unremitting interest and efforts of every single member. Its breadth and height and depth are of such dimensions that it will require the most earnest thought of various minds before we can begin to see our way clear to the necessary steps to take for its ultimate solution. Time will only permit me to suggest some of the lines upon which a working basis may possibly be found for the present.

We do not need more training schools, but better ones. We should aim to build up and strengthen those training schools that already exist and to discourage the establishment of others with insufficient means and unscholarly ideals. The organization schools in the very small and specialty hospitals already appeal directly to us. We should work out some method by which the nursing in such hospitals could be undertaken whenever possible by the association. I believe the day will come when we shall see our way clear toward caring for many of this class of hospitals through its members. We should have no desire to prevent the organization of these small hospitals—we would not if we could, for they have their own particular place and mission to fill in the smaller places and for the specialties they stand for—but we must bear in mind that our first reason for being nurses is to tend, support and care for the helpless in the most efficient way possible. And if we can, as an organization, aid the trustees of hospitals in carrying out their responsibility of giving their patients the best of care by competent nurses, it is our distinct duty to do so, and to furnish them with a high grade of nursing at no greater cost than would be entailed by a small training school and untrained pupils, of which they would otherwise probably avail themselves. This system at the same time would help to materially lessen the number of inadequately trained nurses and, so far as instruction goes, would make the qualifications for membership in State or national associations practically the same for all trained nurses. It would also throw better material, and more of it, into the hands of the better equipped schools, and in this way increase the educational standard of our schools and raise the standard of requirements for women who wish to become trained nurses. Again, it would insure more continuous and agreeable work for a greater number of competent women, who prefer hospital work to other branches of nursing. Such a plan as this, however, can only be rendered feasible by having a supply of specially trained women ready to undertake these positions as superintendents and in such hospitals, and funds in our treasury for the purpose of supplementing, where necessary, the salaries of the nurses. For we should not be willing to have nurses undertake institutional work for inadequate compensation. For this reason, therefore, it might be advisable, in the case of very poor hospitals, for the association to allow their members to undertake the nursing and at the same time to guarantee to them a fair and just remuneration in proportion to the degree of work and responsibility assumed. To insure proper nursing, then, in the poorer and smaller hospitals should be one of our purposes in having money and accepting bequests.

The organization of State and local branches is advisable as a factor in educational advancement. Their importance is manifest in many, but more especially in two ways:—First, because through them only can details of the work outlined by the main organization be successfully carried into effect; and, secondly, because from an educational standpoint the local alumnae societies are of particular value, in that through them the educational interests of the individual graduate can be best fostered and properly cared for. As we all know, a hospital training does not represent the sum total of professional knowledge, and the successful nurse will be she who keeps abreast of the times. The opportunities for further study for the graduate beyond the regular undergraduate courses are often very limited, but where the different alumnae associations of a city or locality become united, they can devise practical ways and means for the encouragement of systematic post-graduate study. It is a source of pleasure to note that in Brooklyn the alumnae associations have already united their forces and are doing good work together.

But it is hardly less important that these local associations should have some outside interests as well. They should identify themselves with educational and philanthropic efforts and take part, so far as they can, outside in such movements, even when not strictly in their own line of work. In this way only will it be possible to avoid the danger of an association becoming narrow and selfish in its life. It is impossible to more than touch upon the educational side of these local associations. Their work will be hard, no doubt, and sometimes discouraging, but, on the other hand, they will have the enjoyment and benefit that comes from unity of purpose, from the element of variety that comes with the broader contact with others in the same work, from the free interchange of all the newest and best ideas outside of their own particular school, and from the added feeling of loyalty to their own society that such contact engenders. They should also lend their aid in endeavoring to direct philanthropy into the most effective channels. From the nature of their knowledge of sanitation and the laws of health, they should in the future have representation on educational boards, State Boards of Health, hospital and training school boards.They may thus use their influence in forming a correct public sentiment in matters of social reform. Another sphere of activity in which associations may engage is the opening of new avenues or branches of work affording means for employment outside of the usual ones of hospital or private nursing. The plan for visiting nurses has already been successfully inaugurated, and at the present time a local society in New York is endeavoring to redeem the application of mechanico-therapeutics from the hands of charlatans and place it in the hands of trained nurses, where it belongs. Last, but not least, there is the nurses' settlement work. In all such ways and many more may the influence of the association be unbounded, not only upon those who directly share its privileges, but upon the community at large. And so we may gradually grow into the third object of our association—that of being useful and honored.

And now just a word on the subject of finances. It would not seem out of place for an association of this kind to interest itself in the future financial welfare of its members. For present needs, in case of illness, members of their own school alumnae associations are assured through sick benefit funds, but it is for the years to come that provision should be made, and that through the thrift of the nurse herself. It is a well known fact that nurses are not very provident as a class, but could some plan be evolved by which systematic saving would be stimulated it would result in a feeling of security and independence for the nurse as to her future maintenance.

It seems to me that there is one feature of work which should prove of the utmost value and aid in helping us to make known and carry out the various objects which have been referred to—I mean the development of publications and of literature dealing with matters which concern directly or indirectly our profession. Just on what basis these developments may be best advanced I will leave for the present. Suffice it to say that this is a point which will bear much discussion and thought, and about which any ultimate plan can only be the result of a consensus of opinions.

Thus briefly have we passed in review some of the objects that we have to work for. Many nurses have asked and more will ask, "What is there in it for me if I join the alumnae association?" In answer we would say through the alumnae association of your school and the national associations all the possibilities that we have pointed out will be opened to you. But more remains; through them you will gain the broader and more unselfish life that comes to each woman who has ideals in her work and does not regard it merely from a commercial standpoint. The first president of Wellesley College said to the college students, "You do not go to college to earn your bread—not this only —but to make every mouthful of bread more nourishing, sweeter. It is to learn how to live—to make life, not a living. You may forget some of your Greek and Latin verbs, your geometry, history, but you need not forget your ideals. They may be yours always, or, better than this, they may be realized, for the students of to-day must be a great body marching toward the solution of problems we have not yet solved. In you we may have our meanings of the stars." How aptly may this be applied to trained nurses of to-day, into whose hands the pioneer nurses in America now place this nursing work, to be carried on to a higher plane to which the eyes of the world may look up, not down, learning to work together in a common interest, with harmony, method, and in a spirit of self-sacrifice strengthening the intelligent loyalty and efficient service of each member for her own alumnae association. It is very natural to look at the outset for the difficulties ahead, but I can foresee few that may not be overcome if skilfully attacked. Necessarily, there is a great amount of labor involved, and patience will be necessary before we can hope to realize any definite results. What we need is to quietly and steadily persevere. Our methods should be direct, simple and easy to understand for any one, and the spirit that underlies them should be generous and impersonal and tempered by a wise conservatism.

Finally, the interests of the individual should be one with those of the whole association. It is impossible to make too strong an appeal to your esprit de corps. Each member should see that the association and its work is loyally sustained in the years that are to come. Such work, though it may be well organized, will always need this individual attention and feeling of personal responsibility from the members, if we would look toward the day when the ideal nurse will be the rule and not the exception; her influence felt in the home, the hospital, our educational institutions and over the broad land.

Early Lessons

By Isabel Hampton Robb, *president*
(Second Annual Convention, New York City, May 1-3, 1899)

Two events have occurred during the past year, both of unusual interest to nurses, the first connected in large part with the past, the other of vital significance for the future of our profession. On March 6th, 1898, a large gathering of trained nurses, physicians and laymen was held in New York to celebrate the close of the first quarter of a century of trained nursing in the United States of America. The year was also marked by the demand for the first time for the services of trained nurses to meet the emergencies of war. I ask you to allow me to look back over the past twenty-five years, because I believe that by so doing I shall be able to put before you more clearly certain phases of the second and more important subject of my address, namely, What lessons has the late war taught us and what bearing or influence may it have upon trained nursing in the future?

It is usually the custom with all well regulated business concerns to take account at stated times of their affairs, to go over their past records and find out just how much has been accomplished and how much, if anything, stands to their credit for the future. As we have just rounded off our first quarter of a century it is then in order for us to re-read our records, and see how we have fared during that time and in how far the outlook for the future is hopeful. The trained nurse is a distinctly modern product. Twenty-five years ago we find her just starting out on her career, without antecedents, without experience, with all before her, and all to learn. Her credentials had to be of her own making, her professional standing had to be evolved; she had to establish her own traditions and in all these undertakings she had to maintain her own personal and professional dignity. She has, however, never lacked for friends, for here in New York the seed was sown by women for women and for the good of suffering humanity. And these founders of a new guild for women have stood through these first years ever loyal and true to watch over the best interests of the young plant, propping where necessary, pruning judiciously and ever giving wise and friendly counsel. So long as the success or failure of the trained nurse was an open question her development was naturally slow, but after the first few years, when graduates began to increase in numbers and the value of their work had been manifest in the hospital and home we find more branches beginning to shoot out, and more training schools springing into existence. In the past ten years more especially there has been a not altogether healthy overgrowth; the increase has been almost alarming and there are now to be found all sorts and conditions of hospitals and training schools, with the result that the country has been flooded with a very non-descript class of women all bearing the title of trained nurse, the term standing for all grades of training and all grades of women. As a natural consequence the public has freely offered its criticisms, various and varied in character, upon the trained nurse, the good and bad having to bear their share equally of praise or blame. Here then was the first problem to confront us—the rapid increase in quantity without a corresponding improvement in quality—and as this discrepancy became more and more apparent, the older and better known schools with the instinct of self-preservation began to draw more closely within themselves, trusting in their own irreproachable names to protect their graduates, with the result that the members of one school were led to hold themselves severely aloof from those of another. Fortunately this narrow and selfish policy could not last long. Gradually but forcibly it was borne in upon the minds of the older and more experienced that in this way did not lie success and advancement, that nurses could not afford to be narrow and self-seeking and that to attain to a fixed high standard in our work, to overcome the evils that were increasing and to collect our scattered forces, we must have unity of purpose and centralization of means. As an expression of this growing conviction a Congress of Nurses was held in Chicago in 1893. During this meeting a number of Superintendents, all of them representing most of the large schools in the country, met together to discuss ways and means by which some of these problems could be met, and some of the evils overcome. This conference resulted in the formation of the American Society of Superintendents of Training Schools for Nurses. Beginning with a membership of 18, the roll gradually increased until now it includes over 100 members. During its five years of work it has labored faithfully to lay a solid foundation upon which a standard for nurses might be built—a standard that all high minded, earnest nurses would be proud to help to maintain and that would attract to the work desirable women. From the first the society was impressed with the fact that only by the nurses themselves could such a standard be created and sustained, and before anything like a professional status could be hoped for, an *esprit de corps* must be established among graduates of the same school with a drawing together in their own work and home interests. The fact that in this short time alumnaes have been organized in almost every training school, both large and small, that the Associated Alumnae is just completing its second year with a membership of 26 alumnaes, representing about 2,500 nurses, and that this year many small general schools will be admitted into associated membership is a convincing proof that trained nurses desire a fixed standard, that they are alive to their responsibilities as professional women, and realize that they have a definite position to maintain. And so we close this brief *resume* of the first quarter of a century of our history with the knowledge that our chief weakness during these years has come from the rapid increase in numbers, from the want of a professional and educational standard and from the scattering of our forces from lack of organization and of working together in our common interests. But there is nothing to be despondent over and much ground for encouragement. We are fortunate in having discovered our weakest points at so early a period in our career. Our strength in all that tends towards bettering the work of the trained nurse is in a fair way to increase. If our efforts towards organization are still incomplete a fair beginning has been made and at least we are free from many factions with their working at cross-purposes for which we may be deeply thankful. Steps have been taken to decrease the quantity of graduates as well as to improve the standard by increasing the term of instruction from two to three years. There is also more uniformity in candidates, requirements, and more system in our methods of instruction. We may congratulate ourselves that we have made a good beginning.

A Look to the Future

And now let us turn and look a little way into the future and mark what it may hold for us in the way of new work, responsibilities and obligations. Nor have we far to look, for right on the threshold we are confronted by a problem that holds grave results and responsibilities for trained nurses. In my last year's address I mentioned some of the branches of work in addition to hospital and private nursing that have been opened up to the trained nurse, all evidences of the growing place which the world is ready to give her as she shows her fitness for it. To these was unexpectedly added another in the demand and need for her services during the Spanish American war. Last spring, when the possibilities of war menaced the nation, individual nurses expressed their willingness to give their services if needed in the military hospitals, and when war was actually declared, the number of volunteers was greatly increased. But unfortunately trained nurses were not the only women thus impelled, for applications and offers to do army nursing began to pour into the Surgeon-General's office from all manner of women, from the well-meaning "born nurse," the enthusiastic patriot, from sisterhoods and from adventuresses, as well as from the cream and slum of trained nurses. Just about this time the Associated Alumnae was holding its first annual meeting in New York, and one of the first acts its delegates had the privilege of performing was to offer the services of representative trained nurses as a body to the government to do its army nursing. This step was taken because the delegates were fully impressed with the fact that nursing in the army is of the greatest importance to the country and that here, if anywhere, incompetence and want of system would be productive of the greatest harm not only in the immediate present but for the future of many valuable lives. You all know how nobly our volunteer forces behaved, but the back bone of our military and naval resources lay in the trained men—the trained members of our army and navy. In the same way it was only logical to assume that the back bone of the nursing should be found in trained women who, for years, had made this their profession. These it was thought should form a nucleus around which could be built up a proper system and efficiency in the nursing. I would particularly insist that the Associated Alumnae of trained nurses did not desire that all the nurses for the army should be selected from their ranks; what they did ask was that the service should be organized from a strictly business standpoint and, that for nursing, trained women should be selected, and each nurse should be chosen only after affording some guarantee that she had been fitted by a proper training for the work in hand. The following telegram was, therefore, dispatched to the Surgeon-General on April 28, 1898:

To the Honorable Secretary of War, Washington, D. C.:

The Associated Alumnae of Trained Nurses of the United States and Canada, including 2,000 graduates of twenty-four Training Schools, offer their services for any work which the Medical Department of the army may demand of them in connection with the war with Spain.

—By direction of Delegates now in session in New York City.

But not receiving any reply, and believing that a personal interview explaining the number and standing of these nurses would result in the acceptance of their services, the president and vice-president of the Association went down to Washington and had a personal interview with the Surgeon-General. But their mission was a failure as they were told that the nursing department had been given into the charge of the Daughters of the American Revolution, with a woman doctor as director. Visions of what splendid systematic work might be done if the nursing might only be in the hands of the nurses themselves, supplemented by the extra supplies so generously provided by the D. A. R., the Red Cross and other Societies, floated before us, but it was not to be. The story of the summer's campaign is familiar to many of us. The chaos and confusion that reigned supreme at first owing to the suddenness and greatness of the emergency was intensified and prolonged by the lack of experience on the part of those into whose hands the work was entrusted. This and the appointments made from all the varieties of women mentioned above resulted in much bad nursing, a worse morale, and in a total lack of standard or system. How long such a condition would have continued to exist it is hard to say had not the situation been saved by the assistance and admirable work rendered by the Red Cross Auxiliary No. 3.

A brief word in explanation of these Red Cross Auxiliaries. They did not form a permanent part of the American National Red Cross Society but were made up of a number of patriotic men and women who organized for the purpose of raising funds to assist the government in any way they might, in relieving the needs and suffering of the sick soldiers. That they might do this the more effectually they offered themselves as Auxiliaries to the Red Cross Society already in the field. After the emergency of the war was over they disbanded. Auxiliary, No. 3, was organized for the express purpose of "supplying and maintaining trained nurses in army hospitals." Too much cannot be said in praise of the work they accomplished, hampered as they were by being only auxiliaries and not the controlling head. It was through this Auxiliary that the best nursing was done; they put themselves at once in touch with trained nurses of experience and ability and continued to co-operate with them to the end. But with lack of experience at the head, and with nurses recruited from a variety of sources, there was necessarily much chaff among the wheat. A certain amount of good nursing was done but not half of what could have been accomplished with proper management. Protest upon protest has come to my ears from the nurses and others competent to judge of these matters, and I have received numerous letters asking if some better condition of army nursing could not be established, and insisting upon the absolute necessity of inaugurating a better system, with more order, discipline and consequently better work. Many good nurses who went into military hospitals during the summer returned home again not because they were not willing to put up with physical discomforts, but because they could not tolerate the lack of discipline and the looseness of work and conduct, and because they could not conscientiously serve under the young, inexperienced and indiscrete women often placed over them.

Do not understand me as saying that all the hospitals and

nurses were unsatisfactory, for just when the stress of work was greatest, the superintendents of experience and ability with their nurses, chosen by the Red Cross Auxiliary, No. 3, did much to minimize the lamentable state of affairs which had existed up to that time. Certainly, then, one of the important lessons to be learned from the war is that the nursing system in the army, as it existed during the war and as it exists at the present day, leaves much to be desired. Sad experience has shown us that those who do the country's fighting and suffer for their flag, do not in the hour of need receive such good care as many a worthless tramp is thought to be entitled to in a civil hospital. At least let the mothers, wives and sisters of the soldiers have the satisfaction of feeling that their loved ones, when wounded or sick, shall have the best nursing procurable. And if women are acknowledged to be the best nurses of the sick in times of peace, why not also in war? Our army surgeons are taken from among the graduates of our best medical schools, our army nurses should be taken from our best training schools for nurses.

But in order to have such a service ready to be utilized in time of war or emergency the work of organization must be intelligently done in the time of peace. No one will dispute the fact that the country must have always at its command a regular army of trained soldiers. Why is it not then just as logical to keep ever ready a standing army of trained nurses who come up to a fixed standard. The day for the volunteer nurse, the born nurse, and the enthusiastic patriotic woman to do army nursing has gone by, just as the old and often haphazard methods in hygiene and surgery have given place to modern scientific surgery and medicine, the result of investigation and training. Nor can the nurse who intelligently put into execution the methods and orders of the scientific physician be made in a day. As a member of the House of Representatives very aptly said: "The work of nurses is a work of their own, it cannot be done by others." There is plenty of work for the energy and generosity of such fine organizations as the D.A.R., and the National Red Cross Society, and our impulse has been and always will be to lend a helping hand to them when opportunity affords. But this one particular branch must be left to trained nurses and if we are to be held responsible for the results of the nursing, the power of making a proper selection of women for the work should rest in our own hands. Only then can our failures be justly cast in our teeth.

But as representatives of the trained nurses of this country, we have felt that before submitting our views to the consideration of the government, it was necessary to make sure that they had the endorsement of the people at large and especially those who had studied the question of nursing in the army. While considering how to reach this opinion, which, judging from numerous articles in the daily papers and in the magazines, was certainly widespread, and while debating how we might get in touch with this friendly aid, we learned to our joy that among the men and women who had so generously given of their time, strength and money to aid in providing skilled nursing during all the long summer, there were not a few who held the same conviction as the nurses themselves, and who, anxious that some permanent good should result from the summer's work and experience, were willing to continue their aid and work for this end when once they were assured that the nurses were willing to undertake permanently this new field of nursing. No time was lost in assuring them of our readiness and the result was that a meeting was called in New York in December, 1898, under the auspices of the Associated Alumnae of Trained Nurses to confer with those interested as to the proper steps to be taken. It was unanimously decided that a bill should be prepared and presented to congress to provide for the establishment of women nurses in military hospitals. To formulate this bill and to secure its success a joint committee was formed, composed of women prominent among those who have deserved well of their country, a certain number of trained nurses from among those who had been in active service during the war or of experience as superintendents of nurses, whose time and services were available for bringing the matter to the notice of the authorities in Washington. After the formation of this committee any active part taken by the Associated Alumnae as a body was at an end since the committee felt that in any bill on army nursing trained nurses should be considered as a professional body and that in its enactments, no exclusive society should be recognized. In drawing up the bill the endeavor was made to embody all the essentials that would assure a high order of nursing. The following statement, read in Washington at one of the meetings held in favor of the bill, admirably expresses what the committee had in mind and will convey to your minds their views far better than could any words of mine.

February 2nd, 1899

The views of the Chiefs of the large Training Schools for women nurses and of the ladies who are especially interested in this movement is that it is a matter of very great importance to select proper women for the first appointments as nurses in the army service, under this or any other bill:

It is not merely that the persons so selected should be able to pass an ordinary examination to determine the capacity of the trained nurse, such as might possibly be provided by the Civil Service Commission, but they should be persons who are selected for their tact and discretion, and, to a considerable extent, for business capacity, and that the only persons who can obtain perfectly reliable information upon these points are the heads of some of the more important Training Schools, or persons who have been connected with them.

The feeling of those who are urging this bill is that it is a reasonably certain way to secure for the army the kind of women nurses whom it is so desirable to obtain, and while the method proposed may not be precisely in accordance with military precedent, they feel bound to urge it in view of the great importance of the matter.

The ordinary method would be, of course, to provide that these nurses should be selected by the Surgeon-General of the Army, which would mean by a Board to be organized by him. But no Board which he could organize, composed of members of the Medical Staff, could by any possibility obtain the information as to qualifications, outside of the purely technical qualifications, above referred to, and it would find itself unable to judge of the relative merits of the various testimonials and certificates with which it is quite certain that every candidate who came before such a Board, would be amply provided. Unless we can make sure that the right kind of women are selected in the beginning to take charge of the introduction of women nurses into the Army, we think it doubtful whether it would be worth while to attempt to introduce women nurses at all at the present time, for a very few women, having more zeal than discretion and not able to cope with the various petty difficulties which are sure to occur at first, will be likely to bring the whole subject of Women Nurses in the Army into unmerited disrepute.

It follows, therefore, that the standard for these first nurses to be appointed must necessarily be high. Our object should be to secure women who can manage, or if necessary, instruct less qualified nurses whom it may be necessary to employ hereafter. It would be the greatest possible mistake to employ any but the very best nurses to begin this work.

The fate of the bill still lies in the future as there was not time for it to come before the Senate at the last session. The work done for it so far goes to show how warmly the public as well as the government approve of it, for it has already received a majority vote in Congress which undoubtedly would have been larger had there been a clear understanding in the minds of all the representatives as to some of its details. There was unexpected opposition on the part of the National Red Cross Society, whose privileges and work we had no thought of interfering with; on the contrary we had hoped by our own organization to render their work in the future much more efficient for the reason that they would no longer have to depend upon Auxiliaries to supply them with nurses in times of emergency. Again it would be a mistake to assume that the bill would debar any Red Cross nurse from serving, for its measures allow for the acceptance of any or all trained nurses, provided they enter the army nursing corps in the prescribed way and can meet the requirements necessary for a fixed standard of ability, health, education and morals.

And now what is the duty of each individual, right-minded, trained nurse in regard to this bill? It is that she shall give it her loyal support in all legitimate ways known to her until it becomes a law. It will be presented to Congress at its next session, and between now and then she should work for it untiringly, for if successful it means that the professional standing and standard for the trained nurse will have been won, for we shall have the seal and the recognition of the nation stamped upon us which should incite us to greater efforts to prove ourselves worthy of so great an honor and trust. At the present time there is no modern system of army nursing in any country and it should be our pride and pleasure to make that of the United States one that would be an object lesson for all countries to follow.

If the bill, however, should fail, then we shall, as a body and as individuals, have a still graver question to face.* Shall we be loyal and strong enough to stand by the standard we are striving to make for ourselves, or shall we dissipate our forces and enlist as in the old way under any society, under any leadership, and with any kind of nurses? The past 25 years has shown a curious apathy on the part of the trained nurses to take care of their own affairs and had we time I could cite several instances in which outsiders are taking the lead and making a profit and sometimes their living out of trained nurses while the nurses themselves seem content to forget the best interests of the profession, and to follow these self-seeking leaders like sheep. For many the temptation to choose the easier path will be hard to resist, for present remuneration is much more tangible and attractive than a possible future standard. During the war the trained nurse has suffered. She has been

* The Army Bill for Nurses was eventually killed.

called to account not only for her own faults but the shortcomings of incompetent amateurs have also been reckoned against her. Can any graduate think it right to help to perpetuate such a reproach by enlisting into any body that lacks a proper organization, and a proper standard? Can we dare to run the risk of making the name of trained nurses more of a reproach than it has been? We need never be afraid that our standard will ever become too exalted for even with our best efforts there will always be those among us who wear the cap and gown who will bring dishonor upon it sufficient to strike a balance and keep us lowly minded enough. But how great the dishonor for all of us if we do not try to maintain a good practical average at least!

During the past quarter of a century we have unconsciously and independently helped to do much, let us now, realizing our strength, resolve to do more; let us by being more closely united as a body become a more powerful factor for good. While working as individuals in other organizations, for their many and varied objects, let us be bound by one common tie to this, our profession; and no matter how great may be the temptations to divert our strength from its legitimate field, let us hold steadfast and thus win confidence and respect which must be jealously guarded and steadily increased by the faithful loyalty and personal interest of every woman within the ranks, each and all, content to put into our work only the highest and best we have to give. Remember we are the history makers of trained nurses. Let us see to it that we work so as to leave a fair record as the inheritance of those who come after us, one which may be to them an inspiration to even better efforts, instead of a regret or a reproach. It rests with ourselves entirely just how honored, how useful, and what place this nursing work shall hold in the world. Certain it is that if we do not get credit for our successful efforts we shall inevitably incur reproach for whatever may sully the work of our profession. Whatever be the result of our efforts, whatever the verdict of the present generation or of posterity, let each of us see to it that we make ourselves safe from the pangs of self-reproach. Then and only then if the consciousness of duty done be our only reward it will suffice.

A General Review of Nursing Forces

By Isabel Hampton Robb, *president*
(Third Annual Convention, New York City, May 3-5, 1900)

Only once during the twelve months is it our privilege to meet together as a corporate body to deal with the common affairs of our common work, to take counsel, as wisely as we may, how we may improve and further that work by mutual and organized efforts, and at the same time strengthen those ties which bind us together as individual workers and as members of a profession, which in a little over twenty-five years has grown, as it were, from a small seed to a mighty tree whose branches spread widely and in many directions. To this yearly gathering also are brought the suggestions of individual members and of individual alumnae associations to receive the consideration and attention of the representatives of the whole body, who deliberate upon them and take such action as seems best. The result of these deliberations, together with the substance of the papers read and of the ensuing discussions, are reported to the several alumnae by their delegates, and moreover are printed in detail in the annual report, which is circulated through the proper channels, so that it comes within the reach of even the most remote member, supplying her, we trust, with fresh food for thought and a new stimulus for the work of the next year.

It would seem, therefore, advisable that we should make use of this annual opportunity to hold a general review of our forces, so that utilizing what we can learn from the retrospect we may be the better able to deal with the present and receive a clearer understanding as regards the future.

We now know that the concentration of our forces came too late by at least a year, for one can hardly doubt that the nursing of our soldiers during the Spanish-American war would naturally have fallen into our hands, had our professional organization been completed earlier. If this had been done, our capacity to meet properly so important a crisis would have been better understood and appreciated, with the result that not only would our soldiers have received better nursing, but we ourselves might have been spared the extra exertion that has been demanded of us during the past two years in our continued efforts in supporting the Army Nursing Bill, and at the same time upholding the honor of our professional status. It may be, however, as well that we were not successful to begin with, for had honors come to us too easily, they might possibly have rendered us careless of our best interests in the future, and the necessity for absolute loyalty and continued personal effort might not have been so early impressed upon our minds with sufficient emphasis. Be that as it may, the events of the past year have made even the doubters among us realize that, in a certain sense, the trained nurse as a unit is nobody; and although at this writing the success or failure of the Army Nursing Bill is still undecided we may still feel that, whether we win or lose the cause for this year, we should be deeply grateful that we were a sufficiently organized and representative body to be able to unite in working to uphold and guard our professional honor and its welfare. No doubt the chief subject that has largely held our interest during the two years past has been army nursing, and the various phases of the problem have been studied by many of us with keen interest.

The growth of our association is steady and encouraging. This year we add five more large schools to our membership and six small general schools will be admitted into associate membership as soon as certain changes in the constitution, which will be made at this meeting, have rendered the step legal. At this meeting also we shall be called upon to consider the question of enlarging our borders in order to admit, on the same footing as alumnae associations, local associations, some of whose members have not had the opportunity of being connected with alumnae (in case such associations do not exist in their schools), but who would bring into a local association the same standard as that required by our alumnaes. It is desired that this point shall be settled before we proceed to the formation of state associations, which the various alumnaes of New York propose to take steps to do very shortly in their state. This will not be the first time the question of local and state associations has come before us for discussion. A large portion of our First Annual Report is made up of papers and discussions upon the subjects of state and local associations. It is not one of my duties to instruct you, but I may at least ask you to remember that our object in associating is to advance the interests of the whole *nursing profession* and not merely those of any one association. After deciding upon the formation of local associations we trust steps may very soon be taken to formulate state associations, beginning in all probability with the state of New York.

As many of us know, the question of registration for trained nurses has been long in our minds, but we were also aware that to advocate legislation for nurses eight or ten years ago would have been to "put the cart before the horse." At that time, no *esprit de corps* existed among the leaders in our schools. Nothing much in the way of systematic teaching was recognized; certainly there was no uniformity in curriculum and not even an attempt at a general education and ethical standard. Among the nurses there was no professional feeling, not even among the graduates of the same school; there was simply nothing organized or professional about us. Collectively we could neither qualify as a profession, a calling, or a trade. For to be a member of a profession implies more responsibility, more serious duties, a higher skill and work demanding a more thorough education than is required in many other vocations in life. But two things more are needful—organization and legislation. A calling, in its accepted sense, implies more exclusively a consecrated religious life, such as that of sisterhoods with their religious restrictions, which are more numerous and exacting than those demanded of the trained nurse; while, on the other hand, a trade is more largely concerned with manual labor. We were, therefore, a most indefinite quantity. How then, could we ask for legislation as a profession, when we did not exist as such? We had, therefore, to know and understand ourselves, in some measure, before we could possibly determine our rightful status. Modern medicine, in requiring of us the professional attributes, has taken the decision out of our hands, and has made trained nursing a profession; but how soon we shall attain to the full profession level depends upon ourselves entirely. Before all, then, it was necessary to organize, and the rapidity and thoroughness with which you went at and accomplished the first steps were truly amazing. These important phases in development, though comparatively rapid, have followed each other in their natural sequence; as a result there has been no time lost in retracing steps, but a gradual broadening out has been going on as need arose. Thus organization has developed through the Society of Superintendents standing for educational advancement, to the school alumnaes, representing home as well as professional interests, to the national association representing the profession, with its larger life and affairs, and where each alumnae has equal representation. Furthermore, after this meeting we may hope for the rapid development of local associations, where each nurse, in one state and town today and in another far away tomorrow, may still have her recognized place and voice in the affairs of her profession; and finally, before we meet again, we look for the formation of at least one state association, the last link in the chain of organization.

Registration for Nurses

With the completion of the chain the fulness of time brings us face to face with the vital question of registration for nurses, the foundation for which was laid just seven years ago. State registration is certainly the next and most important step towards achieving a fixed professional standard. According to the Constitution of the United States, an act authorizing registration for the whole profession and country cannot be passed by Congress at

Washington, but each state must make its own laws for its own nurses. New York with its local and state associations will become sufficiently representative to ask for legal recognition for trained nurses within its domains. It is only fitting that this state should take the initiative. Its educational institutions are controlled by the University of the State of New York, which does not allow members of any profession to practice in the state until they show proper proofs that they have graduated from some recognized qualified school, and have also passed certain prescribed examinations in the studies taught in these schools. Only to those who satisfy these requirements is a license granted by the regents of the university. If then, similar requirements had to be met by trained nurses, nursing would at once be established on a distinct educational plane. Again, as New York is the home of the mother of training schools in this country, it is but fitting that this state should first receive the crowning glory of the work she so bravely undertook. Nor will the other states lag far behind her in this respect if we may judge by the alacrity with which they followed her lead in establishing schools for nurses. Only by a complete system of registration will it be possible for trained nursing to attain to its full dignity as a recognized profession and obtain permanent reforms. As the matter stands at present, the woman who has spent years of hard work and study in acquiring skill and knowledge as a nurse, on undertaking private nursing, finds at once that she is classed on a level with all sorts and grades of so-called trained nurses; nor has she any redress. She is expected to work side by side with the uncertified hospital nurse, who has been dismissed for cause before the expiration of her term as a student, with the half trained nurse from the specialty hospitals, with the nurse who has received the kind of instruction that makes her dangerous, with the adventuress, and the amateur—women masquerading as nurses, a matter of uniforms with no knowledge behind them—with the second-year hospital pupil sent out during the time that should have been devoted to her education, to earn money for the institution. Is it to be wondered at that with such a levelling, with the competent confused with the incompetent in the eyes of the public, that the severe and continual criticism should fall upon the just as well as upon the unjust and that the nursing profession should suffer for the sins and shortcomings of those who should not be ranked as belonging to it. Our sympathies are divided between a long-suffering and much sinned against public and the genuine trained nurse. Such anomalous conditions have gone far towards bringing private duty into bad odor and as a result many of our best graduates prefer to remain in hospitals, at a much less income, because there they hold a definite recognized professional status, since in all hospitals worthy of the name the authorities recognize the necessity and importance of having trained nurses in charge of the nursing department, and the staff is made up either of graduates or pupils, no room or place remaining for nondescripts.

But with registration this unfortunate condition of things will be changed; the professional status of the trained nurse will be defined no less sharply than that of the physician or of the lawyer. By these means also the public would be provided with a distinguishing mark whereby they could know whether any given nurse has been properly trained, and is a suitable person to take charge of the sick; whereas in the absence of a public registry or of a physician to make the selection they are left without any guarantee of the efficiency of the various candidates. Again, since the medical profession must always wish to secure for their patients the best care, it will undoubtedly heartily endorse this further effort to increase and improve the efficiency of the nursing service. Lastly, as regards training schools themselves, the introduction of a legalized registration would naturally stimulate both schools and graduates to reach the required educational standard. Each school would be obliged to give the pupils a sufficiently thorough instruction in the theory and practice of nursing as would enable them to pass the examination prescribed by law, and obtain the certificate, which would authorize them to practice as trained nurses. These examinations could be conducted by properly qualified boards, the members of which would be largely drawn from those among the ranks of the trained nurses who have had special experience in such matters; who know what good nursing is, how it should be taught, and what standard is desirable and at the same time attainable.

Of course such a law would not be retroactive and would not affect graduate nurses, who were already in the field, beyond requiring them to present their diplomas and applying for registration.

With this final step in our professional organization accomplished, we are then ready to set to work to some purpose to define our ethical code.

Although we are nearing the completion of the last links of our national organization there are still others to be forged, by which we hope to unite ourselves in professional bonds with those of our own guild in other countries and become identified with woman's work at large all over the world, this gaining additional breadth and strength for our own more specialized efforts. Last year you may remember, we were proffered the privilege of membership in the International Council of Women; this year we have a similar invitation from the International Council of Nurses, which is one of the outcomes of last year's meeting, and which in itself goes to show that American nurses are by no means alone in feeling the need for organization. Indeed the work that nurses are achieving along these lines in other countries makes interesting and inspiring reading and brings home to each one of us convincingly the importance of personal loyalty, personal interest and personal work, without which we can never hope to attain the full measure of success. If we do not take care of our own affairs, rest assured that outsiders will undertake the task for us to our everlasting undoing and to the detriment of the public, whose sick we have the privilege of ministering to.

Whether we shall take up or lay aside our professional responsibilities is not a matter of choice, but a question of duty and conscience. Do you think it right that any one of us, who has come to a clear understanding of the seriousness and importance of nursing work should go her separate way and take her own ease and pleasure while there is even one human life imperilled for the want of good nursing? Can we be still and let things just take their own way, so long as the stamp of mediocrity marks a work to which should be given the best and highest that the hands, hearts and minds of women can bring to it? This is no work that can be taken up lightly or laid aside carelessly by the first-comer, but one that should be entrusted only to women, each one of whom should be ordained a priestess, as it were, before she presumes to enter into the temple to perform her ministries unto sick and suffering humanity.

Note: During the fourth annual convention in 1901, only a limited amount of business was conducted. Convention delegates participated in the meetings of the International Congress of Nurses being held in Buffalo. Consequently, Mrs. Robb did not prepare a formal address to convention delegates.

1901-1902, 1905-1909

Annie Damer

The second president of the American Nurses' Association, and the only president to have served nonconsecutive terms in office, was, like her predecessor, Canadian-born. Annie Damer studied nursing at the Training School for Nurses associated with Bellevue Hospital and established a program of social service work for tuberculosis patients.

Most of Miss Damer's nursing career was spent in the field of public health nursing. She was a member of the first Board of Nurse Examiners of New York State and later served as its president. Miss Damer also served as president of the New York State Nurses' Association and of the board of the *American Journal of Nursing*.

Miss Damer died on August 9, 1916.

Preparation of the Professional Nurse

By Annie Damer, *president*

(Fifth Annual Convention, Chicago, May 1-3, 1902)

It is very gratifying to our members to be welcomed so cordially to Chicago. Some of us have known something of your hospitality in the past, when our first nurses' gathering in America was held here in 1893. We were then unorganized, but the impetus received then has led to the formation of a society which now numbers over four thousand members.

During the year now past one event in our nursing world has

become a part of history. Our great International Congress of Nurses, representing all the great nursing organizations of the world, met in the city of Buffalo. Representatives of our profession from other lands and from Maine to California, from Northern Canada to Georgia and Alabama, met together in conferencc. Some of the thoughts given to us there we have brought again to you here that we may discuss them and consider their intention and applicability, and that each may return to her home animated by a common purpose and desire towards a common aim.

It would be pleasant to dwell upon the labor and service of those who have done so much for our profession, from our honorary and beloved member, Miss Florence Nightingale, whose rules on army nursing, hospital administration, home nursing, and sanitary regulations are still our models, through the long list of noble and self-sacrificing women, most of them still in active service, still laboring in our training-schools, East and West, North and South. In all our efforts they are still linked with us in service. To our Superintendents' Association we would give all honor. May its spirit of progress and initiative, of usefulness and of unison, remain with us, though we may not as often as in the past have the benefits of its members' attendance at our Annual Conventions, but we can work with them in their efforts towards the advancement of our profession. What our place and our work shall be rests with ourselves.

Let me turn your attention briefly to the work mapped out for the present session. An important report will be that presented tomorrow by our Committee on Revision of the Constitution. Our alumnae associations have multiplied all over the country, but with them have grown up a number of associations of equal standing, formed of nurses many of whom have removed from the neighborhood of their school and who feel the need of fellowship and mutual effort and aid. To many it seems advisable that these societies should become a part of our national association, and this question you will be asked to decide.

Our national society is professedly social and educational. As a social organization it has brought the nurses of the country into a common fellowship, done away with petty rivalries and school jealousies, and brought us to where we are ready to work for the good of not the individual nurse or the individual school, but of the whole profession.

Through five years of education we have been learning how to lay our foundations for a strong organization by first bringing nurses together who were naturally united by their school ties. From these we have been led to take an interest in what concerns the nurses of the country, and now through our affiliation with the Superintendents' Society we form the American Federation of Nurses, sending representatives to the great International Congress of Women. We have been learning, often through our mistakes, the value and necessity of conducting our meetings in proper form according to parliamentary procedure, and that no rules can be lightly laid aside or broken which safeguard the rights of the minority. Hence we are prepared before forming our State associations to proceed in a careful and perfectly legal manner where each step is of so much importance.

What has been emphasized so often of late is preliminary education before entering the wards for technical training. Our present system of training is by no means an ideal one. The work is most exacting and the long hours leave little time for recreation. When off duty in the wards time has to be found to prepare for and attend lectures. Many nurses break down in health and many whose services would be valuable are lost to the profession. In many who have the strength to endure to the end the evil effects of the system are not less apparent. Lack of sympathy and indifference to the feelings of the patient are often charged against the nurse, but it is no wonder if she grow to perform her work in a perfunctory manner when it goes on ten or twelve hours a day, seven days a week, year after year, seeing little of the outside world, not coming in contact with anyone not connected with hospitals. Hospitals are supported by the public, and the public employs the nurses trained in them. If we are to have better nurses, better means must be used to obtain them. More interest shown in the nurse while preparing for future service, and the responsibility to the public of each hospital for the capability and training of the nurses sent out from the school fixed where it belongs, on the hospital authorities, and not on the nursing profession. The time has been when any place was good enough for the nurse's dormitory and anything was good enough for her meals, but gradual improvements are being introduced and more consideration shown for physical well being, and we hope before long to see the preparatory theoretical instruction given in a preparatory school, and the technical instruction obtained in the wards during reasonable hours.

We also feel that we have reached the time when we should demand recognition as a profession through the granting of a proper certificate by a state constituted and maintained Board of Examiners. Though the demand for trained nurses is always increasing, the supply increases still more rapidly. Every small hospital in the country in order to secure service organizes a training-school for its own particular interests, and all sorts of nurses are thrust upon the public, good, bad and indifferent. Our large schools are criticised that they fail to give instruction in the niceties of nursing. Too much attention is paid to operative proceedings and too little to the many little refinements which make the nurse acceptable in a well-bred home. The small schools are supposed to give only the special training required by the hospital and patients under treatment.

We grant that our methods of instruction are very much varied. Nurses have been admitted to many schools without adequate preliminary training and their after training has not been properly supervised and directed, and a lot of half-prepared women have crowded into our ranks with their main idea the acquiring of the almighty dollar, with but little thought for their profession, their vocation, or the public weal. The standard of qualification needs to be fixed, and also guaranteed by some independent authority.

It would seem best to place it in the hands of the Regents where such are appointed, and make our education conform to the general scheme required by law.

The number of schools should be reduced. No hospital which cannot give a nurse a thorough and adequate training should be allowed to establish a school. The efficiency of other schools would be increased by this State supervision and the quality of the nurses improved. There may be a variety of opinions as to the method of conducting these examinations and granting the license, but as to the general proposition there surely can be no objection. It will be seen that this is something more than a question of sentiment, something more than a matter of spasmodic effort or isolated attempt. It is a work worthy of the thought and effort of a great body, which will employ all our energy and resources in time to come. Our work in the past has been of value. There are great possibilities before us in the future. Shall we hesitate and fall back into a disorganized, indifferent, selfish crowd of workers of all sorts and conditions, lacking *esprit de corps*, unity, and strength, or shall we go forward, perhaps through a wilderness of difficulties and trials, to the 'Canaan of our hopes'? Ours is a recognized profession for women, ours unquestioned and unchallenged; for it we need no emancipation, and towards it no antagonistic attitude is assumed by any. Shall we make it a greater and a nobler, held only by women who know the best and love the best, serving our generation according to our opportunities? May the guiding influence of the present lead us to nobler work in the future.

A Growing Sense of Responsibility

By Annie Damer, *president*
(Ninth Annual Convention, Detroit, June 5-7, 1906)

Time is an essential element in the development of strength and character in the individual, and the same is also true of the organization or union of individuals. We all have an important duty to perform in the promotion of our ideals. The Association is not the essential property of the president or officers, nor are they wholly responsible. The constant personal interest of all the members is needed, not merely as spectators but as cooperative workers. It has been said that women are unused to team play or responsibility, and we need to develop this spirit of cooperation. The broadening out means more burdens and more self-sacrifice, but, with confidence in our members and assurance that each will do her part, we can say that the years that lie before us will be years of service and bright promise as have been the past.

We welcome to-day six State Associations into affiliation. One from a state in the far west bearing to-day its burden of sorrow and loss, but with noble spirit of all its men and women,—that *nil desperandum* spirit, inherent, as its president says, in every native daughter, rising above disaster, with strengthened purpose to nobler and greater work.* One joins us from the southland with its own peculiar nursing problems, but the first among us to secure state registration. The others, some but lately organized, but each and all bringing their messages, their plans, their enthusiasm, and their assistance, to the mother organization. To these, with all the new associations of alumnae members, who are joining with us in furthering the efficient care of the sick, and advancing the educational standards of the nursing profession, we extend a hearty welcome. We meet here as a deliberative body, not a legislative, to discuss the matters which affect us as a profession, as women whose vital interest should be the health and the welfare of the nation. We meet that we may still broaden our outlook and be drawn into the fuller current of life out of our isolation and our self-interests, and gain the inspiration and stimulus which we feel each one of us needs.

What are some of the questions which are agitating the nursing world to-day? First of all, perhaps, state registration, which has been secured in eight of our States, in South Africa, in New

* Reference to the San Francisco earthquake.

Zealand and Australia, and lately in Germany, and which seems a little nearer adoption in England.

We hope at this meeting to have reports of the progress made by our affiliated state societies in this direction, and we hope also to give opportunity for informal discussion on matters of detail in our state work, formulation of uniform standards and rules, and for some practical suggestions to those who are in perplexity and encountering opposition in their work. In these efforts towards advancing and regulating our profession let all take part, not considering inclination, but duty; not offering criticism, but assistance; not silent when we should use our voices, nor idle when there is work to be done; each assuming her due share of responsibility, and all working together for the good of the whole, with clear sight as to our aim and vigorous determination as to action. In this extremely practical age we are often not inclined to listen to ideas of a not immediately practical nature. But are not these often the very ones which count most of all in our life? Our national organization should constantly keep before us an ideal. We want to develop the spirit of efficiency and to meet with success, but we want also to remember that these are only the means to the attainment of an end. Our aim! What should it be? To bring intelligent knowledge and service to bear upon the prevention of disease, and ability and willingness to give proper and efficient nursing care to all our sick in all the homes and all the institutions of our land. Does it occur to us that our opportunities and our resources, unless they are made the most of, become our reproach instead of our pride? We are proud of our foundations, our history, our accomplishments and acquiescent acceptance by the public, but let us, too, be working, working to make our real accomplishments the greater.

With the increase of our privileges there must be a growing sense of our responsibility as nurses. Can we say to the public that, as registered nurses to whom the state has certified it considers us efficient women fully fitted to care for its sick, that it is only its rich sick who can pay us well, and its poor sick who can pay us nothing, that we will undertake to nurse? Between them lie a great multitude entitled to the same nursing care as their richer and poorer brethren, but little attempt has been yet made to meet the needs of this large section of the community. Many suggestions have been made, but little definitely has as yet been worked out.

A suggestion has been made that hospital accommodation might be provided by the setting aside of a number of wards for the reception of patients able to pay a certain sum, and be supported in part by annual contributions given in consideration that the subscribers should be entitled to be admitted as patients upon further payment of a small weekly sum. This plan might be helpful to a large number now unable to enter as pay patients and unwilling to enter the free wards. It might also increase the number of subscribers. In these wards, too, might there not be opportunity to give the nurse special training for private duty and time for the little attentions which we are told the rush and work of the large hospital ward do not permit?

A home coöperative scheme has also been suggested by an English nurse, similar to that of the hospital plan, by the formation of a coöperative society of subscribers paying a fixed sum annually, whether sick or well, entitling them to the services of a nurse in sickness. This could be organized in connection with a nurse's registry, or independently, the nurses paid a fixed salary and boarding themselves when not at cases. Another plan being tried in one or two cities is that the nurse lowest on the registry list shall be sent to families unable to pay the highest fees, and being replaced as she rises to the top of the list.

The most feasible plan at present seems to be the system of hourly or visiting nursing. There are many places now where in this way a nurse is proving that her attentions for an hour or two daily are of inestimable benefit and where her services would not be called for in any other way. The great difficulty of providing accommodation for the nurse in city flats or small houses is often so great as to necessitate dispensing with her services altogether even if it were possible to pay for them. There seems no reason why the nurse should not make her daily calls as well as the doctor, and have the possibility of her own home and home life, which are so essential to her well-being. Cannot much of the dissatisfaction with private nursing and criticism of nurses be traced to this fact,—the crushing of her individuality? She is considered as a nurse, not a woman. Nursing, the work of women through all the ages, in mediaeval times the vocation of a chosen few, in these latter days one of the earliest openings for women to independence, still clings to the mediaeval idea of community life and rules for the nurse in training, and as one of the domestic attachments when her services are needed in the home. The conditions of her work both before and after graduation are so narrowing, so lacking in opportunity for contact with others, for friendship and living the normal free life of other women, that no wonder so many become dissatisfied with what is truly one of the most noble occupations for women.

We hope that some plan may be presented at this meeting which will meet a very real need, to give efficient nursing to those who need the services of the nurse, and are willing to pay according to their ability for them.

Training of District Nurses

The spread of district nursing might be touched upon and the need of the institution of a systematic and comprehensive arrangement for the training of district nurses. With the possibility of the Hospital Economics course no longer needing our financial support may we not bend our energies and give our means to establish in connection with one or more of our well-organized district nursing associations, a school where graduate nurses may be trained in district nursing during a six-months or one-year's course? So much is involved in the work, so much need of practical experience, so much knowledge of social conditions and ability to cope with the problems daily arising, that it is pitiable to see how often time, energy, money, and a woman's life are misspent for lack of this training. Working side by side and under the direction of experienced workers, learning their methods, being gradually introduced to and recognizing the value of coöperation, the right relation can be established and more effective work accomplished. From this school, workers might be sent to new fields of work without crippling the society, and women with valuable experience and ability become the pioneers in these fields rather than the women who have served no apprenticeship in this tremendously responsible field of nursing work.

Our training-schools, too, might add to their long lists of lectures a few on the causes of moral and physical deterioration, and the loss of life and ability to cope with life's problems caused by child labor and the unsanitary conditions of living and working of so many patients brought to our hospitals; the life of the poor in our tenements, in its moral, physical and social aspects, and the causes underlying the effects which we see there just a little time to learn the causes of all this sickness, how much of it is preventable as well as remediable, and not have it accepted as a matter of course.

The Responsibility to Study Nurse Education

As a body of professional women, who have undertaken the task of regulating the future status of nurses, it must be our responsibility also to study the whole question of the nurse's education, and to take an interest in the future of nurses yet untrained. Our state registration laws mean more than the registration of graduates; we must stand for and exact a certain standard of requirements from the schools which are preparing the nurses of the future, a definite and faithfully carried out system of instruction (not merely on paper as a possibility or future hope) by fully equipped and paid instructors, with classes and lectures given at proper hours, with sufficient vacation and hours of rest to keep up the nurse's fitness for her work. A great many of our nurses are trained for the work of the hospital and not for the work which most of us have to do after leaving it. The experience which we need is not to be gained by sending nurses out to private duty, but by lessening the ward work, the display work, and many of the unnecessary services demanded by the extravagance of the operating-room, and economies in other directions, so that more time may be given to little personal attentions to the patients and opportunity to know a little more of their daily lives and surroundings.

Many of our schools are now offering better educational advantages, and we as a profession should hold up their hands and give our support to the women at the head of these schools, who are trying to raise them to a true educational standing.

This old world of ours still suffers, more from charlatanism than from over-training in nursing as well as in other professions. The number of training-schools all over the world is increasing at such a rate that sufficient numbers of probationers cannot be secured to keep the hospitals staffed, and undesirable women from the standpoint of nursing qualifications have to be retained because they cannot be spared from the wards. What sort of medical schools would we have if each hospital could maintain one attended by such students as would be willing to spend thirty-six solid months in the hospital wards, often in the doing over and over again of tasks utterly superfluous to their training, with a smattering and irregular course of theoretical instruction?

If we cannot yet have the large central schools, providing nurses for a number of hospitals, let us strive most mightily for the affiliation of schools each of which will supplement the work of the other.

Let us plead, too, in the days of new ideas regarding woman's position, for a more natural home life for our pupil nurses. In the preparation for other professions now open to women there are no such limitations and restrictions as those which bind the nurse. The conventual mode of life, with its combination of conventual and military discipline, may have been thought necessary in the days when a woman never left the shelter of her home except to enter another or become a member of a sisterhood, but now, when women teachers, women ministers, and doctors, and lawyers, are all successfully entering upon their life's work after a system of preparation entirely different from ours, yet equally equipped for it, while their home life has been controlled by themselves, can we say that our schools are sending out women of greater intelligence or skill, of higher moral character or attainment? Might not every feature of this school life be so organized and directed as to lead the pupil to self-determined habits of thought and action, the policy such as to stimulate self-direction under the larger freedom supposed to be granted self-respecting women to think for themselves, to morally look after themselves, and so develop the elements of strong character and helpfulness?

It has been said that men first unite to protest against a grievance or resist oppression; the next form is union for the betterment of their own condition; later they come to the stage of altruism or union for the sake of others. Increasing recognition is being given in these days to the solidarity of woman's interests, and the nurse who is asking rights for herself must not forget that to whom much is given of her also much shall be required.

The nurse with her trained skill, her knowledge of conditions, who sees at close range the direct results of these conditions, should be an interested and powerful factor in the work of women for the betterment of the community. She sees the evil effects of child labor, she knows the consequences following the improper care of mother and child in the period of infancy, and the effect upon the mother who continues at work in the mill or the factory up to and following childbirth,—so is not her place among those who are working for the prevention of these ills? There is a great work to be done, and the field is limitless and inviting.

The old ideas are changing with regard to sickness, just as there is a marked alteration in the attitude of people in their conceptions of the causes of poverty. Both have been considered, if not necessary evils, certainly unavoidable ones, and that all our efforts could only be palliative. We preach now the gospel of prevention of sickness as well as of poverty and pauperism; and in our work we must take cognizance of their fundamental causes, such as ignorance, exploitation of labor and defects in governmental supervision of the welfare of citizens.

A well-known leader in charitable work said recently that if the efforts of the community were to be directed toward the removal of these causes, the time may come when we may begin to contemplate the destruction of charitable institutions, instead of their increase. We find ignorance not only among the poor, but among all classes, of the simplest rules for healthy living, of the proper hygienic and sanitary requirements of the home, and the selection and preparation of food. We find little children working in our southern cotton-mills, in our mines in Pennsylvania, in glass-factories in New Jersey, and in factories in New York and Illinois. When we are called to a mother in a tenement who has broken down striving to support her little family on thirty or fifty cents a day, making the garments which some of us may later be wearing, can we say this is not our concern, ours only to restore them to their former condition that the work may go on again?

The regulation of buildings in our cities, inspection of houses and factories, pure food laws, laws to safeguard the child, are manifestations of awakened interest toward the necessity of safeguarding our citizens against disease and future inefficiency, and the call comes to us nurses to bring our knowledge and our skill, our interest and our influence, to support all the good work where workers are so badly needed, and to further it with all our strength and earnestness.

May our ideals become realities in our lives, real and rational and vital, bearing witness to those best things in which we desire to live.

May we stand for the best and highest in our schools, for an education which will be the best preparation for the opportunities that await us, fitting us for service wherever there is need.

In striving for that Utopia that men have dreamed of in all the ages, when sickness and sorrow shall be no more known, may we too be of those who count in strengthened purpose, with clearer vision, and adequate conception of the work before us.

Sarah Constants

By Annie Damer, *president*
(Tenth Annual Convention, Richmond, May 14-16, 1907)

I approach you, friends and members, with somewhat of diffidence in presenting what may be called my annual address. Sitting at our desks, far away from the busy world of affairs, we think very differently about our work than we do when we come in contact with the force and vitality and interest of the nursing profession. So I want to speak to you to-day very informally on one or two subjects we are talking about in our Association, and things that seem to be floating about in the corridors at this Convention. I have left my written address in my trunk, and I want to talk to you face to face about some of these problems.

This is our tenth annual meeting. The inspiration for this organization was given at the meeting of the superintendents, held in Chicago at the time of the World's Fair. The matter was discussed for a year or two, and in 1897 our Association was organized. I hold in my hand the report of that Convention. There were eighteen people present; a few of them came there individually, women who were interested, and some of them came as delegates from alumnae associations.

I think at that time there were not more than thirty associations organized in the whole country. At the time of the Chicago meeting, I believe only about eighteen had been discovered; they were not known, they had to be searched out. Perhaps you would like to hear the names of those who were present at the first annual meeting, in Baltimore, 1897.

Members present: M. B. Brown, the Massachusetts General; L. L. Dock, Secretary and Chairman Constitutional Convention (Bellevue); Edith Draper, formerly of the Royal Victoria (Bellevue); Isabel McIsaac, the Brooklyn City (Bellevue); Isabel McIsaac, the Illinois; Anna Maxwell, the Presbyterian, New York; Adelaide Nutting, the Johns Hopkins; Mrs. Hunter Robb, Cleveland, Ohio (Bellevue); M. A. Snively, the Toronto General (Bellevue).

Several of those members are with us at this meeting.

The delegates from alumnae associations of training-schools for nurses were: Phebe Brown, from the Illinois; Laura Healy, from the Brooklyn City; Ella Clapp, from the New Haven; Mrs. J. R. Hawley, from the Philadelphia; Margaret A. Mullen, from the Garfield; Helena Barnard, from the Johns Hopkins; M. W. Stevenson, from the Massachusetts General; C. Borden, from the Farrand; Lena H. Walden, from the New York.

All that was reported of the proceedings of that Convention was the adoption of the constitution and by-laws and the appointment of officers. This was our inspiration and our meeting of organization. At the meeting five years later at Buffalo, at the time of the exposition there, we took a step in advance, and branched out into the international work, affiliating ourselves with the foreign societies and taking a greater interest in the broader work of nursing. From then on we have discussed very little of our local alumnae work; we have taken up the state organization and the national work more. Now we meet again at the time of the Jamestown Exposition for our tenth annual meeting. What is to be our inspiration and what is to be the keynote of this Convention?

Just three hundred years ago, the day before yesterday, three little ships sailed up what is now called the James River. The names of those ships were the *Discovery*, the *God-Speed*, and the *Sarah Constant*; names which are perhaps not so familiar to us as that of the *Mayflower*, which made a mistake when it was sailing for the Virginia shore and landed its passengers a good deal further north. That was in the year 1607, and a few years afterwards there were settlements all over this part of the country. In this Henrico county where Richmond now is, five years after that, long before the Pilgrims reached Plymouth Rock, there was a hospital. Bricks for that hospital came from England, and eighty good beds were also sent out from England for the patients. We do not know just where that hospital was situated, but as far as our knowledge goes, it was the first hospital established in what is now the United States of America, in the year 1612.

So it seems that Virginia was the mother, not only of commonwealths, but of hospitals. We do not know what kind of nurses they had here in those days, but we feel sure that in all probability the patients were well taken care of. I mention these things to give us a particular interest in this locality as far as we are concerned as nurses.

The name of one of those little ships has appealed to me,—the *Sarah Constant,*—and it seemed to me a good name for nurses, and in our work we might look upon that, not so much as we know it, as a material thing, but as a memory and an inspiration, as it was to the early colonists.

That little ship was probably not more than one hundred and eighty feet long; it was built very crudely as we consider now, carrying very few passengers. The little settlement at Jamestown soon disappeared; it is said that it was because there were so few women among the settlers, and few homes were established. But the settlements grew and prospered, animated by a common spirit and purpose, and they accomplished what they undertook. Tolerance, loyalty, broad-mindedness, thoroughness in educational matters characterized them, and it is no coincidence that so many of the leaders of the Revolution came from among the descendants of these early Virginian settlers.

From the little local work of building up the homes of Jamestown, just as we began in building up the work of our alumnae associations, they broadened out to the development of their commonwealth, they established their hospitals, and in 1619, I believe, they had made appropriations for a university.

What are we going to do about establishing a school for the training of the women who are going to be the teachers of our profession? If they began their work in those few years when they had all the difficulties of pioneers in a new country to encounter, isn't it time that we began work towards our university? We have talked about it for some time.

Another matter in which we have made the discovery of the need of coöperation is the Red Cross work. We have had the Red Cross association in the United States for a number of years; it was recently reorganized and put upon a better basis. The Red Cross calls upon us nurses in its work in many ways. They wish to be prepared, they wish to have the right kind of nurses in coöperation with them. They have agreed that in those states where we have state registration, they will only enlist nurses who are registered; they are willing to conform to our standards, but they ask that we endorse their work and enter our names upon a list of Red Cross nurses. It has been suggested that we ask the state associations to coöperate in this matter, to form auxiliary societies among their members, or have committees appointed, who will enroll nurses for the Red Cross work. We will call upon some speakers during the meeting who will go further into detail. Ohio is very well organized in that respect, and California has recently started an auxiliary, I think, in the state association, but I will ask some of the California delegates later to explain their plan in detail.

We also, as nurses, should be interesting ourselves more in questions of Public Health. In our schools, are the children being taught as they should be the subject of Hygiene? It was suggested last year that we ought to impress in an official way upon the educational departments of the states and cities, the necessity for more clear and practical instruction of children in anatomy and physiology, and all questions of importance concerning hygiene. None know better than we do the result of this lack of teaching, or understand better the importance of it. I think this knowledge should be brought before these people, and the children should have the right kind of instruction.

Apart from that, as we can be a telling force in the community, we should join in the discussion of all the wider and more important questions of the cities and states. The tuberculosis movement is not receiving our support as it should. The nurses have been going forward in it everywhere; they have been enrolling themselves as individuals, but we can give more impetus to the work. It is not always financial assistance that is required, but we have the knowledge, we see the results of the lack of information, and we can tell better than any one else the effect of it. I would like to see in our association a public health committee, that would take up all of these subjects, and I hope that we will take as much time as possible for those topics, and that you will all be interested enough to discuss them fully. We must not concern ourselves too much with our own affairs; we have broader duties as women who know these things. While we are bound together to take care of the sick, taking care of the well is certainly just as important.

The Situation in the Training Schools

Another matter that seems to be pressing upon us very closely is the situation in our training-schools, because on that depends not only the welfare of the sick in our hospitals, but the future of our profession. We look back perhaps a very few years; our trained nursing work is not so very old, the discovery of that need was not so very long ago (it does not go back as far as the discovery of America). The situation was very different then from now; we had a few hospitals, training-schools were new, there were many applicants after the first few years, women who were anxious for a vocation did not find very many openings outside of their own homes. Now, all over the country, we find there is a lack of suitable applicants for training-schools. What is the reason for it? Our *Journal* gives a great many, but they might be emphasized again. The sick have to be cared for, the number of hospitals is increasing, the public is taking a greater interest in them, and the sick people cannot be properly nursed if they do not have enough nurses in those hospitals. We may say that that question is not to be settled by the training-schools, but it is on them now that the hospital depends for the nursing of its patients. We do not believe that the work in the hospitals should be done by the raw recruits continually, the awkward squad cannot be expected to do the best work; they cannot do it! We need more qualified graduate nurses in our hospitals. Does that depend upon us, or does it depend upon the public, or does it depend upon the hospital itself? Perhaps it depends a little on all of us.

One reason why there are now so few applicants for training-schools is that where there were only one or perhaps two occupations open to women twenty-five years ago, now there are hundreds. But apart from all outside causes which lessen the number of applicants there are certain reasons that are identified with the training-school itself; and it seems to me, as graduates of these schools, the alumnae societies represented here, whose names imply that they are interested in the work of their alma maters, should consider these reasons, and see if some effort cannot be made by us as alumnae societies to improve these conditions and make them more favorable for probationers.

I think the time has come for us to speak pretty plainly. Some of you may say, "these are not the conditions in our training-school." Perhaps not; but I know they are the conditions in a great many schools. A representative of the department of public instruction in Albany, stated to the board of examiners recently that there was not a training-school in New York State worthy, educationally, of the name. Now we think we have several hundred, but he states that he does not think there is a real *training-school* in the whole United States. What we call training-schools, he calls an apprentice system. The probationers go in there, they are expected to work their way all through the course, there is very little time given them for study—that is what he meant; that they were doing little of what he called laboratory and experimental work. Sometimes they do not have time to learn even by experience. The work is hard. In the early days those of us who went into training-schools expected it as a matter of course; we looked upon it as a vocation; we sacrificed a great deal—or our friends thought we did—when we went into the training-schools, they looked upon us as if we were entering a convent, or going off to die somewhere.

The situation is very different now. Young women enter the profession of nursing the same as they do any other occupation, if they desire that work, but the conditions remain about the same as to the long hours, and the work has probably increased. The home life is better, the hospital authorities realize that nurses must not be relegated into an upper story, six or ten in a room, although it is sometimes still done. They realize in some cases that the nurse must be properly fed if she is to do her work, and still in many instances they are not waking up to the necessity of it. The nurses are called upon to do such work as no woman outside is called upon to do, and to work often for from twelve to eighteen hours a day. We have committees for the prevention of overwork of women and children all over the country, but they have not begun to consider the nurses in the training-schools yet. I think that every nurse in a training-school is working as hard as any woman is in a factory, and she is working at night too. The sick demand care in the night as well as in the day, but we should have our hours better regulated.

Now perhaps you all know that there is a wave of retroaction sweeping over the country in regard to the course in the training-schools being three years instead of two. Some years ago, it was the object of the superintendents, by increasing the course to three years, to lessen the work in the wards. The New York State Association last year sent a circular letter throughout the state and found, with perhaps one exception, that the time was being maintained in the same way, that the hours were not lessened, and the vacations were not increased. I know of one school where, in the whole three years' course, a nurse is very happy if she gets two weeks; she has other vacations when she breaks down and is unable to work, and has to make up that time. We found that very few changes had been made in the curriculum, that very little effort had been made to give more hours for study and instruction to nurses. The hospitals have found that there is a lessening number of applicants, and some of them are intending to return to the two years' course, hoping that will be an inducement for more pupils to enter.

I think this is a subject that might be brought up for discussion. It is not altogether a question of the advisability of the two years' course or the three years' course, whether it is necessary that a nurse shall spend two years or three years in the training-school. Some medical men claim that she learns all that she needs to know in two years; in fact, they think she can learn all they want her to know in one year. They claim that the nurses are being taught too much; some of them say there is no need for the nurses studying anatomy, or physiology or bacteriology. But if we are to believe the reports published in the newspapers, the medical examining boards claim that out of every four thousand doctors turned out of the colleges annually, three thousand are not qualified to practice, and that these doctors are not taught anatomy and bacteriology enough to diagnose a case of typhoid fever.

Those are merely reports, but if true they show that progressive physicians are dissatisfied with the conditions of medical education, as we are with conditions of nursing education. We feel that the better educated a woman is before she goes into a hospital, and the better teaching and training she can have while she is there, the better she is fitted for a nurse, no matter where she is placed, whether under the most efficient doctor, or the most inefficient.

But we do want such education for our nurses as will fit them best for what they may be called upon to do. How are we going to get that? We cannot get that if our nurses work the long hours they do in the hospitals; they are totally unfitted, after their hard work they have during the day, to study. An effort has been made to establish preparatory schools. Some hospitals have established them. We hope that some day we will have them apart from the hospitals, where the nurses can be taught the beginnings of their work, and where they can be taught household economics. The nurses cannot be taught to be housekeepers in the training-schools; it cannot all be done there. As Mrs. Robb has said, it goes back to the home. Our work is so identified with the home, the demands of the home are constantly made upon us. The greater part of nursing work is done in the home, only the beginning of it is done in the hospitals, and the rush work in the wards does not allow for that training. In speaking of these needs of our training-schools, I want to place them before you for this reason, that we represent the alumnae societies, and we ought to take greater interest in the work of our training-schools, and not feel that when we leave the school we are done with it, perhaps with regret, and perhaps with gladness. But we must realize that the women who come out of those training-schools we have to accept as members of our profession, whether we will or no.

If we want the right kind of women in our profession, we must do something to make our training-schools what we want them to be. We should ask for representation on the boards of management of those training-schools. Who knows better than the nurse what kind of training should be given in the training-schools, and what is wanted by the public outside? I think we are entitled to it. As nurses who have studied the situation for years and know what is required, we ought to help in every way possible to establish such a system in our schools. I have spoken very disconnectedly, but I wanted to speak looking into your faces, and throw out a few suggestions for your future discussion. We ought all to be interested in the future of nursing.

Let us all be "*Sarah Constants,*" and be as patriotic as those old settlers were. They recognized the great needs of their people, they built for future generations. Some of us are descendants of those old settlers in Virginia, and many claim to be descendants of those who settled further north. Most of us are probably Americans because we could not help ourselves, but a good many of us are Americans of our own free will and choice, just as those early pioneers wished to come where they could have a greater freedom and a greater opportunity for development. May we also be as patriotic as they were, and followers of theirs in establishing all things needed for our profession.

The Need for a Representative Association

By Annie Damer, R.N., *president*
(Twelfth Annual Convention, Minneapolis, June 10-11, 1909)

Our association is getting to be a very big child. We have fifteen thousand members, and we are constantly growing, and it seems that as a national body we should have a more clear and definite form of organization. Whether we can best do that by making some changes in our present organization, or whether we can carry out the work under the American Federation of Nurses is the question. Both have been suggested. I recommend that in order to secure an organization which shall stand as a great national body, a body with power and authority delegated to it by state societies, that shall stand for the things for which we as nurses desire to stand, for which we are working, which shall embody the ideals for which we are striving, that we should form in some way an association which shall include all our state societies or clubs, and take the name of "National Federation" or something that will imply to everybody that we are a national body.

You will find that the name of "Associated Alumnae" is not clear in the minds of the people and not clear to us, because we always speak of ourselves as a national body. The suggestion has been made that the Superintendents' Society affiliate with us and that we have one national society. It appears to me that that would not be possible, and I do not believe it would meet with the approval of the Superintendents' Society. Their membership is individual and their work through the secretary has to be carried on with individual women. Our organization is composed of

Note: Miss Damer spoke extemporaneously to delegates attending the eleventh annual convention in 1908. As a result, no record was made of her remarks.

clubs and associations and the secretary's work lies with associations. But we could reorganize so that instead of having three national associations we could have two national bodies. From the trend of the discussion at our Federation meeting it would seem there was growing up the idea that the Federation was a national body, with judicial powers and authority as a national organization, which it has not. The American Federation of Nurses was organized in order to affiliate with the International Society. That was the sole object. It holds these conferences in connection with the other two societies and forces these two societies to assume the expense of the meeting, which does not seem exactly fair to the Superintendents' Society that they should have to share equally in carrying on the convention. As time goes on it may seem necessary to hold meetings of that general body, meetings which will continue over more than one day. Our Nurses' Associated Alumnae is growing in interest so that it would seem almost as though we would have to have meetings lasting a week if we are to have any papers presented at all. The committee work is most valuable, the interest shown all over the country is great, and the desire to do something is increasing continually, and it seems to me the most important thing we can do is to organize into a national body, and if there is a sentiment about keeping the name of "American Federation" as it is now, let us take some other name and let us affiliate with the other national association. If the Superintendents' Society does not want to come in, although it would seem much easier for one society to affiliate than for two hundred societies to withdraw from the Associated Alumnae and then apply for affiliation with the national association, it would seem best to keep up the organization of this society.

Then we might go further into details. Some very valuable suggestions have been made as to changes in the by-laws, which are necessary. In regard to permanent membership with this national body, that should be recognized on an entirely individual basis. That question can be taken up later for discussion.

Whether the alumnae association remain as a basis of membership can also be determined. There is need and a demand for a national body which is to represent the nurses of the country, which is to give them judicial power and a definite standing before the public as to nursing ideals and work. We do need, either in printed form or some other form, a code of ethics. This is particularly necessary with regard to our relation to the medical profession. The relation in which we stand to them, the relation of our connection with medical work and hospital work, and the objects for which we stand in regard to teaching, the instruction of nurses, our ethical relation as one body to another, and our relation as nurses to one another, and it seems to me we should have a committee to discuss with the medical society committee from each state the establishment of some satisfactory basis of our relations to one another. All these questions come up and we have got to meet them. We are too large a body to go along as we have been going. We have been growing, and now we have reached a stage of growth where we are in a position and in need of formulating something more definite than we are now working under.

We want to take some definite step in regard to our national *Journal.* At the last meeting your society agreed to offer to buy the shares of stock held by individuals and give notes. This suggestion was made on account of the stringent money market and on account of making pledges to the Hospital Economics course, and they did not think it would be advisable or desirable to ask for money to purchase *Journal* stock. The suggestion was made to the owners that they sell their stock and take notes, and as you see we have secured only six shares. The directors would suggest that these notes be taken up during the year from the balance in our treasury. You should also decide whether you wish to raise the money in some form to purchase the remainder of the stock and therefore own the *Journal.*

All through our meetings there has been an evidence of the feeling of unrest among women, and in some cases they have come out openly with a demand for the ballot, and in view of this situation I want to make a plea for the enfranchisement of one class of women, and that is the pupil nurses in our training schools. We are gradually taking the ground that it is woman's place to take part in the affairs of government and the making of laws. We see on many sides women and children being abused and overworked, but we must consider that there is one class of women for whom we can do something as a great body of professional women. We can help the women working in our schools to secure a better adjustment of the hours of labor in our schools. We had a beautiful illustration given us yesterday of the ideals along those lines which we hope to see realized throughout the country. Let us come to the help of those who are striving to make some changes in that respect.

We have had this discussion on the subject of moral prophylaxis, and it has been demonstrated that we, as nurses, know very little about it ourselves; how can we go to the legislature and ask for laws when we know nothing about the subject? We want it taught in our schools and we want to learn a great deal more about it than we do now. We want it felt in our training schools. I am giving my own opinion as a graduate nurse because my whole point of view has been from the position of the graduate nurse.

In going back to the beginning of our training schools I see women who have gone into these schools from their homes. They are not accepted until they are of age, but when they enter such schools they are established in a conventual life, with a strict adherence to military discipline, and when we come out and ask that women be given some share in the national government, let us ask that in our schools our women who are of age may be permitted something along the line of self government, and teach them to govern themselves when they go out as women to take a position in the community. In seeking the ideals for the protection of womanhood we have got to be taught that we have to be self-governing ourselves. I do wish to appeal most earnestly in this matter, and I also wish to say that it is a question which must be taken up by our educational organizations. It is the graduate nurse that is making the laws for registration, which we have now in twenty-three states. I believe it is a question for the graduate nurses, for their national organization to discuss all these matters relating to the improvement of the nurse for her future life, if they have to accept her as one of their members likewise.

I feel very strongly, fellow members, on this subject. When you are asked to begin work for the enfranchisement of women, begin it right at home.

1902-1905

Mary M. Riddle

A graduate of the Boston City Hospital Training School, Mary Riddle served the hospital school in various capacities for 17 years, including assistant superintendent of nursing. Miss Riddle was an early president of the Boston City Hospital Nurses' Alumnae Association, which she worked to establish.

In addition, Miss Riddle was president of the National League of Nursing Education (1910), the Massachusetts Nurses' Association (1903-1910), and the Massachusetts Board of Examiners (1910-1926). Miss Riddle was also a lecturer in the hospital economics course at Teachers College, New York, in its pioneer period, and served the *American Journal of Nursing* as a board member, treasurer, and editor.

Miss Riddle died on November 19, 1936.

Proper Nurse Training

By Mary M. Riddle, *president*
(Sixth Annual Convention, Boston, June 10-12, 1903)

The wheel of progress in nursing matters began in this country about ten years ago to move with greatly accelerated force, and while its rotation has thus far been guarded and safe, it has disseminated knowledge and with knowledge power, until to-day nurses are reasoning upon all schemes for the betterment of their work and enlargement of their opportunities. Heedless of the fact that by the multiplication of opportunities responsibilities are increased, they yet push on and on, demanding more and more of those advantages which, when gained, ultimately call for more and more diligence on their part.

In proof of this, witness the desire of the average nurse for three or more years of training, which, though they are arduous in the extreme, she deems necessary as a proper equipment for her work.

Also witness the new movement among nurses—namely, that for State registration, which will certainly not permit careless methods in either preparation for or the practice of their profession. Surely these changes do not indicate an ease-loving body of women. Furthermore, it is a significant fact that these improvements are not the results of suggestions from the public or the patrons of the nurse, but have in all instances originated with her, the public, as a rule, acquiescing by reason of ignorance or negligence.

But we must not indulge too long in exultation, however honest it may be; rather let us turn to the leading reflections to which this occasion seems to invite us, regarding the objects old and new of our existence, the manner in which we have fulfilled them, and the instructions required along new lines.

Believing that we must educate or perish, it is avowedly one of our purposes to elevate the standard of nursing education. This principle was ever before the founders of our organization, and they have already left visible fruits of their work in the longer period now required for the training of nurses, and in that noble enterprise from which has grown *The American Journal of Nursing*. This is all our own—conceived in the Associated Alumnae, fostered by its members, managed and edited by members, it has risen to a condition of success that is almost dazzling in its brilliancy. But just at this point lies our danger, that of relaxation of endeavor. The success of the *Journal* must be maintained, but will not be without our combined efforts. At our last annual meeting it was decided that each delegate should obtain a certain number of new subscriptions, and by a vote we each gave a pledge so to do—how well those pledges were redeemed may be known only to the individual members.

The enthusiasm of the launching of the enterprise has passed—we now require the gift of continuance in industry. Therefore let every alumna feel it her duty to make a personal effort for the support and more extensive circulation of the *Journal*. It is to be hoped that our Magazine Committee will suggest to us some method by which we may consider ourselves organized into a committee of the whole for that purpose.

The Need for an Enlarged Curriculum

A greatly enlarged curriculum in most of our schools for nurses is also an outgrowth of the determination to elevate the standard of nursing education. Indications seem to say that the school not having the system of university education will soon be the exception, and will find its powers of attraction in inverse ratio to its needs.

The establishment of the course in hospital economics at Columbia University is another result of the desire for elevation. It has heretofore been supported largely by contributions from individual superintendents of training-schools and the Society of Superintendents as a whole. It has certainly been a practical illustration of devotion to a principle for the superintendents so to do, but it is a task which, though self-imposed, they should no longer be allowed to bear alone, and the question naturally arises whether our resources are sufficient to enable us to be of service in the support and promulgation of this course. We may not be justified in thinking that we can draw upon our treasury for any appreciable amount, but do we not represent force and intelligence enough to solve this problem of home missionary work of our own peculiar kind? Have we not among us some loyal, earnest spirits who shall arise within the next two days and suggest the means for the accomplishment of this purpose? It cannot be done without sacrifice of time and strength and money.

The need of adequate post-graduate advantages is an urgent

one, and is to-day more than ever making demands for its satisfaction.

It is not the province of the Associated Alumnae to dictate to the schools their duty in this direction, but might we not be allowed to remind them of that which it is expedient for them to undertake?

Lest many good, practical women be lost to the profession and themselves suffer loss of resources, it behooves us to consider the matter seriously, because the graduate of ten or more years' service in private duty is now considered by the medical profession as belonging to another era, and consequently no longer fit for the more delicate, intricate, and scientific parts of a nurse's work.

We have also by our constitution placed ourselves on record as proposing to promote the *honor* and usefulness of the nursing profession. Possibly nothing sheds more real honor upon our fidelity to this trust than the so-called Army Bill—an act of Congress which placed the trained nurse in service in the army. It may be argued that the nurses were not responsible for this—that their bill did not pass, etc. Granting the truth of some of these claims, we yet assert—and our assertion will doubtless be maintained, even by the most bitter partisan of the opposition—that the passage of the Army Bill was due to the importunity of the nurses.

The election of nurses upon School Boards, as has been done in England, increases their influence in large measure.

The establishment of the position of the school nurse in the city of New York was a long step in advance, and not only increased her usefulness to a vast extent, but multiplied by an untold number the advantages to be derived by the families represented in the schools, and we may expect to see an appreciable diminution in the devastation by contagious diseases as one of the results of her well-timed service.

Again, the usefulness of the trained nurse has been greatly extended in those cities and towns where she has been placed upon Boards of Inspection for tenement houses. Unfortunately, Boards of Health resent her appearance in such work, but they are led to assume the defensive because they fail to understand the real intent and purpose of the nurse. As time goes on and more and more cities make trial of the nurses' services as tenement-house inspectors, and as the nurses prove their efficiency, all animosities will disappear and she will be welcomed to that place as to every other that has called her. Meantime much will be done to overcome prejudice and hasten the day of her kind reception in that sphere if our brothers can be made to understand that we are not supplanting them, but simply asking to be permitted to do the work hitherto left undone or improperly done.

We are proud of our affiliation with other women workers in the National Council of Women, but being a body with no leisure, we have as yet realized little from this connection. Large activities and wholesome growth call for great expenditures of time, and doubtless as we become more able to work with the National Council of Women we shall be benefited in proportion, for there can be no exception to the rule that our greatest personal benefits come through our efforts in behalf of others.

There are hopes also that there is a new avenue opening for the usefulness of the trained nurse. Few will be called to walk therein,—none but the strong and well-equipped,—and when nurses take their places upon Boards of Examiners for the State registration of members of their own profession, as they are sure to do, our hopes will be fully realized.

Maintaining a Code of Ethics

Never in the history of nursing have there come times so auspicious for progress and betterment as these through which we are now passing. To us is given the opportunity to turn them to advantage. May we be wise and wide awake, that it may not pass unimproved.

We have as one of our avowed purposes that of maintaining a 'code of ethics.' In this we have been found wanting. We have looked well to our educational and commercial advantages, but little thought has been spent upon our ethical culture, and this is not because we have not those among us who could and would be our leaders and teachers, neither is it because of the scarcity of apt pupils for the teachers, but because we of the rank and file do not ask for instruction along these lines. There is a vagueness—even a mystery—surrounding the term 'ethics' which causes the average nurse to turn away and wait for another to ask the first question or make the first demand.

It has been said by our critics that by reason of this deficiency we improperly call ourselves members of a profession, that members of all other professions gladly share their professional advantages, that they are willing to give as well as to receive, etc.

It cannot be said that we are more selfish; it must be that we have not been sufficiently enlightened as to our own needs. We do believe, however, it is the want of an ethical sense in some of our members that is placing the trained nurse under the ban of a critical public. Truly the public is often unjust in condemning the whole nursing body for the sins of the individual, but we must bear it and in time overcome it.

In 1902 we placed ourselves on record as believing in the necessity for the preliminary education of nurses and pledged ourselves to work for it. We now know that in some communities are already found secular institutions undertaking this new work, while a few courageous schools for nurses have initiated it for their own benefit. May success attend all their efforts, and may we by our sympathy and deliberations in convention receive from them some encouragement and impetus which shall act and react upon the waste places until every alumna, every superintendent, every candidate, and every member of a training-school committee shall be an ardent believer in preliminary instruction for nurses.

Both extremities of a nurse's training are now under consideration, and they are the two burning issues of the time—preliminary education and State registration. Apparently these must be found upon every banner; they must be the rallying-cry of all our forces until that time shall come when they are an established fact for every training school and in every State.

Preliminary or other education of nurses—that which educates for the care of the diseased body and mind—does not include that which is conducted by correspondence and which pretends, without a practical application, to fit women in the ease and quiet of their own homes to properly care for the sick and disabled. Such sham methods, whose advertisements may be found on the pages of our leading periodicals, must be discountenanced.

Neither can those schools without a physician or trained nurse on their boards of teachers properly *begin* the instruction of nurses. They may be able to impart much valuable information and put their students in the way of acquiring knowledge that is useful to a nurse, and which she would do well to gratefully accept, but they can never even begin a nurse's training. We have not to look beyond our most limited horizon to realize the truth of this—it is taught us by the experiences of every-day life and is easily perceivable through our common-sense. What technical school looks to one who is merely a good teacher of English to instruct its students in chemistry or the mechanical arts? Is not a practical chemist called to teach chemistry and a practical bridge-builder to teach bridgebuilding? How then should nursing be taught? Your answer, by inference, can be but one—*by nurses.*

For securing State registration, of whose progress you will hear in this convention, we of the States in which it is yet but a new question must gird our armor on and with infinite tact and with charity towards all press on for the accomplishment of that which will secure for the nurse a legal status never heretofore enjoyed.

In this we will undoubtedly be aided by the experience of the pioneers in the work, who have already obtained recognition from their State governments and are now prepared to put to the practical test the theories for which they labored so strenuously.

Besides all these which are peculiarly our own incentives to effort for our profession there are yet many others which demand our careful thought, but whose consideration at length must be omitted here by reason of the want of time and space.

Work on sociological lines should be encouraged in the local alumnae associations. Ways and means of preparing for the future should receive some attention, and this preparation should include something more than the provision for the wants of the body. Since our work is particularly absorbing, our tendency is to become more and more unfit for the ordinary walks of life, and to eventually find ourselves stranded upon the bleak shores of time without so much as an occupation. Hence, in all our preparations for the future, it is well that to provide resources for spending time be not neglected.

Present achievements in nursing matters far exceed the expectations of Florence Nightingale or Pastor Fliedner. Even the dreams of our founders are overshadowed by the brilliancy of the realities accomplished.

We have many incitements to duty, but not one to doubt. Our history and our condition, all that is gone before us and all that is with us, justify our belief that as the trusts committed to our care are sacred, so we may hope for all things of the future.

Charting a Course for Nursing

By Mary M. Riddle, *president*

(Seventh Annual Convention, Philadelphia, May 12-14, 1904)

At this, our seventh annual meeting, we hope to redeem our obligations to our profession in *general*, and in *particular* to that great body we represent, the Nurses' Associated Alumnae of the United States.

We are here assembled to renew our acquaintance with one another and to welcome the new associations that have joined our ranks since last we convened, and as we extend to them the right hand in greeting, we do not hesitate to offer a portion of the work we bear in the other hand.

Many problems call for our earnest and thoughtful deliberation, and judging from the audience before me, I conclude that the local alumnae societies realized this and sent a full representation to attend to the work before us.

Perhaps the question now most thoroughly enlisting the attention of nurses all over the land is that of registration by the State. The manner of its accomplishment in the various States depends upon the laws and customs of those States.

It is difficult in one State because the Executive fears to sanction the law lest it give too much power to a body of women; it is restrained in another by reason of the jealousy of a commission, created for a wholly different purpose, that sees in the passage of the nurses bill an opportunity for widening its own sphere, and sees it so plainly as to have an influence with legislators and cause grave fears among the nurses that their bill might become a law, and that they might be placed under a commission which would render their position in the State much less desirable than before. So grave were the fears of those nurses that a small, self-constituted committee sought an interview with his Excellency the Governor and expressed to him the hope that he would kindly veto their bill if it were presented to him during the present session of the Legislature, with the result that that bill is laid over until another year. Thus might be repeated instances of struggles, successes, and defeats wherever nurses are working for State registration.

It would seem that the time for advocating the necessity for State registration has passed; but evidently it has not, or every nurse in the United States would be found working for it. Realizing this fact, your Executive Committee decided to devote a large part of the programme of this convention to that subject; and therefore you will save its principles presented to you from points of view both old and new, all of which you are urged to earnestly consider, judiciously weigh, and conscientiously practise in your homes during the coming year.

We can take with us into our consideration of the question the fact—that in the material things of life those who have conquered have always been they who have ventured into the unknown. Of one thing we may be sure—the preliminary course for nurses is bound to be established sooner or later, and if we do it ourselves, we believe it will be well done.

A very real indication of the trend of public opinion towards the importance of the nurse's work is found in the prominence given wherever philanthropic or social workers meet in council, an illustration of which will be seen when the National Conference of Charities and Correction is held in Portland during the week of June 15 and gives a large part of its time and programme to the work of the visiting and district nurses.

We shall also have another fine illustration of this fact when the International Council of Women meets in Berlin next month for the consideration of ways and means for the betterment of humanity and gives largely of its time and space to questions which pertain to the work of the nurse. Loyal, energetic women all over the world are thus banded together for the promotion of the common weal.

We, through our membership in the American Federation of Nurses, belong to the National Council of Women and thus to the International Council. We are to be represented in the congress in Berlin, where energy of mind, genius, power, will speak in many tongues which the world will hear and heed.

It will be our pleasure later, in convention assembled, to send to them some greeting. We wish to show our sympathy for that great body of women, "endeavoring to comprehend in all its magnitude, and to feel in all its importance, the part assigned to them in the great drama of human affairs."

That they may arrive at conclusions which shall formulate plans for the continued betterment of mankind is our earnest hope and sincere belief; for they, by their works and influence upon affairs,—local, national, and international,—have gained a vantage-ground from whence success must be eventually won.

As a convention we have among the obligations devolving upon as that of reconstructing the by-laws governing the conduct of this association. Happily, the constitution was fixed last year. Doubtless most of you have given the matter some thought and gained much information, as opportunities have been presented you for so doing in your own nursing *Journal.*

You will recall the eloquent appeal made in our last annual meeting for the continuance of high standards in the Associated Alumnae, also the fact that the appeal was appreciated and sanctioned by the assembly.

Eligibility for Membership

Your committee will place in your hands for your approval or otherwise the by-laws as reconstructed by them. The question of eligibility for membership is the one of paramount importance. It would be our pleasure to provide for the membership of all organizations working for the uplifting of the profession, but in this great care and discrimination must be exercised lest we present the spectacle of descending to a lower plane instead of encouraging our co-workers to rise to ours. Experience has taught us that we gain much by insisting upon the inauguration and maintenance of high standards. The curriculum of more than one school has been improved and extended to meet the requirements for membership in the Associated Alumnae. Our organizers foresaw the wisdom and necessity of such a course when they conceived the plans for the construction of this great body.

It is not ours in this day to organize, but it is our great duty to preserve the well-tried and useful methods and, if possible, improve them. It is our duty to develop all our resources and assist others to know and develop theirs. If they can best do it by membership in the national body, it should be our esteemed privilege to extend to them our aid, not by the lowering of all barriers, but by showing them how the barriers may be surmounted.

Most of the work, as you see it mapped out for us, affects us either as a body or as individuals; in it all we have made very little provision as an association for any means of aiding in the promotion of the general welfare.

May it never be ours to meet war or famine, pestilence or fire, flood or drought; but, should any of these grave disasters attend upon us, shall we be found unprepared? We shall never as a nation be *wholly* unprepared. Our national resources and our loyal love of country preclude such a possibility, but sufferers there will always be, disasters will occur even in isolated places; war will threaten and necessity may demand that we withhold not ourselves from it.

How then can this great body of serving-women best serve its country and its country's people when put to such straits? Individuals among us have always been found who would respond to the needs of our fellows—may their number increase and likewise their strength. But the charge has been made, and with some show of justice, that as a body of professional women we respond slowly—we are commercial, we receive more willingly than we give. Indeed, one famous for his good deeds in that profession whose handmaidens we delight to be as well as for his faith in the work of the nurse, has said that until we eradicate this failing we can lay small claim to the assumption that ours is really a profession. However disputed that point may be, it still remains true that we often miss our opportunities for identification with the world's great philanthropies. Is it not time that we should, and may we not here decide to, reverse our methods, and place ourselves on record as being organized for response to any call that may come to us to aid humanity in any needed way?

We have in this country an organization known as the National Red Cross Society, with whose name at least we are familiar, but whose plans for work we do not always comprehend. Our idea would be to ally ourselves with this national body for practical purposes.

Unhappily, the Red Cross Society is not at present able to do much work,—it being in a process of reconstruction,—but it will eventually be as effective as any society of its kind in any other nation in the world.

So strong was the conviction that nurses should be awake to their opportunities and responsibilities in this direction that an informal committee visited in Washington, last winter, members of the Red Cross Association in high official position and placed the matter before them. The suggestions of the committee were welcome, and the committee was advised to make preparations for the work, with the promise that an opportunity would be given the nurses for rendering their service whenever the demand for such service should arise, and with the further promise that if there were then no Red Cross Society with which they could be allied there would be some organization equally effective.

This concession was made because of the very evident fact that neither distinction nor position, neither money nor any other emolument, was sought, but simply an opportunity for work in the most practical and effectual manner. Therefore the appeal is made to you to consider the advisability of getting into form for such work. It is made to *you* because *you* are the rank and file of the nursing profession in this country, and without you nothing can be done, upon you must the dependence for service be placed.

Let us be personally indifferent whether this new work be inaugurated under the auspices of the Associated Alumnae, or the American Federation of Nurses, or some other nursing body: thus shall we prove the sincerity of our request for *only an opportunity to serve.* Then shall we fulfil one of the avowed purposes of our being.

It is indeed a pleasing reflection that for the consideration of these vital questions we are fortunate enough to meet in this grand old city of "Brotherly Love," with its history as the centre of wise deliberations in the past. We gather courage and inspiration from the contemplation of what our fathers here accomplished, and we would show forth our gratitude to the friends who made it possible for us here to assemble and who have to-day offered us kindly greeting and hospitality.

May we reward them by pursuing diligently the great objects we have before us, that they may be able to say in the future, here were inaugurated schemes for the betterment of humanity and the uplifting of an honorable profession.

Nursing Progress

By Mary M. Riddle, *president*
(Eighth Annual Convention, Washington, D.C., May 4-5, 1905)

One of the leading reflections to which this anniversary seems to invite us respects the changes that have taken place in the nursing profession since the formation of your society. In looking at these changes and estimating their effect upon our condition we are obliged to consider not what has been done in this society only, but also that which has been done in other nursing organizations receiving much of their impetus here.

We find that but for the support and encouragement given by this association and others of its kind, nurses in many communities would hardly have come out for themselves sufficiently even to establish directories and clubs of their own. We have seen them in some cities hesitating and wavering lest this important step be misconstrued and they be ostracized or boycotted for such rank independence. By reason of the inspiration delegates of local associations received here the strength for such work grew, as did, ultimately, the work under their hands, until to-day nurses' directories managed by nurses are so assured and so definitely a part of the equipment for the proper transaction of business that they seem always to have belonged to the nurses; and this change has come about in much less than one decade, for we find our predecessors discussing here the possibilities for such advancement within a much shorter period.

Again, so extraordinary has been the progress of the last few years that within a very recent period we find them also discussing here a preliminary or preparatory course for nurses. So intent were they upon procuring this and so satisfactory did it prove where tried that other schools of learning are now found considering the propriety of making it a part of their curricula, and some have even gone so far as to make the practical experiment. Thus we see that in this, as in many other instances, the members of the two greatest and most influential nursing organizations planted well—possibly better than they knew, but, like many individual originators, they to-day are scarcely credited with being the originators or with having first placed the possibilities for such advancement before their societies. But however that may be, results certainly justify the wisdom of their proposals.

So we might go on and on enumerating what has been accomplished by the Associated Alumnae. But there is one accomplishment that outweighs all others, and that is the fact that here is a society that has proved the school where have been drilled and incited the possible members of other organizations. Here, no doubt, State societies were first conceived, and here they must have received in large measure their sympathy and moral support, and who shall say that that very sympathy and moral support may not have been a real source of strength to the pioneers in obtaining registration for nurses and the recognition of our profession by the State?

To Strengthen the Union of Nursing Organizations

We have as one of the avowed objects of this association that it shall strengthen the union of nursing organizations. To those organizations that have labored so assiduously during the year to procure State registration and have met with but indifferent success or downright failure it is a great comfort to reflect that here at least is sympathy, here will be met a complete understanding.

Might we not by our earnestness and *esprit de corps* stand so closely together as to form a solid wall upon which may lean those State societies that find arrayed against them and their efforts an extremely conservative public, an antagonistic medical profession, and an indifferent nursing body. Let us hope that each and every such society is represented here to-day by a good, live delegate who shall gather inspiration for a most active home missionary service upon her return.

Nurses all over the land are asking for much, so much and so earnestly definitely and well that legislators halt before them and, it may be, set the seal of disapproval upon their efforts from sheer astonishment at what seems like audacity from its very uniqueness and scope.

But notwithstanding the realization of the nurses' hopes have in many cases been thus postponed, they have been found to be a power and an element to be treated with.

There have also arisen many prophets who would lead them into the promised land. It is said that someone has called the new movement in England the limited liability company to train, register, and control nurses. Some of these self-constituted leaders hold out to the nurses the possibility of the realization of that much cherished desire,—viz., educational advancement,—knowing that nothing appeals more strongly to the average nurse to-day.

Not all of these newly arisen leaders are insincere or self-seeking. Some there be who truly have the interest of the nursing profession at heart and have much to offer in the way of advice, intelligence, and authority. But others have a system to defend or an interest to advance, and can see their way clear for the accomplishment of their purpose by proposing or opposing, or cajoling or threatening, or possibly by disrupting existing organizations, as occasion may demand. Now, it becomes the duty of this great body of nurses to be a unit in standing by its principles and its traditions so firmly that its influence shall be felt to the uttermost local alumnae or affiliated State society, and it can be done if each delegate feels it incumbent upon herself to go hence and spread the gospel of unity and progress. It is as true to-day of us as it ever was of our country—that "united we stand, divided we fall."

These words are not spoken because there is any evidence anywhere that this association is swerving from its principles, but as a note of warning for the delegates to take with them against that which may arise under the guise of help or philanthropy or *what not* and calls for a departure from the old paths. Not that we should forever remain treading in any one way,—lest we be narrow and cease to progress; such a course would be contrary to the spirit of our originators or the precepts they promulgated,—but we must consider carefully and decide wisely what is to be for the best good of the nursing profession in this country—in short, we must be very thoughtful. In order to accomplish this our eyes must be open that we may select the gold from the dross, that we may know our wise teachers and leaders from the unwise, and that we may act accordingly.

This we must do with a spirit of charity for all and malice for none. We *must* not and *will* not spurn the learning nor theories of those who have given much time and thought to the advancement of our beloved calling, but we will yet, with possibly wholesome and trusted advice, decide for ourselves what is best to accept and what to reject.

As the years have gone on you have had before you many questions for adjustment—among others, the ownership of the *Journal*. You will no doubt hear from the committee of your selection last year just what your relations to that organ are and may be expected to be henceforth.

Your duty to the *Journal* is, however, an unceasing one, and may be manifested by the way in which you support it by your subscriptions. We have no hesitation in saying to you, and through you to your home alumnae associations, that you should subscribe for the *Journal* if you have not already done so. This is not because the *Journal* needs you more than you need the *Journal*. You will have more than value received for your investment, and it is the only organ of its kind in this or any other country published by nurses for nurses.

For years our senior society, that of the Superintendents of Training-Schools, has been agitating the question of how to procure skilled nursing service for people of limited means. They are still weighing the pros and cons, hoping to arrive at a solution which shall be a just one to both patient and nurse. They have been our directors in many matters, but when we seek the actual workers, those who must do the nursing work, we find them in this great body. Might not this, then, be a question to properly enlist the attention of alumnae associations and clubs of graduate nurses? Work of this kind is being done in some cities; might it not be worked out in others? Surely this class is as well worth our care as any other! As has been said, the millionaire is provided for, the very poor are provided for, but the great self-respecting middle class, the bone and sinew of our nation,—with pride we say our own class!—what can we do for them?

Service for Those with Limited Means

We can and must do something. It is unfair that they be left to the mercy of schools which have no hesitation in deploring in the public prints the fact that they are handicapped during their first year's existence because their nurses' earnings cannot be great or sufficient to support the school. Why? We ask of you who have spent two, three, or four years in training—why should nurses' earnings be great in their first year of training? I say, then, with what measure of devotion to our profession can we serve these people of our own class? Does the question appeal to you? Does it merit your attention? Then take it home with you and seek its solution with your colleagues, remembering that concentrated human thought is the power by which human ends are ultimately attained.

We point with pride to that other achievement of our senior society,—namely, the Course in Hospital Economics at Teachers College, Columbia University,—and we commend it to your thoughtful attention. It may lie within your power to aid it—and certainly you need not be reminded of the privilege accorded you in doing so. It has established its usefulness. It must survive as the fittest place where knowledge and learning such as it advances can be procured.

To recapitulate, we have before us for our year's work the opportunity to assist by our moral support and otherwise those nursing organizations that are struggling for the realization of high ideals. When we consider the large number of nurses that take no interest in their professional affairs we realize that the local alumnae societies here represented will have ample scope for their time and talents. It has been truly said that the apathy of nurses themselves in regard to the matters which most closely concern them has often done more for their defeat than active opposition. This apathy can be overcome by the continued, persistent, patient, sympathetic, and concerted work of this large, interested body.

Let us put it off now, this dread apathy, and stand forth in our vigor and firmness ready for the defence of our ideals, which must be cherished at the cost of any effort whatsoever. Then shall no other proof be needed that we are indeed an association that is associated, and for the advancement of the nursing profession.

1909-1911

Jane A. Delano

A pioneer in nursing administration, Jane Delano received her training at Bellevue Hospital in New York City and practiced nursing in a variety of settings, from service at a Florida hospital during a yellow fever epidemic, to industrial nursing at a copper mine in Arizona. She served as superintendent of nurses at University Hospital, Philadelphia, administered a home for delinquent girls on Randall's Island, New York, and was superintendent of nurses at Bellevue Hospital.

Miss Delano was made chairman of the committee that first organized nursing services within the American Red Cross, and she also served as superintendent of nurses in the Army Nurse Corps from 1909 to 1912. After 1912, she devoted her full energies to Red Cross work, and she was responsible for marshalling the more than 21,000 nurses who served abroad during World War I, most of whom were recruited through the Red Cross.

Miss Delano died on April 15, 1919.

The Growth of Nurse Training Schools

By Jane A. Delano, R.N., *president*

(Thirteenth Annual Convention, New York City, May 19-20, 1910)

Our history naturally divides itself into two epochs: one beginning fifty years ago, when Florence Nightingale came back from the Crimea with the enthusiasm and the inspiration which led to the establishment of the first training school for nurses, as we know them to-day; and now I believe that we are on the threshold of a new epoch.

There was a combination of circumstances which led to the development of our profession; first of all was the great need in the Crimea. Other soldiers had lain unprotected, other soldiers had suffered without succor; other soldiers had died unattended; but for the first time in the history of the great wars of the world was the quick transmission of news possible. Telegraphic communication and railroads were just at the beginning of that period. When the news reached England of the suffering in the Crimea it was perfectly natural that women should be found to go to the front. I believe that so long as the heart of woman is filled with sympathy, so long will an appeal for help find responsc.

Soon after the war in the Crimea came the battle of Solferino. You heard last night a splendid tribute to the Red Cross, how the inspiration of one man led to its establishment. On the battlefield after this tremendous slaughter forty thousand soldiers were left dead and wounded. John Andrew Durant, a Swiss, found the conditions most horrible. He organized among the peasant women a relief corps, and he saw the great need for a mutual organization for the care of the sick and wounded in time of war.

We have developed training schools all over the country. Fifty years ago there were no training schools in America. Bellevue is just about to publish its thirty-ninth annual report. So you see ten years after the establishment of the first training school the work began in this country. I would like to pay a tribute to the work of the splendid women, who were, I believe, Florence Nightingale's own nurses, Sister Helen, who was the first superintendent of Bellevue training school, and Alice Fisher, the first superintendent of Blockley.

On my way to New York I stopped in Philadelphia for the twenty-fifth anniversary of the establishment of this training school, and it was my privilege to sit at dinner next to a nurse who was, I believe, the first graduate trained under Alice Fisher. She told me a little story which seemed to me so characteristic of the life and the ideals and the purposes of those splendid first nurses that I want to tell it to you. There was an epidemic of typhoid fever in Plymouth, Pennsylvania, soon after Alice Fisher came to Philadelphia, and the authorities of Philadelphia sent her there to help in the care of the typhoid fever patients. She went without any assistants, but found conditions so bad that she went back to the hospital for help. The nurse who sat next to me was one assigned to this duty. I think she travelled all night and arrived there the next morning. She had been directed to go to a certain little hotel in this town and she found in her room a note from Alice Fisher which told her to rest for so many hours and then report for duty. The nurse did not realize what this meant, but took her rest, five or six hours, I presume, and then reported to Alice Fisher and found that she had been on duty without relief for seventy-two hours.

Following the establishment of the first training schools came their development throughout the country. But even twenty-five years ago there were only thirty-five training schools in the whole United States. Now there are over a thousand. There were perhaps eight hundred pupil nurses at that time, certainly not more, the schools graduating, perhaps, two hundred nurses during the year. It is impossible to estimate accurately the number of graduate nurses in America to-day, but there are probably not far from 75,000.

Now with this increase in our numbers come new responsibilities; and I believe that to-day we are standing on the threshold of a new epoch with new ideals, new hopes, and new aspirations. I believe that the time is not far distant when this great body of women will be joined together in what we now call preventive work. We are inclined to accept conditions as we find them. In the old days we questioned very little the causes which led to the conditions. We found people suffering from typhoid and we felt that we had quite done our duty if we carried our patient safely through to recovery. Now, if we are called into country places to care for typhoid, we have not discharged our duty when we have looked after that one particular patient; we should consider as much as the care of the patient the protection of any one with whom we come in contact, and as far as possible look into the circumstances which led up to this condition.

We hear a great deal these days in regard to the social point of view. I believe there is no body of men or women in the country to whom this duty comes more clearly than to nurses. We have had special training. We have opportunities which do not come even to a physician. We are with our patients twenty-four hours out of the twenty-four. A doctor comes in for perhaps fifteen or twenty minutes; and while his responsibilities are greater than ours, we have unequalled opportunities for service and instruction. And I believe we must give an account of our stewardship in regard to this work. Whether we justify our existence, whether we convince the public that we are really essential, rests with us. We are challenged; we know that we must admit it, we are challenged constantly. In my own mind I think these challenges one of the most hopeful signs. As long as people ignore us it means that we are working to but little purpose underground, like the mole, but when we begin to come out into the light and our work broadens, we may accomplish more, but our faults will be more conspicuous.

I believe that we occupy a peculiar position. It has been said that there is a gulf dividing the submerged classes, from the people above, over which none may pass without contamination. I believe that to us is given the opportunity to pass this gulf without contamination. I think we share with the Sisters of the various religious orders, this privilege.

May I leave this one parting word with you: that you should cultivate in your work, in your studies, and in your lives the desire to benefit all with whom you come in contact, whether sick or well; if well, to help them to keep well; if sick, to help them back to health and to improve the conditions in which we find our patients living.

Organizational Progress

By Jane A. Delano, R.N., *president*
(Fourteenth Annual Convention, Boston, May 31-June 3, 1911)

First, I want to remind you of the growth of our association, how it covers the whole country, and binds us together in one common society, with common interests, difficulties, hopes, and aspirations, and to say to you that our success and our accomplishments depend upon the individuals; not alone upon the individuals as they come here to the meetings, but particularly upon the delegates as they go back to their home county, state or alumnae associations.

The work of the association has progressed most satisfactorily during the past year. The appointment of an interstate secretary was, I think, one of the best things we have done in a long time. We can never again doubt the public spirit of nurses for it has been largely through their efforts that Miss McIsaac's trips have been planned and carried through so successfully. May I emphasize the point which she made in regard to the business-like methods of nurses? My correspondence in connection with the Red Cross has brought me in contact with nurses all over the country and I have been amazed at the enthusiasm and interest found in unexpected places. I am sure that Miss McIsaac and I have both come to the conclusion that the ability to do finished work, the patience to accept suggestions and the willingness to profit by them, will be found in all sections—north, south, east, and west.

We have a year of great opportunities and promise before us. May I say a few words in regard to the *American Journal of Nursing* and your responsibilities concerning it? A year ago last January we owned thirty-eight shares, but since that time we have nearly doubled the number, now owning seventy-four of the one hundred shares. We should begin this year's work fully determined to bring the *Journal* purchase to a completion. We should strive to enlarge the publishing business of the company. We can easily increase the book business, if we will all co-operate, for we have the control of the situation. If we can hold our nursing organizations together and unite upon some general policy there is no reason why the *Journal* should not prove a paying investment, making it possible to increase the usefulness and extend the activities of our association.

You have shown your unselfishness by generous contributions to the Isabel Hampton Robb Memorial Fund and I know you will agree that our united interests bring us more closely together. Do we not come to the convention this year believing more than ever before that we are professional sisters?

May I urge the delegates from the far distant places, the delegates from the northwest and the far west and the south, to take part in these discussions? I shall be bitterly disappointed during these meetings unless we hear discussions from many women whose names I shall need to ask. I am sure many of you may have valuable suggestions, and have had interesting experiences, and we are only too anxious to hear from you.

We have only to glance over our programme to realize the breadth of the interests and activities of this organization. Nothing could outline its responsibilities and aims better than a careful study of this programme. I trust that these meetings may be most profitable and that you may carry to your home inspiration, ambition and hope in your work.

1911-1913

Sarah E. Sly

After several years on the nursing staff of the Pennsylvania Hospital and in private duty nursing, Sarah Sly spent most of the remainder of her career serving the association on both state and national levels.

Miss Sly served as president of the Michigan State Nurses' Association during the campaign in that state for a nurse registration law, and utilized her organizational talents in assisting the national organization in its transition from the Nurses' Associated Alumnae of the United States, with its duplicative membership structure, to the American Nurses' Association, which recognized district, state, and national membership. Miss Sly also served on the board of directors of the *American Journal of Nursing* for several years.

Miss Sly was forced to resign as president of the American Nurses' Association in 1913 because of failing health. She died on May 26, 1944.

ANA's Growth Since 1897

By Sarah E. Sly, *president**

(Fifteenth Annual Convention, Chicago, June 5-7, 1912)

A brief résumé of the history and rapid growth of this association will enable us to better understand the development of the national work and the extent of our responsibilities.

*Miss Sly was unable to attend the convention. Her message was read to the delegates by the acting convention chairman.

At the annual meeting of the Superintendents of Training Schools for Nurses which was held in Philadelphia in September, 1895, a committee of twelve superintendents was appointed, and twelve alumnae associations were invited to send representatives, making a working committee of twenty-four, whose duty was to organize a national association.

In September, 1896, a Constitutional Convention composed of fifteen members of this committee was held at Manhattan Beach Hotel for the purpose of drafting a constitution and by-laws and to unite into one body the alumnae associations of the different schools, but it was not until a meeting in Baltimore, in February, 1897 (at the time of the fourth annual meeting of the Superintendents' Society) that the Nurses' Associated Alumnae of the United States and Canada was organized, and by-laws with amendments were adopted, with an enrollment of twenty-two charter members.

Today we are honored in having with us many of those charter members who have been the pioneer workers in active service during all the years of this organization.

In order to become incorporated in 1901, it was necessary to ask the Canadian associations to withdraw.

During the first five years of organization, eleven associations were affiliated, and in the next ten years there was an increase of forty-two associations.

On account of the affiliation of state, county, and city organizations, the name "Associated Alumnae" no longer fully represented our national interests, so that at the reorganization in Boston last year, the name was changed to the American Nurses' Association.

From the small beginning we have (as the secretary has reported) an affiliated membership of 224 associations with sixty-nine permanent members and twenty-two charter members, representing approximately 20,000 graduate nurses in the United States.

We have reached into the broader fields of nursing activities through affiliation with the International Council of Nurses, the American Red Cross, the National Association for the Study and Prevention of Tuberculosis, and the American Association for the Study and Prevention of Infant Mortality.

One aim, toward which we have worked for the past twelve years, has been to own the *American Journal of Nursing*, and this has at last been accomplished through the generosity, and the faithful, persistent efforts of the nurses all over the country. Their response to appeal has been prompt and cordial, and we feel it an honor to be associated with a body of women whose united efforts have resulted in such a great achievement.

During all these years the responsibility of the *Journal* has been carried by the editor, Miss Palmer, and a small group of women who have from the beginning given liberally of their time and strength to make it a success, and as a result we have a magazine which is indeed a credit to our profession.

The *American Journal of Nursing* stands for national progress and national unity, and is one of the most powerful influences in nursing education that we have in America today. It is the official organ of many nursing organizations, including the three national societies, and is the connecting link which binds the nurses of the country together. Now that it is the property of the American Nurses' Association, every nurse is an individual shareholder in responsibility, and it must be her personal concern to support it, and to help maintain and advance its high standard of excellence. That will insure its prosperity and progress. We need and we must have the interest and co-operation of every nurse in this association, to reach the thousands of graduate nurses throughout the country who are not in touch with nursing organization, and induce them to subscribe for the *Journal*.

A national magazine such as ours should have a subscription list of ten times its present number, and I urge every delegate and every nurse present to carry this appeal back to their local associations, so that in the coming year we will have a substantial increase in the number of subscribers and in the knowledge and intelligence which comes from reading its pages.

Soon after the Department of Hospital Economics (now the Department of Nursing and Health) was established at Teachers' College, Columbia University, New York, the American Nurses' Association joined with the Superintendents' Society to help place this department on a permanent basis. The nurses of the whole country contributed to it individually and collectively. After the beginning was made and its value demonstrated, there followed the substantial endowment of Mrs. Helen Hartley Jenkins, of New York. This splendid achievement, like state registration, is the direct result of all classes of nurses working together.

Registration for Nurses

Organized effort has been the means of securing registration in thirty-two states. The real difficulty lies not in securing state registration, but in the subsequent administration of the law. We should give the boards of examiners and the legislative committees our unqualified loyalty and support in their efforts to enforce the requirements of the law and to raise the educational standards of training schools for nurses.

Seven states make it compulsory for the nurses to register to practise their profession. Until registration is made compulsory for nurses in all the states, the same as for the medical and other professions, any one from any training school may practise and we have no means of protection or redress. As the standards of education become more uniform, reciprocity will naturally become more commonly practised in the different states.

For the past two years the American Nurses' Association has shared with the American Red Cross, the *American Journal of Nursing,* and the Superintendents' Society in the salary of an interstate secretary, the travelling expenses being met by the respective local associations which she visited. Miss McIssac, who was elected to fill that office, has not only presented the work of all the nursing interests throughout the country, but she has helped to lay a splendid foundation for future organization and state registration. It is too soon to see all of the far-reaching influence of her work, but that it has been a successful venture is evidenced by reports of increased interest and activities along all nursing lines. From Miss McIsaac's wise counsel, we confidently anticipate there will be a marked improvement in educational standards, in stronger local organizations, and in more uniform registration laws.

On account of Miss McIsaac's appointment as superintendent of the Army Nurse Corps, she will not be available for interstate work, but it is hoped that Miss Palmer or her assistant Miss DeWitt may be able to arrange to visit different sections of the country, as they have done heretofore.

The Robb Memorial Educational Fund and the Relief Fund are perpetual obligations, and are as much for the nurses of the future as for those of today. Nurses everywhere, including pupils in training, must be educated to realize their responsibility to have a part in maintaining them; and local associations should keep before their members constantly the objects and benefits to be derived from both funds.

The Relief Fund, as its name implies, is for those who have become physically or financially disabled, through emergency or serious illness, and the sooner the fund accumulates, the sooner we shall be able to give needed help.

Our increase in numbers, our broader educational influence mean new and larger responsibilities, and today we stand on the threshold of a new epoch with higher ideals, greater hopes, and aspirations.

In commemoration of this occasion and the final transfer of the *Journal,* it seems fitting that at this meeting we should consider very seriously the establishment of central headquarters for the transaction of our business. We hear much about conservation of energy along all lines of work, and the time has come when the conservation of those who are carrying the responsibility of our national work is absolutely necessary.

This is one of the most important questions which confront us, for our work is increasing each year, while the facilities for doing it are practically the same as in the beginning of the organization. The secretary's duties are at present combined with other work, and she receives only a nominal salary. The constantly changing address has always been a handicap and an inconvenience both to the secretary and to the members. The "Saratoga trunk" in which our valuable records and supplies are packed has long ago reached the limit of its capacity; it is often inaccessible when its contents are most needed, and beside it has the disadvantage of being very unsafe. The *Journal* with its many departments, the various funds which we are establishing, our other increasing and enlarging affairs, and the multitudinous duties of the secretary should all be administered from a permanent, well-equipped business office.

The location of the *Journal* is our first consideration, and wherever it is best to centre its work, there should be the headquarters of the American Nurses' Association, for the interests of one are the interests of the other.

I therefore recommend that at this meeting definite steps be taken to accomplish the centralization of the work of the American Nurses' Association and the *American Journal of Nursing*, and that as soon as possible there be established a permanent business headquarters.

The Red Cross nursing service must become the roll of honor of our profession, and it is our duty to see that only the names of our best women are inscribed there. It is, in a practical way, more closely connected with the American Nurses' Association than any other of our affiliated bodies. The appointment of its National Committee is made through recommendations of this association. It is most gratifying to learn that the National Committee on Red Cross Nursing Service has decided that in the future nurses to be eligible for enrollment must be members of organizations affiliated with the American Nurses' Association. All appointments of committees and all Red Cross work have been done through the national organization, and in many ways this branch of nursing service is more closely connected with the national association than any other. Great credit is due to the chairman of the National Committee, Jane A. Delano, and her co-workers for systematizing the Red Cross nursing service. They have obtained uniform regulations, have organized state and local committees, and have enrolled a large corps of the best nurses in the country for active service in time of need. The local committees have a very great responsibility in the selection of candidates for enrollment. They should exercise the greatest care possible in their recommendations, because they are responsible for the character and the efficiency of the nurses whom they endorse.

The Ninth International Red Cross Conference was held in Washington from May 7 to 17, 1912. On account of the splended work done by the nurses under the Red Cross nursing service, four delegates were appointed by the Secretary of State at Washington from recommendations made by the American Nurses' Association, who represented the nurses of the United States at the conference. This recognition of the efficiency of the Red Cross nursing service is a great incentive for future work.

The private duty nurse and her training in efficiency for her most important work is a subject which engages our thoughtful consideration. Upon her character and her efficiency depends the quality of her service to the largest number of the sick, and no matter what fields of nursing may develop, the number of nurses on private duty will always be in the majority. Every member of the profession is judged by the private duty nurse; as she goes into the homes of the people, she is the exponent of the standards of our profession. The private nurse of to-day may tomorrow be in some other department of nursing and it behooves her to keep in touch with the trend of affairs in the whole nursing world, and to make herself strongly felt in association work and in the support of the *Journal.*

Social service with its animating spirit is leavening our whole profession. The large number of nurses who are engaging in social service has become more and more a very important group and naturally they want more time for the discussion of their problems than can be given them in the regular meetings of the American Nurses' Association.

I therefore recommend that visiting nurses, social service nurses, and all nurses in allied work organize a national association and become affiliated with the American Nurses' Association. That would give them representation in the International Council of Nurses.

No one branch of nursing service is independent of the other, and under the new constitution and by-laws, the American Nurses' Association must stand for all the educational nursing interests of the United States. Our strength is in a united front, and the social service nurses need and must have the American Nurses' Association back of them.

The Sliding Scale of Rates

Among the many unsolved questions which are before us and which call for thoughtful, serious consideration on the part of every member of the association are the responsibility of providing nursing care for people of moderate means, and the sliding scale of rates. The time has come when the nursing body should co-operate with the medical profession to reach a solution of this problem, without lowering the standard of nurses.

Nursing service for all the people must come from some source, and especially for those who have not access to hospitals or who are under the care of relief societies. It would seem to me that the universal adoption of the sliding scale—upward as well as downward—which permits the nurse to increase her charge for those who can pay and to lower it when occasion demands, would meet all conditions. The fixed charge creates prejudice and keeps many nurses idle. This is largely the reason for so many practical nurses, and the cause of the agitation for trained attendants. People must have care. On the other hand, not all nurses are alike capable, competent, adaptable, well-trained, and experienced. Why should a nurse after ten years' or more experience in private, social, or institutional work only receive the amount she did the first year? It would seem perfectly reasonable for those whose training and experience warranted it to charge more, so that they could sometimes work for less. Those who are not progressive will fall into their proper place. In this way all would strive harder, as each would have to stand on her own merits. A sliding scale, with all the states working together, with our splendidly-organized central registries controlled absolutely by nurses, would meet the conditions fairly and squarely. If the nurses in one state would try the experiment, others would follow as they have done in securing legislative enactments. Our nursing organizations have assumed the responsibility of the elevation and advancement of nursing education, that the sick may be more skilfully cared for, so is it not equally our responsibility that such skilled service be available for all classes of people?

All members of this association should stand solidly together for a reasonable, educational standard, allowing sufficient time for training schools to improve their standards, so as not to interfere with the service in the hospitals. There are too many ignorant women in the ranks by whose mistakes in conduct and morals we are all judged. There is a small number of medical men who are inveighing against the educated nurse. Their fear that she will invade their province by trying to adjust medical questions is assuredly groundless. We should not be frightened or discouraged by opposition, even if we must back water once in a while. No good thing is ever gained easily. The more vital the question, the greater the opposition. Any reform to be lasting must be brought about slowly. No one else will solve our problems for us. As we become of greater importance, the more determined certain factions will be to control us. The greatest danger we have to face is failure to stand together for what we know is right. All our efforts lead to the more efficient care of the sick in the home, hospital, army, navy, and in every land. The gain is to come chiefly to those who follow us, not to ourselves, therefore we must build carefully on the foundation which was so securely laid by the pioneer nurses. The opposition with which we are confronted is the natural result of a long, pioneer period, without standards or regulation; during which commercial interests of hospitals, directories, and individuals were unrestrained.

Nothing would so soon dispel the opposition as some means to care for the people of moderate means, who are in the great majority and who must by some means have efficient care.

The enfranchisement of woman as part of a republican form of government, after struggling half a century for a foothold in this country, is gaining respectful consideration. I believe in woman's rights, but the way to these rights is not through noisy, undignified, political agitation, but rather through a careful study of the whole situation, and a definite knowledge of what we want and why we want it. I believe in woman suffrage wherever the women want it, but I do not think that suffrage should be forced upon them. I object to men imposing a share in the responsibility upon women who are adverse, reluctant, or indifferent, because it is unjust to them. For that reason, I think, every woman should decide for herself whether she wishes suffrage or not, just as she decides what her religion shall be. There are few women who want the vote because it is their right but because they recognize that only through having a voice in the laws of the country can they hope to remedy the conditions now prevailing. We as nurses see those conditions as many others have not the opportunity to see them.

United Efforts

By Isabel McIsaac, R.N., *acting president**
(Sixteenth Annual Convention, Atlantic City, June 25-27, 1913)

This meeting of 1913 is a milestone which marks a notable spot in our highway. We began our nursing organizations in a few scattering alumnae associations which were concerned with

*Miss Isabel McIsaac, ANA vice president, assumed presidential responsibilities when Sarah E. Sly was forced to resign for health reasons.

purely local affairs, these were followed by the Superintendents' Society, now known as the National League for Nursing Education—the first national organization, and the first body to lay down definite lines saying, this is our aim, that is our work and these things we propose to do. This society has pursued its way since 1893, carrying a beacon for the guidance of us all, in spite of every possible form of discouragement. While the work of the League has been almost exclusively educational, its members have given help, work, time, money and sympathy to this larger body which is composed of all of our affiliated nursing interests. Last year another definite group, which has developed almost wholly since the first organization in 1893: viz., the Public Health Nurses, laid plans to enlarge the scope of what has become so important a part of the whole nursing profession. This American Nurses' Association is the framework which binds all nursing interests. Its purpose, from its inception, has been to support and encourage every struggling group of nurses and to improve our schools and their graduates. The delegate from the small alumnae has the same opportunity as her neighbor from the large powerful society.

The National League of Nursing Education has furnished the leadership in the long struggle for state registration, but alone the League could not have carried a single state, there had to be behind the movement the strength and unity of this organization. I am trying to emphasize this point: that in the things which concern us all our strength lies in our ability to work for one purpose, just as the power of the United States lies in the unity of the single states.

The American Nurses' Association has, within a few years, begun definite lasting work along lines which concern every individual nurse, not every superintendent, not every private nurse, not every public health nurse, but every nurse who belongs to one of its affiliated societies. It furnishes the machinery through which work may be done for them all, it stands pledged to help the standards of nursing education and ethics; to use its mighty power for the greatest good to the greatest number. For one thing it has pledged its *Journal* to help carry on all of these different lines of work. For ten years we worked and saved and toiled to buy the *Journal.* Now it is ours, and every year it will grow and increase in responsibility. It is the greatest problem this Association faces, a professional problem, a humanitarian problem and a financial problem. Every year it will need, beside its editors, seven nurse directors who will give time, work and judgment to its business and, if they remain long enough in service, will forfeit most of their friends and their peace of mind. These women can not be picked up at random, for they must have not only some business ability but the background of knowledge of nursing affairs over the whole country, because the *Journal* belongs to San Diego as much as to Portland, Maine; to the Navy nurse in Guam and the Army nurse in Zamboango, quite as much as to the superintendent of New York's most luxurious hospital or the visiting nurse in El Paso.

We have undertaken two other heavy responsibilities: the Isabel Hampton Robb Memorial, which is an educational fund; and the Relief Fund, the name of which indicates its purpose. We shall have reports from these committees, but I beg to remind you that these three, the *Journal,* the Memorial Fund and the Relief Fund are yours and are so important that their investment and use are the business of those whom you chose to serve the Association. None of this is news to the older nurses, but to the new delegates or to those who are serving on some of these *hard* committees for the first time, I am trying to say that no matter what our special nursing work may be, we need the help and support of all of the other nurses, and here in the American Nurses' Association is the one place to find it.

In less than five years we will, no doubt, have other groups working out their own salvation, which is exactly as it should be. For instance, the Red Cross Nursing Service began its enrollment a little over four years ago, which could not have been done without the working machinery of the American Nurses' Association, but now, after the experiences of the past twelve months, it is evident that these wonderful experiences must be brought before all of the Red Cross nurses and by another year or two, all day sessions will be a necessity for them. Out of the Red Cross enrollment the new Rural Red Cross Nursing Service was born, of which you will hear more later, and steps have been taken to develop classes in elementary hygiene and home care of the sick. All of our activities, the things which we have worked for in the past ten years, from the course in Teachers College down, have been worked out through the two national organizations; now that we have them, they ought to go on more swiftly. It has been powerfully hard to deny ourselves but we have done it. In the last three years we have raised about $30,000 for the three funds, enrolled nearly four thousand nurses in the Red Cross and started the Public Health Nurses in housekeeping. If that is not something to be proud of, then we are no better than wooden Indians.

What have we ahead of us? First, the careful administration of business, the selection of nurses who are not afraid of work nor even afraid of a battle, if need be. We must make every possible effort to gradually gain more permanency in service for those who must carry the work, and pay them livable salaries to do it.

Now we come to the immediate work ahead of us: this is, of course, the regular routine and an International meeting of nurses in San Francisco, in 1915. We have already, together with the National League of Nursing Education, sent out invitations to the nurses of the world to come, and it is necessary for us at this time to carefully select those who will do this work in order to insure a creditable meeting in San Francisco.

Two years ago the National League of Nursing Education formulated plans for requesting some research body to make a thorough study of the present status of the training schools for nurses of the United States, following the plan pursued in the investigation of the medical schools. The committee from the League presented its request to the Carnegie Foundation but they were not ready at that time to undertake it. Meanwhile there have been a few men in the New York Academy of Medicine who have also come to feel that such an inquiry might help to solve some of the difficulties which beset both doctors and nurses.

For several years we have been buffeted between what we thought was right to teach the nurse and the hostile opinions of our opponents, and until some unbiased judges take up the subject and consider it scientifically, as such rcsearch work is done, the medical profession, the hospitals and the nurses will go on indefinitely in their triangular strife. Personally, I believe that when such an inquiry is made, the nurses who have all but died, fighting for what they believe to be due to nursing the sick, will stand on an enduring pedestal, and still further I believe that no matter how hard nor how humiliating such a rigid inquiry may be for all of us, we should lend every possible aid to make the study a fair and just estimate of things as they are, and to never falter in our steadfast hope that in the end we will be justified for the faith within us during these last stormy years.

1913-1915

Genevieve Cooke

A native of California, Genevieve Cooke was a graduate of the California Women's Hospital, San Francisco, and worked in private duty nursing several years. She received extensive study in the fields of massage and physical exercise, and she taught courses on those subjects in several San Francisco area hospitals.

Miss Cooke was the founder of the *Pacific Coast Journal of Nursing,* on which she served as editor and business manager for some nine years. She served on the board of directors of the *American Journal of Nursing* and held several offices in the California Nurses' Association as well as in the national Association.

Miss Cooke died on January 28, 1928.

Economic Security

By Genevieve Cooke, R.N., *president*
(Seventeenth Annual Convention, St. Louis, April 23-29, 1914)

A scrap of the foundation history of this Association recently came into my possession and though it covered but one typewritten page, it spoke volumes.

For some time, it seems, superintendents had realized a need for an organization of national scope that might bind the young alumnae associations together for mutual good. Toward this end, a conference was held in the early fall of 1896, at which there were some fifteen superintendents and nurses present. That small number of representative women, several of whom are with us this evening, constituted what may be termed the van-guard of this organization which, today, numbers many thousand members. How readily one can picture in mind that group of earnest, far-seeing founders of the American Nurses' Association!

The history of the expansion of the organization has been recounted from time to time, and honor is due the founders and their worthy successors, for its steady growth. It is not my purpose to review that history, but in opening this, the Seventeenth Annual Convention, I am impressed with the evidence here manifest, by the scores of nurses in attendance, that there was need for this national union, and I am inclined to believe this need will increase as the years pass, and the house of delegates of the American Nurses' Association will become the *great clearing house,* if you please, for the vital problems that weigh upon the separate organizations.

Article I of our Constitution states, that we are banded together for the purpose of elevating the standard of nursing education and to promote the usefulness and honor, the financial and other interests of the nursing profession. If you will read that short article carefully, you may interpret a wider adaptation of its meaning than has yet been brought into use, and perhaps, at this time, we may recognize fuller opportunities for promoting the usefulness and honor, the educational, financial and other interests of the nursing profession.

Please consider how many groups of nurses may today be struggling with problems, which a vote or a resolution passed by these delegates in executive session would ease tremendously!

The nurses of New York State, for example, have once more undertaken to blaze a trail for nurses of the world, through their determination to secure a legal and educational status for the simple title nurse. Their recent campaign failed, but their convictions are firm, and if they do eventually secure this title, alone and exclusively to pertain to "a practitioner of nursing," then every other state must follow their lead.

From the opposite side of the continent comes an equally important measure, the eight-hour law for women workers, recently passed in California. This law includes pupil nurses within its provisions, and is of vital interest to hospitals, training schools and the nursing profession. I believe we are to have a paper devoted to that subject in one of our sessions.

Each of these two measures, The Nurse Practice Act of New York State and the Eight-Hour Law for Student Nurses in California, I believe merits the earnest consideration of this body. Other state societies may have equally important problems with which we, as an organization with representation from every state in the Union, should be made acquainted. That there is a greater economic struggle in the nursing world today than ever before is, I am convinced, apparent to all who come into direct touch with nursing organizations.

Many groups of nurses are taking definite steps, in fact, they have found it necessary, to safe-guard their financial interests. A local or county organization may appeal to the state organization for endorsement and support in any problems that weigh too heavily to be borne alone. To whom, I ask, shall the state organization appeal, but to the House of Delegates of this great American Nurses' Association? I use the term House of Delegates, despite the fact that it does not appear in our by-laws, but I think you will agree with me that this term conveys an impression of a unified group, concentrating on matters of national interest and importance to our profession better than does the term "delegates in executive session;" I should like to see this term adopted by the delegates during this convention. The very fact that all through the years since our national association came into being, our main energies have been centered on fulfilling that part of our constitution which pertains to "elevating the standard of nursing education," should clearly demonstrate to all the true, in-born purpose of the founders of the Association, and the desire of the profession, as a whole, to be prepared to render the best possible service to the sick, and to meet the need and ever-growing demand of the public health service.

Since the early years, however, numerous correspondence, and other inferior, short-course, commercial nursing institutions have come into existence; these yearly turn out young women by the hundreds, to compete with the legitimate nurse, and today in some parts of the country I understand, these women have become an actual menace to our members; consequently I ask this question: May we not at this time, carefully consider that part of our constitution which may safe-guard the economic interests of our members? Please note that I use the term members, not the inclusive term—Nurses. Shall we not, as a national body, soon have to answer that oft-heard question: "What will the Association do for me, what benefit am I to receive through my membership?"

Economic Service and Membership

Many, many nurses, we know, actually slave for the welfare of the profession; these women never consider the personal cost, nor do they look for gain, except to the profession as a whole. I believe, however that it is safe to say, that two-thirds of the members of each organization are of a different turn of mind, and I believe there will ever be a large proportion of members whose only incentive for affiliating with an organization is for self-protection and a fancied, or real, financial advantage. Consequently, does it not behoove us as a national body, and this applies to the states as well, to study carefully whereby we can be of the greatest economic service to our membership as a whole? Especially to that two-thirds, which is really not interested in the educational problems with which the other one-third constantly struggles? Would such consideration not tend to weld those two-thirds of the membership more closely to the organization and, possibly, enlist their interest later more actively in, and add their strength to the support of our other measures? Have we not reached the period in our existence as a national organization when we may justly be called upon to weigh some of the vital problems with which isolated groups of nurses are struggling? Shall we not pause and give ear to the economic struggles of many of our worthy members? The house of delegates of this Association is the supreme executive body of nurses in these United States! Think what weight the vote of this body might carry!

Does each affiliated organization, on the return of its delegates, from state or national meeting, receive a stimulus which advances its work, broadens its interest, and adds substantially to its membership during the year?

Do the subscriptions to our *Journal* increase perceptibly after each state and national convention? If not, wherein lies the responsibility? Has the delegate failed to gain substance for an inspiring report to her home organization? Has she been inattentive, or has she simply accepted the office of delegate, as one affording her the pleasure of meeting old friends, forming new acquaintances, listening to interesting papers and discussions, without any due sense of her obligation, to be prepared to convey to her associates at home all of value that she can glean from these sessions? I shall not presume to answer these questions, the answer must come from the conscience of each individual delegate.

We know that the aim of the American Nurses' Association is to stimulate interest in organization affairs, and to extend our field for service, both to the public and to our profession. If, however, we fail to secure proper results in the affiliated organizations, should we not endeavor to ascertain wherein perchance our policies or our efforts may be deficient?

Part of our educational work is, and ever will be, to acquaint the general public with the high ethical and educational aims of our profession, and to demonstrate through the daily life and service of our members, just what constitutes ethics in the nursing world.

Chief among the educational interests of our National organization is our *American Journal of Nursing* and our Isabel Hampton Robb Scholarship Memorial. How encouraging to the young nurse of high aims and studious habits to anticipate that she may possibly be honored with this scholarship and the splendid avenues for service which it can open to her! And as to our *Journal,* the growth of this Association, and in fact its very existence, would have been impossible without it. Appreciation is due to the splendid women who serve our interests faithfully in the directorate, and especially is appreciation due those two women who are ever at the helm of the *Journal* and hold it steady through troublous times. Our *Journal* has it in its power to open new avenues of service to the profession, and to create a coöperative and professional spirit among our members, forceful and promising, far beyond the fondest hopes, of its founders. One of its chief values to us and to the public is the relation which it establishes, between our profession and the public; in this relation it is very essential that the editorial department of our *Journal* should always be represented at our national convention, and at other gatherings of note, the better to serve our interests and the more spontaneously to stimulate our membership. This will tend to increase the number of our subscribers which is an important factor in the educational work of the *Journal.* Should we in any measure be satisfied with its growth, as an educational medium or, as a financial interest, until we know that it reaches a large majority of the members of this great national organization to which it belongs? Its growth and part of its value, however, as an educational medium and as a financial interest, is largely dependent upon the interchange of nursing news which it is able to carry on for the scattered groups of nurses throughout this vast country, and a very important factor in this, is the timely presentation of such news.

I trust that the delegates may recognize in some of the questions touched upon in this paper, matters sufficient and worthy for their official consideration during a business session. I wish to extend to you most cordial greetings from California and to assure you of a very warm welcome to San Francisco in June of next year, when our great International Congress of Nurses will convene at the very entrance of the Golden Gate.

One Who Protects and Nourishes Mankind

By Genevieve Cooke, R.N., *president*
(Eighteenth Annual Convention, San Francisco, June 20-25, 1915)

Never before have we had the privilege of welcoming to California the National League of Nursing Education, the membership of which is made up from the teachers in our profession, meeting at this time in twenty-first annual session. Also for the first time we are honored with the presence of the newest of our national organizations, namely the National Organization for Public Health Nursing, now holding its third annual session.

Three short years ago a message was flashed from the Old World which brought joy to the members of the California State Nurses' Association and which filled us with enthusiasm. The message was that the International Congress of Nurses in session at Cologne had accepted California's invitation to meet here in San Francisco in June, 1915. Then came acceptance from the American Nurses' Association, from the National League of Nursing Education, and from the National Organization for Public Health Nursing. There is no occasion for me to dwell upon the heart-rending calamity to the human family, which has made our International Congress an impossibility. There is no individual in this great audience who is not seriously affected through the knowledge of the continuous slaughter in our parent countries. Many members of our International Council who but one short year ago were anticipating with so much pleasure the wonderful congress planned, have for weary, weary months, been serving the cause of humanity in those blood stained countries. But looking beyond the present sorrows* and separations, two members have come to us from England, one from Holland and one from Australia to meet with our International president and charter members in executive session, for the sole purpose of maintaining the continuity of the Council, so to proceed with its unifying work some years hence when peace may again be upon

*Reference to World War I.

earth. Inadequate as the numbers of nurses may be to succor more than in infinitesimal fraction of the precious lives now being sacrificed in battle, it is some small consolation to realize that even the simple title Nurse means one who protects, one who nourishes, never one who destroys.

The nurse of today is educated by widely different methods and to meet widely different demands from those of yesterday, and to lay a wise and adequate foundation to efficiently equip the nurse of tomorrow, is one of the serious problems which concerns our teaching body, and our far-seeing sympathetic associates and medical officers. We may indeed be thankful that in the education of the present-day nurse, a wider interpretation of this simple title prevails, and whether the demand for service today calls her to the private home or to the hospital, or to serve in time of general calamity, such as earthquake, fire, flood, or to succor the wounded on cruel battle fields, the ministrations of the true nurse may be anticipated not only with a confidence that she possesses technical skill and the experience which makes her the chief assistant to the great surgeon, but also with trust and belief that in her experience in the School of Life, she has come into possession of that knowledge and sympathetic understanding of souls in distress, which fit her to be the chief assistant to the Great Physician.

We must all in time come to recognize the truth of the statement that the development of a soul is not a peaceful process like the growth of a plant. The realization of a divine purpose within ourselves, we are told, is not in obedience to a tranquil necessity. Forever there is conflict between high ideals and low standards, a wrestling with the principles of evil; hand to hand, foot to foot, every inch of the way must be disputed. It is thus in our struggle for lifting the nursing profession to higher efficiency.

Consider if you please, the promise that awaits the service to humanity if in some future time the majority of the young women who yearly graduate from our schools of nursing shall begin their public service not only with full technical knowledge and practical experience in the principles of nursing, but with their early ideals unshattered and their faith strengthened.

One of the problems long under consideration by our profession is how we can best serve the people of moderate means, that large majority of self-respecting home people who are the real bone and sinew of every country. One organization has suggested as a possible solution of this problem, the grading of nurses in First, Second and Third Classes, in accordance with the proved efficiency of each. Under such a plan would it not be logical to assume that the nurse of greatest skill and experience should be assigned for care of the patient who is in the hands of a second or third rate physician or surgeon, in order to insure the life of the patient? On the other hand, when one considers the assignment of a correspondence-school product or any other untrained, poorly-equipped woman to care for the patient of a first class skilled physician or surgeon, are we not at once confronted with the fact that all the skill of the greatest surgeon is set at nought and the patient's life placed in jeopardy by so doing?

The question is, Shall we have one good standard? If not, to whom then shall the second and third rate nurses be assigned?

1915-1918

Annie W. Goodrich

A leader in the field of nursing education, Annie Goodrich's dream was to move the basic preparation of nurses into institutions of higher learning. Miss Goodrich's early career included direction of the schools and nursing services of four New York hospitals, a term as inspector of training schools for the New York Department of Education, teaching assignments at Teachers College, Columbia University, and direction of nursing service of the Henry Street Visiting Nurse Service.

Miss Goodrich was chosen the first dean of the Army School of Nursing. The establishment of the Army School of Nursing during World War I came as the result of a study and recommendations submitted to the War Department by Miss Goodrich. In 1923, she established the Yale School of Nursing and served as the school's first dean. Miss Goodrich served as president of the International Council of Nurses and of the Association of Collegiate Schools of Nursing, and she was the recipient of many awards, medals, and honorary degrees.

A nursing leader for more than sixty years, Miss Goodrich died on December 31, 1954.

The Nursing Care of the Future

By Annie W. Goodrich, R.N., *president*

(Nineteenth Annual Convention, New Orleans, April 27-May 3, 1916)

It seems to me that this year when the best and strongest of many nations are being crushed and crippled and the Mother countries are bowed with anguish, it is singularly fitting that we should meet in New Orleans that breathes so harmoniously the spirit of the old and the new world, this city that has suffered and wept, but always smiled again, and therefore for this opportunity and what it will mean to us, again we thank you.

My message, members of our Associations, is a brief one.* Never before have words seemed of so little value, never the deeds of many of such stupendous import. Another year has rolled by and we have met to discuss again our problems that do not seem to lessen, but rather increase with time, nor would we have it otherwise, for problems and progress go hand in hand.

The most casual observer of our program could not fail to note the rapid growth and expansion of our profession. We shall within the next few days hear of the increasing demand by municipalities, states, and the Federal Government for nurses until the number needed reaches into the thousands. We shall hear of new branches of work in already established fields, and also of new and undeveloped fields themselves, and we shall wonder through what avenues the varied and extensive preparation required for effective service in these fields can be supplied.

But as we listen to those concerned with the problems of nursing education, we shall find that here too the growth and expansion have been rapid beyond our highest expectation. New courses, new and more efficient methods of teaching and training have been developed and ever increasing affiliations with other educational systems are bringing our system into line with the progressive educational thought of the day.

The reports from those concerned with standardizing nursing education through state laws, will be of no slight interest. We shall find that one state has but a few weeks since, through some amendments, placed upon its statute books, the most comprehensively progressive law governing the practice of nursing, that has yet been enacted, a law that requires every women desiring to

*Members of the American Nurses' Association, National League of Nursing Education and National Organization for Public Health Nursing.

practice as a graduate, certified or registered nurse, shall have not less than four years of high school and three years of professional training in a school of accepted standards; that provides for inspection and a registration fee sufficient to enable the work to be effectively carried on; and finally provides a reciprocity clause which is the most equable that has yet been drawn, since it permits a graduate in nursing of a training school maintaining standards equal to those of the state of Maryland, it matters not in what state the school may be, if already registered, to register without further examination.

We shall learn that another state has failed to pass a mandatory law although the requirements of this measure are far below those of the Maryland law, but we shall also hear as we have heard for the past four years, that unquestionably that measure will be passed next year, and that every cent and every moment that has been spent in the effort to pass this bill, has been justified by the public education that has resulted.

Not less significant of growth and progress is the call to consider incorporation under a Federal charter and the reconstruction of our form of membership. Twenty years ago there was no American Nurses' Association, there were a few schools of nursing, less I think, than a hundred; there were a few alumnae associations, even as late as 1900 there was not one state nurses' association. But there was a group, twenty years ago, of progressive women to whose vision we owe it, that we stand today a great body of professional women, numbering over 30,000; owning our own journal; issuing benefits and scholarships through our relief and educational funds; issuing each year an ever increasing and sounder body of literature; with forty-three state nurses' associations, through whose efforts, laws have been placed in the statute books, state curricula drawn up, training schools accredited, and educational standards maintained.

This is but the barest outline of what has been and is being accomplished, but before we raise our heads with pride, let us remember that there is another aspect of this situation, another side to this picture and to this side we should give our most careful consideration. We are wont to say that the greatest value of these gatherings arises from the renewed inspiration and the broader vision with which we return to our field. What, I wonder, would be the result if we could be carried to every corner where those who cannot be with us, are serving. From the Atlantic to the Pacific, from the Gulf of Mexico to the Canadian borders, even across that great continent and beyond the seas we should find them and from the service we should see them rendering we should draw a greater inspiration for renewed effort than we have ever felt before. But I wonder what would be the result if we should go from place to place where they are needed, and are not found.

In twenty-two small blocks of one of our great cities, live 30,000 citizens; nearly 90 per cent it is said, in time of sickness receive neither medical nor nursing care. An investigation of a suburban district gives statistics that hardly differ. We do not need to go into the almshouses, the foundling asylums or the prisons, not yet I fear is the highly trained nurse found there. In the next few days we shall hear pleas for the inclusion in the general preparation of an experience in contagion, tuberculosis and mental disease. Why? Because those suffering thus are not receiving what we mean by nursing care. What do we mean, what should we mean, and what will the whole world some day mean, by nursing care? We mean that skilled and intelligent service that is only ensured by a sound foundation of theory and a wide practical experience and through which only shall we correctly interpret as we alone have the opportunity of interpreting, the message of the scientist to the people.

One of the wise men of the ages has said that the whole history of man could be written in three words—"Born, suffered, died;" and the whole history of science, covered by one—"perhaps." What a depth of hopeless suffering in these words that never seemed truer than today in this great world crisis, but what a volume, what a world of hope in that one word *perhaps*. Perhaps those whose bodies are lying on the battle field garbed as enemies may, through the supreme sacrifice, be united in an immortal brotherhood. Perhaps the little group of men and women who are facing shot and shell and pestilence armed only with the red cross are sowing seed we know not of, of an enduring peace. Perhaps those most austere religionists, through their untiring search for truth, the scientists, may make the lame to walk, the blind to see, the deaf to hear; may open the door of the prison cell never to close again upon a fellowman; perhaps our part in this may be greater than we ever dared to hope; perhaps dear fellow members through our most bitter failures, others may succeed. As long as we can say perhaps, though we may fail and weep, we too shall rise again to toil and hope, and hoping, *smile.*

Letting in Light and Air

By Annie W. Goodrich, R.N., *president*
(Twentieth Annual Convention, Philadelphia, April 26-May 2, 1917)

I am not going to inflict upon you a history of the progress and growth of the nursing profession. That you can find eruditely set forth in the *History of Nursing* by our great leaders, Nutting and Dock. I am not going to dwell upon our rapidly broadening educational opportunities through our university affiliations and our graduate courses, nor the advanced fields to which nurses through these opportunities are being called. Nor shall I take these few precious moments to review even so important a matter as the progress in state legislation. These and many other topics will be ably and amply dealt with in the conferences and meetings of the coming week. I do not propose to present in detail a picture of the innumerable institutions with their ever extending departments, splendid in construction, extensive in equipment, that have come into existence during this period. Operating rooms with marble and tiled floors and walls; pathological and X-ray departments; comfortable, even luxurious, provision for private patients, that have attracted all classes of society to these institutions and have wiped out the traditional odium imposed by their classification under the charities—those developments have followed one another in bewildering succession in institutions for the sick, striving ever to keep in touch with the rapidly progressing needs of the scientists.

I shall not even permit myself to yield to the temptation of comparing the days when fifty percent of the compound fractures not only meant a loss of limb, but the loss of life, with the present absence of infection, or of operations then infrequently performed requiring weeks for recovery, now so frequent as to be barely noted and recovery from which is only a matter of a few days.

It would not seem possible, however, that any retrospection should fail to mention the way in which institutions, equipped as they never were before, expanded effectively to receive the little sufferers of the great epidemic that swept over our cities last year, or to enlarge upon the sense of social responsibility, illustrated by the great philanthropic and municipal organizations that established at once after-care that will reduce the crippling to a minimum.

It would be impossible certainly not to linger for a moment to recall the fact that it is within this short period that the Red Cross Nursing Service in America has been developed and established, and through such development stands today with an army of qualified nurses prepared to answer to all too imminent call of the country.

Not, I say, upon all these wonderful and rapid developments of medical and nursing science does my retrospection rest, but rather upon, may we say, their cumulative interest into one great, splendid, outstanding result, namely, that evils that for centuries have demanded a heavy toll in human life, in human suffering, in crippled efficiency, and the expenditure of vast sums of money, have during this period been unhesitatingly pronounced preventable.

As I turn from one evil-removing, health-restoring achievement to another, the list is long, beginning with smallpox, diphtheria, tuberculosis, typhoid, malaria, yellow fever, typhus, syphilis, infant mortality, insanity, and crime. In comparing the statements of authorities concerning them, the words of that most representative American, James Russell Lowell, "Democracy in its best sense is merely the letting in of light and air," seem to attach themselves to each statement like a refrain.

Let me present a few concrete illustrations. Concerning tuberculosis, that disease which Hippocrates 400 years before Christ pronounced the most fatal to man, Dr. Biggs writes recently of the therapeutic benefits of sunlight and ventilation. No fiction could ever be more thrilling than Dr. Gorgas' narration of the application of Walter Reed's discovery, that not only made possible the greatest engineering feat of the ages, but also made life in the tropics possible for the white man. Not less important to the world is the knowledge that not through hospital care, not through artificially prepared feedings, a heretofore accepted loss of maternal and infant life is rapidly being prevented.

Although the victims of mental disease still may be found in prison cells, their freedom in the near future is assured, for here we find again accepted this new doctrine of prevention.

The last, and shall we say the most marvelous message of all, comes from the criminologists and penologists, who report successes in changing autocratic systems into democracies with responsibilities vested in the prisons themselves.

There is still one great evil that we have not mastered. It spells the maximum of waste, agony, and ruin. For two years it has held the old world in its clutches; today we are its victims. There are those who still believe war inevitable as long as men are men. There are others who see in this war the triumph of a great cause, and they will go forth gladly to make the greatest sacrifice that can be made. There are others, and I am among them, who believe that no more than can the knife prevent cancer, can war prevent war.

This is not the time for any nurse to falter. The splendid army of Red Cross nurses that seems so adequate today, a terrible need tomorrow may reduce to insignificance. Fewer than ever will the messengers of health, too few at best, who go from door to door of the long street, their skillful hands and needed services securing eager admission and a readier ear for the message of the health-giving properties of light and air. Not less faithfully, not less courageously, even more strenuously than those who see in this step of their country the triumph of their causes, must those proceed who see their cause deferred by many years. No cause worthy to be a cause can ever die.

Nursing and the Great War

By Annie W. Goodrich, R.N., *president*
(Twenty-First Annual Convention, Cleveland, May 7-11, 1918)

We have come together in the most momentous period not only in the history of this county but in the history of the world, to consecrate ourselves anew to the service of humanity through our chosen profession.

For the first time in the history of our country included in the military establishment is a division of women in an almost definite ratio to the number of men: one million men, ten thousand nurses; four million men, forty thousand nurses. Upon this body whose function is the conservation of life, not less than upon the body whose function is its destruction, is imposed a service that no personal sense of inadequacy permits of escape. Such service as can be rendered must be rendered by every member of our profession today that through the forceful hands of men and the healing hands of women a purified world may be prepared for the generations that are to come.

It is therefore our highest duty during the few days when, gathered together from all parts of the United States, we meet for the consideration of each aspect of the situation in which we are involved, to prepare a programme of work that looks to the most far-reaching results in every field, that leaves no stone unturned to treble, not alone in numbers, but in efficiency, our nursing strength.

Through simple and effective organization we must make it possible to carry to the most remote corner of each state our message to every member, that each member may make her full contribution of nurse power. Our reorganization was indeed timely; the effort of the national organization to decentralize, throwing back upon the state the burden of its responsibility, is in strict accord with the policy of the Federal Government and is in contrast to the policy pursued at the time of the Civil War in such matters as the draft and other similar measures. Little did those whose vision brought these great associations of ours into such early existence, providing them with an official organ, dream of the public service they would be called upon to render and through these means, only, could effectively render.

Through ever closer and closer cooperation with all sister organizations must the woman power of the country, so increasingly great, be brought to strengthen our hands so overfull and still so pitifully weak.

To the institutions of higher education already responding to our needs must go a stronger and more far-reaching appeal, that the rest of our girls be aroused and not alone to the dramatic element of the nursing field at this time, but to the great varieties of its service to civilization: its potential contribution to the happiness of the race through the conservation of its health; its potential contribution to its spiritual and mental development so dependent on the normal body; the part it may play in the diminution, or even the eventual abolishment, of those institutions that are as much monuments to the defects of our social state as are our institutions of learning and religion to its virtues—our institutions for dependents, for incurables, our prisons, penitentiaries and jails. Their heavy doors have closed and are still closing, not only on the men and women victims of our social system, but on the children, blotting the sunshine out of little lives that can only reach an efficient maturity through its rays. Of whom should we expect a more penetrating vision, a broader social interpretation, than from those in whose hands is placed the shaping of the thought, and through the thoughts the lives, of the citizens of tomorrow; and those whose thoughts have been so shaped. I would not think that there would have to be a war to call our students to the nursing fields or to make faculties perceive its social values. Inspired by visions of its usefulness, equipped with sounder tools through which to reach their goal, these nurses of tomorrow should break down walls that we of today have never tried to scale.

There is another group that we must reach and make our call ring in their ears, for their own sake not less than for the sakes of those who need their services—the young women who through the fortune of environment are not compelled to earn their daily bread. Until they take their place beside their sisters who have always toiled, sharing in their renunciations and rendering a service so complete that they shall not suffer the after smart of undeserved applause but reap the benefits that accrue to those who have demanded of themselves a full conformance to the requirements for a chosen field.

And last—ourselves! What is our programme for ourselves? The army of trained workers called to the side of these men, picked men, men that it was planned, or so we thought, should build through years of healthy, happy manhood, our democracy. Never in our history have we been so under fire; never perhaps again will there be such a period of testing. With all the strength we have, with all the undreamed of strength we can summon, in every manner of which we can conceive, through every avenue of service we can find we should seek to raise the standard of nursing so immeasurably above the service rendered in all previous wars, in the military field today and in civil life, that after this ghastly struggle is over, freed through a record of high service from commercial uses, the hamperings at social prejudices, the limitations of inadequate preparation, our profession may contribute in fullest measure to the restoration of the crippled, scarred humanity. *This is our sacred legacy of labor from the young fathers of the country, that their supreme sacrifice may bear fruit through a fair unblemished manhood of tomorrow.*

I wish, if it would make my message stronger, that I might have come to you with knowledge gained first hand, not alone from our camps of preparation, but from those under fire. But what I have seen leaves me in no doubt as to our attitude or action at this time, whether as part of the military establishment or serving our country through some other field. In my conception of this service the military system plays no small part. In this establishment we have, through the unification of forces, a body of labor that gives the greatest return in the shortest period of time, a system of control and direction that establishes simply and incontestably the authoritative voice. Its demand that all accessories that consume space, time, or thought that are not needed for its own designs shall be abandoned, commands a maximum of individual service. Through it was achieved the greatest engineering and sanitary feat of the century, if not of the ages. However short it may have fallen of its own or the communities' desired achievements at this time, its great accomplishments already justify its methods and commend its system for situations where concentrated effort and concerted action are acquired.

The official bulletin for April 8, reviewing the first year of America's participation in the war, states as follows:

> The outstanding feature of the first year of war has been the sudden transformation of America's young and able manhood into an army that today numbers 12,380 officers and 1,528,924 enlisted men, whereas one year ago today the total actual strength of this uniform force was but 9,524 officers and 202,510 enlisted men.

Gathered from every walk in life, accustomed to an individuality in thought and action, through citizenship under a Government that has not heretofore expressed itself in terms of autocratic control, this great army is uncomplainingly learning its rapid and rigid lesson in the subordination of self to the machine. For it, and in no small measure through it, plains have been converted into cities and the great hospitals scientifically equipped have arisen almost overnight. Here we have been called to take our place but with no stern exactions, rather with all the considerate thought that could be given in this time of stress and strain, and to render not a new and unchosen service but one of our own election. In order that we may discharge all tasks more heavily weighted with responsibility than appears on the surface, we are asking the device whereby authority in the military system is universally recognized. It should be given us, it must not be denied. Its accordance may mean a conformance to its customs and traditions not hitherto required. I think such conformance should require no military action.

'Our Service Is Our Recreation'

Is it too much to ask, I wonder, that we have seen life at such close range, that have been privileged to come close to its great truths with all its foolish trappings stripped away, should of our own accord demand of ourselves a strict observance of these military customs so that in every way we shall promote and not retard the efficiency upon which so much depends? Is it too much to require of ourselves that as long as this war lasts, we conceive of our service, wherever it is rendered, as our recreation and our recreation as a service that we will not now endure? Such an attitude of mind would find no hours too long to devote to the accomplishment of its self-imposed tasks, no heretofore diversion would have power to attract and no time and space-consuming customs of dress be tolerated. The service to be rendered by our profession in these great camps, even as in our cities, is only limited by the vision of those who perform them, and nursing procedures are not the only items in the list. With minds purged of all selfish interests, intent alone upon the consummation of a gigantic task, let us perform our part. The manhood of our country has been called to undergo a testing not less cruel and searching for soul and mind than body; are they to emerge triumphant helped by our hands or hindered by our presence? Pray God that in this crisis of the nations we nurses may not fail.

Let us therefore, tonight, consecrate ourselves and our services anew for all the days, the months, or years, if need be, of this great struggle.

1918–1922

Clara D. Noyes

The successor to Jane Archer Delano as director of the American Red Cross Nursing Service, Clara Dutton Noyes was a graduate of Johns Hopkins Hospital School of Nursing, Baltimore, and became head nurse at that hospital after her graduation. She went on to become superintendent of St. Luke's Hospital, New Bedford, Massachusetts; New England Hospital for Women and Children, Boston; and Bellevue Hospital, New York City.

Miss Noyes was summoned by Miss Delano to serve with the Red Cross as director of the Bureau of Nursing, and her contributions to that nursing service were many, including the organization of base hospitals and other nursing units, the standardization of surgical dressings, the development of a course of instructions, and guidelines for the use of nurses' aides. When the United States entered World War I, Miss Noyes was responsible for the assignment of nurses abroad, and on Miss Delano's death in 1919, Miss Noyes became director of the Red Cross Nursing Service. She held several offices in the International Council of Nurses, served as president of the National League of Nursing Education and president of the board of directors of the *American Journal of Nursing*. The impact of Miss Noyes' work was duly recognized through the many honors, medals, and awards she received, both in the United States and foreign countries. In 1933, she received, by popular vote, the Walter Burns Saunders medal sponsored by the American Nurses' Association for distinguished service in the cause of nursing.

Miss Noyes died on January 3, 1936.

The Changing Career Patterns of Nurses

By Clara D. Noyes, R.N., *president*
(Twenty-Second Convention, Atlanta, April 12-17, 1920)

At our last convention, now two years ago, the deep shadow of war was hovering over us; our hearts were heavy with sadness, our minds torn by anxieties and our bodies weary with the prolonged physical strain of extra work thrown upon us by the exigencies of war. To-day, nearly one and a half years since the signing of the armistice, we are deeply concerned with the task of readjustment.

While the pressure of actual war conditions has been lifted, the period of reconstruction brings pressure of quite a different type. The deliberations of the next few days will cover a wide range of subject matter, which will be an index to nursing conditions as they now exist and which we sincerely hope, will bring forward suggestions of ways and means of solving some of our problems.

Before declaring the convention open for the conduct of necessary business incident thereto, it seems logical to direct your attention to the character of the profession as it now appears. One has only to face an audience like this to gain an impression of the numerical strength of our organization. At the same time a thrill of pride in its solidarity is instantly "registered." Could there be anything stronger or more simple than our plan of organization—the alumnae, the local and state associations heading up in a national organization, with a delegate system of voting? This general form of organization prevailing in all three of our national associations offers, with its sections and special committees, an opportunity to all its members for expression.

It has been roughly estimated that 100,000 nurses have registered in order to conform to the nurse practice acts which exist in forty-six states, that we have about 3,000 schools of nursing from which probably 13,000 student nurses are graduated each year, and for which superintendents and instructors are required. The hospitals with which these schools are connected need large numbers of qualified nurses to fill the supervisory and other positions that exist in these institutions. The Army, with a personnel of 2,000 graduate nurses; the Navy, with 700; the rapidly developing United States Public Health Service, to which about 900 nurses have been assigned by the Red Cross alone during the past year; the Red Cross, with approximately 275 nurses working under its auspices in many foreign countries; 2,380 in its fourteen Divisions and many of its chapter offices, (1,800 of these as instructors in its classes of Home Hygiene and Care of the sick) while 8,000 nurses listed in the ranks of public health nursing, indicate in a measure the distribution of our members.

Sweeping hurriedly through this rather rough and more or less approximated classification, we can easily visualize this vast army of professional women nurses, pledged to service and, I firmly believe, the highest type of service that a woman can enter.

In viewing our development we find our associations engaged in raising great funds, one for relief of its disabled members; one to build a school of nursing in France as a memorial to those nurses who gave their lives during the war for the purpose of extending and perpetuating a modern system of nurse education under proper conditions and suitable environment. We find our periodicals well established and our literature increasing. Laws capable of improvement are constantly in need of amendment and, furthermore, must be almost constantly policed. During the past year the nurses have raised large sums of money to finance the committee working for rank for nurses and success in this direction appears to be close at hand, for it has become part of the Reorganization Bill of the Army and the special section providing for relative rank for nurses has passed both the Senate and the House. Large scholarship and loan funds have been placed within the reach of nurses who were desirous of preparing for public health nursing and as instructors in schools of nursing, while postgraduate courses in public health nursing have been increased in numbers.

A plan for national and divisional Headquarters will be presented for your consideration. It is hoped that the delegates will not reach a conclusion too hurriedly. The need for headquarters has never been greater. With our rapidly developing interests headquarters are almost indispensable. We must not let personal or political ambitions sway us, we must stand together, for unless we go forward we must drop back, something we cannot afford to do.

Conditions in schools of nursing, such as long hours and scarcity of pupils, are matters with which all nurses are deeply concerned and for which remedies are being sought. The National League will give the most careful consideration to this subject.

What about nurses themselves? Necessarily some unrest prevails. The nurses who went into active service, an army 20,000 strong, have come back from overseas or from military hospitals in this country, or from naval stations to which they were assigned, with a new point of view; some dissatisfied, it is true, some exalted by a broader and wider insight into the wonderful possibilities lying within their grasp; some physically unfit for nursing, but equal to some other form of work, ready and eligible for the re-education which our Government offers; others, and alas, there are too many! held in the grasp of that dread disease, tuberculosis, for whom arrangements for care under proper conditions are being developed as rapidly as possible by Federal departments.

The Scarcity of Graduate Nurses

We hear of a great scarcity of graduate nurses. This was particularly noticeable during the recent influenza epidemic,—where are they all? We should have many more nurses now than we had a year ago. Estimating rather roughly, it is true, upon about 15,000 released from active service, add to this the graduates of 1919, of probably 13,000 pupils, we should have at least 28,000 more nurses available for service than we had a year ago. What has become of them? From such information as can be secured, many seem to be leaving the profession entirely, many enter the business field which at present is offering lucrative positions and alluring possibilities; many are establishing homes for themselves in the country or are taking up land grants; as secretaries they seem to excel, while matrimony and tea-rooms beguile many from the ranks of active workers. We also find many, not leaving for something quite different, but entering related fields of activity, such as social service, anesthesia, X-ray, and laboratory technique; more recently our attention has been called to the fact that many are entering the field of oral hygiene. We are naturally concerned by these deflections from the straight path of nursing, for every one turning aside for what may seem a more attractive opportunity weakens our strength and scatters our power for usefulness. The unrest is not confined to nurses, it is noticeable in other professions as well. It has been stated that 140,000 teachers entering other fields of work last year.

The exodus from our own ranks, however, is our problem and is a genuine cause for alarm. We should like to see a definite campaign of education of the public to their responsibility in this direction undertaken. The importance and value of a nurse's education, her place in the economic and social scheme, proper schools, separate endowments, should be more generally and better understood. A different attitude should be developed toward the nurse. For example, at one moment she is declared by leading medical authorities to be the most important factor in our public health movement; at the next she is discredited, her work is belittled, she is deprived many times of an opportunity for initiative, a veritable barbed wire entanglement of restrictions is frequently erected about her that is not only humiliating, but crippling to initiative and development. At one moment the nurse's brain is used, at the next her hands only, are required, at the next both brains and hands and perhaps at the next, neither brains or hands. Can any profession grow and thrive under conditions as they now too frequently exist? Is a nurse necessary in the field as a public health worker or in the institution? Is she an important adjunct to the medical profession or is she not? If she is, then what can be done to interest her to enter the profession and keep her there after she has once entered? What can we do about it all? Isn't this one of the questions that we, as nurses, must try to answer?

If it seems necessary to retrace our steps and begin all over, then we must begin the education of a nurse back in the public consciousness. There seems little use of urging young women to enter schools of nursing if, because of conditions within, it becomes impossible for them to remain after they have entered. Every pupil that does withdraw is a propagandist against the system. Nurses alone cannot make good nurses, they cannot alone support or endow good schools. They need, as does every profession, the public back of them. They require the sympathetic understanding of the medical profession, they also require the support of an intelligent and educated public, at the same time they need to educate themselves to a wider comprehension of their own responsibilities toward the profession they represent and to the public they serve. We hear quite generally that commercialism is invading the ranks of nurses and some rather distressing stories are being told of excessive charges and of arbitrary and un-nurselike attitudes.

Perhaps this is what one might expect as a natural reaction to years of servitude and it is at least in keeping with the times. It is unfortunate, however, if there is any truth in these statements, as the nursing profession because of its uncommercial attitude and high-minded devotion to the principles laid down by the founder of modern nursing, Florence Nightingale, has been able to obtain a position in the minds and hearts of the great public that I believe no other profession enjoys.

While it is true that "Every laborer is worthy of his hire," we believe that we must still continue to make a a few sacrifices, we are still pioneers and we should count it still a glorious honor to keep the lamp, lighted by Florence Nightingale so many years ago, trimmed and filled and always burning, we cannot allow it even to dim lest we lose the priceless position that we have gained in the world's work.

Progressive Steps

By Clara D. Noyes, R.N., *president*
(Twenty-third Convention, Seattle, June 26-July 1, 1922)

On the twelfth of May, at the beautiful city of Bordeaux, France, the Memorial to American nurses who died during the World's War in line of duty was, with appropriate exercises, dedicated as a home and school building for the faculty and students of the Nightingale School of Nursing. The anniversary of the birth of the patron saint of nursing was a fitting occasion for this ceremony. The building is clearly and suitably marked, externally and internally, showing its origin and purpose, while a representative from each of the three National Nursing Organizations has been appointed to serve on its Advisory Committee. They will serve to maintain a close link between this Memorial School in France and the nurses of America whose small contributions (for the majority were of low denomination) were eagerly given in order that the daughters of France might have an opportunity to prepare under ideal conditions to "carry on" in the name of our beloved dead.

The materialization of the spiritual gifts of these nurses, whose passing is there commemorated, symbolizes in a measure the progress made in nursing since our last biennial convention. It seems customary on occasions of this nature to review achievements. This summary of accomplishment might be likened to the "slap on the back" given by the captain of a football team before the game, and if I do not review our weaknesses and our failures, which of course I should do, it is because I do not wish to rob you of the exhilarating effect of the encouraging prod.

Has there been progress, if so, is it of a constructive and lasting character? Is the criticism that our organization has developed a spirit of commercialism, a deserved one? Has the pitiless publicity directed toward the nursing profession, classing it as "the most autocratic closed shop in the world" been entirely without foundation? These and many other questions will be discussed during the deliberations of the next few days.

Organization, however, is essential to the growth and development of our profession. The purpose of organization is to promote professional and educational advancement, to elevate the standards of nursing education and ultimately to improve the character of nursing care of the sick, whether it be in the field, through public health nurses; in the home, through private nurses; or in the institution, through the student and graduate nurse. Every profession has felt the necessity for organization, not only for the purposes indicated above, but for protection as well.

Military rank for Army nurses favorably reported at our last Convention has become an effective law. It is almost too early to state whether it is as successful as its advocates hoped. We have heard some rumors that it is not, but I at least have not spoken to any member of the Army Nurse Corps who would wish to give it up. Furthermore, it is reasonable to believe that its full value could hardly be determined in time of peace.

The discussion regarding an inadequate supply of graduate nurses and candidates for schools of nursing seems at the present time to be less animated and from reports, the good schools, at least, seem to be well filled. This condition has been helped by the Student Nurse Recruiting Movement, launched under the auspices of the three National Nursing Associations, and the American Red Cross. This movement was directed toward a definite and continuous educational measure. While Student Nurse Recruiting was one of the objects, the educational work in connection therewith was of far greater importance. Hundreds of committees have been formed and many unique plans have been developed for arousing interest both in nursing as a profession and in the educational aspect of the work. Special reports will give in detail the record of accomplishment, and plans for the future.

The final establishment of a national office for the American Nurses' Association at 370 Seventh Avenue, New York City, adjoining that of the National Organization for Public Health Nursing, and for the present, at least, conducted in conjunction with the National League of Nursing Education, has been one of the most important and progressive steps that we have taken. The funds to maintain this office have so far been derived from several sources: the American Red Cross, our individual treasuries, gifts from alumnae and state associations, whole hospitals which have benefited by our placement work have become subscribing members. Such means of revenue, however, are too uncertain. It is hoped that the amendment to our by-laws, therefore, to increase the dues from 15 cents to 50 cents per capita, will be adopted. This increase will enable us to maintain headquarters of the American Nurses' Association on a dignified scale. This will also make it possible not only to develop, but conduct the Association and its affairs in a thoroughly businesslike manner.

The Headquarters Office is in a building with many other national health and social organizations, a position we should continue to hold. Representing, as the American Nurses' Association probably does, the largest organization of professional women in the world, with our Relief Fund, our magazines, our publications, our scholarship fund, we cannot afford to occupy a less conspicuous position than that which we now hold.

Nurses have become accustomed to hiding "their light under a bushel." It has been part and parcel of our training, an inheritance from the cloister. While we should regret to see the qualities of sacrifice and service so essential to the success of nursing lost or subordinated, yet we cannot afford, as an organization, or as individuals, to take a lesser part in the affairs of the world than we are now taking. The World's War settled (if it needed settling) the question of position for the nursing profession.

We can no longer stand aloof from other organizations working alone, solely on our own problems. The work of nursing touches the child, in the home and in the school, it is concerned not only with the care of the sick in the home and institution, but is concerned with the great questions of causation and prevention of disease, and therefore touches the work of other groups, the physician, the nutritional worker, the teacher, the social worker. Its interests are interwoven in the very fabric of civilization. For this reason we cannot go back, neither can we stand still, we must therefore press on.

Members of this organization, under the banner of the Red Cross, may be found in all parts of the world,—organizing schools of nursing in Poland, Czechoslovakia, Turkey, Haiti; in Child Welfare and general public health nursing in nearly every country in Europe,—in Porto Rico, the Virgin Islands and the Philippines while hundreds of Red Cross Chapters in this country are also utilizing our members in rural nursing work, or as instructors in the Red Cross course in Home Hygiene and Care of the Sick. For this reason and many others, we cannot afford to decrease our efforts to maintain good schools of nursing and satisfactory postgraduate courses for special training. We must give these "Missioners of Health" the best possible equipment, their work is too valuable, their responsibilities too serious, their privileges too great, we can send no less than the best among us to foreign countries; at the same time we need the best in this country.

During the deliberations of the next few days, consideration will be given to the problems and opportunities in nursing. Each one is here not only to learn, but to contribute something to the success of the meetings. We invite most cordially free discussion, we wish everyone to participate, we desire that each may go back to her daily task refreshed and satisfied.

Let me, therefore, in closing urge upon each the necessity for full and free participation in the affairs of the meeting. We extend the warmest and most cordial welcome to all, but most especially to the younger delegates, for upon their young shoulders we older workers must eventually place the burden of administration. In their young hands we must place the torch. To their youthful enthusiasm and devotion we must trust, not only the individual task, but ultimately the affairs of this great organization, knowing full well that they, like those who have preceded them, will find a way.

1922-1926

Adda Eldredge

A leader in the field of nursing education, Adda Eldredge served as the first educational director for the Wisconsin Bureau of Nursing Education. Miss Eldredge was a native of Wisconsin and a graduate of St. Luke's Hospital Training School, Chicago. Her career also included private duty nursing, teaching, and several positions with the American Nurses' Association, the National League of Nursing Education, and the *American Journal of Nursing.*

Among Miss Eldredge's accomplishments in the field of nursing education were improved housing, shorter working days, and longer vacations for students; better prepared faculties; and encouragement of completion of high school by nursing students. Because of the efforts of Miss Eldredge to improve the standards of nursing education in Wisconsin, the Wisconsin Bureau of Nursing Education was chosen by the Rockefeller Foundation as the basis of study for the establishment of similar bureaus in foreign countries. Miss Eldredge also served as executive director of the Nurse Placement Service of the Midwest States. She died on October 24, 1955.

Current Challenges

By Adda Eldredge, R.N., *president*
(Twenty-Fourth Convention, Detroit, June 16-21, 1924)

We do feel that there is a great deal which we have come here to discuss that may seem to one who does not know what nursing means, outside the question; but we all know that the questions which we are discussing here are as vital to the service of the people of this city, the people of the United States, and of all the countries of the world, as anything which is being discussed today.

I want to speak tonight of a few of the things of which we in our convention must think, must discuss, and for which we must find a solution.

We have had many difficulties in the organization in the last seven years; and as you know, we have been making our re-organization during all of that period; you have heard today that there are a few alumnae associations and a few districts which are not yet re-organized. You know, however, we now have an organization in every state in the Union, and that we have an association in Hawaii; and today you have had introduced to you a delegate from our latest addition to the American Nurses' Association of Porto Rico.

Before you tonight, as I hardly need state, are the officers of our three national associations, those organizations which have been and are so closely associated, where there is most perfect coöperation and which in our joint board meetings discuss any matter which is of importance to all.

There are times when we feel that possibly we might do better work with one organization. There are times when we feel that the work we are doing is much better done because we have the three organizations. As you know, we appointed a committee which we named the Committee on Self Analysis. You also know that one of our States has made a survey of our national organizations and has printed its conclusions and sent them out to each state. We have voted in the Board of Directors to use that report as a basis for the work of the Committee on Self Analysis and to ask that each one of you study conditions where you are, and send your suggestions to this Committee of which your President has been made the Chairman. Any action that may be taken regarding our three organizations must be taken on the basis of the questions; in which way can we do the best work? Where can we give the best service? There may be other things which may enter into it, but that is the great thing, how can each one of us in each of our organizations do the greatest amount of good?

The question of whether or not we may lessen our dues is a very trivial question, is one which we can hardly see, because if the work progresses, as the work must progress from time to time, that would be an impossibility. You cannot cut down as the work goes on; you must add to. There is not a nurse in this building tonight—and it really is a wonderful thing to look at this great body of nurses—there is not one here who desires one step to be taken that is not well thought out and that does not tend for better and more constructive work. The ideals of our three organizations are identical. The plans for work and the basis of the work to be done, do at times differ. The American Nurses' Association is an organization of nurses to make them conscious of their responsibility as nurses, as individuals and as citizens, to the public, to the profession, and to the state. We have accepted, in the American Nurses' Association, the standards which you have set in your States. We feel that these standards should be elastic enough that, once a member of the American Nurses' Association, the nurse can always be a member, unless for some grave ethical failure.

A tremendous responsibility rests upon us for the care of the patients, for the care of the sick, in the United States—a challenge not only to care for those who are ill, but a challenge as teachers of those who are well. One of the great challenges before us today is, how are the sick to be taken care of in our hospitals, not those hospitals running training schools, but those great hospitals for the care of the mentally sick, the care of those suffering from contagious diseases, those in our sanitaria for the care of tuberculosis. Many of our schools have not in the past given experience in the care of these different classes of patients. If every nurse will consider whether she could not give in these different hospitals even a few months, from three to six months' time, she would find, at the end of that time, that she had not only increased in experience, in efficiency, but that she had made a tremendous contribution. Also, if we fail, what? Is it to be Sairy Gamped again? We trust not. We hope that if the plans of the nurses are efficient their education will only tend to make them realize more completely the great opportunities for service, and that they will not fail.

There are other things that I would call to your attention, one is that we must work until every nurse is a member of our Association. We must work to see that those who have not our advantages, are given opportunities to come forward and to belong to our organizations.

These are some of the problems which we, as nurses, as members of the American Nurses' Association, must meet. Other problems will come to us during the Convention, which we trust you will take back to your Associations, through the Advisory Council, and through the National Headquarters, and later on, through the State Headquarters, and that you will help to solve the problems which are presented to you here. We hope the American Nurses' Association will be alive to all of its opportunities, realizing that if a branch of the tree be dead, the whole tree is affected both as to its beauty and as to its usefulness.

The challenge which the community offers us, is the opportunity for service, a challenge which we hope you all will meet.

Years of Progress

By Adda Eldredge, R.N., *president*
(Twenty-Fifth Convention, Atlantic City, May 17-22, 1926)

It is my pleasure and privilege to speak to you tonight as the President of the American Nurses' Association who has served you for the last four years and who, now about to give up that work, wishes to render to you an account of what has been accomplished since the meeting of our Association in Seattle, in

1922, when you honored me by electing me President.

At that meeting we raised the dues of the American Nurses' Association so that it was possible for us to start on a career with a chance of expansion that we had never before had. Headquarters was, as you know, already started through the kindness of the American Red Cross, and it had been under the control of the American Nurses' Association for about a year.

We were decided upon our headquarters by the fact that the National League of Nursing Education was ready to place its Executive Secretary in charge. We appointed a full-time Director on January 1, 1923. The expansion has been gradual. We began with the Director and one stenographer and added an assistant to the Director, but in January, 1924, a change in the plans outlined by the Headquarters Committee changed somewhat the functions of Headquarters, and the decision was made that a Field Secretary and a Publicity Secretary were needed for expansion, instead of an assistant to the Director.

Gradual expansion meant that we had a large balance on hand our first year. The Finance Committee budgeted for the Association and the Headquarters Committee budgeted for the Headquarters. There was a gradual unloading of the bookkeeping, and the mechanics of the work was placed at headquarters. Careful budgeting is still necessary. The size of the income seemed large, but it has been necessary to study and plan not to exceed the budget.

The Placement Bureau was one of the original projects and was a joint activity of the American Nurses' Association, the National League of Nursing Education, and the National Organization for Public Health Nursing. A plan was submitted for combining with the Placement Bureau of the N. O. P. H. N., but this plan of the Common Activities Committee for the three organizations was found to be too expensive, and was not adopted. Dual control was found impracticable for the American Nurses' Association, and its participation was merely a contribution of money. In 1926, as the scope of the work of the Placement Bureau seemed to be more or less confined to the eastern states, the American Nurses' Association withdrew its support, because of the requests of the National League and other organizations throughout the country for our assistance with the project of the grading of schools, for a survey of private duty nursing, and for many other urgent things.

In 1925, the President suggested a reserve fund. This was adopted by the Board of Directors, and $5,000 was set aside. In 1926, $2,000 more was set aside, for the reason that it didn't seem sane and sound for an organization of this size to exist without having a good, financial basis.

Plans for international expansion were approved by the delegates, necessitating $2,700 in the 1926 budget, as the share of the American Nurses' Association. It was most gratifying at a meeting of the Advisory Council of the American Nurses' Association to find how directly the states stood back of us for some of them were willing even to raise the funds rather than have them taken from our budget.

Two field secretaries were appointed, in the belief that cultivation of the field was necessary for proper development of the states and that the only sound way of increasing our work, our activities, and our membership, and at the same time, our budget, was in the states and through the states.

We have tried to encourage headquarters in the states. Interesting material is available at the National Headquarters on every state and is for their use.

A new division, the Middle Atlantic, has been formed. It held its first meeting in December and includes the states of Pennsylvania, New York, New Jersey, Delaware, Maryland, and the District of Columbia.

There has been an initial meeting of the states of Wisconsin, Michigan, Illinois, and Iowa to form a Lakes Division.

A number of committees have completed their work. The incomplete work is on the grading of schools, and the study of private duty nursing. The Chairman of the Grading Committee has said that he believes that the study of private duty nursing is a logical part of the whole nursing situation which must be studied in the grading of schools.

We have appointed several committees which have done little work at the present time, but for which we see a tremendous scope. One of these is the Committee on Professional Relations. All of us know how much what we are doing needs to be understood by the medical profession and by the community, and perhaps we need to study both the medical profession and the community to see what they need from us.

You know that our section of the Government nurses, which was formed at Detroit, has meant a tremendous increase in the membership of the American Nurses' Association and has greatly strengthened and helped not only the American Nurses' Association, but also the Government Services.

We are all to be congratulated, as well as the Army and Navy Nurses, on the passage of the Nurses' Retirement Bill.

You are going to hear something later at this meeting from the Grading of Schools. We hope to hear of a program for the raising of funds, in which we shall need your assistance. We do not see this grading of schools as a short-time problem but one which may stretch out indefinitely into the future.

Plans should be cultivated and carried out, for bringing a knowledge of the International to every nurse in the A. N. A. There is much to be learned from the development of nursing in foreign countries and much that we need to learn of the different ways in which nursing can develop and in these new countries we shall see many things tried that to a conservative mind may seem strange but we should keep an open mind with regard to them.

I have already written regarding the American Red Cross and the fact that we must keep this unique connection and do all in our power that we may always have the fine reserve that we had at the beginning of the Great War.

Anyone who has served for four years as President of an organization must, of necessity, look over what has been done with a somewhat critical attitude and, if she has gained anything from her years of experience, she must have a vision of some of the things that are yet to be done. On the basis of a careful study of what we have done during the last four years and with, I hope, a vision of much work still undone, as your retiring president, I wish to suggest that the following recommendations be given at least careful consideration.

Some Suggestions for the Association

First. A steady increase in the reserve fund. It is unsound for an organization with such responsibilities as this one, to lead a hand-to-mouth existence. We should be building for a firm financial foundation. This will make for slower expansion but it will make for surer growth. It will prevent frequent curtailment of plans made, or a deficit. Therefore, we need a conservative Finance Committee which will carefully budget from year to year and a conservative Board of Directors which will not exceed the budget.

Second. Increase of the income which means increase of membership. Our growth in the last four or five years has been from 49,000 to 54,000,—but 100,000 nurses are registered. Why have we only 54,000 in the A. N. A.?

Third. Use of the field secretaries to help the states see their possibilities for growth and advancement. It is important that the secretaries get to the district and alumnae associations instead of talking only to state meetings. Of necessity they will be more needed in states without headquarters than in those with headquarters.

Fourth. Encouraging visits of state secretaries to Headquarters that they may see the work of the whole country. Field secretaries may give valuable help to the state secretaries in the states by helping to survey the conditions and by serving in an advisory capacity.

Fifth. The continued use of the publicity secretary to help formulate an interest in ethical news of nursing; the sending of material to the states which can be supplied by the publicity secretary; suggestions and information to be sent in from the states of the publicity secretary for use; use of the publicity secretary by the two other organizations and the *Journal.* The editor of the *Journal* having been chairman of the Public Information Committee of the A. N. A. has prevented any conflict between *Anagrams* and the *Journal.*

Sixth. Making material sent to states more useful, seeing that it is properly distributed without waste, and finding a way to have it reach all the members of the association.

Seventh. A tie-up between the representatives on the Women's Joint National Legislative Council and members of State Legislative Councils.

Eighth. A caution to the Sections that they are not separate organizations, and that their function is neither legislative nor executive, but that their recommendations must go through the Board of Directors if we are to grow as a profession. We must be careful what advice the Legislative Section makes to the Board of Directors on specific action in the states, beyond the setting of a minimum, and where possible that minimum should be the same in all states. It is impossible to have state laws all exactly the same; and it is important to bear in mind that laws are only set-up machinery and that the work must be done according to the constitution of each individual state, remembering that all states have not attained equal growth. Sections are discussion groups; they may recommend to the Board of Directors, but it requires care on the part of the chairman and secretaries to see that all information goes through Headquarters—otherwise, the President and Board of Directors may be unaware of action for which they may definitely be held responsible.

Ninth. As to the officers of the A. N. A., judging from past experience, it would be wiser for member states of the A. N. A. to select the president from the Board of Directors, electing vice-presidents with an idea of making them president or else having a president-elect. It is impossible, or at least an Herculean task, to ask anyone who has not had experience to step in to do such a piece of work. She should at least be selected from the Board, and therefore, the Board should be chosen with this idea and also with an idea of representing the country.

Tenth. It is a bad plan to put in new officers while plans of the old Board have still some time to run. It makes the term of office variable, as the time of the biennial meeting varies with the seasons, according to the part of the country in which the association is to meet.

Eleventh. We must consider that the time is coming when the A. N. A. headquarters will have to be nearer the center of the country and more accessible to all. We will have to consider some other place than New York.

Twelfth. Greater interest and more intelligence on the part of the states regarding nominations, or else some other method of nomination. We need more care and thought in the distribution of members of the Board of Directors. It is interesting to note that, although your President announced at Detroit that she would not run again, a number of states wasted their nomination by putting her name in, and that a number of women who had retired were put on the ticket, thereby losing to those states their nomination. It is surprising, too, what a large number of states never send back the nominating blanks.

Thirteenth. More effort should be applied to training our younger members. Don't be afraid of youth! Youth will make mistakes but so do their elders, although perhaps not always the same mistakes.

Fourteenth. It is very important that with the formation of new divisions they avoid becoming political. It is necessary to keep always in mind the fact that the division is not a separate organization, not an executive or legislative body, but is intended to bring the adjacent states together. In other words, to bring the A. N. A. home to those who do not and cannot attend national meetings. In the state, we have home problems, in the A. N. A. these come from all states to the nation.

Fifteenth. As brought out in the Committee on Self-Analysis, we must bear in mind the thought of one national organization, but let us not move hastily and not on the basis of dues but on the basis of intelligent thought as to needs and services to be rendered.

Sixteenth. We should also give thought to our interlocking directorates. With such a large association and with comparatively few members on each Board of Directors, and a limited time which the Directors can spend at meetings (even when not considering the large expenditures of funds for the organizations), a representative being on one, two, or even all three boards, has to select one whose meetings she will attend. If an effort is made to attend the others, her knowledge of each Board is apt to be so limited that she cannot act intelligently.

Seventeenth. We are increasing expenses at Headquarters as the work grows and we realize more and more what the tremendous burdens are that our women have been carrying. The devotion of those at headquarters and in the field cannot be paid in money.

As my parting words to you I will say, let the star which is our guide be that ray of hope which makes us see into a future for nursing which leads to a perfect realization of the highest ideals of womanhood; a world such as Florence Nightingale saw when she dreamed of every mother capable of so caring for her child that it should have a chance for perfect health, and in it we see every nurse with an ideal of service which shall spring from that ideal coöperation between boards of directors, the medical profession, educational institutions, and nurses, that the education of the nurse shall not be a slogan of discord but an aim for all; and that our great united profession shall move on as one with an ethical standard which is a living, breathing part of every nurse's life, an American Nurses' Association crowning the work for humanity through the membership of every graduate registered nurse. Let our goal be 100,000 members in the American Nurses' Association in the next ten years. Ever higher our ambitions for our profession soar and ever our vision sees more to be accomplished.

1926-1930

S. Lillian Clayton

A graduate of Philadelphia General Hospital School of Nursing, Lillian Clayton served as superintendent of nurses at the hospital 15 years. Her prior experience included service as assistant superintendent of the hospital and training school at the Miami Valley Hospital, Dayton, Ohio; superintendent of nurses at the Minneapolis City Hospital; and educational director of the Illinois Training School for Nurses, Chicago. While holding her position at Philadelphia General, Miss Clayton also served as director of nursing of the Bureau of Hospitals of the Philadelphia Department of Health. She was also president of the National League for Nursing Education, the American Journal of Nursing Company, and the Pennsylvania State Board of Examiners.

Miss Clayton died unexpectedly on May 2, 1930, the only ANA president to die in office.

An Activity Update

By S. Lillian Clayton, R.N., *president*
(Twenty-Sixth Convention, Louisville, June 4-8, 1928)

From the standpoint of the organization, I desire to present to you a picture of its relationships, of some of its accomplishments during the past two years, and some of the questions that together we must meet, and for which we must find an answer if the

American Nurses' Association is to continue to carry out the purposes that brought it into being.

When going to the several states during the past two years, I have been increasingly impressed by the splendid work done by the local and state associations, and by the effort that is being put forth by them to carry out the recommendations made by the national body. At times, I have wondered how so much could be accomplished, and have asked myself why they have had such faith in the parent body, as to cause them to be so willing to put forth such effort. An affiliating student nurse gave me the answer, without realizing in the least that the answer to this examination question meant more to me than any other answer. She said she looked forward with great dread to the time when she would complete her course in the school of nursing and go out into the community, leaving the friendliness of her school behind, but that now, since she knew something about the American Nurses' Association, she no longer had that dread, because she would go from the friendliness of the school, into the friendliness of the American Nurses' Association. That was the answer to my own question, regarding the source of the spirit found in the work of the state associations. *The American Nurses' Association has grown out of the needs of the individual nurse.* It would never have been started, nor would it have been continued all these years, had there not been a necessity for it. Its objectives consider the individual needs as they exist, and look forward in anticipation to future needs. The American Nurses' Association has taken into account the condition of the age, and has been forward-looking, so that the needs of the individual, and of the group have been thought of, and planned before the need became a conscious one to the group mind.

As we look back over the years, one great fact stands out very clearly. The continuity of effort and achievement. Every year sees the problems of the various parts of the country brought to our local, state and national meetings. Always one hears the careful deliberations, realizing the time and effort that are put into the study of these problems of the various committees, realizing that the effort put forth, and the recommendations made by one group, are carried on to the next, that the effort goes on and on, that in every generation, new workers come to the front, but always with the same desire—to serve the good of the whole by meeting the need of the individual, and through the group and the individual—the citizen.

In making a study of the reports sent to us by the Director at Headquarters, we realize that a great deal has been accomplished during the past two years, in continuing to make very close connections between the states and Headquarters. In the past two years, the problems arising from the changed conditions influencing the work of the private duty nurse, have made heavy demands upon the parent organization in interest, time and money.

In the wise solution of these problems to the best interest of all concerned, lies, we believe, our greatest usefulness at the present time to the patient, to the nurse, and to the physician.

The Grading Committee is assembling valuable information which you can use, but you must not think it can be used only by the large organizations in your interests. You must familiarize yourselves with this information, and acquaint everyone in your locality who has any interest in these problems either as a consumer or professional. If you do not find interest, create it, so that in your locality, a nursing service may be established to be available for all who need it, in such form as can be paid for.

It is not the policy of the American Nurses' Association to support legislative matters, except as they are particularly related to nursing and health problems. It has, however, used its influence to gain support for the Education Bill, for the creation of a Department of Education with a secretary in the President's Cabinet. This kind of legislation has been sought for some time, and we have been glad to urge its support by sending communications to the congressmen, and by supporting it in our official organ.

Our effort to serve the states has resulted in a great increase in correspondence, a large part of this consisting in giving information concerning our organization problems. The interviews at Headquarters show an interesting and significant trend. Visitors from at home and abroad, singly and in groups, state and local officials, lay people and professional—all coming to the American Nurses' Association for advice and guidance. Through both correspondence and interviews, requests for information as to meeting the need of patients, nurses, and doctors, run like a constant refrain.

One of the most helpful contributions to the states has been the compiling of a Presidents' Portfolio, the material covering the rulings on organization matters, answering written questions and arranging these in loose leaf form so that newer needs making changes necessary, can be readily corrected. Copies of these have, during this convention, been given to every state president, to be transferred by her to her successor, and to be the property of the American Nurses' Association. It is hoped that this material will eventually form the basis for the American Nurses' Association Hand-book, and that it will help the president to carry out the policy of the organization, and help her to help the individual nurse.

Work on the 1928 edition of the Accredited List of Schools is under way.

Our membership is a matter of great import to us. In 1926 there were fifty-three thousand members (53,000). In 1928 there are seventy thousand, one hundred and eighteen (70,118), a growth of thirteen thousand (13,000) nurses in two years. This is a great gain, you will say, but we are told by Dr. Burgess that we have two hundred thousand nurses (200,000) in the country. The question confronting us is where are the one hundred and twenty-nine thousand eight hundred and eighty-two (129,882)? Do we need them? Do they need us? Have you any responsibility toward the answers to these questions, and if so, what do you consider this responsibility to be?

The Relief Fund is a vital matter to every nurse. An analysis has been made of our present plan of giving relief, and an effort made to determine whether our present plan, to be of assistance to our membership, during their illness, is the one best suited to their interests. The details of this will be given to you, and we hope that you will all be keenly interested. As a friend, the American Nurses' Association recognizes its responsibility to provide leadership in thought along this line. Much has been written concerning the so-called Harmon Plan of providing annuities for nurses at their retirement age. You are familiar with the statement prepared by Miss Carrie Hall relative to the findings of the Joint Committee appointed by the three national organizations to study the plan. I should like to quote from the summary of that statement so that the nurses of the country may call to mind at this time, the position taken by the committee, and later approved by the joint boards of directors:

"If the endorsement of the nursing organizations is to be secured, any plan must be sound, that the officers of the organizations can recommend to their own members without hesitation, not only the principle, but the details of the plan:

"1. Such a plan must not jeopardize the relation between the nurse and the public.

"2. It should be available equally to nurses doing all types of nursing work.

"3. It should provide not merely a retirement fund, at a definite age, but should safeguard to the individual nurse her payments into the plan, as savings with interest, if she be forced to withdraw before the retirement age."

To this statement, I should like to add that Mr. Harmon is still eager to assist us in this project, and the committee has not been dissolved. We are in direct communication with Mr. Harmon through his secretary, Mr. Coddington, and through Dr. Haven Emerson. We have kept three very important thoughts in mind:

1. The need of the nurses for some project of this or a similar nature.

2. The importance of studying the plan most carefully, so as not to commit the nurses to any plan unwisely or hastily.

3. The great importance of not closing the door on the future development of the plan.

We have, as you know, a Committee on Insurance. The chairman will have a very important report to make. We must bear in mind the great responsibility we have as individuals, and as groups to plan wisely for sickness and retirement. This is a personal obligation, and a civic duty. Much will be brought to us during the week from persons who have devoted time and intelligent study to the problem. We should think carefully of the information presented, and consider wisely such recommendations as are made.

Two years ago, the American Nurses' Association assisted in carrying out the recommendation of the Sesqui-Centennial Committee by contributing time, interest, and funds. An exhibit, showing the field of nursing, was, as you know, prepared by Mrs. Stella Booth Vail, and used with great success during the months of the life of the Sesqui-Centennial. We believed that it would have real publicity value. It has more than served that purpose, for it has traveled from coast to coast, and from north to south, proving to be of real educational worth.

Our financial responsibility is great. Our treasurer and finance committee are painstaking and wise. We have, however, at their request, appointed the Farmers' Loan and Trust Company to advise them on investments, as the guidance thus provided will give them a greater measure of confidence. Because of the important place our organization holds in relation to community interests, it must be closely connected with many other national groups. This necessitates sending representatives to the various meetings of these groups, making possible a mutal interpretation of function, accomplishment and growth. When you hear the reading of these reports of our representatives, try to realize with pride and humility just what our part as individuals should be personally and professionally, if we are to hold on to the position we have gained, and continue to go forward as community and professional needs develop.

Our predecessors have been standard bearers, and this brings us to the work of another important committee—that of Ethical Standards. The committee expects a great deal of discussion of the code that it has prepared. We are told by some teachers of philosophy that ethics is no longer needed or understood. Call it by whatever name you wish.

There will be presented to you a report of the Interim meeting of the International Council of Nurses that was held at Geneva, July 25 to 31 in 1927. I shall not, therefore, do more than refer to it at this time.

Every state should look forward with great eagerness, and do much planning for the meeting of the International Council that will be held in Montreal in 1929. An International Hospital Association has also been formed and will hold its first meeting next year in Atlantic City in conjunction with the annual meeting of the American Hospital Association. I hope that many of you will attend both of these meetings, and that you will have the experience that I had at Geneva—that the meeting will renew ideals, strengthen discouraged delegates, and give to all the countries represented, something truly worth while.

I returned from Geneva with faith 100% strong in the principles for which the International Council of Nursing stands—self government of nurses in their associations, and raising ever higher the standards of education, professional ethics, and public usefulness of its members.

Publicity—One of the Largest Tasks

I have made an effort to touch upon some of the facts in the life of our organization that would be of interest, and that would help us all to realize something of the tremendous responsibility we, the American Nurses' Association, carry. In order to continue the carrying of this responsibility, we must look forward to our program for the next year. There are so many important activities for us to consider, but first I should like to call to your attention that early in the year, eighteen nursing leaders stated that publicity, or giving the story of nursing to the public, is one of the largest tasks confronting us. What is the story of nursing that we are telling people? Are we understanding our own problem sufficiently to be able to interpret it to others? Are our patients, our doctors, our hospitals, understanding our profession and the problems surrounding it, because we are giving the proper interpretation? Our director at Headquarters has been telling the story of nursing by means of radio talks. She tells me her story has been the old, old story of nurse, patient, home and the home problems involved, and as a result, she knows the public does like nursing.

We must be actively interested, ourselves, in our profession. We must get a picture of the whole situation, nursing in its relation to the past, present and future—our relation to the patient, to the doctor, and to the community. There has never been a time when it was so necessary for the individual nurse to be able to interpret her own profession, and her place in it, as at the present time. The report just coming out by the Grading Committee will help us do this. Let us be responsible for reading this report ourselves, and for giving it to a patient and a doctor. This will be a concrete form of publicity in which we can all help.

There are further needs of our organization, each one of which I should like to enlarge upon, but time will not permit—a legislative secretary—more field workers—greater facilities at Headquarters to gather information. We are not truly a profession until we have some research work to our credit—research work in our own field. A registry study is needed. A membership campaign should be launched. Every group should consider the importance of developing leaders. Find some one in your own locality with native powers of leadership. Then do everything you can to help in her development. If such a one be found, let her assist in the development of her own abilities by never refusing to accept the responsibility placed upon her by the members of her group, and having accepted it, to carry it through to completion. Let her not be afraid of failure.

Last, but most important of all, let us remember that nursing was introduced in this country because patients needed nurses. Patients need nurses today. The need is not being met. What are the reasons? If we are emerging into a profession, or if we have emerged, let us remember that the fundamental principles of a profession are the ability to assume individual responsibility, and the having of altruistic motives. If nurses met the needs of patients fifty years ago because they believed it to be their individual responsibility to do so, and if their altruistic motives led them to assume that responsibility, what are the causes preventing our profession today from accepting these same fundamental principles? If we will earnestly seek the answer to this, we shall find it, and in finding it, we will serve our patients, our profession, and ourselves.

1930-1934

Elnora E. Thomson

A graduate of Presbyterian Hospital School of Nursing, Chicago, Elnora Thomson began her nursing career as superintendent of nurses at Elgin State Hospital, Elgin, Illinois. It was there that she acquired an interest in and knowledge of mental hygiene. She served as superintendent of the Illinois Society for Mental Hygiene and as director of public health nursing education for the American Red Cross in Italy during World War I.

Miss Thomson became director of the public health course at the School for Civics and Philanthropy, Chicago, and then undertook direction of the program of public health nursing at the University of Oregon. Her career also included operation of the San Francisco branch of the American Child Health Association and teaching public health nursing and history of nursing at the University of California at Los Angeles.

Miss Thomson died on April 24, 1957.

ANA and the Patient

By Elnora E. Thomson, R.N., *acting president**
(Twenty-Seventh Annual Convention, Milwaukee, June 9-14, 1930)

In preparing this report I have made every effort to follow the lines of thought which were Miss Clayton's for her report, so I ask

*As a result of the death of S. Lillian Clayton, ANA president, the first vice president, Elnora Thomson, was made acting president.

that you will feel as I do that this is not my message, but that it comes from her and that she asks us to carry forward her ideals for service and education, as well as our own, in the democratic spirit in which she believed and which she did all in her power to foster.

Nursing came into existence because of human need for such service. As we look back through history we find many interesting figures who stand out with striking distinctiveness because of the service they rendered humanity.

We find Phoebe, the early Christian, concerning whom St. Paul said, "She was the succorer of many and of mineself also." And we know that St. Paul did not always speak so favorably in regard to women.

After Phoebe there were many who devoted themselves to the care of the sick and the poor. In these early days the only requisite for those wishing to enter upon the career as nurses was that they had a service ideal, an ideal, however, strong enough to lead them to devote their lives to helping those who could not help themselves. There were among this group many eminent and learned women such as the Abbess Hildegard, who ruled over a large establishment and was skilled in the art of medicine as well as in that of nursing. But not until the time of St. Vincent de Paul did any one clearly help others to see that the service ideal was not sufficient, that there must be education as well if this ideal were to be made effective. When, with the help of Mlle. Le Gras, he organized the Sisters of Charity, there was a definite plan for nursing education. A similar plan was later followed by Pastor Fleidner who, with his wife, Frederike, organized the Deaconesses of Kaiserswerth.

These two organizations, based as they were upon the service ideal and the need for education in nursing, and working in both hospitals and homes, gave Florence Nightingale her opportunity for observing methods in caring for the sick, for while traveling on the Continent she spent some time with each of these groups. She put her observations into effect when she utilized the method observed in developing the military hospitals in Crimea, when she was asked to help her country.

Many people think of Florence Nightingale vaguely as some one who intuitively knew nursing and organization and not at all as she was in her younger years when she not only had an overwhelming desire to serve the sick, but was also an indefatigable seeker after knowledge as to how this might be done in the best way possible. They do not realize that it is because of this intelligent preparation that she was able to give the service for which she stands today, as she has stood through all of these years, as a symbol of all that to obtain which the nursing profession is still striving. For nursing today is attempting, as did St. Vincent de Paul, Pastor Fleidner and Florence Nightingale, to meet human needs effectively by acquainting itself with all available pertinent knowledge so that its service may be effectively rendered.

There were others of her time, besides Miss Nightingale, who were interested in the education of lay women as nurses. Two other schools were established before the Nightingale School of Nursing came into existence, but Miss Nightingale, with her personality, experience, and spectacular service in military hospitals, stands out because, according to her biographer, Sir Edward Cook, she was prepared to "make public opinion perceive and act upon the perception that nursing was an art and must be raised to the status of a trained profession, and that the means by which she achieved this great work were three—by her example, her precept, and her practice."

It was not long after the development of the Nightingale School of Nursing before such schools were formed in the United States. With a look into the future the women who had put forward this movement here soon began to appreciate the need for some form of organization for nurses. So the Superintendents' Society was organized, now the National League of Nursing Education, and was followed very shortly afterward by the Associated Alumnae Association, which is now our American Nurses' Association. This year this Association celebrates its thirty-fourth birthday.

When the history of our Association is reviewed, it is appreciated that many things have happened during these years, and it seems appropriate at this time to note a few of them.

First of all, we take pride in our form of organization, which has come to us through the forward thinking of those nurses who in former years have led the nurses of this country to act soundly in developing this Association, which now counts in its membership more than 84,000 individual nurses. These, however, come to the American Nurses' Association not as individual members in the national association, but as individual members in their state association.

The state association is divided into district associations and these are made up of alumnae associations and of individuals whose alumnae associations happen to be in other states.

We are frequently asked how can an organization with so large a membership as ours and scattered over so large a territory serve the individual patient. Our answer is through our democratic form of membership, from the individual nurse to the district, to the state, to the national, and even to the International Council of Nurses, and vice versa from the national Association, with its House of Delegates and its Advisory Council, made up of state presidents to the states, to the districts, to the individual nurse and through her to the individual patient.

The effectiveness of our organization has been demonstrated. In an effort to protect the patient who needs skilled service and to give nursing a professional status, as well as to protect the well prepared nurse, the American Nurses' Association has through its state association, secured in all but one state and in Porto Rico and Hawaii, a nurse practice act. Some of these acts carry only minimum standards, but some of them are quite advanced.

Another impressive thing is the multiplication of schools of nursing in the United States. In the life time of the first graduate nurse, Linda Richards, schools for nursing have been started in all but one state of the United States, so that now there are some 2,000 or more. This all indicates that there is a need for the service which the nurse, when educated, is prepared to give. However, this rapid growth has not always been sound growth, so that now an attempt is being made to find out about the quality of the product of these schools, with the idea that quality is more important than quantity.

To do this, nursing has undertaken to examine itself through the Committee on Grading Schools of Nursing, which is now in the fourth year of its five-years' study. This study has brought to light information about the lack of employment experienced by many graduate nurses, and this has led this Association to consider its responsibility for the graduates of schools of nursing in the matter of economic security.

It would seem that in the past, to some extent, the distribution of the services of nurses has followed the needs for nursing. Thus district nursing developed to serve the economically dependent group and this service has expanded and changed so that it now enters the field of the prevention of disease and the building of health. In some instances it has even met the needs of the economically independent in the smaller incomed group, through a cost charge for bedside service. This latter group, however, is still largely without skilled nursing service, and therefore, the American Nurses' Association is somewhat concentrating its resources in the study of the nursing needs of this moderate salaried individual and family in an effort to find out the part which the nurses' official registry, now pretty firmly established, may have in giving this needed nursing service.

Too long in many instances, the registry has been regarded as merely an employment bureau for nurses rather than as, in addition, a distributing center for nursing service in the community. It has been found through trial in several places, that it can be such a distributing center, so that this larger view of the registry is not only sound from the standpoint of service to the patient in extending nursing service to all those who need nursing care, but also from the standpoint of the nurse. For in the light of our knowledge of economic conditions in the United States, it is obvious that the time has come when it is essential that the distribution of the services of nurses must be done more in line with modern practices.

Much more information has come from the studies of the Committee on Grading Schools of Nursing which is in reality, because of the methods employed, a self analysis of our profession by ourselves. As a result we believe will come knowledge of the needs of the present day patient whom we serve in co-operation with the present day practitioner of both curative and preventive medicine.

Judging the present in nursing by the past, we believe there will be worked out by our nurse educators and leaders new programs, not only for the education of nurses, but also for the practice of nursing as a profession. These plans will then be discussed in our state groups, modified by suggestions from the clear thinking individual nurses, and then in their modified form they will be accepted by our Association as a whole and put into practice by each of us as individuals for our service to our individual patients.

With our form of organization, nothing can be imposed from the national Association to the state, but rather must decisions be made by our groups of states in our House of Delegates.

So, granted that the nurse is still actuated by the service ideal and seeks knowledge as did Florence Nightingale as preparation for service, then when we are in majority, agreed upon our newer plans of procedure in nursing education and practice, we shall by "our example, our precept and our practice" create a public opinion which shall make effective through our 84,000 members our service to our individual patients and also make our contribution a part of the larger contribution for service which is being rendered by organizations similar to our own, working in other fields of endeavor but actuated, by the same ideal for service.

Nursing Comes of Age

By Elnora E. Thomson, R.N., *president*
(Twenty-Eighth Convention, San Antonio, April 10-15, 1932)

The past two years have brought to many people and to many professions problems which are difficult to solve, and the way in which these problems have been met demonstrates whether or not the people who meet them and the professions who meet them approach them with the judgment of an adult or in the way of children.

The nursing profession has faced difficult problems and perhaps, to paraphrase a caption which has been applied to America, we might say that the profession of nursing has through its method of meeting its problems, demonstrated that it has "come of age." In the face of difficult financial conditions the American Nurses' Association has grown from 82,000 members in 1930 to 110,000 members in 1932—a total which there is every reason to believe will be increased, in the next biennium, to a considerable extent and which means that in approaching the problems of nursing and nursing organizations we have this large number of individuals, and therefore the decisions we make as an organization have behind them the force of large numbers.

With the other nursing organizations and other organizations interested in nursing education, we have been facing our problem through the studies we are making of the profession. These studies show us very clearly that there is an overproduction of nurses and that there is still much to be done in improving the education which is provided for the average student nurse. We are also facing the problem of developing new fields in which nurses may be active; and the problem of distribution of nurses and of nursing service, as well as many other problems of a like character.

We know that there are too many nurses graduating each year. We therefore have a responsibility to decide upon some course of action which will reduce this number and to work out a plan for a proper ratio of nurse to population which will ensure a fine type of nursing care for each patient needing such care, and then with all the force of our numbers and our belief in our decision we must attempt to carry forward such a plan.

Such decisions and such plans can not be worked out by the American Nurses' Association alone but must be done in cooperation with the National League of Nursing Education and the National Organization for Public Health Nursing; and indeed, inasmuch as schools of nursing are closely associated with hospitals, we must also in making such plans have the cooperation of the medical profession and the American Hospital Association.

In the matter of the education of the student nurse, we of course look to the National League of Nursing Education for the direction of our thinking, but, as plans are developed by the League for the improvement of the education of the nurse, it is important that each nurse in her own community should get back of the program. We are quite sure that there are many patients needing nursing care either from a sickness or health standpoint, who do not have such care, and therefore we have a responsibility not only to the nurses who are now unemployed but also to the uncared-for patients, to work out a plan whereby everyone needing nursing service may secure it at a price which he is able to pay. In order to find out what the situation in this connection really is and what can be done about it, we have a committee working on Distribution of Nursing Service and have employed a field secretary to work with this committee so that we may make a workable plan which will put such service into effect and back of which we can stand.

We believe also that we are evaluating our services as individuals and as groups from other standpoints, particularly those which have to do with our service ideals. Two years ago Dr. Glenn Frank spoke to us about the art of nursing and reminded us of the danger of neglecting the art in the practice of the science of nursing. It is fairly easy to measure the quality of the science but it is very difficult to evaluate the quality of the art. In nursing, the art must be interpreted in service and to measure service there must be the appreciation of the quality of service by the person served and the analysis of the type of service which the individual nurse has given by that nurse herself.

Such a self-analysis would help us as nurses to realize the strong points and the weak points of our relationships. Have we been able to help the patient appreciate that we have a keen interest in his welfare? Have we helped the patient to realize that we consider him as an individual worthy of the best type of care? Those who were at the biennial meeting in Detroit and heard Dr. George Vincent give his memorable talk will remember that he asked us to consider him just an average person who ordinarily was not very important but who, when he was sick, felt himself to be very important and wanted everyone around him to recognize his importance. Have we in our contacts with physicians helped them to see us as supplementary adjuncts in the care of the patient; have we in our contact with the relatives and friends, hospital boards and other boards of directors, helped them to see nursing and the nurse as a helpful individual in all hospital and community projects; have we ourselves had a sense of satisfaction in our service which has made us determined to improve its quality and brought with it the joy which comes from service well done? Do we recognize our importance as individual nurses in making public opinion relative to the nursing profession? Isn't it true that the public thinks of the nursing profession, not as an organized group, but rather according to their own experience with the individual nurse?

Relationships

By Elnora E. Thomson, R.N., *president*
(Twenty-Ninth Convention, Washington, D.C., April 22-27, 1934)

As a review is made of the work of the American Nurses' Association during this last biennium which closes with this convention, it is found to be characterized by an effort to face the reality of the situation in which nursing finds itself, a situation which appears to be common to all other professional groups. At the very beginning of this period the members of one large group in the American Nurses' Association were finding it difficult to maintain themselves economically and as this period advanced more and more members were affected. As time went on it also became clear that a better state of affairs would not come quickly, but rather that any real improvement might be a long way off.

Therefore the Board of Directors of the A.N.A. could not assume a Macawber-like attitude and wait for "something to turn up," but rather had to consider our organization and our services to the end that we might make the most of all our resources. This meant that we had to look at ourselves, our services, and our form of organization in a constructively critical way to see if improvement could be made so that the organization might be more effective and thus make its service to the membership more adequate.

First, then, for the organization itself—its strength and its weakness. How could the strength be made stronger and how could the weakness be eliminated? As a result of looking at our organization and the way we functioned through it, the Board of Directors has asked the Committee on Revision and Membership to present to you at this meeting certain changes which, in the opinion of the members of the Board, will strengthen the organization.

Second, relationships. What could be done to improve relationships within our own group, with our sister associations, with allied professional groups, and with the public itself? Within our own group there had been developed sections which were, in the beginning, merely a place in which to gather together a group of nurses whose services were alike or similar. Gradually some of the sections have grown and have become conscious of needs for which help was sought from the association. One section in particular, the Private Duty Section, had many problems, partly because of the economic situation and partly because many members of this section felt they had little representation on the

Board of Directors, the governing body between biennial meetings of the association.

In an effort to meet these needs a conference for the officers of the Private Duty Section and the Headquarters Committee of the American Nurses' Association was held in the Fall of 1932, and the chairman of the section was also invited to attend the meetings of the Board of Directors held in January of 1934. That this was a step in the right direction is evidenced by the fact that the chairman of the Private Duty Section made certain recommendations at the January Board meeting which had previously been proposed by Board members and favorably acted upon. These recommendations, too, appear in the report of the Committee on Revision and Membership.

To study intensively our set-up and services, special committees were elected by the Board of Directors and these committees have given largely of their time and of their energies, and as a result we have a pretty clear picture of where we are going and excellent suggestions as to how we should carry forward. Recommendations received from these committees have also gone to the Committee on Revision and Membership and come to you as a result of the report of that committee.

As our services were studied it became quite obvious that in these services we could not work effectively alone, but must work with and through the National League of Nursing Education and the National Organization for Public Health Nursing.

To accomplish this the directors and assistant directors of the three national nursing organizations at Headquarters have established what they call a cabinet. They meet regularly once a month and discuss problems which are common to all, and through this method it has been possible to work out plans of many kinds that are far reaching in their implications for nurses in every state and district.

When in the Summer of 1933 the NRA came into existence the directors at Headquarters for the three national nursing organizations worked together to see to it that everything which could be done would be done to protect the nurse. Close contact was maintained between Washington and the Headquarters office. Conferences were held with the representatives of the American Hospital Association, and while the results may not have been pleasing to all nurses, certainly no effort was spared to safeguard nursing service.

Later, when the Federal Emergency Relief Administration announced through *Bulletin No.* 7 a medical care program, the three nursing organizations again collaborated and when the Woman's Committee came into existence the American Nurses' Association sent a representative from the Headquarters office to Washington to be sure that the interests of the nurses were safeguarded, for we are certain that if the interests of the nurse are safeguarded the patient also is protected. The whole story of this service will probably never be written.

The National League of Nursing Education is functioning well as the educational division of the American Nurses' Association and the National Organization for Public Health Nursing maintains the policy which it enunciated some years ago that all matters which affect the nurse professionally are the function of the American Nurses' Association, the function of the National Organization for Public Health Nursing being the service of the nurse in the public health field.

Relationships with the American Hospital Association have been maintained in a most cordial manner. Several members of the American Nurses' Association, the president of the National League of Nursing Education and the president of the American Nurses' Association, have appeared on the programs of the American Hospital Association at its last two annual meetings and the courtesies extended to the nurse representatives have been many and are greatly appreciated. At the meeting of the American Hospital Association in the Autumn of 1933 that association went on record as approving in principle the statements made by the American Nurses' Association relative to the nurse and the NRA.

Joint committees of the American Hospital Association, the National League of Nursing Education, and the American Nurses' Association are now functioning.

The American Nurses' Association cooperated with the National Council of Women in relation to the Century of Progress Exhibit in Chicago in the Summer of 1933. Nurses from the Illinois State Nurses' Association acted as hostesses for the American Nurses' Association at the exhibit and reports indicate that they served, as was anticipated, with tact, courtesy, and generosity.

Our committee on joint relations with the National Association of Colored Graduate Nurses has been active and several joint projects are under way.

In July, 1933, occurred the Congress of the International Council of Nurses in Paris and Brussels. Effie J. Taylor, Susan Francis, Adda Eldredge, and Evelyn Walker, together with your president, were the delegates for the Grand Council, and your president for the Board of Directors. There are now thirty national nurses' associations which are members of the International Council of Nurses—thirty associations with self-government working constantly to raise the standards of nursing education and nursing service in their respective countries to the end that the patient who needs the service of the nurse may have a service which is adequate and effective.

Christiane Reimann, secretary at the headquarters of the International Council of Nurses, reported regular correspondence with seventy-five national groups of nurses. Can anyone measure the value of this organization in its field of service or its influence in other international affairs?

Some time ago the National Health Council, of which we are an associate member, and from which we rent space for our headquarters and our *American Journal of Nursing,* gave us notice that they would move to Rockefeller Center on West Fiftieth Street, New York City, in April of this year. A special committee was appointed to study the matter. It was found that the National Organization for Public Health Nursing had decided that they must go with the National Health Council as public health nursing service is involved with the services of so many of the other member organizations, all moving to the new location.

The National League of Nursing Education awaited our decision. It was deemed most important that the three national nursing organizations remain together at this time for so many of our services, as has been previously stated, demand frequent conferences and cooperative effort. We also need the common services that are offered through the Health Council and the rent at the Rockefeller Center is a trifle less per square foot than we formerly paid. The neighborhood is much better and hotel accommodations can be obtained quite near at rates no higher than are paid in the hotels in the vicinity of the old location. We are therefore moved and are now located at the Rockefeller Center, 50 West Fiftieth Street, New York City.

While these studies were being made the regular work of the association went on. The work which was under way under the guidance of the Distribution of Nursing Service Committee has been completed and the information which resulted has been made available and is already being utilized by some of our state associations. The Registry Committee continues and it is anticipated that it will be more and more helpful to the individual registry and to the individual nurse.

It is encouraging to know that so many securities held for the Relief Fund Committee proved to be so satisfactory that they could be sold at par or better, thus making it possible to prorate a considerable sum to the state associations at a time when the need was great. It is to be hoped that more will be forthcoming in the near future.

You will remember reading in the September, 1932, number of the *American Journal of Nursing* a description of the completed work on the figure of the American nurse which was painted into the famous panoramic painting known at the Panthéon de la Guerre. This was a very real achievement for it represented persistent effort on the part of our association over a period of years and now will become a permanent record of our service in the World War.

Due to the illness of Dr. May Ayres Burgess the final report of the Grading Committee has been delayed, but there is no doubt that the work of this committee has been most worth while and effective. It is also of interest to know that similar studies have been made in Canada and in Great Britain.

We shall, during this meeting, achieve one of our ideals when we dedicate the Jane A. Delano Memorial and enshrine in our own lives its beauty and its message.

The Acting Director of Headquarters will report on the work which has been accomplished through that office. As a result of the study of a Committee on Functions, Policies, and Program of the American Nurses' Association, changes have been made which have resulted in economies as well as for greater efficiency, and the employment of more nurses on the staff. The American Nurses' Association closed the year with a budget balance on the credit side, and with 99,231 members.

The *American Journal of Nursing* Board, which is elected by your Board of Directors who are the stockholders, will make a report relative to the *Journal,* which is quite astonishing, for during the past year savings have been effected which have made it possible to declare a dividend, an action not many companies have been in a position to take. This dividend of course has been paid to the A. N. A.

These are trying times not only for nurses but for all people in this country and in every other country. There is much unrest and there are many divergent ideas and opinions. There is a lack of security which, whether for an individual or for a government, makes for a condition which is characterized by unstable emotions. Shall we recognize this, face the problems which are involved as adults, count the blessings which adversity has brought:—in many states larger graduate staffs, fewer schools, and fewer student nurses in these schools;—in other localities, shortened hours for the special duty nurses and in some localities new opportunities—and have faith to believe that we shall press forward to even greater accomplishments in our professional associations than we have had in the past? This will come through individual effort co-ordinated for service in alumnae, district, state, and national associations.

1934–1938

Susan C. Francis

A native of Philadelphia, Susan Francis was a graduate of the Reading Hospital School of Nursing. She served as a private duty nurse, staff nurse, and head nurse, and was superintendent of City Hospital (later Gallinger Memorial Hospital), Washington, D.C.; Touro Infirmary, New Orleans; and Jewish Hospital, Philadelphia. Miss Francis was also director of the Pennsylvania-Delaware Division of the American Red Cross during World War I.

For over 21 years, Miss Francis was the superintendent of Childrens Hospital, Philadelphia, and she also served as superintendent of its school of nursing. She held several offices in the Pennsylvania State Nurses' Association as well as in the national association.

Miss Francis died on October 18, 1962.

The Value of Group Effort

By Susan C. Francis, R.N., *president*
(Thirtieth Convention, Los Angeles, June 21-26, 1936)

For the American Nurses' Association, the biennial period just closing has been notable in two respects—in the continued effort to safeguard professional nursing service to the community, and in the strengthening and widening of the association's circle of relationships. All other activities have been carried on as a result of or in an effort to support these two. Indeed even the second is a corollary of the first.

Since early 1934 we have had, successively, the Federal Emergency Relief Administration, the Works Progress Administration, and the Social Security Act of 1935. Each measure brought problems affecting nursing, particularly affecting the professional status of the worker who was to carry on nursing service in the community. No crisis has shown more effectively the value of our organization. The A. N. A., jointly with the National League of Nursing Education and the N. O. P. H. N., has been able to work with the states, on the one hand, and with representatives of the Federal government, on the other, pointing out the dangers to the community if the nursing care of the sick and the nursing aspects of public health, were entrusted to workers of less than the status of the professional nurse.

Because the A. N. A. is organized as it is, states could easily and quickly refer their problems to national Headquarters. Headquarters staff members were able to confer with the appropriate bureau or departmental representatives in Washington on short notice and, in turn, to interpret their rulings to the states. The final classification of nurses by the W. P. A. as "professional and technical workers" was one result of this type of cooperative action.

But whatever success such efforts have had is due largely to the effective relationships which our Association has built up—relationships with the other two national nursing associations; relationships between the A. N. A. and the states; and those between the A. N. A. and other organizations and groups.

A professional association, such as ours, comes together in the beginning because its members have common interests, problems, and ideals. It exists to serve its members and through them the community. If it honestly tries to make this service effective, it soon finds it necessary to establish new and ever widening relationships with other groups.

Our three National Nursing Organizations are finding this increasingly true. The A. N. A., the N. L. N. E., and the N. O. P. H. N. have carried on some joint board and committee activities for years. At first this amounted to little more than a sharing of information about what each was doing. Gradually and quite recently we have come to realize that the three organizations have *joint* responsibilities to the community and to their members. The nursing service offered the community must be a coordinated service, not a series of narrowly defined units of service in which there is marked emphasis on division into private duty, institutional, and public health nursing.

The Joint Committee on Community Nursing Service of the three National Nursing Organizations, which has lay members also, is an outstanding example of this feeling of joint responsibility. It is an outgrowth of the earlier Committee on Distribution of Nursing Service, though its immediate forebear was the N. O. P. H. N. Committee on Community Nursing Service which had representation from the League and the A. N. A. This committee was appointed in 1933, at the request of the A. N. A. Board. In January, 1935, it became a Joint Committee of the A. N. A., the League, and the N. O. P. H. N., with representation also from lay groups.

Its purposes are twofold: to analyze the needs for more satisfactory nursing service; and to study—and possibly to experiment with—ways of meeting these needs. As part of its work it hopes to stimulate interest in more complete community nursing service and offers help in studying their problems to communities which request it. It is a working committee, with a full-time secretary, much of whose time is spent in field work.

Although working under the direction of the *American Journal of Nursing,* which is essentially an A. N. A. activity, the Nursing Information Bureau cooperates with the League and the N. O. P. H. N. It too is the result of a conviction shared by the three nursing organizations—that the responsibility for public information about nursing is theirs. The Nursing Information Bureau was established following the 1934 Biennial. It has been very active during the two years of its life, in preparing and releasing informational material about nursing for the use of prospective students, vocational counselors, speakers, and the general public. It too has a director, and a full-time secretary at A. N. A. Headquarters.

The Subsidiary Worker

Since the beginning of organized nursing in this country the subsidiary worker has been a major problem. She has competed unfairly with our private duty nurses, but she has at times given needed services which the patient has not been able to get from nurses. More than one committee of our associations has studied the problems involved in controlling her practice. The subsidiary worker, and the control of her practice, her preparation, her supervision, touches us at many points. She enters into our legislative programs, our registry development programs, our federal nursing projects, our nursing information program, even our personal lives.

We have come to see that the problem of the subsidiary worker is not that of one nursing organization alone, but a problem which must be shared by all three. A Joint Committee of the A. N. A., N. L. N. E., and N. O. P. H. N. is now working on various aspects of the whole problem.

In 1932 the A. N. A. and the N. L. N. E. established a functional relationship whereby the League became the Department of Education of the A. N. A. As the A. N. A. Educational Department, the League has held conferences for members of state boards and has compiled and published a list of Schools of Nursing meeting the minimum requirements set by law. Working with the American Psychiatric Association it has studied Nursing Schools in psychiatric hospitals. A Joint Committee on Legislation of the A. N. A. and the League is studying existing nurse practice acts and, with the special legislative committees of the three nursing organizations, hopes to formulate principles which will guide states amending and perfecting their present laws. Another A. N. A.-League committee is studying staff education programs. With the Division on Nursing of the Council of the American Hospital Association the League, still acting as the

Department of Education of the A. N. A., has prepared and published a *Manual of the Essentials of Good Hospital Nursing Service.* The League has also shared with the A. N. A. in the educational problems referred to A. N. A. Headquarters.

It should be said that the location of the offices of both organizations literally within the same wall has been of inestimable value in saving time and effort and in making possible the further sharing of services.

With the N. O. P. H. N. the A. N. A. has a Joint Committee to study health insurance and its implications for nurses. The subject is fraught with public health and legislative problems as well as with personal and economic interest for the nurse. Many questions instantly raise their heads: What nursing services should be provided in connection with health insurance plans and for what groups? How can the public be safeguarded against the unethical, nonprofessional worker? What place should the subsidiary worker have in the scheme? What new nursing services will be demanded or developed? How shall we prepare workers for these services? Where and how shall we find the nursing leadership needed to safeguard and to develop the nursing phases of health insurance plans? We shall look to the work of this Committee with interest.

The placement of nurses and vocational counseling for nurses present problems to A. N. A. and N. O. P. H. N. alike. The two organizations have cooperated in studying the effect which a placement and vocational counseling service, under the direction of both or possibly all three nursing organizations and on a national scale, might have on the distribution of nursing service.

As one result of the work of the A. N. A. in promoting the development of official registries and nursing bureaus, there is no question but that methods of placement—of choosing the right nurse for the task, that is—have improved recently in many localities, but there is still much to be done on placement methods as well as toward providing more adequate vocational counseling. The N. O. P. H. N.—which serves a considerably smaller membership than does the A. N. A.—shares with the American Association of Social Workers in the services of the Joint Vocational Service—a placement service operated nationally. You have already had made available to you through the pages of the May, 1936, *Journal* the many problems to be considered in determining whether a national nurse placement service would or would not be the best way to assure the best type of service to nurse and community.

From time to time nurses ask "Why do we have two magazines?" Several years ago the possibility of combining the two magazines—*Public Health Nursing* and the *American Journal of Nursing*—was the subject of careful study. It was found at that time that the two served different purposes and different readers and accordingly thought of a combination at that time was dropped. With the converging of interests of nurses following on recent events, the question has once more been raised and again a Joint A. N. A.-N. O. P. H. N. Committee is studying the question of the possibility of amalgamating the *American Journal of Nursing* and *Public Health Nursing*.

Efforts to improve the care of patients in hospitals have continued to bring hospital and nursing groups nearer together during this period. The American Hospital Association and the Catholic Hospital Association, with the A. N. A., are studying the place of the graduate nurse in the hospital, including standards of nursing care. With the American College of Surgeons the A. N. A. hopes to set up minimum standards for nursing service in hospitals seeking approval by the American College of Surgeons.

The activities carried on by our A. N. A. Headquarters are planned, as has been the rest of our program, with the needs of nurses and patients in mind. These activities will contribute to and coordinate with the work of our committees.

Many of you are cooperating in the study of incomes, salaries, and employment conditions in which thirty-two states are participating. This study is directed by a committee, the work of preparing the questionnaires and compiling and tabulating the returns being carried on at the Headquarters office. In preparing the questionnaires, we were fortunate in having the advice and help of the statistician on the staff of the League—another piece of helpful cooperation.

The work with professional nursing bureaus in their efforts toward greater development has continued through our Headquarters office. The number of registrars reporting regularly to A. N. A. Headquarters has increased from fifty in March, 1934, to ninety in April, 1936. Their reports have been yours to read in the *Journal* each month and indicate to you the services our registries give, or are not able to give; the progress of the eight-hour day; and other information of the greatest importance concerning private duty nursing.

The Eight-Hour Day

In 1934 in Washington, our association adopted a resolution on the eight-hour day. Since then a large part of the field work carried on by the A. N. A. Headquarters staff members has been directed toward helping nursing groups with the problems which they encounter in trying to establish the eight-hour day. An increasing number of hospitals and communities report the successful use of the shorter day, though there are still many communities in which private duty nurses work a twelve- or a twenty-four-hour day. There is still much to be done by enlightened nurses in showing hospitals, lay groups, and other nurses that the shorter day can improve the service to the patient and to the hospital and can make it possible for the nurse to live and use leisure time as do other professional workers.

During this biennial period, there has not been a meeting of the International Council of Nurses, but the President attended a meeting of the I. C. N. Board in Geneva last July. These have been difficult times for all nurses, perhaps more so for nurses in other countries than for our own, but the I. C. N. is evidence that nurses the world over are determined "to hold fast that which is good." The Congress in London in 1937 should indicate the extent to which this has been possible. Meanwhile nursing maintains an international center in Geneva and with the reorganization of that Headquarters office recently has been able to undertake again the publication of the *International Nursing Review.*

The President also attended the second meeting of the Grand Council of the Florence Nightingale International Foundation held in London, England, July 2-3, 1935. The challenge to the nurses of the world offered through the establishment of this Foundation, is one to be accepted with courage and carried forward with zeal. The resolution of the American Committee—which was presented in detail at this Biennial in the report of that Committee—was received. This resolution, in essence, conveyed to the members of the Grand Council of the Foundation our conviction that the educational facilities for research and for advanced work in nursing education would not be assured by the Foundation, until such time as a Chair of Nursing has been established in the University of London.

The sum of $7,318.30 which constituted the first contribution from the American Committee, a joint committee of American Nurses' Association and American Red Cross representatives, was presented at the Grand Council meeting.

The Florence Nightingale International Foundation, if and when established on a sound and secure basis, cannot fail to make an invaluable and far-reaching contribution to the world.

This convention closes the period of which I have been speaking. The record of the work of the association and of its aspirations is before you. Throughout the world, in our own nation, and within our own group, it has been a period of social and economic unrest and of considerable social experimentation. *We* are fortunate. Our organization is so structurally sound and its Headquarters office functions so smoothly, that the carefully-thought-out policies of the Board of Directors, and the arduous work of the committees, have been effectively carried forward. Because of these things, we are prepared to take advantage of such social planning as may further the twin purposes of the association—the extension of nursing service of appropriate kinds and amounts to all who need it and social security for nurses themselves.

The convention program has been planned with exceeding care to further these ends. A convention is a costly thing: costly in time, in money, in human effort. These expenditures are fully justified if we highly resolve, individually and collectively, at our opening business meeting, to keep the great and shining aims of the profession steadily before us; to absorb from the program those nuggets of practical information which have been provided for us; to remember that although "a man's reach should exceed his grasp," we move forward into the next biennium with a more united front than ever before and with well-founded hopes of yet greater achievement.

Coming Together for Common Purposes

By Susan C. Francis, R.N., *president*
(Thirty-First Convention, Kansas City, April 24-29, 1938)

Since man first joined his neighbors for mutual protection and pleasure, certain periods have been set aside when the accomplishments of the immediate past could be reviewed and plans made for the future.

And for these reasons we, members of the American Nurses' Association, meet together today.

A review of the biennial period just closing reveals clearly that for us as an organization, this period has been marked by a growing unity of purpose.

Today we, the largest organized body of professional nurses in the United States, have reached a period of concentration of effort; a period of working together for the good of our patients as well as for our own individual welfare; a period when we realize that we must work not only with each other but with the members of the communities which we serve, if that service is to leave the nurse and the patient the richer for their reciprocal experience.

To illustrate this statement,

I call your attention to the steady growth in membership of the Association and to the large amount of joint activity of the ANA, the League, and the NOPHN which is reflected, or we might say, is a reflection of, similar joint efforts within the state and district associations.

There are many other evidences of this growing unity. Requests for help which have been received at ANA Headquarters from state, district, or alumnae associations and from individual nurses throughout the country during the past two years show that state and local projects are being evolved which deal with community nursing needs and registry development, placement and vocational counseling, the extension of the eight-hour day, improvement of salaries, incomes, and employment conditions for nurses, and with the development of coöperative relationships with other welfare groups in the community, to the end that better nursing care may be provided to all who need such care in the community; all of which are part of the present program of work of the American Nurses' Association.

Even the official names of the state associations and the by-laws by which they are governed are gradually being made uniform.

Certain state associations have asked for a book which contains American Nurses' Association policies and which will serve as a guide in establishing uniform state association policies and the ANA is at the present time preparing such a book for release. Also, the state associations are asking for the help of the American Nurses' Association in the establishment of certain broad policies of coöperative relationships with other groups such as the hospital and the medical associations, and for guidance in legislative matters which relate to, or many affect, nurses and nursing.

Many of you will think of other illustrations of this "coming together for a common purpose" which is so evident at the present time.

But this accord, this tendency toward uniformity might be a dangerous trend for the good of those we serve, and for ourselves too, if it were not accompanied by a wholesome tendency toward the adaptation of national policies to meet state and local needs. The nurses in America, like all other citizens of this country, must realize and cherish the right and the necessity of *thoughtfully modifying* any national policy so that it will serve well the locality in which it is used. I use the words "thoughtfully modifying" with intent, for the pattern of national unity must not be broken while local adaptations of national policies are being made, or our right recognition as a profession will be jeopardized.

A good way of achieving this unity of purpose with a diversity of method is by putting to local use the materials which are published by the American Nurses' Association.

During this biennium there has been wider use of material prepared by the ANA and by the Nursing Information Bureau, and there has been a greater tendency to use and to adapt this material for clearly defined purposes.

It is gratifying too to report an increase in the subscriptions to the *American Journal of Nursing.* The circulation at the present time is approximately seven thousand five hundred greater than in June 1936, when we last assembled for the convention held in Los Angeles, California.

With this brief review of some of the developments which have strongly influenced the professional organization during the past two years, let us now consider what we should like to accomplish during the next biennium.

We must remember that it is still necessary to choose our goals wisely and work toward them steadily, even though at times progress may seem to lag unreasonably. Also, we have been through a major depression recently enough to know that what we are able to do as a profession will be inextricably affected by the social and economic conditions in our country and in the world. We realize that any plans we make must be flexible enough to meet those unknown emergencies which may be around the next turn in the road. However, there are some definite needs of the profession for which we must plan, and plan carefully.

We know through the study of salaries, incomes, and employment conditions affecting nurses which has recently been completed by the ANA,* and through correspondence, fieldwork, and interviews with nurses employed in all sections of the United States that many professional nurses throughout the country need the assistance of the American Nurses' Association and its units, the state nurses' associations, in securing better incomes and working conditions, in order that they may give better service to their patients. This involves a continued and continuous program of education, not only for the employing groups and of the public but of ourselves. For any student of man and his needs will tell you that more money and more leisure time will be of benefit to a man (or a woman) only if that individual knows how to use that money and that time to enrich his personality. The opportunity to serve and to so serve that the effort involved is creative, is especially important to the nurse, and we must not lose sight of this fact in our programs for the improvement of incomes and working conditions for nurses.

Study of Working Conditions

A study of general staff nurses and the conditions under which they work is being prepared for publication at ANA Headquarters at the present time. You will be interested to know that the analysis of turnover among general staff nurses included in this study shows that hospitals which have adopted the eight-hour day and have increased salaries over those common during the depression have less turnover among the nursing staff. Yet there are other factors which seem to influence the staff turnover almost as much. And these factors relate to the type of care which the nurse is allowed to give to her patients. When her patient load is too heavy so that good nursing care is impossible, the staff turnover is relatively high even though hours and salaries are

* *Study of Incomes, Salaries and Employment Conditions Affecting Nurses* (exclusive of those engaged in public health nursing). Published by the American Nurses' Association, 1938.

satisfactory. The general staff nurse's satisfaction in her job is influenced too by the degree to which she is allowed to participate in planning the conditions under which she will render her service to her patients and to the institution. As a professional woman why should she not be permitted to participate in such planning? The nurse is the person nearest to the patient in the hospital. Unless her relationship to the hospital is satisfactory, the whole of the hospital service to the patient is thrown out of balance.

These same facts have been repeatedly demonstrated in the study of community nursing needs and registry development carried forward by the ANA since March 1934.

If the employing groups and the public, in other words the lay men and women for whom and to whom we render our services, are to understand that nurses need and are asking for better incomes and working conditions *in order that the patient may receive better nursing care,* we must find ways in which these lay persons may work with us in solving these problems. Further, because nursing is but one of the many services which are essential to the welfare of the community, we must ask lay men and women to help us find ways to fit nursing into the whole pattern of community life.

We must continue to seek the help of lay persons, also, in the improvement of the preparation of nurses. The ANA has studied the question of lay participation during the past two years and will continue to do so and we know many of the state associations are doing likewise.

As you all know, the American Nurses' Association through the National League of Nursing Education, which functions as the Department of Education of the ANA, has a clearly defined responsibility toward the advancement of nursing education. This is only proper, for upon the basic preparation of the nurse rests the whole question of whether or not in the end the community will be well nursed.

But it will take the concerted vision and efforts of all professional nurses throughout the country to solve the many problems which are involved in adequately preparing the individual nurse for community service and in making it possible for her to give a high type of care to her patient after she receives her education.

This means that ways must be found for all nurses registered in any state who meet the requirements for membership in the ANA, to become members of the state and district associations in which they are residing and practicing.

To allow this, state nurse practice acts and regulations controlling nursing schools will need to be more uniform throughout the country.

Special provisions will also be necessary in the by-laws of some state nurses' associations, so that nurses employed in the government and other nursing services, in which they are frequently transferred from one state to another, may become members of the district and state association in which they are residing and practicing.

Moreover, certain adjustments will be necessary in the dues required for both resident and non-resident membership in alumnae associations and reinstatement fees in many instances should be reduced to the maximum of two dollars which has been recommended by the ANA Board of Directors.

However, if each nurse is to become a member of her professional associations, membership must be made attractive. For this reason the work and plans of the American Nurses' Association and its organization units, the state, district, and alumnae associations, must be clearly outlined and brought to the attention of all members and prospective members. Also, it will be necessary to continue to include topics which will contribute to each nurse's knowledge of her work and her profession, in the programs for meetings, whether local, state or national; and more ways must be found in which each member may participate in these programs.

Whether or not the individual nurse recognizes and is willing to assume her responsibility to the community she serves and to the profession of which she is a part depends upon many factors. Some of these are rooted in the heredity and early home life of the young woman who is allowed to enter the school of nursing. Others may be determined during her basic nursing course.

Much may be done, however, to arouse this sense of responsibility through the work of the professional associations and one of the surest methods is to help each nurse to feel that the good of the community and of the nursing profession depends, at least in a small measure, upon her own individual efforts.

In the early part of this review, I mentioned the growing unity of the profession. But a further consolidation of effort is necessary if nursing is to find its rightful place in present-day life and if it is to move forward to new frontiers of service.

An old folk tale recounts the story of a man who had seven sons. He sent the eldest son into the woods to bring home a stick. The son did so and when he brought it to his father, the father bent it over his knee and the twig snapped.

The man sent his second son into the woods for the same purpose and this son returned with a larger stick. Again the old man bent it over his knee and broke it in two.

He sent his third and his fourth sons and one by one each of his seven sons on the same errand and each time, though the sticks grew larger and stronger, he was able to snap them in two.

After he had broken the last of the seven sticks each of his sons had brought to him, he said, "Now my sons, go out together and each of you pick up a stick and put it together in a faggot then bring it to me."

The sons did so and by no amount of effort could the old man break the bundle of sticks which his sons had gathered together and bound in one bundle.

One by one we, as individual members of the nursing profession, may be defeated even though our goals are chosen for the good of all and our courage is of the highest, but together our "bundle" of efforts will be indestructible, as long as we strive for the good of those we serve.

1938-1944

Julia C. Stimson

One of the several nursing leaders to emerge from the First World War, Julia Stimson was a native of Massachusetts and received her baccalaureate degree from Vassar College. She went on to receive her training in nursing at New York Hospital Training School. Prior to the War, Miss Stimson served as superintendent of nurses at Harlem Hospital, New York, where she developed a hospital social service department, and as administrator of Hospital Social Service and superintendent of nurses of the hospitals and dispensaries of Washington University, St. Louis, from which school she received a master's degree.

When the United States entered the World War in 1917, Miss Stimson joined the Army Nurse Corps and was Chief Nurse of a base hospital in France, Chief Nurse of the American Red Cross in France, and Director of Nursing Service of the American Expeditionary Forces. In these capacities, she supervised the more than 10,000 members of the Army Nurse Corps abroad.

Following the war, Miss Stimson succeeded Annie Goodrich as dean of the Army School of Nursing and became superintendent of the Army Nurse Corps, an office she held for 20 years. In 1920, following the amendment by Congress of the National Defense Act giving relative rank to members of the Army Nurse Corps, Miss Stimson received the rank of Major, the highest rank thus allowed. Major Stimson was the author of the *Nurses' Handbook of Drugs and Solutions.*

Major Stimson died on September 30, 1948.

Nursing in a Democracy

By Julia C. Stimson, R.N., *president*
(Thirty-Second Convention, Philadelphia, May 12-17, 1940)

For this National Biennial Convention we have chosen as a main topic "Nursing in a Democracy." We believe that a true democracy is that social order which deliberately seeks to secure for every one of its members the best the universe has to offer, and help in moral and spiritual growth to new levels of personal and social cooperation. We believe in critical *re*construction of any pattern that hampers personal and social freedom and obstructs efforts toward the enlargement of life for communities. Health is a fundamental factor in social or individual progress. We have dedicated ourselves to mental, physical and social health.

We have come together to examine the old patterns and to learn of new areas of science and philosophy and to get a creative understanding of them, that we may apply them to our own lives and our organized efforts. Adequacy of service is what we seek. Our hearts are heavy as we contemplate the spreading battle fields of the world on which human decency and dignity fight for life against a reversion to savagery. We see a world rent by envy and ill will, divided into warring nations and hostile races. We suffer with our sorrowing, heavily-burdened colleagues and friends of other countries, and pledge ourselves once more to unity and tolerance and renewed efforts toward understanding.

History, if it means anything at all, means that no civilization has a chance to survive except as the forces of knowledge and skill can prevail socially and victoriously over self-interest, except as all vocations rest upon the basis of that freedom which not only ennobles but inspires men and women to put the honor of their calling above the reach of their own weaknesses.

In our thankfulness that we American nurses live in this beautiful country, this true democracy, and that no emergent national crises are hampering our efforts to make our service adequate to the entire public, irrespective of class or creed, we have come to share our experiences and aspirations, to hear ennobling words of justice and beauty, to be confronted with something loftier than ourselves. We look for an increased consciousness of inner power, together with greater technical knowledge based on the experience of others. We expect the feeling of a new moral imperative to save us from self-sufficiency and soft complacency. We know from similar past gatherings of this sort that we shall go away with greater faiths, resources and loyalties and from them we shall derive courage and strength to combat the awful sense of life's futility which weighs us down in these dark days. We are deliberately exposing ourselves to lofty ideas and God-given personalities that we may strengthen our devotion to something greater than ourselves, in which we can everlastingly believe, worth serving, worth sacrificing for, something that gives to life dignity and meaning.

May this Convention release power within our own souls, fill us with convictions which cause us to attach ourselves to something more lasting than the moment in which we live and tap resources of divine energy from beyond ourselves for our daily need.*

Nursing at the Nation's Service

By Julia C. Stimson, R.N., *president*
(Thirty-Third Convention, Chicago, May 17-22, 1942)

The theme of this convention is *Nursing at the Nation's Service.*

We have come together in the most momentous period not in the history of this country but in the history of the world, to consecrate ourselves anew to the service of humanity through our chosen profession. No other purpose would justify our turning for the briefest moment from the various fields—the demands of which not less in one field than in another, cannot today be adequately met.

As in our desire to render our fullest service we fix our eyes upon the overwhelming tragedy into which the world is plunged, and in some measure there is borne in upon us its unutterable

*Medical Archives, New York Hospital—Cornell Medical Center

anguish and despair, its superb endurance and renunciations, its marvelous scientific achievements in the destruction and construction of the work of God and man, how infinitesimal, how almost inconsequential and trivial does any individual contribution seem.

But even as the tiny mountain streams growing ever and ever mightier in their consolidating strength find themselves at last in a vast ocean through which they present an overwhelming force; so our puny individual efforts through unification of purpose becoming a greater and greater factor in the conservation of human life, have merged into an army that has been called to take its place with the greatest army that has ever been brought into existence.

Such service as can be rendered must be rendered by every member of our profession today, that through the forceful hands of men and the healing hands of women, a purified world may be prepared for the generations that are to come. It is, therefore, our highest duty during the few days when, gathered together from all parts of the United States, we meet for the consideration of each aspect of the situation in which we are involved, to prepare a program of work that looks to the most far-reaching results in every field, that leaves no stone unturned to treble, not alone in numbers, but in efficiency, our nursing strength.

These thoughts were expressed by Annie W. Goodrich when responding to the address of welcome at the Twenty-first Annual Meeting of the American Nurses' Association, held in Cleveland, Ohio, in May 1918. They are as true today as when they were expressed twenty-four years ago.

We are defending the democratic way of life, and in this struggle each nurse must be qualified to participate. This is necessary if she and the association of which she is a part are to retain those fundamental principles of democracy and qualities of service, which throughout the ages have been developed step by step through persistent and conscientious effort directed toward improving nursing in the home—the hospital—in industry or on the field of battle.

It is important for every registered nurse to realize that she is making a contribution to the total war effort, regardless of whether or not she is serving with the armed forces. It is her duty to keep informed about all that is happening in the world about her as well as developments in her own profession and particular field of practice. She should constantly be on the alert to detect ways in which she can modify or change the type of service which she is rendering in order to be of maximum assistance. Advantage of every educational opportunity which will enable her to make a better contribution should be sought. Active participation in all organized nursing effort should be regarded as a privilege and not accepted as an obligation or ignored altogether.

Nurses who have enrolled in the Federal Government Services, and who are serving in other countries must be made to feel that we will not fail them, and that the responsibility for safeguarding their professional interests has been left in good hands. Upon their return they should find a stronger nursing profession, one entirely worthy of the sacrifices which they have made.

All that has been said of the individual nurse applies to the profession as a whole and has special significance for the American Nurses' Association. This association is involved in the greatest effort in its history. The plan of organization and the program which determine its activities have proved to be sound. This is a source of satisfaction to all of us. The American Nurses' Association has provided certain organization machinery and working channels whereby the defense and war programs for nursing throughout this country are being carried on.

Stimulation for the organization of the Nursing Council on National Defense* in July 1940 came from the American Nurses' Association and until the employment of the Executive Secretary for the Council late in 1941, the work of the Council was centered at Headquarters of the American Nurses' Association. The organization of the Nursing Council on National Defense fol-

* Now changed to National Nursing Council for War Service.

lowed by the appointment of the Federal Subcommittee on Nursing required the establishment of effective working relationships between all official and non-official nursing groups in the United States. This has required constant study and evaluation in order that the privileges, functions and responsibilities of each of these groups might be preserved and the resources of each utilized to the fullest extent.

This has been a difficult task—constantly we are being reminded that time is short—decisions must be made at once (but not without giving thought to their implications for the future), projects must be initiated—studies made and data tabulated in an incredibly short period of time. This has meant that nursing organizations frequently are finding it necessary to transfer attention from usual and necessary programs and activities to those occasioned by war demands.

However, in our endeavor to fulfill obligations for war service, we must not lose sight of responsibilities for the future. The ideals which have motivated the achievements in our profession must be guarded and cherished with zeal and determination. Professional values have significance only in so far as they inspire the finest type of performance. Values relating to nursing education, nursing legislation, personnel practices and distribution of nursing service must be preserved.

This responsibility rests with each one of us. Let us accept this challenge embued with a desire for service. In this way only, we shall be able to make our greatest contribution.

Nursing's Pledge to the Nation*

By Julia C. Stimson, R.N., *president*
(Thirty-Third Convention, Chicago, May 17-22, 1942)

When the national nursing associations met in 1918 there was a war and we were in it, but our own country was not in danger. We were fighting to help other countries defend their liberties and

* New York *World Telegram*, March 5, 1942.

every soldier, sailor, or nurse who sailed away in those days had the comfortable feeling that business as usual, homes, friends, all that they were accustomed to and took for granted, would be waiting for them on their return. We were glad to help. We were filled with altruistic feelings. We were going to win the war for people who were hard-pressed, but it wasn't really our war.

Now things are different. It is our war and we are in it to the last ditch. We are awakening to the full gravity of the peril that confronts us and we are beginning to appreciate how badly we have been defeated so far. It is beginning to dawn upon us that the United Nations can lose this war and suffer the fate of France and all the other subjugated countries, and that this possibility may become a probability if the tide does not change. We are told that we must have maximum production and that we will not have maximum production unless we fully realize our own awful peril, and as a recent editorial says* unless we get over the "gimmes" of recent years,—gimme shorter hours, gimme higher wages, gimme higher profits, gimme more overtime, gimme more pensions, et cetera. France had the gimmes too, and had them 'til the Germans were close to Paris. Then everybody went frantically to work, too late. France has no gimmes today except gimme food for my baby, gimme a place to lay my head, gimme death.

We have come together in the darkest period of our whole history as a profession, and in the darkest period of our country's history, to see if by taking counsel together, facing facts, and rallying our forces to a higher pitch, we can get new inspiration to find out if we can develop greater individual and collective capacities and get new strength to unite them in the most effective way. Our job, and our first job, whatever we have hitherto thought was our primary function, and the job every other organization and every other individual of the 130,000,000

*Inasmuch as Major Stimson's address to delegates attending the 1944 convention was not recorded, her opening address during the 1942 joint session of the American Nurses' Association, National League for Nusing Education, and National Organization for Public Health Nursing is included.

people in these United States, is to win the war. That means two very positive things: first, accepting as our personal quota our full personal capacity and, second, understanding and using our personal and collective resources.

If each person determines that her quota is to be her full capacity, the sum of the efforts of each of us will be a total war effort, the magnitude of which is beyond anything we have ever dreamt of accomplishing before. More than the accumulation of thousands of individual war efforts, it is force, a power, a unified overwhelming surge, an outpouring of professional strength on every level—national, state, district, city, local, adding its abilities to those of other groups, sweeping all indifference, all complacency before it. War means a dislocated life for the men and women in the services and it means a dislocated life for us. If we fail to fill the quota of our individual capacities we may have no normal life to which to go back.

Before these meetings are over, it is probable that each of us will have new ideas of what our professional capacities may be. The personal ones will take much conscientious thought. Moreover, here we are going to learn much about the resources, plans, possibilities, and tools for using our strength as a profession, strength to help the fighting services win the war, and strength to help the men, women, and children of our cities, towns, and rural areas win the war.

But unless we see our part as citizens in winning this war, we can never take our full part as nurses. Now it is all or nothing. We are forced to realize the life or death nature of this war and what defeat—and an entirely possible defeat—would mean.

Defeat would mean in addition to the loss of our outlying territories, such as Alaska, Hawaii, and the Philippines, the surrender of our fleet, our arms; and it would mean we would have to do anything the conqueror might choose to demand of us. The things we believe in as a free and self-governing people will no longer exist if we do not win this war. Moreover, there will no longer be free and self-governing people in the world if we do not win. But we will not win the war unless all of us have a burning, passionate conviction, angry and deeper than fear, that the winning depends on us. Death, destruction, deprivation, and sacrifices are beginning to be felt, but what we have hitherto suffered will be but small compared to the inevitable consequences of defeat.

An enumeration of these consequences, such as control by our enemies of great sources of raw materials, reduction or virtual destruction of our export trade, increase in cost of living, decrease in standards of living, continued state of internal and external tension, militarily, psychologically, and politically, et cetera, all these things seem far-off abstract ideas that leave us pretty cold. Actual bombing of our cities and possible invasion—these too have not changed our way of living much, as yet.

There is more than one way in which we, as nurses, can do our part to win the war. There are many ways. But there must be agreement on our main efforts. It is not so important what we do as that we do it together and do it well. We must be sure, however, that we are not expending our energies on activities other people can do, neglecting those things that we can do which other people cannot.

In the past few years the nursing profession has been united as never before. Ours are democratic organizations and the processes of democracy are orderly and necessarily slower than those forms of government in which orders are issued from the top. The three national nursing organizations, with a total membership of about 198,000, constitute an unwieldy body, but with a purpose behind which we are all so wholeheartedly united, we are moving forward as a solid army. It is a Cause that is leading us.

We are not losing sight of the fact that our present work and our present plans must serve the future, for we are determined to contribute to the durable peace in the new kind of cooperative life we envisage on a world scale. To win the war and to achieve the peace we are here to expand our personal capacities to their greatest limit and to accept them as our personal quotas, and to forge anew our united capacities into such a prodigious united quota that it will astonish even our most optimistic selves.

It is not only ardor that I call upon you for, but single-minded effectiveness—single-minded in objective, single-minded in attack—that we may continue as a free and self-governing people.

We, as a strong, free, and self-governing profession in a free and self-governing country, are determined to preserve those things which make us free, not only for ourselves but for our professional sisters and their countries throughout the world.

Exercising the privilege of personal self-sacrifice and collectively uniting our total capacities, we pledge ourselves anew to the Nation's service.

1944-1948

Katharine J. Densford

Prior to entering the nursing field, Katharine Densford Dreves taught history, having earned a Bachelor of Arts degree from Miami University and a Master of Arts degree from the University of Chicago. Mrs. Dreves received her nurse training from the Vassar Training Camp for Nurses and the School of Nursing and Health at the University of Cincinnati.

Early nursing assignments included positions as head nurse at the Cincinnati General Hospital, public health nurse in Hamilton County, Ohio, supervisor of nurses at the Cincinnati Tuberculosis Sanatorium, and instructor of tuberculosis nursing and public health nursing at the University of Cincinnati. She also served as assistant dean of the Illinois Training School for Nurses, later renamed the Cook County School of Nursing, and assistant director of the nursing service of the Cook County Hospital in Chicago.

In 1930, Mrs. Dreves was appointed director of the School of Nursing and professor of nursing at the University of Minnesota, the oldest university school of nursing. During World War II, the institution trained the largest single United States Cadet Nurse Corps in the country.

The fourteenth president of the American Nurses' Association has given much of her time and interest to the work of state and national nursing organizations. In addition to her two terms as ANA president, Mrs. Dreves has served as president of the Minnesota Nurses' Association, president of the Minnesota League of Nursing Education, a member of the Board of Directors of the Illinois State Nurses' Association, a member of the Board of Directors of the American Journal of Nursing Company, and chairman of the Minnesota Nursing Council for War Service.

In addition to writing articles on nursing education for professional journals and contributing to various textbooks, Katharine Densford Dreves co-authored *Ethics for Modern Nurses* and *Counseling in Schools of Nursing.*

An active participant at ANA conventions, Mrs. Dreves maintains a keen interest in nursing issues.

Postwar Demands for Nursing Services

By Katharine J. Densford, R.N., *president*
(Thirty-Fifth Convention, Atlantic City, September 22-27, 1946)

This is a tremendously important moment in the history of nursing. The war is over, but peace has not been restored, nor has the upheaval that war brought to all countries and all occupations spared our own profession.

On those European battle grounds which I recently visited, where our own American nurses served so devotedly and at such risk to their lives, I could not help thinking of the great debt all of us, as American citizens, owed to the 76,000 nurses who served in the Army and Navy. My own travel arrangements were not luxurious and we missed many of the comforts of home, but we traveled safely—without fear of enemy attack—in the very areas where scarcely more than a year ago the hazards of war filled air, land, and sea. To those splendid women, and to their fellow-nurses who bore the brunt here at home, filling in as gallantly on the civilian health front, I pause to say: Never has a president of this association had more reason to be proud that she is a nurse.

Today we face the paradoxes of peace. Here, for instance, in our own United States, we have one-half of all the professional nurses of the world. Yet what do people of other lands read in our newspapers? "Nurse shortage . . . nurse shortage." How strange, how lacking in perspective that must seem, when we have here in the United States one professional nurse for every 400 people, by far the greatest concentration of nurse power in the world.

But the man in the street is asking you and me, "What about it?" Therefore, let us look at the record. In 1945 there were actually 20,000 *more* nurses employed in hospitals and other institutions than in 1944. There were about 1,300 *more* private duty nurses employed in hospitals in 1945 than in 1944. Student nurses increased from 112,000 to 126,000, many of them members of the U. S. Cadet Nurse Corps.

What was happening in the hospital world? According to the annual surveys by the American Medical Association, admissions to *all* hospitals in the United States rose by 220,000 in the same period, and the average daily census rose by 105,000.

You know some of the reasons for this rise in hospital service: growth of population, increase in family incomes, spread of Blue Cross hospital insurance, overcrowding in homes, overburdening of physicians, new techniques in medicine, increase in birth rate, and most of all a growing realization by the public that they want the best medical and hospital care they can get.

Demand for nursing service, in other words, has been going up like a skyrocket, while supply of that service has been going up like a skyscraper. The tempo of nursing education has been accelerated during the war, but we believe the foundation must be firm if it is to meet the demands of the future. The result of this difference in rate of speed is that whenever you compare the number of nurses needed with those who are available, you find a mathematical deficit.

The most recent estimate is that made by the Committee on Statistical Research of the National Nursing Council. This indicates that with 359,000 estimated as *needed*, and 317,800 actually or potentially *available*, there is probable deficit of at least 41,700 graduate professional nurses. That is to say, demand has outstripped supply in a ratio of 100 to a possible 88. That probable deficit of 12 per cent can be widened or narrowed, only as a great marginal number of nurses or potential nurses decide whether their requirements for working and living can be met in a nursing position. We do not know when supply can catch up with demand—if ever. But this vast expectation of the public for the best of nursing services challenges us to meet it as soundly and as wisely and rapidly as we can.

Some of the steps we must consider here are for us as a profession to take; some we can take only with the help of the related professions, medicine and public health, education, hospital administration; some will be possible only if the public as a whole understands and will help us.

The same elements of ferment and unrest which we recognize in the nursing profession are at work in teaching and other professions. Let us view our problems not as unique to nursing, but as a part of the upheaval in all planes of thinking and living, in all other countries as well as our own. If there is comfort in viewing our relatively fortunate position, let us remind ourselves that nurses have not been interrupted by war in their practice of nursing. We have just gone on nursing—harder and more continuously, in more difficult conditions, taking on more of the physician's responsibilities as they were laid on our shoulders. Never once have we been asked to stop nursing in order to man a machine gun or to make ammunition. We have been, throughout it all, never the destroyers of life, always the healers and conservers and builders.

Because the economic security of the nurse is a matter of vital importance to all of us, it is particularly gratifying that we can soon find out the real economic status of nursing today. The socio-economic study of nurses in comparison with other occupations, which the National Nursing Planning Committee asked the Bureau of Labor Statistics to undertake should bring us invaluable information.

This question of economics is one of many which we must answer if we are to fulfill the purpose for which we have come together: to make possible good nursing service for all who need it. We should not have traveled these thousands of miles and devoted these thousands of hours to committee and convention activities if we were not determined that we shall move forward, on many diverse fronts, toward that one goal.

Suggested Platform for American Nurses' Association

High on the list of issues which I urge the House of Delegates to take action this week, are the following:

1. Improvement in hours and living conditions for nurses, so that they may live a normal personal and professional life.
2. Specifically, action toward (a) wider acceptance of the 40-hour week with no decrease of salary, thus applying to our postwar conditions the principle of the 8-hour day adopted by the American Nurses' Association in 1934; (b) minimum salaries adequate to attract and hold nurses of quality, and to enable them to maintain standards of living comparable with other professions.
3. Increased participation by nurses in the actual planning and in the administration of nursing service, in hospitals and other types of employment.
4. Greater development of nurses' professional associations as exclusive spokesmen for nurses in all questions affecting their employment and economic security. Such a development should be based on past successful experience of professional nurses' organizations in collective bargaining and negotiation.

In this connection I wish to read the economic security program which the Advisory Council voted yesterday to present to the House of Delegates for discussion and action:

"The American Nurses' Association believes that the several state and district nurses' associations are qualified to act and should act as the exclusive agents of their respective memberships in the important fields of economic security and collective bargaining. The association commends the excellent progress already made and urges all state and district nurses' associations to push such a program vigorously and expeditiously.

"Since it is the established policy of other groups, including unions, to permit membership in only one collective bargaining group, the association believes such policy to be sound for the state and district nurses' associations."

5. Removal, as rapidly as possible, of barriers that prevent the full employment and professional development of nurses belonging to minority racial groups.
6. Employment of well-qualified practical nurses and other auxiliary workers under state licensure, thus protecting both the patient and the worker.
7. Continuing improvement in the placement and counseling of nurses, to give greater stability and job satisfaction to the profession and to facilitate better distribution of nursing service to the public.
8. Further development of nursing in prepayment health and medical care plans, in order to spread the cost of nursing service to the public.
9. Maintenance of educational standards, and development of educational resources, that nursing may keep abreast of the rapid advances in medicine and other sciences. Such a development may well require federal subsidies and contribution from foundations and other educational philanthropies.
10. Appraisal of our own national organizations, through the report of the structure study, and fearless action based upon such appraisal, to make sure that the nursing profession will be organized and equipped to deal most effectively with its problems and its opportunities.

In conclusion: If the nursing profession is ready to take decisive action on hours, salaries, economic advancement, enlargement of nursing resources while maintaining standards and the possible reconstruction of its own organizational structure, we shall this week be making nursing history.

Nursing's Goals

By Katharine J. Densford, R.N., *president*
(Thirty-Sixth Convention, Chicago, May 31-June 4, 1948)

At our last biennial, we were just emerging from the shadow of war. The world has moved on since 1946. Today America stands as the leader of the free nations, sharing with them the responsibility for maintaining and strengthening the democratic way of life and for setting patterns of world behavior.

In the field of nursing, no less than in that of social reconstruction, leadership, whether we like it or not, has passed into American hands. The challenge thrown down to us by history is something to give us pause. It is through accomplishments in the work of social reconstruction, through the example it sets, and not through words that the United States must prove its qualities of leadership. And the same holds true of the nursing profession.

To lead means to march at the head of the parade. A profession, in its making, should always be a generation or two ahead of the public. Keeping abreast of the world situation is not enough. At the same time its position of leadership demands that the nursing profession take on more and more responsibilities for service, locally, nationally and even internationally.

As leaders of world nursing, we need fresh, constantly revitalized points of view. We cannot hope to attain the universal outlook essential to leadership on our own, with no assistance from the public. Many schools of nursing, for example, are poorly equipped to meet the ever-broadening requirements of the profession. The general public must help to reorganize these schools before they will be able to set new patterns in such fields as psychiatric nursing.

We must not forget, however, that outside forces beyond our control affect the nursing situation. The public, in the last analysis, determines the social and economic factors governing all of us as professionals. And those factors, in turn, bear importantly on the number and quality of students in nursing at any given time to the profession. Without some guarantee of economic security, without legal control of the nursing profession and without proper distribution of its members, we cannot measure up to the role of leadership we are expected to assume.

A moment ago I said that the public determines the conditions under which we nurses have to work. Usually it does so by sheer inertia. Our problem has been to overcome that inertia, to make the public get up on their feet and start moving, as it were. During the past year, I know you will agree we have had not a little success along that line. And we nurses have taken the initiative by arousing the American people to the nursing crisis and showing them how it can be overcome.

If the United States is to lead the way to a healthier, happier world, it must first improve the health of its own citizens. We can count on the American people to adopt any sound idea of ours after it has been explained to them. Social reconstruction begins where the people live, in the community. Every nurses' association, whether on the state, district or local level, can play its part. Once the group makes up its collective mind on the right way to participate and goes to work, improvements on the national and world level should follow as a matter of course, but the job can be accomplished only if the public joins the nurses in the fight.

All of us, in the profession and out, acknowledge the desirability of reaching the general goals nursing has set itself, or rather those which have been set for it. Our sole disagreement is over the means of reaching them. In the things that matter, nurses and public alike stand shoulder to shoulder. The delegates of the American Nurses' Association, representing approximately one hundred and sixty thousand professional nurses, meeting in convention in Chicago, are deeply concerned with their responsibility as American citizens. They reaffirm their faith in the United Nations and in the constructive leadership of the United States. They continue their support for the promotion of common health goals for the United States and the world at large. The members of the nursing profession are alive to their responsibility for providing sufficient nursing of superior quality to safeguard the health of the American people. To attain these goals the members of the association ask the public to share with them the responsibility of promoting the social, economic and professional advancement of nurses so that adequate and improved nursing service may be furnished the American people. This active support is essential if the safe professional nursing care demanded by the public is to be provided. To achieve these goals the following platform is placed before the delegates for their study and action:

I. EXPANSION OF THE ROLE OF THE AMERICAN NURSE IN WORLD AFFAIRS.
   A. Endorsement and support of membership of the United States in the World Health Organization.
   B. Securing recognition of the International Council of Nurses as the official representative of organized nursing in the World Health Organization.
   C. Continued participation in American Overseas Aid—United Nations Appeal for Children.
   D. Expansion of the program for the international exchange of students and teachers of nursing.
   E. Participation in the development of an Inter-American Association of Nurses.

II. INCREASED PARTICIPATION OF THE NURSE IN NATIONAL AFFAIRS.
   A. Membership of the ANA in the United States National Commission on UNESCO.
   B. Promotion of the goals stemming from the 1948 National Health Assembly.
   C. Cooperation in the organization of nursing services for civil defense in the event of war or other national emergency.

III. PROVISION FOR THE RAPID EXPANSION OF NURSING SERVICES TO MEET THE HEALTH NEEDS OF THE AMERICAN PEOPLE.
   A. Continued endorsement of nursing service in prepay-

ment health insurance plans.

B. Improvement of nursing supply and distribution through cooperation with the United States Bureau of the Census as well as through nursing organizations.

C. Extension of the professional counseling and placement service.

D. Cooperation in accrediting practical nursing schools as one step toward the solution of the present nursing crisis.

E. Promotion of state licensure of practical nurses to protect the public.

IV. FURTHERANCE OF THE PUBLIC'S HEALTH THROUGH PROMOTION AND PROTECTION OF THE WELFARE OF THE PROFESSIONAL NURSE.

A. Further development of the economic security program in response to the urgent needs of the public and the desires of nurses.

B. Further development of public recognition of the nurses' right to participate in the setting of employment conditions in harmony with economic and social principles as practiced in contemporary employer-employee relationships.

C. Extension of social security benefits for nurses as part of society's obligation to the profession.

D. Promotion of the principles of education already carried out in other professions of integrating professional schools of nursing into the framework of institutions of higher education.

E. Promotion of federal and state and local aid for nursing education to assist in establishing schools of nursing on a sound financial basis.

F. Participation in programs directed toward the selection and preparation of tomorrow's nurses.

G. Participation in advanced programs of study to prepare today's professional nurses to meet expanding needs of the profession.

H. Continued effort to establish a unified program and an integrated structure for all national nursing organizations.
I. Promotion of effective working relationships with other social, scientific and professional groups as a contribution to our national health service.

1948–1950

Pearl McIver

Pearl McIver, a well-known figure in the public health field for over thirty years, served as first chief of public health nursing for the United States Public Health Service.

A former public school teacher, Miss McIver received her initial training from the School of Nursing at the University of Minnesota. Some years later, she earned both her bachelor's and her master's degrees in public health from Teachers College at Columbia University.

Early in her career, Miss McIver served as a visiting nurse for the University of Minnesota and as director of public health nursing for the Missouri State Board of Health. In addition to her position as chief of public health nursing, Miss McIver was a public health nursing analyst for the Research Division of the United States Public Health Service. Following her retirement from the United States Public Health Service in 1957, she served a two-year term as executive director of the American Journal of Nursing Company.

Miss McIver was extremely active in a number of organizations. In addition to her work with the American Nurses' Association, she served as president of the American Journal of Nursing Company, president of the Graduate Nurses' Association of Washington, D.C., vice president of the American Nurses' Foundation, vice president of the American Public Health Association, secretary of the National Nursing Council and chairman of the Postwar Planning Committee of the National Nursing Council for War Service.

In 1956, Miss McIver was the first recipient of the Public Health

Nurse Award, an honor bestowed by ANA's Public Health Nurses' Section. The American Nurses' Association honored its fifteenth president in 1957 by establishing the Pearl McIver Public Health Nurse Award.

Although Miss McIver has been retired for a number of years, she still takes an active interest in nursing and the activities of the American Nurses' Association.

Issues in Nursing

By Pearl McIver, R.N., *president*
(Thirty-Seventh Convention, San Francisco, May 7-12, 1950)

Today we hear much about atom bombs and hydrogen bombs. Some of us are wondering if our time as human beings isn't running out! But, as organized nurses, we believe that given half a chance, the shattered body of the world can be nursed back to health, can be unified once more. Therefore, it is appropriate that the theme of this convention should be: HEALTH—A UNIFYING WORLD INFLUENCE. Those of you who had the privilege of meeting with nurses from more than forty nations in Stockholm last June must have realized the unifying influence of health. Gathered in Stockholm were nurses from countries which had been at war with each other a few short years before. But with a common desire to provide more and better nursing service for all people, political disagreements faded into the background. We were united to do our share in conserving life and improving the health of the world.

It is my privilege to enumerate briefly some of the major accomplishments of our association since our meeting in Chicago in 1948.

The American Nurses' Association is a growing organization. The membership June 30, 1948, was 144,199.* The membership at the close of 1949 was more than 170,000. This increase in members is gratifying but it may be likened to physical growth.

* "News About Nursing," *American Journal of Nursing*, Vol. XLVIII (August, 1948), 540.

Physical growth, if not accompanied by mental growth and development is tragic. Increase in members without a corresponding increase in vision and enrichment of service would be no cause for rejoicing. However, we believe ANA's program has expanded in direct proportion to the increase in membership. I shall enumerate some points of progress:

1. The platform you adopted at the biennial in 1948 pledged us to promote "effective working relationships with other social, scientific, and professional groups." Active participation in the Commission for the Improvement of Patient Care* has brought about a united front on the issue of licenses for practical nurses and a desire to cooperate actively in various measures to improve patient care. The Inter-Association Committee on Health,** upon which the ANA has representation, represents an attempt on the part of all the health professions to prepare a plan for meeting the health needs of the American people which will conserve that which is sound in our present systems of medical care and meet the changing and expanded health needs of our country.
2. Progress has been made in implementing the admission of Negro nurses to ANA. In all but four states and the District of Columbia, Negro nurses now join the ANA through their district and state associations. The admission of Negro nurses directly into the ANA from those four states and the District of Columbia is progressing well and through the fine work of the Liaison Committee between the American Nurses' Association and the National Association of Colored Graduate Nurses, excellent relationships are being developed.
3. One of our major programs is the economic security

* This Commission is made up of representatives of the ANA, the AHA and nursing organizations.

** This Committee is made up of representatives of the AMA, ADA, ANA, AHA, APHA and APW.

program. Definite gains have been made all along the line but during the past two years outstanding progress has been made in Minnesota and Washington. Compensation commensurate to the services nurses render to society is only one of the benefits of this program. The development of democratic relationships and work satisfaction are invaluable assets in the attainment of true professional status.

4. Completion of the nationwide inventory of registered nurses, at the request of the National Security Resources Board, was a costly and time-consuming job which the ANA has pledged itself to keep up-to-date. These data are the basis for planning in many of our ANA programs as well as being an essential tool in planning for national defense.
5. Progress has been made in carrying out a number of the planks in our 1948 platform through joint activities with the other national nursing organizations. At long last, nursing has taken its place among the other health professions which have a national accrediting service for the schools which prepare their practitioners. The National Nursing Accrediting Service is now organized and functioning as a joint activity under the aegis of six national nursing organizations. Our responsibility in the recruitment of student nurses is carried out by the Joint Committee on Careers in Nursing. Progress has been made in securing the inclusion of nursing in health and medical prepayment plans. These are but a few of the many activities which have been promoted more effectively through the united efforts of all nursing groups.
6. One of the strengths of our type of organization is the activity on a local or state level. To stimulate more active programs within the states, ANA has sponsored numerous institutes and workshops for section chairmen, state executive secretaries, counselors and personnel of state boards of nurse examiners. In addition to these conferences, headquarters staff has carried an exceedingly heavy schedule of

field work which has extended into local areas. All of these activities have contributed to a better informed profession and a greater interest in association activities.

7. Accomplishments in the interest of world health have been gratifying. Since the 1948 biennial convention, the Congress has approved U.S. membership in the World Health Organization. The International Council of Nurses has been recognized by the World Health Organization as the non-governmental spokesman for nursing. Each year the American delegation to meetings of WHO has included a nurse advisor. This has done much to increase the prestige abroad of American nurses. The American Nurses' Association has been granted observer status at the United Nations Assembly. Our headquarters staff has assisted in arranging educational and work experience for hundreds of foreign nurses who have come to America to learn of our methods in nursing and, we sincerely hope, to appreciate our American way of life.
8. And finally, the diamond jubilee of nursing developed in the general public, as well as among allied professional groups and our own members and students, a new interest in and an increased appreciation of the contributions of nurses in meeting society's needs for health service.

The examples of progress cited above do not include all of the regular on-going programs of the ANA. Professional counseling and placement, federal and state legislation programs, not to mention the work performed in preparation for this convention, are important ANA activities.

A few of the major issues which require your consideration and decision before we leave San Francisco are:

1. What shall we do with regard to the structure of our national nursing organizations? More than ten years ago, one of our state associations requested the ANA Board of Directors to take steps toward the possible amalgamation of all national nursing organizations. No issue has been studied more

seriously by nurses throughout the entire country than has this problem. Your board of directors, at its meeting in January, recommended a two-organization plan as being the most feasible at this time, provided: (a) the ANA corporation be retained and new or expanded functions be provided for through amendments to or revisions of the existing ANA by-laws; (b) the proposed joint board be a subsidiary corporation jointly owned by the American Nurses' Association and the proposed Nursing League of America, and (c) the organization of specialty councils be delayed but that appropriate sections be encouraged to develop the functions proposed for the councils. In response to requests from several of the ANA sections, a postcard opinionnaire on structure was sent to every member of the ANA, and each was asked to check one of three possible choices. The replies have been tabulated and the results have been sent to each state. Approximately twenty-six percent of the cards were returned. About thirty-one percent of those responding preferred a one-organization plan; a little more than thirty-nine percent preferred a two-organization plan, and almost thirty percent preferred no change in our present ANA structure. It is time a decision is made, and this house of delegates has that responsibility.

2. Shall we adopt a professional code for nurses? About twenty-five years ago the nursing organizations were asked to prepare a professional code to which all registered nurses could subscribe. Later the Joint Committee on Ethical Standards became an ANA special committee, and during the past two years this committee has been very active. More than five thousand nurses participated in evaluating the data prepared by the ANA committee this past year. The tentative code was published in the April *American Journal of Nursing.* Your decision this week will climax almost a quarter of a century of discussion.
3. What shall we include in our platform for the next two

years? Because at the 1948 biennial some delegates felt that the platform had been rushed through at the last minute without adequate opportunity for study, great care was taken to ensure that no such charge would again be heard. The proposed platform was framed after long and careful study of suggestions received from the states. It was then submitted to the board of directors in January, 1950, and when approved by the board, it was sent to the state associations for study prior to this convention. It appeared in the March *American Journal of Nursing* so that every member had an opportunity to review the items suggested.

4. How many kinds of nurses do we need and what shall be the functions of each type of worker? The ANA Board of Directors has had numerous requests to undertake or to promote studies which will determine what should be the functions and relationships of all types of nursing personnel (professional nurses, practical nurses, and auxiliary workers) and to determine what proportion of nursing time should be provided by each group of workers in various situations. The questions to be answered by you are: Who will undertake the research and how shall the cost be met? Unless the nursing profession assumes the responsibility for such studies some other group will probably do so, and we may not approve of their methods nor of their findings. One of the criteria in judging the professional status of any occupational group is the amount of research and the type of critical analyses carried out by the group. Is nursing truly professional when measured by that criterion? Would ANA members be willing to contribute a dollar a year for a period of five years to a fund if that fund were earmarked for research?
5. Shall ANA headquarters remain in New York or be moved to the Midwest? This question has been under consideration for sixteen years. Our headquarters lease in New York expires this year. Uncertainty creates a feeling of insecurity

among the staff and it hampers efficient planning. Now is the time to make a definite decision with regard to this problem.

6. Shall we provide associate membership for retired or inactive nurses? An amendment to our bylaws will be presented to you at this meeting. The national inventory of registered nurses reveals 200,000 nurses who are inactive or retired. Would nursing be strengthened if their active interest in organized nursing could be maintained?

These are but a few of the many important issues facing the delegates at this meeting. Not all the problems will be solved in a manner that satisfies everyone. One of the fundamental principles of a democracy is that the minority accepts the decisions of the majority, and together, both groups try to make the decisions work for the best interest of all. In arriving at our decisions this week, let us try to put ourselves in the place of those who may not agree with our point of view. I am sure the decisions reached will be more objective if we try to understand opposing points of view and establish goals which will be of the greatest benefit to nurses and nursing, not only for today but during the years to come as well.

1950-1954

Elizabeth K. Porter

Awarded the Florence Nightingale Medal by the International Red Cross, Elizabeth K. Porter has devoted her career to nursing education.

Some years ago, the Governor of Pennsylvania named Dr. Porter, a native Pennsylvanian, "Pennsylvania Ambassador" in recognition of her distinguished service as a nurse educator.

Upon graduation from West Penn Hospital School of Nursing, Dr. Porter accepted a position as a teaching supervisor. She received her Master of Science and her Doctor of Education degrees from the University of Pennsylvania while serving on the faculty of the University's School of Nursing. She is a Dean Emeritus and Professor Emeritus of the Frances Payne Bolton School of Nursing at Case Western Reserve University.

In addition to serving as president and a member of the board of directors, Elizabeth K. Porter worked on the committee studying the functions of the American Nurses' Association as well as the committee identifying current and long-term goals.

She has also served on the boards of directors of the American Journal of Nursing, the National Health Counsel, and the association's Professional Counseling & Placement Service.

Following two terms in office as president of the national association, Dr. Porter was selected president of the Ohio State Nurses' Association. She also functioned as chairman of numerous committees established by various nursing organizations.

Now residing in Cleveland, Dr. Porter serves as a nursing consultant.

Reorganization of the National Nursing Organizations

By Elizabeth K. Porter, Ed.D., R.N., *president*
(Thirty-Eighth Convention, Atlantic City, June 16-20, 1952)

A biennial convention of the American Nurses' Association cannot fail to excite the emotion and challenge the imagination of all who know its history. It is no longer the comparatively simple organization of nurses that it was in the years immediately following its founding; it has become highly complex. Changes have come in its field with such breath-taking rapidity that its story constitutes a modern Arabian Nights Tale.

With equal rapidity, we must add, changes have come in other fields. General education, religion, business and industry—all show a similar pattern of change in accordance with one basic principle, namely, that all life is integrated, and therefore, each profession and business today must, if it is to fulfill its purpose, integrate itself into the life of this mid-century. In brief, the seemingly startling changes that have taken place in nursing, in schools and colleges, in churches, in government, in mills and factories, but mirror the changing life of our country and reflect the growing interdependence of all nations of the world. For us, those changes mean that there are thrilling social and professional frontiers that await our crossing. They mean that nurses united are now seeking new goals, and searching for the best means to realize them.

This is not to say that there will be a forsaking of old goals. Probably everyone in this assembly throughout her professional life has worked to attain the highest standards of practice and education for the profession and will continue to work for them. You have worked for health education and the prevention of illness as well as cared for the sick.

You have approved and been a part of the increasing emphasis upon an understanding of child growth and development, the need of parental education, and, since our population is living to a greater age than ever before, geriatrics.

You have been increasingly aware of the significance of human behavior and the importance of improved human relations. Though there have been miraculous advances in the physical sciences, there has been comparatively little in the area of human relations. We do not yet have the techniques, the knowledge, the wisdom to solve human relations problems arising in a world that is one big neighborhood. Some of the major problems in our own profession lie in this area, and the field is wide open for study and research.

You have worked for public recognition of nursing as a profession and for the welfare of the nurse herself.

You have worked, through the larger resources and organized efforts of the entire profession, for those services and conditions of efficiency in the field of nursing which nurses, individually, cannot secure.

These long-held goals are still before us, but they take on new aspects with the new times; they require a different approach. These interests bring nursing directly into the social field, since they impose upon us an obligation to improve conditions that menace health. The social field, in turn, needs the contributions that we can make; and the public needs a clear interpretation of our profession and its philosophy and policies. The two—the social field and nursing—are working toward a fuller integration. But in the forefront of all our thinking and planning, our hopes and aspirations, must ever remain the fact of present-day America with all its tensions and atmosphere of emergency. As one of the largest groups of professional women in the world, we are obligated to give top priority to the defense needs of our country.

Immediately after the 1950 biennial convention the ANA Board of Directors gave consideration to the fact that in the event nurses are suddenly needed in large numbers it would be imperative to be ready with plans for action.

Therefore, in July 1950 the board expressed the belief that if any sudden emergency developed which would deplete nursing service, it would support the selective service act for all women to be supplemented by a general service act to augment reduced civilian nursing service. In other words, the board indicated its willingness to accept a draft for nurses if it is a total draft of women power in order that our civilian nursing services would not suffer because of the sudden withdrawal of nurses.

In these last two years the ANA participated in various programs which were intended to stimulate recruitment of nurses for military nursing service. This included assistance in the preparation of a statement on the mobilization of nurses for national security by the Joint Committee on Nursing in National Security. State quotas for extended active duty in the Army Nurse Corps were established and states were urged to give every possible assistance in stimulating recruitment for the military service.

The achievement of all the goals of the American Nurses' Association is in large measure dependent on the welfare of the nurse herself.

The pioneering work of ANA toward improving employment conditions of registered nurses is well known. Our economic security program, launched at the instructions of the 1946 house of delegates, established a unique principle which is today being closely studied by many other professional groups as a guide and model.

In the short space of six years we have made very encouraging progress when you consider that we live in a profession beset by age-old traditions and customs which are not lightly laid aside. We have had necessarily to proceed slowly, recognizing that nursing has responsibilities far greater and graver than most other groups. Despite these factors, the principles and philosophies inherent in the economic security program have at last seen the bright dawn of recognition and acceptance, both within our ranks and outside of the profession.

There are many other important aspects of the economic security program which perhaps are not so well known, such as guidance in collective bargaining. The ANA Committee on

Employment Conditions for Registered Nurses has, for instance, assumed responsibility for keeping the association alert to economic and employment factors involved in current mobilization to meet additional military and civilian nursing needs. It has spoken out for nurses' welfare in regard to wage stabilization and price controls. It has kept nurses informed on their status under the new social security law. And it has concerned itself with study and promotion of various types of group insurance and retirement plans for nurses.

A convention that is to vote on the continuance or modification of old policies and the adoption of new ones reaches its conclusions in no ivory tower; in no single meeting or series of meetings over a period of days. Rather it reaches its conclusions through long hours—sometimes years of study; through experiences in actual service and exact analysis and interpretation of those experiences; and through conferences with nurses and nursing groups, with other professional groups, and with laymen both here and abroad. And always it looks upon its past history as a springboard for new achievement.

'We Work Not Alone'

What exactly has keynoted our program in recent years? Most of all, perhaps, the idea that we work not alone, but in cooperation with many groups in our own profession, in other professions, and in government. To illustrate: in order to create a corps of nurses equipped to teach others in local and state defense groups, the Atomic Energy Commission, the United States Public Health Service and the National Security Resources Board have cooperated in giving courses on the nursing aspects of atomic warfare. Nursing, as you know, has also had representation on committees in the Health Resources office of the N.S.R.B. and on the Joint Commission For Improvement of the Care of the Patient. Representatives of our national associations are serving as civilian consultants to Army, Navy and Air Force Nurse Corps, have attended the Mid-Century White House Conference on Children and Youth, the national conference on International Economic and Social Development, a conference on Women in National Defense and many others. Indeed the number of national and world organizations on which our nursing associations have had representation is legion. Most impressive, perhaps, is the official status that the International Council of Nurses has with the World Health Organization under the United Nations—a status that allows it consultative relations with the United Nations Economic and Social Council. It may be added that the WHO has now eight nurses on its staff; that two psychiatric nurses are on its advisory council; and that a public health nurse was assigned to help in formulating survey guides. Further, the UN Commission on the Status of Women has adopted a resolution on the importance of wider recognition of the professional status of nursing and of legal protection for that status.

It is heartening that so many groups have recognized in a practical way that nursing is a great social force in the present world crisis. Foundation gifts, WHO Fellowships, Fullbright Awards for nurse specialists, the Mary M. Roberts Fellowship for study in journalism, and scholarships set up by schools of nursing, women's clubs, every kind of lay organization—all testify to the current opinion that nursing must be given every opportunity to equip itself well for its unique contribution to health and to the fields of human behavior and human relations.

'More Aggressive Programs Necessary'

Now, to meet the new problems and responsibilities that have grown out of two world wars and a world neighborhood, social changes, scientific progress, more aggressive programs in the world of nursing are necessary, if our profession is to go forward.

When the National Association of Colored Graduate Nurses was disbanded, its program was taken over by the ANA which immediately set up an intergroup relations unit. Probably no single program of ANA has received such widespread and favorable acclaim outside of our own profession as had the intergroup relations program which had its genesis in 1946. This program is concerned with the tensions, rifts and cleavages between nurse groups of different origin, stemming from different peoples or races.

The bold and forthright action in 1946 recommending that all state and district nurses' associations eliminate racial bars to membership, and the subsequent record of progress, has earned for nursing the proud right of enlightened leadership among all the professions. Indeed, our action has been a real contribution to the entire nation in our present world-wide struggle for ideologies. And might I add, not only is the integration of colored graduate nurses into the association a deserved recognition but, the American Nurses' Association will, as the years pass, continue to be enriched by their contribution.

With the disbanding of this group, there now remains the task of reorganizing the remaining national nursing organizations. All here know that they have long cooperated in many phases of their work. Indeed there has been a steady increase of joint committees. All here have followed the proposals and plans for a closer union of all national associations. In such a union of our professional associations it is believed that overlapping can be eliminated, that attention can more economically and effectively be focused on over-all problems and interests, and also on the concerns of special interest groups; and that the end result will be a nursing service suited to the need of this modern world, which, we hope, will eventually be a united society. Here again, nursing parallels action in the world at large.

A recent writer in nursing has pointed to the likeness between our governmental structures and the structural plan for nursing that we are considering in this convention. In earlier years, there was a disposition to think of government in terms of the local community. But with the growing complexity of our way of life no community can provide for all of the needs of its people; it can do only part of the job. So we have the wider communities—the state and the nation with their richer resources of specialists, organization, money, authority, but always the local community and the state to influence national policies. Our district and state associations will have the same relations to the new American Nurses' Association. The structure is in its nature democratic.

There are probably a few in every organization, but very few in ours, I hope, who cry out against any change of pattern in the profession and in life generally. They pin their faith to what is static, not what is dynamic.

The American Nurses' Association can be only as strong as individuals are strong for collective action, and that strength must be fostered in district and state groups. The individual nurse in the association is an important entity. Just as, as a citizen, she needs to be informed and to make her influence felt, so as a nurse, she needs to be an informed, committed, and alerted-for-action member of her local, state and national associations.

The individual nurse, concerned with bedside care on hospital wards and in the homes, may feel that she is remote from her national association but she, too, can make history in the ANA, if only she will inform herself and use the channels open to her. She must know in broad outline what the policies of the ANA are in its deliberative bodies and in its specialized agencies; and she must make her opinions about those policies known in the same way she makes her opinions known about local, state and national policies of political government. But she must have facts in order to make wise decisions.

At this historical convention, you, as delegates, will be faced with many momentous decisions which will affect the 175,000 nurses you represent. You have a very great responsibility, therefore, for getting full and accurate information about the ANA programs you will be asked to act upon. One sees frequently a variety of statements and facts which must be looked at with a critical and questioning eye. You should be extremely wary of incomplete and unsupported data.

For example, you may see a statement that the average salary for nurses in state "X" is $230 a month. That statement is absolutely meaningless unless you know certain other essential facts. You must know what fields of nursing or what types of positions are covered and how many nurses are included in each. You must know what the basic work week is, that is, does the figure apply to a 40-hour week, a 44-hour week, or a 48-hour week. You must know whether the figure covers maintenance or other benefits. The ANA has been most careful in all programs to use only facts and figures that are complete and accurate and that have been obtained according to accepted statistical methods and procedures. Sometimes this policy handicaps us because we do not seem to be informed. But at least it is an honest policy.

There has been such a wide variety of activities in ANA over the past two years. The individual states cooperated in follow-up activities by distributing materials sent to them, by reporting findings and recommendations, and by reviewing with the membership on the state and local level, the ways in which they can help to achieve the objectives.

As you know, the program is developed through recommendations and suggestions of members wherever they are. It is translated into action by members in groups or as individuals. The program follows the main objectives outlined in the platform adopted by the House of Delegates and points the way to specific goals for nurses and nursing.

In conclusion, as we face the greater and inevitable changes in our profession in the years that lie ahead, may the American Nurses' Association grow and prosper as never before.

Calling American Nurses to Action

By Elizabeth K. Porter, Ed.D., R.N., *president*
(Thirty-Ninth Convention, Chicago, April 26-30, 1954)

When the American Nurses' Association met in Atlantic City two years ago, the whole country was caught up in a fever of the national campaigns for the Presidency of the United States. Every periodical headlined the question: "Who Will Be the Next

President?" Second in commanding front page space were articles on "War News from Korea," "Higher Taxes for All," "Is the Next Depression Near?" "New Atom Weapons," "Strikes Big and Little." And along with these we read reports of unrest in Indonesia, Palestine, Iran—almost, it seemed, in every corner of the globe.

Now what is the situation as we meet today? Dwight Eisenhower is President. The war in Korea is over. Taxes, though still high, have been reduced this month. Many persons are still jittery about the possibility of a depression. Strikes are still frequent. The hydrogen bomb has been exploded at Eniwetok. Jet planes streak through the sky with twice the speed of sound, and there is in preparation a railroad at the Edwards Air Force base in California that has a proposed speed of 1,200 miles an hour.*

At our last biennial convention some of us dared to question man's mastery of things. Just recently our own President, Dwight Eisenhower, in a radio and TV address to the nation, spoke his concern over "science outracing our social consciousness." President Eisenhower observed that the crucial events of one lifetime reflect our inability to emotionally and intellectually adapt to vast scientific advances.

Our awareness of this situation is reflected in topics selected for program meetings. Hear some of them: "Human Values in a Scientific Age," "Social Responsibilities of a Professional Organization," "Professional Progress Through Personal Growth," "Dynamics of Human Relations."

But why, you may ask, dwell upon these depressing items when science has wrought in the healing arts miracles just as stupendous as those of the hydrogen bomb and supersonic speeds, miracles that are constructive, that are for the good of mankind? Because all of these factors tie in with the theme chosen for our convention, "Calling American Nurses to Action."

The first challenge to nurses in this year of 1954 is that we

* "Fastest Railroad Ever," *Newsweek*, February 1, 1954, 64.

understand, so far as possible, present world conditions. It is impossible to carry well our share of the responsibility for adequate service in hospitals and homes, for joint action with allied professional and lay groups, for research projects, for International Exchange-Visitor Programs, and for membership in World Health Organization teams, unless we understand conditions responsible for man's present ills and his impaired health.

Parallel with the first challenge, especially in this Florence Nightingale Centennial Year, is the call to study anew the history of nursing that we may accept added responsibilities imposed by a legacy such as ours in nursing education, nursing experience, and nursing opportunity; and that, without making a break with the past, we may emerge from past professional performance to a broader and more efficient service.

At the last biennial we responded to a call to action by adopting the new structure for our nursing organizations—a change which resulted in more efficient machinery for achieving our purposes. That change was not a hastily made decision, but a culmination of many years of painstaking study on your part and on the part of other nurses.

Today, many of you, for the first time, have assembled to discuss and vote on matters that affect all members. You are here because you have been selected by the occupational sections in your own states. Included in this house of delegates are representatives chosen by the general duty, private duty, industrial, and public health nurses who give direct care to patients; delegates chosen by nursing educators who teach nursing to graduate and undergraduate students, and by administrators responsible for nursing services. The states' special group sections and individual members of the American Nurses' Association are represented. In addition, there are three delegates-at-large from each state nurses' association, plus ANA officers and the board of directors.

Here we are truly a Congress of Nurses. Delegates have a marvelous opportunity and a heavy responsibility to take part in discussion, to contribute knowledge and experience, to weigh the contribution of others, to appraise suggestions, to debate issues, and to register their votes. And in addition, to summarize for the good of the group at home the findings of each hour.

Inventory of Accomplishments

An inventory of accomplishments in the various areas of the association's program is essential before indicating follow-ups or new attacks. Opportunity for these inventories and plans for action you will find in business meetings and programs arranged for specific units. The list of "Timely Issues" calling for decisions is quite extensive, namely: proposed amendments to the bylaws; strengthening the structure of the organization; legislation (federal and state); counseling and placement; human relations; the economics of nursing; functions, standards, and qualifications of nurses; nursing in national defense; international nursing.

For this week's concentrated attack upon crucial problems, we are bolstered by the recent public recognition given the nurse in the birthday celebration of the World Health Organization on April 7. As you know, our nation joined in that celebration by calling all persons in the United States to center their attention upon health. The attractive brochure prepared and circulated by the regional office of WHO carried across its cover in large type a theme that stirs the pride of every nurse: "The Nurse—Pioneer of Health."

And the voices speaking on that theme pay honor, not only to Florence Nightingale and her initiative in the field of nursing and the thousands of missionary nurses and government nurses who have for many, many years been pioneering throughout the world, but place special emphasis upon present-day nurses and present-day nursing, and the outlook for the future; for nursing, they contend, is still a pioneering, not a static job. High commendation is given to nurses and their achievements in this present era: expansion of the objectives of nursing to include the promotion and conservation of health, broadening the meaning of health to a positive concept of physical, mental, and social well-being, emphasis upon the sociological as well as the biological in the preparation for this truly professional calling.

The hope of the American Nurses' Association, World Health Organization, and workers in bilateral programs like the American Point IV Aid, is that these celebrations will result in an all-out campaign to attract a much greater number of highly qualified young people into the nursing field for our own country and the countries of the world. A goal of complete health for the world means more, and yet more nurses. In the more fortunate parts of the world there is one professionally trained nurse to three hundred population. But in some other countries the ratio is one to one hundred thousand. We nurses can fire the gun for recruitment. Here is a call for effective public relations. Right public relations, both at home and abroad, is a powerful weapon for mutual understanding and progress.

In addition to knowledge gained through the study of world affairs, nurses are gaining greater understanding of the cultures, customs, and interest of others through contacts at international conferences, through social and professional association with exchange nurses, exchange teachers, exchange students, and exchange social workers. Arrangements for some of these opportunities have been made through the American Nurses' Association working through the International Council of Nurses; some are the result of Fulbright grants, Rockefeller fellowships, and others are grants by individual philanthropists. We count ourselves fortunate to share in the work.

Included also in association activities in the international domain is the planning for observation, study, and clinical experience under the Exchange-Visitor Program of the Department of State, and for salaried employment. During the year 1953, fifty-three nurses arrived in our country to begin assignments under the Exchange-Visitor Program and thirty-nine for salaried employment. Four study programs and forty-five observation tours were arranged. Almost 300 nurses from other countries were interviewed personally by the assistant executive secretary.

On the home front we are moving as rapidly as possible to remove barriers that prevent the full development and full employment of nurses belonging to minority racial groups. Eight years ago at the biennial we voted to give integration our support. Our efforts have resulted in definite progress. Naturally, the progress was facilitated greatly by the increasing readiness of the American people to extend the privileges and responsibilities of citizenship to every American regardless of race, religion, or national origin. The number of schools of nursing now enrolling students on the basis of qualification without regard to color is approximately 710. All except one state nurses' association accept Negro nurses into membership. Two state nurses' associations submitted to the governors of their respective states the name of a Negro nurse for membership on the state board of nurse examiners. Increasingly, committees on the district, state, and national levels concerned with various American Nurses' Association programs are considering questions in intergroup relations. Again, increasingly, agencies which employ nurses are choosing the nurse who meets the established qualifications regardless of the nurse's racial inheritance.

Intergroup Relations

There are still inequities. Too infrequently in our professional organization is a Negro nurse appointed to membership or chairmanship of a committee, or elected to office. No matter how high the qualification, colored persons are seldom considered for a position above the level of general duty, and too frequently they do not receive equal salary for equal work.

Intergroup relations in nursing is of vital concern to all of us, as nurses and as citizens of our United States and our world.

As for the program of the American Nurses' Association in research, we know that every industry, every business, every profession for long years have been dependent upon research for better techniques and new developments. Without new knowledge there is no progress. Billions of dollars yearly are spent in research in fields as widely separated as medicine and automobiles, law and textiles. But research has traveled a rocky road in our profession. It has suffered from the preconceived idea that nurses must be kept busy about routine tasks. Schools of nursing and nursing service administration have sometimes promoted this idea. Now, however, that allied professions and laymen are recognizing that nursing research is the concern, not just of nursing, but of the whole social order, there has been a growing interest and support. Heretofore, our progress in nursing has been due in large part to unselfish, far-seeing nurses who contributed freely of their time and talent to volunteer research. But a profession such as ours, touching every phase of life, can no longer depend wholly upon occasional research or interrupted research. Although such research will always make a contribution, we must have, in addition, a very definite program of full-time nursing research.

The American Nurses' Association is now advancing in this field under its own power, following authorization by the House of Delegates in 1950. Action at first was slow, but is now stepping up rapidly as you will note at the program meeting on the topic "Professional Functions and Nursing Practice." Five new grants for studies were made under our program in 1953. Six grants, totalling $80,000, have been made available for 1954. Persons outside of nursing have told us that this research program of ANA is one of the most creative and enlightened undertakings ever initiated by any profession.

So far I have discussed specifically intergroup, international, public relations, and research, as each relates to our work. I should like to headline another ANA program, which touches every group, namely, the economic security program. Our organization has two broad general purposes. The first, to promote the continuous improvement of the service we give; the second, to promote the welfare and protection of our membership. The aspirations of the nursing profession in all of its programs cannot be realized if we neglect strategic resource—the nurse herself.

The story of the economic security program is a puzzling chapter in our history because the basic principle of a democratic organization, i.e., "the right of decision belongs to the majority" is so frequently violated. Nevertheless, although the story is not one of "paradise gained," only a rank pessimist could fail to be impressed by the difference between our situation today and eight years ago. There are new issues, new needs in this field, and an imperative call to American nurses to carry on. A new phase of nursing evolution with respect to the welfare of nurses lies ahead—the challenge for leadership. Will the sections of ANA assume it? Will they take advantage of their golden opportunity for leadership? They cannot stand still and let well enough alone. If they do, other groups and professions will pass us by. You and I must face up to the question of our role in shaping this economic security program in the future.

What, you may ask, is the role of the individual nurse in these broad affairs of our association? She has an exceedingly important role to play. The individual nurse concerned with bedside care makes her first contribution by giving the finest possible care to patients. Because of her very close association with patients, she is in a position to make a unique contribution to the development of healthy, well-balanced individuals, and to the building of an environment conducive to health. But she must do more. What she can do to give the general public an idea of nursing as a strong social force, stirs the imagination. Further, as she studies the policies of her professional organization, she will form her own opinions about those policies and make them known through her section at its various levels. As small tributaries feeding into the main streams make mighty rivers, so do individual nurses working intelligently and creatively at their appointed tasks give a distinctive character to our great profession.

This is the last time I shall address you as President of this great association. I cannot let the occasion pass without telling you that these four years have been for me, as I hope they have been for you, personally and professionally, rich and rewarding. There have been three major steps undertaken to advance the cause of the American Nurses' Association. First, we had some dreams for nursing of "what were fair provided it could be." These were dreams of heights to be obtained knowing that "a man's reach should exceed his grasp, or what's a heaven for." The second step was the creation of plans to translate our dreams into realities. Third was the organization of specific programs that would implement adequately our planning. Continued progress in relation to all three steps must go on.

When I leave this highest office, I shall continue to work closely with you, but from a different vantage point. Side by side, as always, we shall strive creatively for the best interests of our profession and our association. An inspiration for the task we may draw from Cicero's words, "In nothing do men more nearly approach the Gods than in giving health to men."

To you, my colleagues, to you the finest professional women in the world, I pledge my unwavering and eternal devotion.

1954–1958

Agnes Ohlson

An alumna of the Peter Bent Brigham Hospital School of Nursing in Boston, Agnes Ohlson was awarded a Bachelor of Science degree in nursing from Teachers College at Columbia University in New York City and a Master of Arts degree in government from Trinity College in Hartford, Connecticut.

Miss Ohlson began her nursing career as a supervisor at the Wesson Maternity Hospital in Springfield, Massachusetts. In later years, she worked as assistant superintendent of nurses at Truesdale Hospital in Fall River, Massachusetts, director of the nursing service and school of nursing at Connecticut's Waterbury Hospital, and chief examiner of the Connecticut Board of Examiners for Nursing.

During World War II, Agnes Ohlson was a consultant to the U.S. Cadet Nurse Corps. In this capacity, she was instrumental in organizing an emergency nurse training program to satisfy wartime needs for nurses. Following the war, Miss Ohlson worked closely with state boards of nurse examiners, serving as chairman of the ANA Bureau of State Boards of Nurse Examiners and the Committee on State Board Problems of the National League of Nursing Education.

ANA's seventeenth president also served as president of several other nursing organizations, including the Connecticut State Nurses' Association and Connecticut State League of Nursing Education. She was the first president of the American Nurses' Foundation. While serving her second term as president of the American Nurses' Association, she was elected president of the International Council of Nurses, the oldest continuously functioning international council.

Today, Miss Ohlson maintains an interest in the activities of both the American Nurses' Association and the International Council of Nurses.

Nursing in the Future

By Agnes Ohlson, R.N., *president*
(Fortieth Convention, Chicago, May 14-18, 1956)

There is a time for listening, a time for speaking, a time for thinking and a time for doing. This week there will be time for all of these . . . We will be listening, speaking, thinking and doing, not only for ourselves but for the nurses at home, whom we represent, for the nurses who preceded us in such conventions and for the nurses who will follow.

This year marks the 60th birthday of the ANA. Sixty years during which nurses have worked together to better their profession in every way and to improve patient care. Sixty years during which we have learned as an organized group, to listen, to speak, to think and to act.

Today, as we look at our professional organization, it is difficult for most of us to comprehend the changes which have occurred in the past 60 years. We see the ANA as it is today—one of the largest professional organizations in the country, with a membership of more than 177,000; constituent associations in the 48 states, the District of Columbia and five territories; and an extensive program undreamed of in the days when nurses first organized nationally. It would be impossible to describe from this platform all that ANA is and does today in the time available. It has taken more than 600 pages of print to report the activities for the association during the biennium alone.

This year also marks the end of a decade for us. The sixth decade in ANA's history. It has been a decade of rapid expansion and great change, both in nursing and in our organization. Ten years ago our activities were governed by a budget of approximately $289,000. This year, our budget is three times that amount, and the programs and activities we carry on have expanded accordingly.

This is a particularly auspicious decade for us to consider, since it marks the time during which nursing has officially been recognized as a profession. Some of you will remember that it was in 1946, after a great effort on the part of ANA that the Civil Service Commission reclassified graduate nursing positions in Federal government agencies from the subprofessional to professional status. During this decade we adopted the first Code for Professional Nurses, and were gratified to see our Code used as a model for the one adopted by the International Council of Nurses.

We launched an extensive program of research, and following that established the American Nurses' Foundation, Inc. We developed the Professional Counselling and Placement Service, which was established in 1945. We created a formal economic security program. We expanded our legislative activities with the opening of an office in the nation's capital. We created a comprehensive public relations program, an inter-group relations program and have expanded our activities in international relations. All this has been reflected in the development of the platform of the ANA.

What makes this expansion of program most significant, I believe, is that it occurred during a decade which also saw a tremendous reorganization in the structure of the ANA and the development of section programs. This has resulted in a greater ability to meet the needs of members and greater opportunity for participation.

Another aspect of our growth which should be mentioned here, has been the broadening of our relationships with other groups. ANA meets with many of the health and professional organizations concerned with the myriad problems relating to the health needs of the public. Exchanging views with representatives of these groups and noting the increasing acceptance and desire to work with nursing on their part has been one of the most thrilling experiences I've had as president of the ANA.

We have passed through the adolescent stage of organization. We have learned to cope with many problems; we have learned through successful, as well as trying experiences. We have reached a stage of maturity, as an organization, and as a profession, when we can meet the challenges which face us. The challenge to our profession is to progress with our times. The challenge to each of us is to think broadly and the challenge to our organization is to plan beyond immediate needs and problems.

If we do not meet these challenges, we shall find ourselves members of a profession without stature and an organization without strength.

To Progress with the Times

In order to help our profession keep in step with changes in society, and to cope with other than immediate problems, we must plan now so that we can function effectively as an organized group ten or twenty years from now. We must study the social and economic trends which will help fashion the world of tomorrow. We must look to our association and its ability to function successfully in that world. The ANA has already taken steps toward such an appraisal. The committee on current and long-term goals which was created at the last convention has begun this tremendous task. It is our eye on the future, and will help us to make a realistic appraisal of the present.

This committee's study should give us a basis upon which we can plan, as an organized group, to use our resources to best advantage, anticipating the needs of our profession and the patients whose care is in our hands.

The experts tell us that we can, in the future, anticipate a larger population, an older population and a population with more money to spend on health care. Our people will have increasing freedom from drudgery, increasing freedom from disease and an advancing level of education. These trends will affect us as individuals and as a professional group. They will influence not only what we are able to do but how we do it. In view of such changes, we must consider the future of our profession and the needs of patients.

What will be the character and nature of nursing care ten or twenty years from now? This question cannot be answered by one person. It must be answered by the nursing profession. Each of us has a part in formulating the answer. With the great changes in disease patterns, the increasing number of cures possible, the very nature of illness has changed. Many diseases which once were devastating in their effect, are under control. Yet new health problems arise and with them new nursing problems. How we solve these problems will partially determine what nursing is in the years to come.

Developments in related health professions also will have a great effect upon nursing in the future as they have in the past. For example, there is an increasing emphasis on medical education in the human as well as biological sciences, an increasing tendency to educate physicians to see not just a body, but a human being in relation to his family and community. As this trend gains momentum, physicians will find they are unable to carry out new medical practices while continuing those of the present. Assuming, as figures in the past indicate, there will not be enough doctors to go around, so to speak, physicians will pass on more and more tasks to other professional persons. This pattern is not new. We know, today, professional nurses are performing many functions formerly carried on by doctors. But, the tempo of this trend will, I believe, increase. This, of course, has obvious implications for nursing. As professional nurses take on more of these additional functions, they must in turn delegate more of their activities to others. This will gradually bring about a reallocation of responsibilities and, I believe, an increasing correlation between medicine and nursing. The nursing profession must help such a correlation mature.

At the same time, nursing must not neglect its responsibility in helping the development of nonprofessional health personnel. The increasing need for persons trained to give care, under professional direction, is obvious. Practical nurses and auxiliary health personnel are integral components in today's health care picture.

Changes in nursing will, of course, affect the needs of nurses and hence the future of our organization. We must consider carefully what it is we need most from our professional association, and then find a method of meeting those needs if they are not already provided for.

For example, will it be necessary, one day, to make the ANA a source of information for nurses on new techniques, new trends, new procedures? Where else will nurses find such information readily available?

Right now, in view of the tasks we are called upon to do, and the challenges which face us, perhaps one of our needs as a professional group is to develop leadership experiences. The need for leadership in professional nursing is obvious today. More and more, both on the job, and as one of many professional groups, we are being called upon to assume this role.

As times have changed, as nursing has changed, we have extended and adjusted the activities of the ANA accordingly. We have learned organizational adaptability. We have made the study of our structure a continuing process. Every two years, assembled as we are this week, we review changes in bylaws, changes in our platform, so that we can adjust to present needs. One of the planks in our platform specifically provides for this. We know we will probably never have perfection, improvement is always possible. If we give careful thought before each contemplated change, we will accomplish what we intend, "to facilitate effective action in nursing."

Importance of Organized Groups

Perhaps, one of the most significant trends today, of which we must be cognizant, is the growing importance and influence of organized groups in our society. One can accomplish little alone these days. Community action, group action, are the order of the day. There is a growing tendency for groups to speak for and represent individuals. This is a trend which gathers momentum obviously. For as soon as one group acts in this way, other persons find they cannot stand against the pressures exerted unless they, too, are organized. The objective of any group is to change the status quo. We ourselves are an example of this. When nursing first organized, one of the major objectives was to change the situation regarding the licensure of nurses. Underlying all our programs is the aim to improve patient care. This denotes change. Today, many of our programs are designed to change present situations. It goes without saying that there are bound to be organized groups whose objectives do not match ours, whose aims may be contrary to ours. To cope with such situations we must be united, and firm.

As nurses we must develop the techniques which other groups are using to make themselves effective. Group activity of this kind requires that we present a united front to the public. This is not as simple as it sounds. Yet it is, I believe, perfectly compatible with the democratic principles upon which the ANA is based. We need dissenters in nursing. We need varying viewpoints. We need alert, inquiring minds. Yet, once a majority decision has been reached, those with varying viewpoints must stand together and speak with one determined voice. We must be firm without being arbitrary. We must not permit opposition to "divide and conquer." For group activity, participation is necessary. The thought, energy and effort of every member is required.

Nursing will, in the next decade, play a much more important role in the health care of the nation than ever before. The result will, I believe, mean a great improvement in patient care.

Year by year, nursing has assumed more and more responsibility in care of patients and greater participation in preventive medicine. One has only to look at the functions which have been outlined by the various sections to see what nursing is today. The idea of "planning for the total nursing needs of the patient" recurs in one statement after another, and such practice requires judgment, self-direction, and an understanding of human behavior and relationships.

Through the years, nursing has acquired a body of knowledge of its own. The independent nursing functions which are a part of practice today are increasing and it is in this area where nursing is assuming more and more responsibility.

The benefits of such care for patients are being documented through some of the research under way in nursing. For example, one of the studies shows that given the opportunity, a head nurse's potentiality to plan nursing care is so great that it cannot be accurately estimated. Where such a condition existed, remarkable results were apparent for the patients. While the study does not infer that nursing care alone was responsible, it indicates what can be acomplished when a head nurse is able to "plan for the total nursing care of the patient."

The main reason I am so confident in predicting a much larger role for nursing in health care is that nursing today is strong enough, as a profession, and as an organized group, to have an impact on public opinion. The tremendous advances of the past decade to which I referred earlier are indications of this strength. Not only has nursing much to say, but it has a voice and a means for unified, constructive action.

We have the strength and the means—with the will to carry through we have only to decide the course of action and the method. This is in your hands.

Toward Better Nursing in Our World

By Agnes Ohlson, R.N., *president*
(Forty-First Convention, Atlantic City, June 9-13, 1958)

We have achieved much in the past. Nurses can be proud that they have helped our nation to attain one of the best health records in the world. Our profession has been ahead of many others in efforts to achieve integration for its practitioners on the basis of competence without regard to race, color, or creed. Furthermore, I assure you, American nursing is looked to for leadership, for guidance, and inspiration by nurses in many other countries. We have achieved here things which our professional colleagues in many parts of the world are still hoping for.

Yet further improvement of our practice, of health care for all people, is the real challenge which faces us at this, the 41st Convention of the American Nurses' Association.

We know there is no miraculous solution to the problems which face our profession. There is no quick and easy way to achieve our goals. We also know that the problems involved in providing better nursing care cannot be solved by nurses alone. Rather, the situation calls for staunch cooperative effort by the public, by other groups and professions concerned with health care, and by nurses.

Since World War II, the most discussed problem in nursing has been one of sheer numbers. We *have* grown in numbers, in fact we now have 258 nurses for every 100,000 population. Yet looking ahead at tomorrow, we find that by 1970, we will need a 40 per cent increase over the present number. Clearly, our *nursing education facilities must be expanded—but this expansion* must *be qualitative, not just quantitative.*

There is an increasing need for nurses adequately prepared by the baccalaureate level to meet the enormous advances in health care. Further, the increasing scope of responsibility, together with the enormous advances in science and medicine, require more and more nurses with a master and doctorate level of education. If we hope to meet future demands for nursing care, we must, by 1965, graduate at least 5,200 nurses annually from advanced degree programs. The present rate of enrollment in master's degree programs, however, is only 800 graduations annually, about 15 per cent of future needs.

To achieve qualitative expansion, nursing must have adequately prepared practitioners. Even if we *could* increase the number of qualified nursing students by 40 per cent, and provide the physical and clinical facilities for them, we would still lack the faculties to teach them. Even if we *could* increase our nursing staffs by 40 per cent, we would still lack the nursing administrators and supervisors to coordinate their work. Yes, expanding our nurse population alone is not enough.

Let us extend this thought still further. The fundamental body of knowledge upon which nursing practice is based has only been partially explored. We lack, at this time, a corps of nurses specializing in research; we lack adequate funds for basic research; and perhaps we have not sufficiently nurtured among nurses in the past the degree of intellectual curiosity and the knowledge of critical inquiry so essential for maximum professional competency. A profession has a basic responsibility to continually undertake research in order to enlarge and perfect the knowledge on which its practice rests.

To do this we must have nurses qualified to undertake such research. We must secure resources in sizeable amounts to provide for research of this magnitude and consequence. The profession must embrace the concept that scientific inquiry underlies the advancement of nursing practice. Improvement of nursing practice also requires continual evaluation and a readiness to apply research findings for the improvement of nursing practice.

A Course of Action

Toward a solution of these underlying problems, I would like to suggest a three-way course of action—a course of action which will require the cooperation of the public, other groups concerned with health care, and nurses.

Let me turn first to those things which, I believe, involve public support.

The *paramount need is support through tax funds to expand nursing education programs* at both baccalaureate and post graduate levels. Bold, broad measures by society as a whole are required.

Public Law 911, known as the Health Amendments Act of 1956, has been enormously helpful. However, it is limited and the act expires in 1959.

Since 1956, $5 million in grants has been awarded under Title II of the act to approximately 1,400 nurses in advanced educational programs. During the past year, more than 3,000 nurses applied and qualified for such grants, but the $3 million appropriated for 1958 provided traineeships for only 773 of these applicants. The American Nurses' Association has urged that the appropriation for the next year be increased to at least $7 million so that more of our eligible candidates can be assisted.

Title I of the act provides traineeships for public health personnel, and to date, 460 nurses have received study grants to prepare themselves for staff positions in public health nursing. Yet, the $2 million appropriated for this part of the program for the next year is woefully inadequate to meet the present needs. We have asked that this be increased to $3 million. With increasing emphasis on preventive and rehabilitative services and upon home care programs for the chronically ill, the demand for a larger number of qualified public health nurses will increase.

Title III of the act provides grants to state vocational education departments for expansion and improvement of practical nurses training. The ANA has supported requests for $4 million for this purpose.

Our association also is requesting Congress to provide funds for research in nursing and to assist nurses to prepare themselves to engage in research. Public support for this financial assistance by government is essential.

We also must have public support behind our efforts to achieve a better economic base for nursing if we expect to attract and hold qualified nurses in the profession. Employment conditions must be such as to permit nurses to work at their maximum level of ability. The public is responding to a similar critical economic need in the teaching profession, and, we believe, the public will do so for nursing when the facts are understood.

Historically, nursing has been regarded as a dedicated calling rather than an economic pursuit. Yet, professional nurses must have a standard of living comparable to persons in other professions and occupations requiring similar preparation and ability.

The present income level for nurses makes it difficult to attract and hold the best personnel, and it acts as a deterrent in upgrading the standards of practice. The argument that improved salaries and working conditions for nurses will add an impossible burden to the nation's health bill is a fallacious one. Increased costs can be met; for example, through inclusion in prepaid health insurance plans in the same manner as are hospital and medical expenses. Costs can also be affected by better planning, administration, and utilization of nursing skills and services.

Let us turn to the second aspect of our three-way course of action. If the nursing profession is to provide the quality and quantity of service needed, we must call on other groups and professions concerned with health care to do certain things. We live in a society of group action, and, it is in this sense of cooperative effort that I suggest we ask support in two matters of grave concern.

Employers of nurses must respect nurses' rights to participate in decisions concerning their own welfare. To be sure, nurses employed in some institutions do enjoy such rights, and results have proved beneficial to all concerned. But in general, nonprofit hospitals are under no legal compulsion to discuss such matters with their employees and this presents a stumbling block to necessary economic improvements.

There has been resistance and fear of the idea of nurses engaging in collective bargaining, through their professional association. Nurses themselves recognize that their first and foremost professional and ethical responsibility is the care of their patients, and as evidence of this we have voluntarily relinquished the right to strike.

Employers remember that this decision was an act of good faith on the part of nurses. Employers forget, however, that this imposes on them an equal obligation to sit down with the representatives of nurses for full and free discussion of questions concerning employment conditions.

We must also seek from related groups and professions concerned with health care, a greater recognition of nursing's own sphere of expertness and acceptance of nursing as a discipline of equal status. Nursing is increasingly emerging as a distinctive health science. A further mark of our growing maturity is evident from the fact that nursing is consulted by many groups in deliberations regarding the health care of our citizenry. While our viewpoints do not always agree with those of other organizations in the health field, it is through meeting together that we resolve some questions and we achieve an increasing respect for the role of the practitioner in each of the several health disciplines.

I have suggested ways in which the public and other groups and professions in the health field can help us improve nursing care. Now let us turn to ourselves!

In all candor do we believe we are carrying out fully the responsibility society expects of a professional group such as ours?

Do we believe that our standards of practice reflect more than the minimum required for the safety of the patient?

Do we constantly evaluate our practice and set for ourselves ever higher levels of competency?

Are we alert and ready to apply the new findings in both science and technology to improve our practice?

Are we gearing our practice to the demands of the time in which we are living and those which we predict will occur in the years ahead?

Let us be both critical and constructive. Let us be proud of what has been accomplished, but not satisfied.

We must be our own severest critics. We must safeguard the public from unethical and unqualified practitioners. We must control the practice of our profession. We must set our own standards, publicize them widely, and then effectively implement ever-improved excellence of practice. We must continue to search for ways to recognize and reward members of our profession for outstanding competency and performance.

No nurse alone can hope to achieve the improvements we have been discussing. It will require the power and force of a unified profession working through the professional nurses' associations in districts, in states, and on the national level.

Therefore, let us strengthen our state and national associations so they *can* meet the changing needs of members, taking on new responsibilities and casting off outmoded activities.

Since membership in our nurses' associations is purely voluntary, the tasks I have outlined will not be easy. Today, the question of membership is based on a mature decision by each individual nurse. This means that we must work toward building a larger and better informed membership. We must assist student nurses to take an interest in association activities so that upon graduation they will be ready and anxious to participate in their professional organization.

Our convention theme this week is, "The Professional Nurse: Practitioner and Citizen." As practitioners, I hope you will be challenged anew to improve the practice of nursing in our country and to meet the increasing health needs of the public both now and in future.

As citizens, I hope you will be challenged anew to take appropriate action in your communities through your government representatives, and through meetings with your professional colleagues towards the further achievement of these goals.

The House of Delegates is the voting body of the more than 181,000 members of the American Nurses' Association. You who are here today are representatives of the leadership group within our profession. The decisions you make will have extended and extensive effects. Indeed, these decisions will determine the measure of progress which our association can achieve in the next biennium. Will the momentum of our progress be accelerated or will it be impeded?

Furthermore, the decisions you reach this week must be interpreted and implemented through your state and district nurses associations. It will be your challenge to stir the imagination of your colleagues to help achieve the objectives we will set for ourselves during this convention.

In closing, I will repeat something I have said before because I believe it can never be said too often.

We, as members of the association, do have the *strength* and the *means*—with the will to carry through we have only to decide our course of action and the methods. This is in your hands.

1958–1962

Mathilda Scheuer

Interested in nursing at an early age, Mathilda Scheuer devoted her life to caring for the sick. A 1910 graduate of Mercy Hospital School of Nursing in Baltimore, she received additional training at the University of Pennsylvania and Teachers College at Columbia University.

During her career, she served as regional supervisor of nursing in convalescent and nursing homes for Pennsylvania's Department of Welfare, regional supervisor of the Pennsylvania Bureau of Services for the Aging, and acting director of the Philadelphia Visiting Nurse Society. Miss Scheuer was active in a number of nursing organizations, serving as president of the American Public Health Association, Pennsylvania State Nurses' Association, and the Pennsylvania State Organization for Public Health Nursing.

It is said that Mathilda Scheuer worked timelessly to protect nurses' rights and the rights of the American Nurses' Association to speak for the nursing profession. During her term as ANA president, the Association undertook an examination of its functions and structural organization. Miss Scheuer died on January 29, 1974.

The Far-Reaching Plans

By Mathilda Scheuer, R.N., *president*

(Forty-Second Convention, Miami Beach, May 2-6, 1960)

At the 1958 convention you accepted a very far-reaching goal which relates to research. It was stated it is to stimulate efforts made by nurses and other specialists to identify and enlarge the scientific principles on which nursing rests, and to encourage them in the affirmation of these principles through nursing practice.

We heard at that convention that the subscription rate of the *American Journal of Nursing* was going to be raised. A new plan in subscription rates for your state and district associations was reported to us. At that time, one of the projects we put before the board of directors was to study and evaluate, with the help of the *Journal*, all these matters to show what we had done or had not done.

Upon recommendation of the Committee on Economic and General Welfare, we adopted a resolution to be sent to the American Hospital Association. In 1958 the House of Delegates resoundingly supported the principle of social security insurance to include health insurance for old-age, survivors, and disability insurance, or what is known as the OASDI. We asked that prepaid health insurance include nursing service and nursing care in the home.

The House of Delegates adopted a resolution recognizing the obligation of ANA to protect the public from unqualified practitioners.

In 1958 you approved the increase of dues from five dollars to seven and a half dollars. You adopted a resolution with regard to the difficult question of one organization.

In connection with the program you gave us, a conference group on research was established in 1958. On Thursday of this week a general program session to last four hours has been scheduled on the use of research to improve practice. A joint meeting will be held of the research and studies committee with the section representatives, with the editors of the *American Journal of Nursing*, in nursing research, and with members of the technical committee of the American Nurses' Foundation. A joint meeting of this group is scheduled for 1961. When they meet they plan to examine carefully what research has done to further coördinate research activities.

You have already heard something about the expansion of the American Nurses' Foundation program and this, of course, we are very eager to have because, if we get the money, that will also be used in the field of research.

In 1959 the study and evaluation of the American Journal of Nursing Company was begun. In 1960 the bylaws were revised by the stockholders at their annual meeting. Eleven directors are now designated by ANA, and five by the National League for Nursing. The *American Journal of Nursing,* at our request, has been exploring the matter of offering the *Journal* with the ANA membership. Please do not go home and say you will have the *Journal* with your membership, because that is far from true. We are exploring that possibility. If you want to go home and talk about it, that will be fine, but we do not have the real figures to give you. The *American Journal of Nursing* staff has worked very hard to give us something on that and the study they have submitted is a beautiful one but they do not feel they are ready to present it to this House of Delegates at this time.

In this study we learned that while the American Journal of Nursing Company operated at a profit, the financial statement did show a continuing and increasing loss each year on the publication of *Nursing Outlook.* The AJN Company is now studying ways and means to eliminate this deficit.

Approaches to Problems

It was recommended also in 1958 that we study comprehensive approaches to problems of patient care and, for the first time in the history of the ANA, a liaison committee was formed with the American Medical Association. It was to consist of the top officers of the ANA and AMA. We had a purpose. We wanted to meet, to try and identify our areas of agreement, but also to study our areas of disagreement, if we have any. We wanted to build a bridge of common belief. That is still in the early stages, although we have met with the AMA representatives.

The resolution we sent to the American Hospital Association following the 1958 biennial convention was really a sincere plea for them to join in the spirit of good will, with a common objective of helping to solve critical employer and employee problems by taking steps to implement collective bargaining. Our resolution was sent in the form of a telegram and I think their answer came at the end of fifteen months. They said, "We do not accept, we do not agree."

We take no joy in the nature of their response.

On the question of health insurance—the old-age, survivors, and disability insurance beneficiaries—we supported the principle of health insurancc but we also wanted nursing service and care improvement, which the immediate bill did not give. Our constituent states have been under great pressure from county or state medical associations to change our position, but most of our states have remained firm in their belief in the care for their patients. We must dare to stand up and be heard on what we believe to be right for our patients and our nurses.

Someone has said that nursing is at the crossroads. I would hope that we will take the right road.

We passed a resolution to protect the public from the unqualified practitioners, so we asked the state associations to form committees to study the problem. Forty-one states have such committees. Of course, we have not accomplished everything we need to do, but we hope in the next biennium we will go way out and extend this resolution and do something about it. It must have a far-reaching effect. It concerns educational needs, licensure, section committees on functions, standards, and qualifications and this, too, will require courage, to carry out the letter and the spirit of this resolution.

The increase in dues from five dollars to seven and a half dollars was not what we had asked you for, but those of you who are here as delegates remember that was what the House voted as an increase. We had asked for a five-dollar increase. You had requested from the ANA more workshops, more institutes, more conferences, and more help from the staff of ANA headquarters. While we did not get the increase we thought we needed to carry through your requests, we believe we have made progress with what we had and to date we have held two conferences on psychiatric nursing practice, one in New York and one in Chicago; an institute for operating room nurses was held in Chicago; a five-day conference on economic security, or a five-day workshop on economic security, was held in Minneapolis; a three-day conference for the PC&PS counselors was held there, and a three-day conference for executive secretaries. These were all held at Minneapolis because one followed the other. We did that with a motive. We thought that would be a saving of expense for transportation.

Further conferences, institutes, and workshops are planned for the next biennium. I would like to say that we can help you only insofar as we have the budget for it and we will try to make the budget stretch as far as possible.

We reaffirmed our intergroup relations program which was established in 1946.

We have given the Mary Mahoney Award which was under the auspices of the National Association for Colored Graduate Nurses. When that organization was dissolved, we took it upon ourselves to carry that on. Tonight we will give the Mary Mahoney Award again.

Your platform contains the principle of nondiscrimination and it is embraced in every program of ANA. This question is broader than nursing. We are being closely watched by groups all over the world and what we do or fail to do has many implications.

You gave us a resolution in 1958 on organizational functioning. I am calling it that. It was known then as "One Organization." You voted and gave that to our board of directors and with it you gave us three directions. You believed that one organization would best serve the purpose of nursing and nurses. You directed us to invite the board of the National League for Nursing to coöperate in appointing a committee to study this question.

You directed us to invite the NLN to co-sponsor a meeting of presidents of state leagues and presidents of state nurses associations in Philadelphia because the league was holding its convention in Philadelphia. We were to meet there last May and give a progress report on how far we had gone if this joint committee had been formed. The board of the National League for Nursing replied that they could not agree to the invitation as directed by the House of Delegates. Then, if you remember, we called together the state presidents and the executive secretaries and asked them to meet with us in May in New York to advise us what they thought we should do then, since we could not carry through the resolution as directed by the House of Delegates.

Upon advice the ANA board has instituted its own study of the functions of a professional organization.

I am not going to mention all the functions of the American Nurses' Association, such as the newly formed committee on infections; licensure—one-half of the states have a mandatory licensure law; the Professional Counseling & Placement Service, Inc., which is now limited to members of ANA; the American Nurses' Foundation of which you will hear more; the program we have for exchange visitors which we are trying to carry out as well as possible; our professional liability insurance—the reports are in your printed book and you will hear some reports from this platform during the convention.

I would like to express my admiration for our board of directors. They have worked long hours and many days. They have never hesitated to take action when they believed it right. I have never seen that in all of my experience in professional organizations. I know I express for you your many thanks to them and I will say they must have a common satisfaction of an important job well done.

I have tried to give you cold facts about your own organization. I have not attempted to solve all the problems. They are difficult. The answers are not easy. I have said to you before that I have great faith in our membership and never in the two years that I have tried to serve you have I had any reason to change that opinion about our members.

On the stationery that we send to you from time to time we carry the United Nations insignia, which says, "We believe." I ask each one of you to weigh carefully the issues before you at this convention and ask yourselves, "What do I believe?" and then vote accordingly.

Now, as I end, may I repeat what that great man and wonderful leader, Abraham Lincoln, said during one of the most troubled times of his office. "The dogmas of the quiet past are inadequate for the strong present. The occasion is piled high with difficulties and we must rise with the occasion. We must think anew and act anew."

The Largest Professional Organization of Nurses

By Mathilda Scheuer, R.N., *president*
(Forty-Third Convention, Detroit, May 14-18, 1962)

I would like to review with you how far we have come in the last two years. In some areas, we have reached our objective; in others, we have made real headway.

The House acted to gain full acceptance of ANA's long-standing principle of nondiscrimination. In 1960, one state had not yet adopted this principle, and a resolution was passed to encourage that state "in its efforts to provide membership for all qualified professional nurses so that, by at least the time of the next biennial, all states will have accepted all professional nurses as members."

Now we have reached "the time of the next biennial," and the wisdom and spirit of cooperation expressed in the resolution have led to achievement of our objective. Now, *all* state nurses' associations accept all professional nurses as members.

Under a continuing charge from the House of Delegates and building on a report presented in 1960, the Study Committee on the Functions of ANA has been engaged in a huge job since

1960—developing a proposal for organizational rearrangements for consideration by the membership.

In developing its suggestions, the committee has devoted long study as to how ANA can best meet immediate needs—and how ANA should be organized so that we can meet the changing needs of nursing and of the public for nursing care. In the end, when the House has finally taken its action, ANA will be better prepared to mobilize its forces, to intensify its efforts and to enlarge its achievements even when these are more difficult than before.

During the past two years, there has been a truly notable advance in the recognition and prestige of ANA. I can speak to that very well, because I have traveled this country a little bit, and I believe this is directly traceable to the steadfastness of ANA, and when I say that, that is you, as members, the state nurses' associations, district nurses' associations, and individual nurses across the country. With the determination and courage to maintain professional responsibilities in the face of all outside oppositions and pressures, where others have forecast defeat, you have scored victory.

In 1960, the House of Delegates overwhelmingly reaffirmed the position on health insurance for the aged. I do not think you can pick up any paper today, wherever you live or wherever you are, without reading, with a great deal of interest, the comments about the so-called King-Anderson Bill. We reaffirmed the position on health insurance for the aged, first adopted in 1958. In 1960 the House of Delegates approved a resolution for increased public information about the economic conditions in nursing.

In both these areas, there has been increased activity and information and continued pressures. There also has been increased recognition of ANA as a result of its position, and many public expressions of praise and support. As ANA continues to speak out in meeting its professional responsibilities, we find more and more professional, governmental, and other groups coming to us for information, guidance, and for cooperative activities. And we find published statements by doctors and others, urging support for nurses in our efforts to improve standards and the nursing care of the public. I do not want you to think that doctors never speak for us, because they do.

ANA Accomplishments

During the past two years, ANA has achieved almost universal recognition as the organization representing the profession of nursing—the *largest* professional organization of nurses in the world.

In 1960, nursing education came in for serious attention. The House of Delegates adopted a plank calling for ANA to "Continue to elevate the standards of nursing education by formulating basic principles of the education essential for effective nursing practice." A report from the Committee on Current and Long-Term Goals focused on nursing education and posed a question and suggested an answer as to what should be the education basic to the practice of nursing on a professional level. The House asked that consideration be given to this during 1960-62.

Since then, a number of ANA committees and groups have given thoughtful and continuing attention to the important subject of nursing education.

For the first time in the history of ANA we are having as a major focus 21 clinical sessions at this biennial convention. These have taken months of planning and preparation and they are good clinical sessions. Also scheduled are clinical films and clinical tours of outstanding caliber. This growing emphasis by ANA on improvement of clinical practice will be reflected in reports and resolutions to come before this convention.

During the past two years, we have stressed the importance of the *American Journal of Nursing* in the professional life of each member. The *American Journal of Nursing* is the professional, official publication of the ANA. We have been exploring ways to make sure that the *Journal* is available to all members, as probably the most important single way in which they can get the latest clinical information, find out what is happening in nursing and other health fields.

You will also learn, through the *American Journal of Nursing,* significant developments, both inside and outside nursing, and what the ANA is trying to do about them. It is a vital communications link between ANA officers, committees and staff, and the members.

The *Journal* can be a truly powerful voice of the nursing profession. To do this, it must have the support and readership of *all* members.

Though we have decided not to propose at this time that *AJN* be included with dues, consideration of this possibility has resulted in greater interest and understanding of the role of the professional journal, and you will hear about the result of that survey.

In still another important area, a much closer liaison has developed during the past biennium between ANA and the National Student Nurses' Association. Several productive meetings have been held. The students have shown their desire to strengthen the bond with ANA and they proposed the following changes for their bylaws: Do not think I am giving them to you as something already accomplished. This is what they propose:

> That one function of the National Student Nurses' Association shall be to prepare for membership and participation in the American Nurses' Association, the professional membership organization for nurses.

And as young nurses join the ANA, they can take a more and more active part in the work of the professional organization.

Over the years, there has been a steady increase in the service aspect of ANA operations—the providing of data, information, consultation and other kinds of special services to health groups, government, other organizations, and individuals, as well as to state and district nurses' associations and members. The increase in this kind of ANA activity has been especially notable during the past two years.

Field service to states, for example: In 1960, there were visits to state nurses' associations by ANA board and staff to attend SNA conventions or for special field service and consultation on specific programs. In 1961, 107 field visits were made. I made a few of those visits.

This biennium has brought a distinct rise in governmental interest in nursing. ANA has met at various times with many different government officials—to outline issues in nursing and objectives of the ANA program. In his health message to Congress in February 1961, President Kennedy included special comment on the needs of nursing. Again, this year, the President's message specifically pointed out nursing needs.

Certainly you know that the President of the United States, through the Surgeon General, Dr. Terry, has appointed a special Consultant Group to the Surgeon General, to study and make recommendations on needs in nursing education and service. Although members were appointed as individuals, not as representatives of any organization, there are 11 professional nurses on the consulting group and included in this particular group is our Executive Secretary, Mrs. Whitaker, as well as Dr. Merton, our sociologist consultant—and we can be very, very proud—because of their wisdom and their knowledge, not because of the ANA.

These then are some of the principal accomplishments of ANA during the past biennium. I hope you will feel that something has been accomplished.

Association Needs

Not everything I have to report is pleasant. At this time of vastly increased interest in health care and expanding opportunity for nursing, ANA is severely handicapped by lack of funds. This is not new to you.

ANA committees continue—and rightly so—to report needs for expansion and to point out new areas requiring attention of the professional nursing organization. It would not be possible to list for you all the services our board members and staff have given to the state nurses' associations in these past years. We would like to offer more assistance.

Needs of nurses for more information and assistance in improving clinical practice must be met. Two new clinical conference groups, for example, are to be organized at this convention, to bring the total of such groups to six. Requests have been made for regional conferences on nursing practice in 1963.

ANA must expand its liaison with other organizations. Even if we only meet the requests from other groups, it means increased activity. And, in addition, ANA must take the initiative in setting standards, preparing policy statements, providing official guidance in those areas where nurses have primary knowledge and responsibility. For example, during the past biennium ANA developed and published the *Statement of Standards for Nursing Care in Nursing Homes.* Attention is now being given to accreditation of nursing homes. We are being asked to take part in a proposed new division of the Joint Commission on Accreditation. We have been asked to co-sponsor institutes with allied organizations. To meet these and other responsibilities of the professional organizations, we must have adequate resources.

Instead of having the resources to capitalize on new opportunities and to accept responsibilities, the ANA board, committees, and staff are periodically faced with the necessity to cut back, to go slow, to limit programs and services, and even to suspend important activities.

As I review the programs and needs of ANA, I ask you how many will be left if we do not have adequate resources. Will there be an ANA? What if there had not been an ANA? The very thought is appalling.

Let us remember that the American Nurses' Association actually predated nurses as we know them today. We originally became organized to set up criteria and get state governments to determine by examination who could and who could not have the right to call themselves Registered Nurses. In 1896, when ANA was founded, there were no R.N.'s because there were no licensing laws. Now nurses are licensed in every jurisdiction, and the laws governing practice are still being improved as a result of organized planning and effort.

Not too long ago, nursing had no real recognition as a profession. Today, we take the words, "the nursing profession" for granted. Let us not forget that this was achieved largely through organized effort by the ANA. In fact, a decision issued by the U. S. Civil Service Commission in 1946 officially declared nursing to be a profession and specified reclassification of graduate nurse positions in federal agencies from subprofessional to the professional service.

In more recent years, ANA strongly promoted in 1956 and achieved passage of a federal traineeship program—later extended—which has enabled thousands of nurses to secure advanced education.

Though we have far to go, we have achieved substantial improvement in the area of economic security. We have achieved widespread recognition—and especially lately—increasingly voiced support of nurses' efforts to improve the conditions under which nursing care is provided.

Through the organization, nurses have developed *The Code for Professional Nurses* (first outlined in 1926, and changed many times since) to guide the members of our profession—and to advise the public, as well, of those standards which the profession has set for itself.

Setting standards is, of course, one of the chief functions of a professional organization—standards for practitioners, for those who would become practitioners and to protect the profession from exploitation or misuse by outside forces, to guard the public interest in its use of services provided by the profession.

All programs of the association are in one way or another designed to establish, maintain, or protect the integrity of the nursing profession and enhance its standing and its contribution to society.

To achieve this, it is obvious that a professional organization must be in a position to keep up with the times—even to keep ahead of the times, to be aware of—to anticipate—those developments that affect the profession and its members.

If an organization is not in a position to do this, then it is in trouble, because events will not stand still to allow any individual or group to catch up. You have to *keep* up—to move ahead and lead the way.

It has been said we do all things big without question—everything has changed except the way we think. I ask of you to "think big"—that is not original—as you hear these reports and stand firmly for what ANA means. Not only in this country but all over the world they will be waiting to hear what we are doing.

Please do not be afraid. Have real courage. And whatever we do we must do with honor and integrity of purpose. Many of you have heard me say this before. You have heard it a number of times. You have heard me say that I believe in the membership. I do still believe in the membership of the ANA. I repeat; I have said it a number of times.

Last May the Philadelphia Conference of the Methodist Church opened its 175th session.

They exhibited some of the old records and I want to read you one of the resolutions dating back to 1880. On the retirement of ministers they said:

> *Resolved,* That Albert Benham be considered a worn-out preacher.

So you retire this worn-out preacher, and she says goodby, with a nostalgic feeling, reminding you that we live in a time when there is no easy solution, nor will there be for a long time—and as Machiavelli has said: "There is nothing more difficult to take in hand, more perilous to conduct, or more uncertain in its success, than to take the lead in the introduction of a new order of things."

1962-1964

Margaret B. Dolan

Margaret B. Dolan was recognized as a national health leader, having served as president of the American Nurses' Association, the American Public Health Association, and the National Health Council. Between 1960 and 1961, she also served as president of the American Journal of Nursing Company.

Mrs. Dolan obtained her initial training at the Georgetown University School of Nursing, her undergraduate training at the University of North Carolina, and her graduate training at Teachers College, Columbia University. For her work as a nurse-educator, she was honored by a doctorate degree bestowed on her by Duke University in her home state.

A recipient of the Pearl McIver Public Health Nurse Award, Mrs. Dolan spent her career advocating creative use of nursing skills in primary care. She served as a consultant on public health for the Department of the Army and the Department of Health, Education, and Welfare. She was professor and head of the Department of Public Health Nursing at the University of North Carolina.

Well-known in the nursing profession as an outstanding spokesperson for nursing, Margaret Dolan promoted health care legislation at state and national levels. She presented Congressional testimony on behalf of the American Nurses' Association for more than twenty years. She also served on a number of government advisory bodies, including the President's Committee on Health Resources.

Mrs. Dolan died on February 27, 1974.

The Accelerated Decade—1954-1964

By Margaret B. Dolan, R.N., *president*
(Forty-Fourth Convention, Atlantic City, June 15-19, 1964)

Ten years ago, in Chicago, the House of Delegates met for the first time under a new structure. After six years of study and discussion, delegates to the 1952 convention had adopted a plan for the amalgamation of six national nursing organizations into two. Our convention ten years ago—the first under the new structure—seemed to be the start of a new era. It was—perhaps more than any of us realized.

Ten short years. And yet, in those ten years, we have lived through a period of extraordinary change. This has been the fastest moving decade in the history of our country.

Ten years ago, most of us still considered space flight largely in the realm of science fiction. Today, nine men, one woman, a dog, and a chimpanzee have orbited the earth. And even those of us who are more nearly earth-bound can fly from coast to coast in half the time that it took us in 1954.

Great social changes have taken place. College enrollment has doubled, having increased from a little less than 2½ million to nearly 5 million.

The number of women in the work force has grown by 5 million in the past ten years. Today, more than a third of all workers are women.

We have seen an accelerated trend toward government action in areas of health and education; and great social advance is taking place in the growing effort to achieve full civil rights and equal opportunity for all citizens.

The Knowledge Explosion

In this same decade, we have seen a sudden and vast expansion of knowledge that has given us our theme. The focus of this convention is "The Knowledge Explosion—Its Implications for Health Care." In 1964, that theme is truly significant.

During this ten-year span, the rate of growth in basic knowledge has exceeded that achieved in any other period in our history. This increase in knowledge has been largely in science.

Some of the most remarkable discoveries have been in the field of genetics. Scientists have isolated the basic life molecule, DNA, and the actual breakdown of the genetic code seems firmly under way.

Other breakthroughs in the field of mental retardation and mental illness face us with a bright new prospect for the control and cure of mental afflictions.

Great advances have been made in the study of viruses and in the development of drugs capable of curing virus-caused diseases. The Salk and Sabin vaccines have virtually erased poliomyelitis.

What About Nursing?

All of these changes have profound implications for nursing.

Nurses are having to learn the nature and reaction of a whole range of new drugs, to master the intricacies of complicated lifesaving machines. They are having to study the import for nursing of new information and changing concepts about the nature of disease and its effect on the human body and mind.

With the so-called population explosion, there has come an expansion of all kinds of health care facilities and an especially sharp rise in demand for nursing services.

Nursing functions have mushroomed. A wide variety of duties have fallen to nursing. Nurses now supervise an army of auxiliary personnel. They carry out many functions once performed only by physicians.

This change and growth has accentuated the importance of the true role of professional nurses. It means that, more than ever, we must identify the unique basis of nursing practice and the scientific principles on which it rests.

It means that practice must change to meet new demands.

It means that education must change to meet today's needs.

It means, in short, that nurses must rise to the challenge of the accelerated decade.

This was anticipated by the House of Delegates in 1958 when it adopted a goal to: "Stimulate efforts by nurses and other specialists to identify and enlarge the scientific principles upon which nursing rests, and to encourage research by them in the application of these principles to nursing practice." As we said at that time: "Professions grow and develop by adapting to technical, social, and environmental changes and by extending and advancing the knowledge upon which their practice is based. Most professions have identified for themselves the intellectual bases of their practice. Through extensive research they constantly enlarge the body of knowledge and thereby improve the effectiveness of their service. While no profession is entirely autonomous, many have successfully defined the extent of their authority. Where this is true, these professions can be selective about the kind and amount of authority and responsibility they assume."

In 1961, ANA Regional Conferences stressed this theme, examining, as Sister Charles Marie put it: "The nurse's orbit in relation to improved nursing care."

In 1962, convention clinical sessions emphasized the scientific bases of nursing practice. And, in 1962, also, the House of Delegates adopted a resolution calling for cooperation of the Medical and Hospital Associations in *supporting and promoting the primary role of the professional nurse as a clinical practitioner.*

Companion to this has been recognition of the enlarged responsibilities of the nursing profession brought about by developments largely outside of nursing—both in the private and governmental sectors. The rapid increase in number of nursing homes required attention to standards for nursing care in these institutions. Government programs, such as manpower development and training and area redevelopment, have provided new training programs for health occupations. Again, guidance from professional nursing has been essential in the interests of a high quality of nursing service.

Increasingly, the pressure of developments outside nursing has required us to take action to protect nursing and the public interest.

In one important sphere, nursing has been ahead of the accelerated decade. In 1946, we initiated an active program to promote full employment and professional development of nurses from minority groups. We adopted a policy for support of civil rights legislation in April, 1954—even before the Supreme Court decision for school integration. We have not solved all of our problems. But our role has been one of leadership.

The Next Decade

There will be no deceleration in the decade ahead.

The population will soar to 225 million. The percentage of both younger and older people in our population will increase. Income will rise and the work week will shorten. College enrollment will probably double again.

There will be further sweeping advances in science and technology. Automation, particularly of record keeping, will help free the nurse for her primary functions in patient care. But the nurse will be expected to take on increased responsibility.

Demands for health care services will continue to rise. And government will play an expanding role in meeting the basic health needs of the people. Other groups, too, are taking action that will affect nursing care.

We must be prepared to represent nursing—wherever its concerns are involved—or to surrender this responsibility to others.

With the rapid pace of the past decade, many of our problems have intensified and multiplied. The next decade will bring new demands and new problems for nursing.

How well have we anticipated the impact for nursing of the swift development of scientific and social forces in this country? How well are we prepared to meet future demands? These are the questions that should be continually in our minds.

Our past achievements have been many; some have been

accomplished in the face of massive obstacles. But today, we need even more.

We must proceed quickly, steadily, and swiftly to build nursing into a true profession with its special realm of knowledge and its special province of authority. This we can do if we are willing to key our pace to the accelerated decade.

We are all interested in changing many things in the current nursing situation, but we cannot evade the fact that we have been slow to unite in action to bring about needed reforms.

But our interests as individuals can only be served if we are members of a strong profession. Each of us is only as strong as our profession and our organization. Our chief objective is to serve the individual—whether it is the individual patient or the individual nurse. To do that, we must have a strong, united association.

Issues Before The Convention

This week, we have an unprecedented opportunity to take a giant step forward, if we look at each problem and question to come before this convention in terms of the total association and the total profession, and in terms of the future, not the past.

Certainly one of our major concerns is for the future of nursing education. Nursing has lagged behind other fields in the area of education. We raised questions about this in 1960 with proposed Goal III. The House of Delegates did not at once adopt the Goal but voted to take it under serious study. Now we have established a Committee on Education to take a deeper look at the whole question.

Though some of us thought Goal III precipitous in 1960, the Committee on Education is enlarging and adding to that report to bring the profession's concept of nursing education more in line with developments in the changing world around us. Considering the demands that will be placed on our profession in the next decade, we are attracting far too few young people—especially college-bound young people. Between 1955 and 1960, admissions to schools of nursing increased from 46,500 to 49,500, an increase of 6 per cent. During that same period, the number of girls entering colleges and universities increased from 257,000 to nearly 387,000, an increase of 50 per cent.

The number of graduates from basic nursing programs has changed very little—from 28,500 in 1954 to 31,000 in 1962. Only 43,500 nurses have baccalaureate degrees and 11,500 advanced degrees. There are nearly 1,800 vacancies in faculty positions in schools of nursing.

The Surgeon General's Consultant Group on Nursing estimated that to meet the needs of the nation in 1970, there should be 850,000 professional nurses, including 200,000 holding baccalaureate degrees and 100,000 with graduate degrees. Realistically, considering the potential supply of students and the potential capacity of schools, the consultant group set a more modest goal: 680,000 professional nurses, including 120,000 with academic degrees. Even this may seem optimistic.

We are making progress. This year we have a major nursing education bill before Congress. It calls for $294.6 million for construction, traineeships, loans, and funds for improvement of educational programs.

Education does not stand alone. It is closely linked with economic returns from professional work. In the next decade, we must achieve *real* improvement. We must improve the economics of our profession in order to attract qualified young people into nursing. We must improve its economics in order to retain nurses in the profession. We must improve its economics in order to attract inactive nurses back into the profession.

We must improve our economic position because—for good or for bad—the economic measure in this country is an important measure of the standing of a profession.

Improvements have been made. General duty salaries, for example, are 43 per cent higher than they were in 1954. But they are still far too low.

In spite of the tremendous effort that has been expended in the

18 years since the Economic Security Program was founded, we have a long way to go. As we all know, we have not always been successful.

Our efforts to achieve recognition to represent Veterans Administration nurses are an example. The VA was perfectly willing to grant recognition. But at a price. At a price the Board of Dircctors of ANA was not prepared to pay. The VA would have deprived many nurses of their full membership rights. If a single state nurses' association was recognized as a bargaining agent the VA would have prohibited every VA nurse from head nurse up, from serving as an officer, as a board member, or on any committee related to the Economic Security Program, in any district association, any state association, or the ANA.

In any hospital where recognition was accorded, no nurse from head nurse up would have been able to serve as an officer or on the board of their district association, their state association, or the ANA.

Nurses in managerial and supervisory positions throughout the country would have been prohibited from promoting or encouraging membership in the professional organization. Once recognition was given, the VA would no longer have encouraged membership or given leave for attendance at meetings.

For these reasons, the Board made the only decision that it could. Concern for the total association and the rights and contributions of all members everywhere made it mandatory.

This should only reinforce our determination to bring about improvements for all nurses everywhere, and to use every means open to us. We must exercise initiative and imagination in seeking the support of other health groups and of civic, business, and professional groups, and in fostering greater understanding and support among nurse themselves—all nurses.

We know that collective bargaining is a technique—an important and often essential technique.

But it is not enough. In the decade ahead, let us unite in action to improve the economic standing of nursing—using *all* approaches that our imagination can devise—so that by 1974, the salaries of professional nurses will be truly professional.

I think this is one place where change is very much on our side; with new determination, in ten years, we will see genuine progress.

Accelerated change requires periodic evaluation. This House of Delegates must re-examine the Professional Counseling & Placement Service, first established in 1945.

The idea for a counseling and placement service was first conceived in 1936 when the House of Delegates appointed a committee to consider the possibility.

Impetus for establishing the service came ten years later with the approaching end of the war, when many nurses would be returning to civilian life.

As conceived, the program was to be carried out through state and district nurses' associations and registries. The national office was to supply consultant service, hold institutes for state and local personnel, collect data on the needs for nurses, and act as a national referral agency for both positions and nurses who could not be cared for at the state or local level. ANA was to assume "leadership and administrative responsibilities" for a nationwide program.

We know that the services did not develop, as expected, on state and local levels. As a result, ANA has assumed a function not originally anticipated—the function of attempting to provide direct counseling and placement to nurses and employers in the 32 states and territories that do not have their own services.

At this convention, we are asked to consider PC&PS in terms of today's needs and resources.

As I said earlier, ten years ago the House met for the first time under a new structure. Change is rapid. And this House of Delegates is receiving a plan for reorganization.

Speedily and comprehensively, we have begun to think in broader concepts than ten years ago. We have been forced to think in broader concepts by the changes around us.

The Study Committee on Functions has been working for nearly five years. Their purpose has been to design a plan to permit the ANA and its constituent units to better perform the functions assigned to them; to provide balance and spread activities without duplication of effort; to permit greater initiative, to conserve the Association's human and financial resources; to provide flexibility to meet changing conditions. It is based on the idea that structure of national, state, and district associations should be suited to the functions that can be best performed by each.

Of course, much more work will have to be done before any changes can be made in the structure of the organization. Those of you who remember the changes of 1952 know that this is a tremendous task. Our task at this convention is to provide a sense of direction for the committee at work on this. The study committee was given its assignment because the membership had made it very clear that they wanted changes. I believe it is imperative that this House of Delegates come up with a consensus of response so we can get on with the job of making ANA the best possible mechanism to carry forward the interests of nursing.

We face many choices in this convention. But there is one major choice. How can we best change to meet change?

We are in an era of social and scientific revolution. A period of ferment and frustration, but a period of excitement and unlimited possibility.

At such a time, we all look for points of identification—points of identification that give larger stature and significance to our individual needs and objectives. More than ever, in a time of change, we need the identification that is possible through the professional organization. In the accelerated decade ahead, we shall need this professional point of identification more than ever. It must serve us as never before, both as an anchor to hold fast to the fundamental beliefs for which we, as nurses, stand, and as a beacon to show the way to the future.

1964–1968

Jo Eleanor Elliott

Named one of Colorado's Women of Achievement, Jo Eleanor Elliott is currently director of nursing programs and a project director at the Western Interstate Commission for Higher Education in Boulder, Colorado. She is also secretary of the Western Council on Higher Education for Nursing.

Miss Elliott received her Bachelor of Science degree in nursing from the University of Michigan, where she later served as an instructor in surgical nursing.

The 1952 recipient of the Isabel Hampton Robb Scholarship, she completed work on her Master of Arts degree at the University of Chicago.

During and following her two terms of office as president of the American Nurses' Association, Jo Eleanor Elliott has served as a member of the boards of directors of the International Council of Nurses, American Nurses' Foundation, and the American Journal of Nursing Company. She is currently president of the American Journal of Nursing Company.

In addition to functioning in a consultant capacity for various agencies, including the National Commission for the Study of Nursing and Nursing Education, Miss Elliott is a frequent contributor to nursing publications.

In 1975, the National League for Nursing presented the Mary Adelaide Nutting Award to Miss Elliott for outstanding leadership and achievement in nursing education.

The Challenge of Today: Directions for Tomorrow

By Jo Eleanor Elliott, R.N., *president*
(Forty-Fifth Convention, San Francisco, June 14-17, 1966)

The House of Delegates has major tasks before it in these four busy days. However, all our past ANA history shows that the House of Delegates proves itself equal to the tasks it faces.

In the mid-50's, the ANA went on record requesting federal funds for support of baccalaureate programs in nursing and for preparation of teachers and administrators. The Nurse Training Act of 1964 is the fruition of efforts of many—including the American Nurses' Association.

In the 1940's, the association undertook the Economic Security and General Welfare Program. Progress reports, succeeding action, ongoing activities have been before you at each biennium since then. This year, you will discuss and decide whether or not the ANA will set a national salary goal.

Concern for Clinical Practice

Over a period of time, emphasis has been going increasingly into the area of practice. A concern for improving practice on the part of members has, I believe, had an ascendancy in the association. In the 1950's, we organized conference groups. In 1962, we held our first clinical sessions.

The emphasis on practice is healthy in terms of our demonstrating to the public that we have as great a concern for the quality of work our members perform as we have for the necessary economic and general welfare activities which relate to fair return. I think it is important that we continue to emphasize our efforts in the field of practice.

In reference to research, I would like to comment on the regional clinical conferences that were held during 1965, one in Washington, D.C., and one in Chicago. They were well attended, and excellent papers were presented. One senses the growth of nurses, individually and as a professional association, when one can sit and listen, discuss and interact for three days and discover the caliber, the high quality of the clinical material that is being studied, collected and shared with colleagues in the association.

During the past biennium, we held the first two research conferences sponsored by the American Nurses' Association for nurse researchers. This too, I believe, is a milestone; we now have enough researchers to sit together and share their research methodology, and their plans and patterns.

Actions of the House of Delegates

In 1958, the House gave the Board of Directors a mandate regarding organization. In 1959, the Council of State Presidents indicated the association should undertake a study of the functions of the ANA, and a look at how the association might be rearranged organizationally, to better meet the needs and professional concerns of its members. Since then, every two years, you have heard progress reports and/or taken action on directions of change.

In 1962, you added the functions of responsibility for setting standards for nursing service and nursing education.

In 1964, you adopted a resolution which read as follows:

RESOLVED, That this House of Delegates commend the work of the Committee by endorsing the principles and recommendations of their report as the basis for the future development and structure of the ANA, and be it further

RESOLVED, That the Bylaws Committee be instructed to draft as rapidly as possible the bylaws, new and revised, needed to embody these principles and recommendations in the ANA structure, and be it finally

RESOLVED, That in order to take definitive action at the House of Delegates meeting in 1966 the following should occur during the coming biennium: 1) Continued active study of the present proposals and materials at all levels of the organization, and 2) Preparation and distribution of tentative proposals for bylaw changes as rapidly as possible so that they can be a part of the ongoing study, and 3) Continued work by the Committee for further clarification, definition, and refinement of proposed structural changes and the inherent functional relationships.

Ensuing action has been the preparation of the Supplemental Report in 1965, the early distribution of proposed bylaws last fall, the continued reaction of groups within the association, the discussion in state and local areas, and now the forums held on Sunday and this afternoon to assist in reaching conclusions.

Out of the 1962 action came the Committee on Nursing Service, and the production of the Standards for Organized Nursing Services during the past biennium.

Also out of the 1962 action came the Committee on Education; and the association's first position paper on education for those who work in nursing was set forth publicly in December, 1965.

Collaborative Relationships

Collaborative relationships with other organizations have moved apace in 1964-1966. We held our Second ANA-AMA National Conference for Professional Nurses and Physicians. We have issued an NLN-ANA Statement of Working Relationships and this week we will issue an ANA-NLN Joint Statement on Community Planning for Nursing Education. We have initiated an AHA-ANA Liaison Committee.

We have continued our work with the National Federation of Licensed Practical Nurses and with the National Student Nurses' Association. We have been expanding our collaborative relationships, not just because of what this does for the ANA, but because of our concern. I believe that we cannot accomplish all that we want to accomplish alone, that we do need the assistance, the collaborative efforts of other people.

The Bylaws Proposals

But of all these developments, it is clear to all of us that two have loomed largely in the past biennium: the study of structure and the bylaws proposals, and the publication of *Educational Preparation for Nurse Practitioners and Assistants to Nurses: A Position Paper.*

The board has taken the work of the Study Committee, the Bylaws Committee and other groups within the association and has brought to bear its best judgment. Now, as always, it is the task of the House of Delegates to act on the proposed bylaws since they represent transition to a new form of organization.

Whatever you enact, remember that these are only bylaws—made by delegates and subject to change by the delegates on the basis of experience. You will be making needed change this week on the basis of past experience and bringing to bear your best judgment on the direction of the future of the association. Your decision, we will all live with for the next few years; but your decision is not an eternal decision.

Position Paper on Education

The major item of consideration, discussion and concern for many people is the Position Paper, issued by the Board of Directors for the association last December.

The history of ANA's concern in education goes back to its Articles of Incorporation. But again the emphasis has been present in the relatively recent past. You recall that as early as 1960, the Committee on Current and Long-Term Goals proposed a goal leading toward baccalaureate preparation as a beginning base of professional nursing.

It is a large, monumental, complicated and lengthy task to move from statement of position to the effecting of change through orderly transition.

No such change can be carried out without the full participation of nurses at every level of the organization.

No such change can occur without community planning involving many other groups.

No such change can be introduced so rapidly as to threaten needed services to people.

No such change can come about merely because nurses wish it to occur. Changes in society will affect what occurs.

No such change can be allowed to be at the expense of the health services of this country or at the expense of the nurses of this country.

Change will occur. Our task is to see that it is a more orderly change rather than a chaotic one—a planned change, as opposed to letting things "just happen."

Directions for Tomorrow

I think the spirit of this convention will be one of thoughtful debate, much participation and action, and that most of us will leave San Francisco with the feeling of "well done for now; let's get on with tomorrow."

A colleague reminds us, relative to democratic organizations, that the ability of an organization rests on the democratic rules of the game which require that when debate has been closed, the various plans or opinions must give way to the commitments of the association as a whole.

We are concerned about directions for tomorrow, and we are here to set them. I believe that in this coming period of time, nursing and its professional association will be better than they were in the past, only as nurses take, one from the other, the light of invention and not the fire of contradiction.

Positive Action for Meeting Health Needs

By Jo Eleanor Elliott, R.N., *president*
(Forty-Sixth Convention, Dallas, May 13-17, 1968)

Two years ago we thought a biennium was not a very long period of time in which to accomplish the organizational rearrangements and move forward with the new plan to reinforce the strengths and correct the fallacies in nursing education, service and practice.

Those two years have proved to be extremely productive—far more than a "transition" period. At this point in time, the transition seems to have taken place long ago.

Following the 1966 convention, the sections very expeditiously made arrangements for dealing with ongoing activities. The divisions on practice have organized; the development of standards is underway; and plans for initiating the certification boards are also in progress. The commissions have been extremely active in the two-year period since they came into organized being.

The board of directors is charged with carrying forward the work of the association between meetings of the House of Delegates. As the board has considered the things to be done, and the association's resources, it has given much of its attention to the setting of priorities to guide both board and staff members in planning short- and long-range goals.

One of the pleasures of reviewing eight years of service on the board, and a four-year tenure as president, is that of seeing in a new perspective the increasing strength of the association in the four areas now officially designated by the board as priority areas—nursing practice, education, nursing services and economic and general welfare. Our actions in these areas have reflected both the forces in society with which we need to be involved, and the needs of members to fulfill more effectively our reason for being: that people need nursing care.

The Concern for Clinical Practice

I have been particularly pleased with the new developments in the area of practice, and the association's efforts in this direction over these past several years.

Many of you may well remember the first clinical sessions at the 1962 Biennial in Detroit. This was indeed a major step forward. It was the increasing success of the conference groups that demonstrated need for the divisions on practice as our primary organizational arrangement for membership.

At the clinical conferences held in the years between biennial conventions—in particular, the extremely successful conferences in Kansas City and Philadelphia in 1967—the members of this association shared their knowledge of what nurses are doing to expand the dimensions of practice.

Throughout 1967-68, the divisions on practice have been very busy—getting their standards committees underway and moving forward with plans for the certification boards.

At this convention, you will be participating in program sessions of the divisions, in clinical sessions, in nursing debates, in the transoceanic discussion, and all of the other activities reflecting the association's concern and belief in its members' interests in improving nursing practice.

Related to, and stemming from, the divisions on practice will be the Academy of Nursing. While some of us always wish to progress in leaps, the board has agreed that the movement to the Academy must be an orderly process, as we have indicated in the past. There will be more developments in this direction in the next biennium.

You now have before you a proposal for a Congress for Nursing Practice, designed to highlight the concerns of the association for practice; to make the organizational provision for practice a visible entity within the structure of the association; and to give emphasis to what the board has agreed should be the ANA's top priority.

The Work of the Commissions

Education, nursing services and economic and general welfare will, we believe, continue to be very important areas of priority for the association. As I look back at these two years, it seems that some groups have made more progress than others. Where we previously had committees, there are now commissions that are carrying on the work of those committees, and expanding the association's base and direction in education, service and economic and general welfare.

We have had considerable leadership from the members of the Commission on Nursing Education, both in planning for the future of nursing education and in assisting the association in other efforts to improve the quality and quantity of opportunity available in the field of nursing education. We have published *Avenues for Continued Learning* to assist our members in choosing among the various ways of moving ahead.

In the area of nursing services, we have placed particular emphasis on our relationships with other associations concerned with the delivery of organized nursing services. We need to strengthen these relationships, even though there has been real progress in this direction. As the board agreed at its pre-convention meeting, it is impossible to know how many other organizations are interested in what the ANA is doing until we have established relationships that facilitate this kind of interaction.

The Commission on Economic and General Welfare has moved forward very rapidly. I must comment on this because we are still being questioned by other groups about the purposes of our economic and general welfare program. For the record, I state that I believe this activity must be a function of the professional nurses' association, and a vital part of our many-faceted effort for nurses and for better care of the American people.

The Obligation to Society

The program sessions, the clinical sessions and, especially, the House of Delegates will deal with issues that are vital not only to nurses but also to society as a whole. Increasingly, we see and must deal with broad social patterns—the ways in which the problems of nursing (and of ANA as the organized voice of nursing) interface with the major social problems of our country today. I have no doubt that you will deal with these problems in ways that are appropriate to the needs of society, and our association, in 1968.

I believe that this association has been maturing very rapidly. We are assuming our appropriate functions, and we are behaving like a professional organization. I think it is time for ANA to consider the possibility of adopting the president-elect system. This is not an agenda item for this year; but I ask you to think it over for a couple of years.

There is something I think we must do as we develop standards for practice through our divisions and our criteria for certification—as we sort out the kinds of nursing practice that people need. We must take leadership at the national level of the American Nurses' Association to assist the state associations to work with nurses in their places of employment in designing and using new means of assessing the quality of practice of the individual practitioner. As we achieve gains in our economic and working conditions, we must insure that we are producing the best possible kind and quality of individual, and individualized, professional nursing practice.

A last word: today is bright with accomplishments to date; tomorrow is full of the many things yet to be done.

The road ahead demands new goals and courageous implementation. Insights must be deepened and an unknown future envisioned.

I believe that our future is full of greatness: great service to all of society as well as to the members of our own profession.

1968-1970

Dorothy A. Cornelius

Dorothy A. Cornelius has received national and international recognition for outstanding service to the nursing profession. Miss Cornelius was the first nurse to be appointed by President Johnson to the Health Insurance Benefits Advisory Council. In 1970, she was one of five "distinguished American women" invited to France by the French government.

Miss Cornelius has served as general duty nurse, private duty nurse, public health nurse, and director of nurses. She received her initial training from Conemaugh Valley Memorial Hospital in Johnstown, Pennsylvania, and a Bachelor of Science degree from the University of Pittsburgh.

In May, 1972, ANA honored Miss Cornelius for her exceptional leadership during a time of financial crisis for the organization.

In May, 1973, ANA's twenty-first president was elected to a four-year term as the president of the International Council of Nurses.

Miss Cornelius currently serves as executive director of the Ohio Nurses' Association.

Is ANA Relevant in the Seventies?

By Dorothy A. Cornelius, R.N., *president*
(Forty-Seventh Convention, Miami Beach, May 3-8, 1970)

Traditionally, the president's message is a recounting of the activities of the last biennium, with projections and identifications of directions for the future of nurses and nursing. It is a time for epilogue and prologue.

Two years ago, I stood on a similar platform in Dallas, Texas, after having been elected president of the American Nurses' Association. I was then confident of the future of the American Nurses' Association. I am still confident.

There was no portent then of the seriousness of our financial situation. The Board of Directors looked forward to continuing the work of our predecessors in advancing ANA's programs. We could not forecast the volatile and paradoxical financial situation at ANA. We did not anticipate the extent of the fiscal constraints that ANA was to experience. We did not anticipate the drastic cutbacks in staff and programming, nor did we suspect that an appeal for voluntary dues assessment would be necessary.

However, as the situation unfolded, it became apparent that finances would not be available to achieve all our goals. Consequently, this message does not contain all the program advances that we hoped to report.

As we know, stress and failure capture the headlines, while response and success appear on the back page. But there are many back-page successes to report. I should like to highlight a few.

The collaboration with allied health groups has been the greatest in our recent history. We are no longer talking to the American Medical Association via the news media. The presidents and executive staffs of ANA and AMA are meeting and talking together in free and unrestrained dialogue, as colleagues who share the same concerns for the delivery of health care for all people.

The ANA and the American Hospital Association are developing a more meaningful relationship. Although for some time there has existed an ANA-AHA Joint Committee, that committee's primary function was to share reports of the activities of the two organizations. Both organizations have now expressed a desire to expand the role of the committee.

An invitation has been extended by the ANA president to the

AHA president to initiate dialogue between the presidents and executive staffs as a means of working for and promoting common objectives relating to nursing and nursing education. Arrangements have been made for such a meeting.

The National League for Nursing and ANA have had continuing discussions this past biennium. We have recognized the need to analyze the programs of ANA and NLN in order to facilitate the unique functions of both organizations.

The basic philosophies emerging from the discussions of the steering committee of the Coordinating Council were that duplication of effort should be avoided and that activity should be coordinated to best fulfill the obligations of each organization in the most economical, expeditious and productive manner. We have moved from rhetoric to action.

Relationships have been strengthened with the National Student Nurses' Association as ANA has sought the involvement of students. There is great recognition of the need for nursing to speak with one voice on social issues in the areas of poverty, malnutrition, hunger and discrimination, all of which profoundly affect the health and well-being of the people of this country.

Another area where we can see progress is the development of an open communications system between members and ANA. Members are speaking to ANA, and ANA is listening; more than listening, ANA is responding.

ANA is actively seeking the views of members and constituents. Members are being urged to exercise their freedom of expression.

All these developments have a positive potential for ANA's future. Each of these advances holds the promise of a more effective, cohesive, professional association. The ANA has a potential as a force in society which we have only begun to tap.

Nursing is the conscience of the health care system. Through the years, nursing has taken leadership among the professions to secure the rights of human beings to receive adequate health care.

Many times nursing has stood alone to support the principle

that health care is a right, not a privilege. If we are to continue to advance the health care system and to fulfill our role as professionals, we must be prepared to stand alone again.

ANA has moved into the seventies with its forces diminished by financial difficulties. While we work to restore ANA's financial health, we must also address other questions. What kind of ANA do we want? What should ANA's core concerns be? How should it relate to society? And what involvements should ANA assume that have not been a part of our program? Are there areas in ANA's functioning that have no relevance in the seventies?

Indeed, the overriding question is, Is ANA itself relevant in the seventies? The happenings of the past two years have given this House of Delegates a unique opportunity: one that may not come again in ANA's existence.

We have the opportunity of redesigning ANA, of changing its nature and its characteristics, of adding to and subtracting from its concerns.

We must accept this challenge and deal with it decisively. The dignity of every human being is of vital concern to all of us, both as nurses and as citizens. Do states and districts seek positive avenues of action to make our commitment to human rights a reality—not merely words inscribed on an official document? Does ANA provide leadership in this area? Is it enough to write papers and give awards? Should we be establishing, or consider establishing, a highly visible unit at the national level, with its own place in the structure, so that members of the association can come together to speak to these concerns?

How long can ANA go along with a narrowly conceived commitment to abolishing poverty, hunger and other miseries of millions of Americans? How long can any health organization look over its shoulder at these kinds of problems? Any human relation that is not productive of health is productive of sickness.

Nurses, with their special skills and knowledge, can help to change the face of poor America. We can do it through our organization, and we can do it as individuals. The "BE-INvolved" nurse search has proved what I have long believed: that one nurse can make a difference, even in this overpopulated, mechanized, impersonal world of the seventies. In nearly every ANA constituent, the "BE-INvolved" search found nurses whose courage and love of humanity have put them where the action is, where any degree of change is massive change, where caring has worked miracles.

If a handful of nurses can do so much, think of what the combined strength of ANA's members could do! You and I may not live to see a world in which all men live in peace and enjoy the full measure of life's securities: food and clothing, shelter, education, employment and health care; yet we can be a part of what makes it happen.

By and large, nurses—the largest group of professionals in the country—have paid little heed to the hazards to our environment which have been clearly identified in recent years. How long can ANA remain aloof from pollution problems?

Nurses are uniquely prepared to speak to this issue. Certainly the ANA membership includes nurse experts in environmental health. How long can we stay out of the fight to save our planet, and still maintain that we are an organization concerned with health?

There are other questions we should raise as we plan priorities and shift our emphasis.

How can we enlarge ANA's collaboration with other health professionals in the interest of improving the delivery of health care?

What new kinds of communication systems can we develop in ANA that will provide a free-flowing, back-and-forth exchange among the three levels of the organization?

What is the nature of ANA's relationship to the student nurse association? Is it what it should be? And does NSNA think ANA is relevant?

How effective is ANA in influencing the federal government, the Congress? How can we get more input from members in legislative activities?

What involvement should the consumer, the buyer of nursing services, have in ANA and the state and district associations? How can the expanding role of the consumer contribute to the improvement of health care?

What role should ANA play in defining the parameters of nursing practice? How will our efforts to clarify the nature of nursing practice be influenced by the consumer, by the disadvantaged, and by other disciplines?

Are we ready, and do we have the means, to recognize our divergent points of view in the association, to deal with them, but to move ahead nonetheless with the job to be done?

What issues in nursing education will we see in the seventies? Will ANA search out the issues and seek solutions based on the best judgment of nurse educators? Or will ANA merely react to what already has happened?

Building a New ANA

There is much more in ANA that has been initiated in the past few years, but is far from coming to fruition—the Academy of Nursing, the certification boards of the divisions, the work of the divisions. Careful assessment must be made of this important work in relation to the immediate future and in terms of long-range objectives.

I am not a revolutionist; yet I would have revolution in nursing. I am not an extremist; yet I would seek extreme measures in dealing with human suffering. I am not a pessimist; yet I fear for the future unless we can gather our forces quickly. I am not an optimist; yet I have high hopes that nurses will involve themselves with humanity as participants instead of bystanders.

My last official message to you is a clarion call for nurses to muster all their professional, unique and responsible caring values into a ground swell for a vigorous, relevant ANA that will stand against any force.

I think you will understand why I especially wish to thank the

Board of Directors for their courage and their decision to tell it like it is.

My profound thanks, both to the staff and the Board of Directors for their commitment to ANA and for their support of the president during two difficult years for the organization.

My thanks are also given to thousands of ANA members who responded generously to the appeal for supplementary funds; to all of you, I express my gratitude and affection.

I believe in ANA. I shall continue to work for its objectives in every way possible. I ask you to join me in that resolve. Let's begin anew. Let's build a new ANA together.

1970-1972

Hildegard E. Peplau

Hildegard E. Peplau has conducted clinical workshops and nursing institutes in almost every state in the United States as well as several foreign countries.

A graduate of Pottstown Hospital School of Nursing, Dr. Peplau earned a Bachelor of Arts degree in interpersonal psychology from Bennington College, and a Master of Arts degree in teaching and supervision of psychiatric nursing and a Doctor of Education degree in curriculum development from Teachers College at Columbia University.

Dr. Peplau has had experience in private duty and general duty nursing, operating room supervision, and teaching in undergraduate and graduate nursing programs. She has been a consultant to the United States Public Health Service, Veterans Administration, and World Health Organization for some twenty years. A frequent contributor to health publications, Dr. Peplau is the author of two books, *Interpersonal Relations in Nursing* and *Professional Experience Record.*

In addition to her work with the American Nurses' Association, Dr. Peplau has served on many committees and advisory groups of the National League for Nursing. In 1952, she was employed by the NLN to blueprint a study on "Desirable Functions and Qualifications of Psychiatric Nursing."

In September, 1969, while serving as professor and director of the Graduate Program in Psychiatric Nursing at Rutgers University, Dr. Peplau was appointed interim executive director of the American

Nurses' Association, a position she held until May, 1970.

In 1970 and 1972, ANA's twenty-second president was awarded honorary doctoral degrees from Alfred University and Boston University for distinguished service in nursing education. In 1975, she was admitted to the American Academy of Nursing.

Now retired, Dr. Peplau frequently serves as a nursing consultant.

A Time To Stand Up and Be Counted

By Hildegard E. Peplau, Ed.D., R.N., *president*
(Forty-Eighth Convention, Detroit, April 30-May 5, 1972)

Much has been accomplished by the American Nurses' Association during this biennium. A renewed forward movement is observable. There will be a hiatus with relocation to Kansas City, Missouri, later this year. The forebearance of every ANA member will again be needed. Nevertheless, a substantial groundwork has been laid toward realization of a revitalized ANA. But ours is a society in turmoil, and ANA reflects that.

ANA will, in the years just ahead, need continuously to find new ways to be socially responsive to shifting influences and to accommodate to them as these emerge in our rapidly changing world. In this biennium, much of the activity of the association has been reactive to events underway.

Once the move to Missouri is accomplished, and operations are fully restored, ANA must boldly address itself to nursing's response and participation in shaping an anticipated future. Long-range forecasting of trends and planning of strategies to reshape nursing and health systems must occur side by side with responses to emergent events. Everything is changing—the world, health affairs, and the work of the nursing profession. In relation to these changes, our profession must be both provider and pacemaker.

The First Hundred Years

We come to the end of the first century of nursing with much work still to be done. It was 100 years ago that the first "training school"—the New England Hospital for Women and Children—received Linda Richards, who in 1873 was considered to be the first American "trained nurse." All of the nurses who followed in her path—Mary Mahoney, Isabel Hampton Robb, Lavinia Dock, Lillian D. Wald, Adelaide Nutting, and many others including you and me—have been guided by a singular devotion.

The health needs of people everywhere, whatever their circumstances, have been the focus of our work as nurses. It can be said in all truth, at the close of this first century of nursing, that the character of nurses and nursing has been forged, not by self-interest, but by intelligent, imaginative, innovative responses to a maelstrom of changing social needs. It can be said now, with the same assurance as at the beginning: Nurses care about people.

It is sometimes said that the first hundred years are the hardest. They certainly were not easy. The struggles, sacrifices and efforts of the women and men in nursing have not yet been fully documented. We must get to the task of recording our history fully and documenting our heritage very soon. This could indeed be a worthwhile contribution that nurses could make to the bicentennial celebration of 1976.

But what we know now with certainty is that the nurses who preceded us, and we with them, believe that nursing services were good for the people—sick and well—and that health was a right as important as any other humanitarian value. A profession was shaped in bringing alive these ideals in nursing practice.

At this juncture in our history, there are clear signs of the ever-enlarging usefulness of nursing. There are also evidences of forces that countervail the advances of the nursing profession. Things sometimes seem darkest at the dawn, and perhaps this applies as we approach the dawn of the second century of nursing.

New Questions for Nursing

Or, to put the matter another way, the power of the forward thrust of the profession, and the counterpulls upon it at this time, seem roughly equal. And this is the test: Whether or not the will and the energy of nurses can be mobilized sufficiently to meet the new challenges now on the horizon for the profession of nursing. One side of a seesaw goes up while the other side goes down. On which side will nursing be?

As the profession moves into its second century of service to society, new and harder questions lie before us. It will not do to soothe ourselves by sweeping any of them under the rug. Nor will preaching about the goodness of nursing and the size of the occupation meet the requirements of the new challenges. A renewed realism must be brought to bear. A more disciplined approach to the study of problems will be expected of all nurses.

The major question in the first century—Is nursing good for people?—could easily be answered with a resounding "Yes!" The people who experienced the fevers and discomforts of illnesses of an earlier day also experienced directly the beneficial, tender ministrations which we call nursing care. Today, the illnesses and, indeed, the very definition of health have changed.

So the question must be rephrased. In what way is nursing good: In relation to what? What phenomena are the focus of our practices and what effects upon those phenomena are our practices expected to produce? That is a hard question. Nurses in the past few decades have begun to grope for some answers.

The Need for Nursing Research

Yet nursing research so vital to this effort to bring specificity and understanding to our work is undersupported. Indeed, the American Nurses' Foundation—the research arm of our profession—receives very little economic support from ANA's members. All nurses must come to appreciate why researchers in nursing must have our full support. Their work benefits all of us. Their work clarifies ours. Activating the authority and accountability and defining the productivity of nurses calls for new kinds of effort and new kinds of discipline from all of us; but mostly it calls for nursing research.

But even demonstrations and systematic studies of the effectiveness of nursing practices, in relation to the focus of our work, may not suffice in the decades ahead. There is little doubt that nursing practices in relation to actual or potential health problems of individuals will be needed. The spectrum of our work has broadened toward both a wider area of activity shared with physicians and new expansion of nursing to fill unmet gaps in health care.

At the Educational Conferences of the Council of State Boards of Nursing, a few days ago, one of the speakers urged nurses to "step briskly into the void" that exists in health care today. The largest void has to do with prevention of illness: Promotion of health, if you prefer that phrase.

Nurses have always had an active interest in health-optimizing practices, and this concern is being activated more widely than ever; but more effort is needed. In fact, a new kind of complementary partnership between nurses and physicians is evolving, although slowly. In this partnership, each has independent practices and both have shared practices.

The overriding issue that impedes full development of a nurse-physician partnership in health care is the matter of control. Will it be unilateral or shared? Nurses must focus their attention on this issue, and on resolving it.

Health programs to meet the needs of people must be our central concern. In such programs, control of nursing services is our responsibility, and we must exercise it fully. Even so, while all of these developments have significance for bringing about a higher quality of health care, they may yet not be enough to meet new requirements that are in the making.

Will Nurses Act on Social Issues?

Every day it becomes more apparent to the health scientist, to the professional practitioner, and to laymen, that deleterious social conditions breed health problems. Mental illness occurs more frequently among the poor. We know that. Shall we then, as nurses, address our activities only toward correction of the individual's difficulties, and overlook the poverty?

Greed has a lot to do with allowing work in unsafe mines. Shall we concern ourselves only with the nursing care of miners who are injured or suffer "black lung" disease, or is the unsafe mine also our business?

And what of the deprived child—exposed to leaded paint, to drugs, to mediocre education—all hazards to health in some way? Should nurses speak out and seek remedies for social conditions that breed illness?

Crime, drug abuse, air, water and noise pollution, overpopulation, unemployment and other social problems that impinge on health—are these our business? The question for the second century of nursing is not "Do nurses care about people?" They do! We all know that. The question is, "How deeply do we care?" And if nurses care deeply, and if they abhor the thought of any child anywhere in the world being hungry or deprived of a decent education, then what are our suggested collective actions?

Almost from the beginning of nursing in this country, some nurses have involved themselves locally in these problems. How far are all nurses willing to go to promote health: Through individual practices as nurses and through joint action as a professional group?

There is another hard question before this nation. Quality health care, easily accessible at reasonable cost for all, is being recognized as an individual right. Yet everyone here today knows that in some degree there are serious shortcomings in our health care system. Some call it a crisis. Others call it a nonsystem.

How Will Health Care Systems Be Reformed?

It is of interest that the President of this nation has not yet seen fit to call a commission on health care: To define health care as more comprehensive than medical care and to identify and seek solutions to the real problems inherent in the continuing crises.

Manpower shortage is not the major problem. More than a decade ago, ANA's House of Delegates endorsed a resolution calling for such a commission. That House recognized the extant problems that are still with us, only more so: Fragmentation, unilateral control, proliferation of personnel, under-utilization of qualified people, outmoded facilities, economic motives—not to mention the more recently recognized discrimination against minority groups and employed women.

There is a tendency to divert the public focus from careful analysis of this urgent national problem and to apply ill-conceived, stopgap measures as if they would magically resolve the problem. One solution—and only one—is full utilization of registered nurses.

All of us here know that registered nurses can do more than many situations permit. Their ability to provide primary care, in the absence of and in collaboration with physicians, has been amply demonstrated. Nurses in schools, industry, clinics, health centers, in ghettos, Indian reservations, rural areas, nursing homes, military installations, and the like have illustrated this fact for many years—long before Medicare, Medicaid and the physician's assistant.

The guiding incentive of nurses is concern for the people, and not economic gain, although we must certainly pay attention to our own needs. Why then is this substantial resource not now fully encouraged and supported by government, and by our colleagues in other professions, to redouble its efforts to meet growing gaps in health care delivery systems?

Will Nursing Be 'Phased Out'?

Now the problem may be more serious than any of us may wish to acknowledge. The issue is whether or not the men now in government, who control public funds, really believe that nursing is an outdated female role. Is this but another variation of male chauvinism? And if so, the problem is greatly compounded if the women in nursing act as if they are in agreement with that view.

Silence gives consent, it is said. This is a time for nurses to stand up and be counted as men and women who intend to continue the advancement of the profession of nursing in the public interest. Nurses intend to humanize the system of health care, to build into it more choice for the consumer, and to insure that health care is more than medical care and more than hospital care during illness.

Why Do Nurses Fear Power?

All of our efforts in these first 100 years have been in this direction. Nurses, particularly the women in our field of work—and I do not mean to overlook the men, but I speak now to the women—have to confront the reality of their socialization experience. The Equal Rights Amendment, not yet ratified by the states, attests eloquently to the need to recognize inequalities heretofore meekly accepted, and to rectify them.

More women than not are fugitives from leadership and power; all too many shrink from the task of developing fully their capabilities and feeling good about using their competencies. Some do not recognize that relationships normally seen as benevolent—relationships between physicians and nurses, students and teachers, for instance—have elements of power in them. All too many nurses have yet to learn strategies for getting and using power constructively.

Some say that women are afraid of power and yet feel its absence: namely, powerlessness. Some nurses use particular behaviors that are appropriate to work with patients, and use the same behaviors in their relations with health colleagues. They thereby lose the struggles that could otherwise result in an improved collaboration in health care. Distinctions must be made between the sick and the well, the competent and the incompetent, the authority of the physician and the authority of the nurse.

It is irresponsible for nurses to negate, or fail to develop and use fully, the power and authority which they now have. If nurses believe that nursing service is good for society—good for the people—then they will embrace their capabilities and address them fully to the destiny of our profession and enlargement of the benefits that it provides for all of the people.

The Turning Point for the Profession

Responsible, well-informed, observant nurses know that there are threats to the nursing profession. These nurses are uneasy about countervailing pressures upon our progress that deter us at every turn. The profession of nursing is at a turning point. The courage of our convictions about people is being challenged. Our pride in our profession is being checked. Our disciplined ability to be definitive about nursing practice is being questioned. Our willingness to stand together to sustain the forward movement of the nursing profession is being tested.

Indeed, the astonishing development of nursing and its substantial impact—not only on the health of this nation but on the development of this entire society—too often go unrecognized by our professional colleagues, and by the public, and sometimes by our own profession.

All of us must mobilize our best resources to sustain and enlarge the work that nurses do to improve the health of people. Courage is contagious, and we must show it. The intellectual affluence of nursing is considerable; it must be respected, supported, encouraged and put to use to inform us all of that which we do not yet know about our work. We must share what we learn from our individual work with each other through publications, and conferences, and continuing education.

Innovation has been a hallmark of our profession. Even though it involves risk-taking, we must support it widely. We must design ever more effective strategies to make our work known and our needs known to the lawmakers, our colleagues in health work, and the public at large. Every nurse must help activate these strategies in some degree.

We must learn to respect and trust each other, take pride in the achievements of all nurses, and make our common cause the health of all of the people. And in all of these efforts, only a strong, united, disciplined organization of nurses can do the most in behalf of us all.

The American Nurses' Association has a record of achievement, of service to its members and for the common good—a record of which all of us can be very proud. Its 75 years of work, celebrated this year, are but the beginning. At this convention, this House of Delegates will once again debate new questions, weigh alternatives, and propose actions to guide ANA in the years ahead. I would urge you toward thoughtful debate, careful analysis of all questions, consideration of the consequences—the long-range consequences—of decisions that will be made here, and the formulation of clear directions for the forward movement of the nursing profession.

1972-1976

Rosamond C. Gabrielson

Rosamond C. Gabrielson, twenty-third president of the American Nurses' Association, has served in the capacity of nurse administrator for a number of years.

A graduate of the Hotel Dieu School of Nursing in El Paso, Miss Gabrielson received her Bachelor of Science and Master of Arts degrees from Arizona State University in Tempe.

In addition to her work with national nursing organizations, she has been active in state health groups, having been president of the Arizona State Nurses' Association and the Arizona League for Nursing. She has also served as member of the Arizona Advisory Council for Vocational Education and the Arizona Board of Nursing.

Miss Gabrielson was a contributor to the book, *Nursing Reconsidered,* edited by Esther Lucile Brown. She has also had articles published in various nursing journals.

In 1971, Miss Gabrielson was appointed by President Nixon to serve on the Committee on Health Services Industries, an advisory body to the Cost of Living Council.

As ANA president, Miss Gabrielson traveled to Australia and New Zealand in 1974 to participate in the Association's first Trans-Atlantic Nursing Conference. She represented ANA at the 1973 Quadrennial Congress of the International Council of Nurses in Mexico City and the Council of National Representatives in Singapore in 1975.

In June, 1976, Miss Gabrielson completes her second term as president of the American Nurses' Association.

Toward a New Reformation

By Rosamond C. Gabrielson, R.N., *president*
(Forty-Ninth Convention, San Francisco, June 9-14, 1974)

In this, my 1974 presidential message to you, I don't want to be in the position of over-simplifying what I believe are the issues facing the association, nor do I want to ignore our most obvious accomplishments. I do, however, want to share with you some concerns I have about the American Nurses' Association, and the impressions I have received while representing you as president of ANA.

When the Chinese write the word "crisis," they do so in two characters—one meaning danger, the other opportunity. I choose to believe the opportunities available to the American Nurses' Association at district, state, and national levels are unlimited. Consequently, if we are able to move in the appropriate direction, nurses, nursing, and the health care of people will benefit.

As a result of impressions gathered during all my visits, I decided very early during my term of office that I had to deliver a specific message to you today.

The message is this: It is most urgent that the association direct immediate attention to utilization of the vast energies and talents of its member practitioners, the staff nurses in this country. With their involvement in the work of the organization, the association can truly speak with a united and powerful voice for the profession.

Diversified Membership

The membership of ANA is diversified. We have philosophers, historians, researchers, educators, administrators, and, the largest group of all, practitioners of nursing; members represent all ages, backgrounds, and degrees of educational preparation. I have met with representatives from all these groups, talked with them, and listened to them. Their relative values and allegiances for the profession are tied up with these diversified groups. These allegiances are all important to us. However, I tend to believe that we can all agree upon whatever is necessary to advance the profession and ANA, regardless of our different interests. Agreement among ANA's diversified membership will be reflected in improved service to the public.

However, with the increase of knowledge, there seems to have arisen a paucity of new philosophy and a lack of humanity which have polarized our membership. As a consequence, we find that only 25 or 30 percent of the practicing nurses in this country hold membership in ANA. Retention of membership is a continuous problem. Why have we been unable to unite nurses? Why have we been unable to convince nurses that through ANA, the professional organization, their cause can be furthered?

In too many of my visits and contacts with nurses, I have been saddened to hear nurses describe themselves as "just staff nurses." I've not only been saddened, but also shocked, by the way staff nurses negate their importance and denigrate themselves by the words they use. Fortunately, such a self-image does not prevail with nurse researchers, nurse educators or nurse administrators.

There is growing feeling among many staff nurses that they are helpless—helpless in shaping their collective destiny as practitioners, helpless in changing the system in which they practice, and helpless in providing the kind of care they know and believe in. These are concerns we must deal with through cooperative and concerted effort.

I fully realize, as you do, that ANA has developed major programs to recognize practicing nurses. The *Book of Reports* is replete with evidence of the productivity of the commissions, the congress, and the divisions on practice. But how much do these reports reflect the infusion of ideas of staff nurses? Can we not recognize and accept as reality that most of our practitioners are staff nurses? These are the nurses who deal with the day-to-day realities of caring for people.

Reports of our thinking are insufficient. We must take measures to enhance the self-concept of staff nurses; we must identify their worthwhile contributions to the nursing profession; and we must encourage them to become increasingly involved in the affairs of this association.

A Tangible Effort

I must be very direct with you today and emphasize that the most tangible effort this association has ever made on behalf of staff nurses has been the economic and general welfare program. Through this program staff nurses have gained a sense of importance. They have realized that they can affect their destiny, as well as the destiny of the professions. They have *certainly* achieved involvement through the use of collective bargaining.

You are aware that the board of directors took action to commit substantial financial resources to support the 53 constituent nurses' associations to bring about collective action in health care facilities. This revitalized commitment of ANA and the state nurses' associations must continue. However, I have been concerned with the covert and overt messages I have received to the effect that it is all right to go this way in 1974, but . . .! I've been concerned also with some of the language used to describe the actions of staff nurses in this program. There must be appreciation and acknowledgment that staff nurses are just as interested in standards of practice and standards for the quality of care as they are in economic gain.

The Problem

The profession's cause cannot be represented by a collective sense of imminent, self-inflicted defeat. If this occurs, the feeling of helplessness will increase among staff nurses. Neither ANA nor the nursing profession can afford to let this happen.

I submit to you *again* that the group I am speaking for are those nurses who frequently feel that they have no real voice in this association. It is this group of nurses, staff nurses, who can be the most powerful group in this association, who can accomplish what needs to be done for the profession and for the public.

What is the problem? The problem, as I view it, can be

addressed by seeking answers to these questions: What motivations, what values, and what allegiances take priority at any given time? Who is in the position to change or alter the course of this profession and the professional association, and, in so doing, who may be alienated? I have met nurses who believe there is only *one* way of accomplishing the profession's goals. Such rigidity causes internal conflicts, and vested interests seem to take precedence over what is right for the profession and ANA.

Colleagues, we must increase our risk-taking, with full realization that, in taking risks, we may fail. However, unless we are willing to risk change—a change marked by the working together of all diverse groups in the association—we will accomplish very little.

This is not to say our history has not been without failures. But failure is not the ultimate fact of life; it is an aspect of life in which transient or poor judgment plays a larger role than it should.

We must convince staff nurses and help them internalize the belief that they are not creatures of failure so long as they have a vision of what nursing should really be; so long as they can comprehend the full meaning of the power they really have. We must demonstrate that we can work together to face the future, and future choices, with great expectations. We need to convene meetings of staff nurses all over this country. We need to say to them: "You are not helpless; you have never been helpless; you may have been dispirited."

A New Thrust

The new thrust in this association must be a reformation and a reaffirmation of this faith expressed in ANA programming for the staff nurse and programming for the clinical interests of nurses. We must make human and financial resources of the association available to enhance the power of the staff nurse. If we can accomplish this, we will do more to further the profession of nursing than anything else we might dream of. All our magnificent position papers, all our statements of belief, all the other programs we hope to implement will come to naught unless we accomplish this thrust and involve the staff nurse in the decisions made in this association.

Many nurses' values and allegiances might be sorely tested by this thrust, but, if we all have sufficient trust, we can achieve a common goal: The advancement of the profession of nursing for the public good. This is not an unreasonable demand to make of ourselves.

I am reminded of a speech John Gardner make when he was secretary of the Department of Health, Education, and Welfare, and I will attempt to recall a portion for you:

> As I pass the Washington Monument, and the Lincoln and Jefferson Memorials, I try to recall . . . that this nation was conceived by human beings, who were capable of mistakes, and subject to doubt and confusion, just as you and I are subject to such human fallibility, but they had the courage and heart to believe that man might create a democratic society, and that made all the difference. A nation is never finished. You can't build a nation and let it stand like the pyramids in Egypt. It has to be recreated in each generation by living, caring men and women. It is now our turn, and if we don't believe or don't care, nothing can save the nation.

While I travel from one state to another, I frequently think about ANA, nurses, and nursing. My thoughts are often a paraphrase of John Gardner's as I recall the efforts of our early nursing leaders who conceived and believed nursing could be different. The design was conceived by human beings, imperfect, as you and I are imperfect, but even with all their human fallibility, these nursing leaders had the heart and the courage to believe that nurses would someday be free to practice as they wanted to and knew they should, and this made all the difference. It is hard unending work and it involves great risks. This association, ANA, is never finished. We can't build the organization and let it stand like the Pharoahs did the pyramids. ANA has to be built and rebuilt. It has to be recreated in each generation by living, caring men and women who are nurses. The time is now to rededicate ourselves, to state clearly our beliefs, to operationalize those beliefs, to be renewed. If we don't believe or don't care, then ANA cannot be what it must be.

The Challenge

I am challenging all of you to, and I am calling on all of you for, a new openness, a new directness, and a new acknowledgment of what are my hopes for this association. We must increase our trust in ourselves and in others. We must open the profession to the ideas of the consumer. We must open the profession to the ideas of those intimately involved with the feminist movement—for nurses are really not liberated. Most importantly, we must open this professional association to the ideas and the dreams of the staff nurses in this country. We must show a new respect for human capacities, whatever our background or vested interests. If we can truly demonstrate this openness, this willingness to change, this willingness to involve the bulk of the practicing nurses, then we will find vast new resources and strength for the profession.

Tomorrow's Challenge

By Rosamond C. Gabrielson, R.N., *president*
(Fiftieth Annual Convention, Atlantic City, June 6, 1976)

Whenever I speak before a large gathering of individuals, I am reminded of a story about Thomas R. Marshall, who was vice president of the United States between 1913 and 1921. Vice President Marshall was once invited to speak at a political meeting in a small Iowa town. The meeting hall was very stuffy and, for some reason, it was impossible to open the windows. So it was decided that one window pane be broken. It was feared that the noise would startle the audience and, perhaps, throw them into a panic. The mayor of the town, who was on the platform with Thomas Marshall, stepped forward to give warning and to calm the audience. However, the audience had not assembled to listen to the mayor and overwhelmed him with cries of "We want Marshall! We want Marshall!" Rebuffed, the mayor yelled at the top of his voice, "I'm not going to make a speech, I have something to say!"

Tonight, it is not my intention to make a lengthy speech, but I do have something to say—something to say about the future of this organization and the future of nursing.

This year, the nursing profession celebrates two significant events: the two hundredth anniversary of this country in July, and the eightieth anniversary of this association in September.

Nurses have cause to take part in the nation's bicentennial celebrations. Nurses have served in every war, conflict, and disaster which have affected this country. Through intelligence, compassion, and hard work, they have brought about many social changes for the benefit of mankind. The improvement in health care through nursing, from colonial days to the present, is phenomenal.

In September of this year, the American Nurses' Association will observe its eightieth anniversary. The nursing profession did not gain prominence in America until nurses banded together in 1896 to seek standardization of educational programs and laws to insure practitioner competence. The establishment of the American Nurses'Association was a direct outgrowth of an interest in the professional and educational advancement of nurses. Since its founding, the association has had a significant impact on the growth and development of the nursing profession and the quality of nursing care.

Contributions of the American Nurses' Association

It would be impossible to relate all of ANA's efforts to foster nursing research, to promote nursing practice legislation, to stimulate the implementation of standards of nursing practice, nursing service, and nursing education, and to safeguard the economic and general welfare of nurses. However, I would like to mention several significant endeavors of the association.

During the 1922 convention, ANA President Clara Noyes observed:

> We can no longer stand aloof from other organizations working alone, solely on our own problems. The work of nurses touch the child in the home and in the school. Nursing is concerned not only with the care of the sick in the home and institution, but is concerned with the great questions of causation and prevention of disease and, therefore, touches the work of other groups, the physician, the nutritional worker, the teacher, the social worker. Nursing's interests are interwoven in the very fabric of civilization.

Since the 1920s, ANA has fostered liaison activities with over sixty-five health-related agencies and organizations, including the American Medical Association.

Since the 1930s, ANA has studied salaries, incomes, and employment conditions affecting nurses. As early as 1934, the association was fighting for the eight-hour work day for nurses. During the past forty years, it has spoken for nurses' welfare in regard to wage stabilization and price controls and concerned itself with the study and promotion of various types of group insurance and retirement plans for nurses.

In an effort to protect the patient who needs skilled nursing care and to protect qualified nurse practitioners, ANA, through the efforts of its constituent associations, secured nurse practice acts in every state by 1941.

During the early part of the 1940s, ANA provided certain organizational mechanisms and working channels to enhance the operation of a defense and war program for nursing. Over 76,000 nurses voluntarily served in the army and navy during World War II. The establishment of the National Nursing Council for

War Services in 1941 came as the direct result of the efforts of the American Nurses' Association.

Since the early 1940s, ANA has worked to develop a pool of licensing examinations for state boards of nursing and now owns the process by which the nursing examinations are developed.

During the 1940s, ANA began to work to remove barriers that prevented the full employment and full development of nurses belonging to minority racial groups. In 1946, ANA recommended that all state and district nurses' associations eliminate racial bars to membership. In 1951, when the National Association of Colored Graduate Nurses merged with the American Nurses' Association, its programs became an integral part of ANA's program.

In 1946, after great effort on the part of the American Nurses' Association, the Civil Service Commission reclassified graduate nursing positions in federal government agencies from the sub-professional to professional status. Many believe this action marked the official recognition of nursing as a profession.

The development of a code of ethics is an essential characteristic of a profession and provides one means whereby professional standards may be established, maintained, and improved. In 1950, ANA adopted the first code for professional nurses. This code was later used as a model for the code for nurses adopted by the International Council of Nurses.

In the last five years, ANA has concentrated its efforts on developing tools which will assure continued quality nursing service in light of changes in nursing practice and in light of changing consumer demands. Standards of nursing practice, nursing service, and nursing education; guidelines for continuing education programming; a program of certification for excellence in clinical practice; definitions of various nursing roles; and guidelines for the establishment of peer review committees are all measures aimed at judging and improving the quality of nursing performance.

In eighty years, the ANA has developed into a cohesive,

nationwide organization with ONE STRONG VOICE—one strong voice for nursing education, one strong voice for nursing practice, one strong voice for nursing service, one strong voice for the economic and general welfare of nurses.

As nurses and as members of the American Nurses' Association, we have a past worth remembering, but, more importantly, we have a future to shape. It is time to close one chapter in nursing history and the history of the American Nurses' Association and time to open another one.

State of the Health Care System

In order to maintain a viable position in the health care system, nursing must become a futuristically-based profession.The profession must begin to anticipate the health care demands for the next thirty years and, as quickly as possible, initiate innovative nursing programs aimed at satisfying these projected demands. The process of forecasting consumer needs can best be achieved within the framework of the professional association, which has at its disposal appropriate mechanisms for systematic investigation. Forecasting involves at least three steps: 1) the critical appraisal of past and present developments in health care and nursing, 2) the determination of significant goals and priorities desired for nursing, and 3) the development of innovative approaches to the achievement of the desired nursing goals.

In 1956, the Committee on Current and Long-Term Goals identified those sociological and economic trends which, it believed, would have a profound impact on the health care system and the nursing profession between 1960 and 1980. The list of trends included: population growth, technological and scientific advances, increasing medical costs, higher education in the general population, and the growth of government concern in meeting the public's health needs. In the last twenty years, as the result of these trends, the provision of health care services, on a national basis, has become fragmented, uncoordinated, and incomplete.

Population growth alone has resulted in greatly increased demands for more health care facilities and additional personnel. In the face of the dislocation of population patterns, orderly planning of health care services has become almost impossible. Moreover, technological and scientific advances in the health care field have occurred at an accelerated rate. As a result, there are more elderly, more chronically ill, and more patients on complex medical regimens requiring careful observation, health education, and supportive measures.

Today, the high costs of essential services prohibit the effective delivery of existing health care services to a significant portion of the population. In the last twenty years, health care expenditures have increased by almost 600 percent. Unfortunately, over fifty percent of this cost increase reflects price inflation rather than the addition of more comprehensive health care services. Compounding the rise in health care costs is the lack of health insurance coverage and the limitations to coverage provided through voluntary and other social insurance and tax-funded medical programs.

A more informed public is beginning to conceive and identify health not only as freedom from disease, but as a positive state of physical and mental well-being. Health care is viewed as a right of ALL people. Writers in the health care field have focused on the concept of wellness and, in so doing, have focused attention on the role of health workers in helping individuals, families, and entire communities establish comprehensive health services which include preventive, health maintenance, diagnostic, treatment, restorative, and protective health care services.

Finally, the shortcomings of the present health care system have prompted the federal government to take increasing steps to set the terms and conditions under which health care services are provided.

In light of the present health crisis, are nurses initiating change or reacting to the need for change?

It is my contention that, in the past few years, the nursing profession has been reacting to the need to revamp the health care system. There can be no doubt that the nursing profession feels the need for change. However, to recognize the need does not necessarily reflect the intent to initiate change. Feeling the need to change may be a reaction to conditions or circumstances which necessitate innovation. In recent years, role adaptation on the part of the professional nurse practitioner has been necessitated by at least two factors of change in our society: 1) the technological and scientific advances which have introduced innovative methods and new approaches to the diagnosis and treatment of certain health problems, and 2) changes in patterns of demand for health services which warrant provision of a more comprehensive continuum of care.

Fortunately, although the nursing profession has not initiated change in the immediate past, nurses have not fallen victim to change. Henry Steele Commager once remarked that change does not necessarily assure progress unless there is evidence of growth and development. In the last few years, the nursing profession has experienced growth and development. The nursing profession has been able to identify more efficient methods of practice, strengthen relationships with colleagues in the health care field, and establish much needed nursing service in the community. However, nurses cannot continue to merely react to change and still maintain a viable position in the health care system.

Recently, the profession has been confronted with two serious problems:

First, the general public, the government, and other health care disciplines are reluctant to acknowledge that nurses function in primary care roles. This is evidenced by the fact that nurses are still working to achieve unconditional recognition of direct fee-for-service reimbursement from both private and public third party payors. Moreover, the role of the nursing profession in health planning is often overlooked. Consequently, nursing services are limited or totally excluded from many health care proposals and programs.

Secondly, the introduction of a number of ancillary health care workers has created confusion and conflict regarding the delegation of responsibility for certain nursing duties. Unfortunately, an increasing number of non-nurse personnel are assuming miscellaneous nursing tasks. Such delegation of duty jeopardizes the profession's ability to insure continuity of nursing care.

Had the nursing profession initiated innovative nursing programs aimed at satisfying the projected health needs of the 1960s and 1970s, these particular problems would not exist.

Future Trends

The first step in futurizing or charting a future course for nursing is to identify those basic issues which confront nurses. An analysis of nursing history suggests that the profession of nursing has always been confronted by issues regarding standards for educational preparation, legal safeguards, and recognition of levels of competency. If the profession is to grow and develop, nurses must continually weigh these issues in light of relevant changes in society.

A second step in futurizing is to predict socioeconomic, political, and scientific and technological trends for the next two to three decades. One method of predicting trends is to analyze past events in order to delineate those trends and forces which would appear to remain operative in the future.

According to experts, population growth will continue to have a negative impact on the orderly planning of health care facilities and services. As this trend persists, authorities foresee greater governmental regulation and control of the health care system.

In the next thirty years, there will be continued proliferation of knowledge and increased use of technology. The acquisition of new knowledge and the more extensive use of technology will enhance the trend toward professional and occupational specialization. According to health care experts, an increasing dependence of health professionals on technology will tend to remove incentives for innovation, creativity, and personalization of health care services. It is predicted that, in an accelerated age of technology, health care providers may become mere technicians.

In the next fifty years, many more lives will be prolonged as the result of the discovery of more curative methodologies and wonder drugs, greater utilization of transplants and organ substitutions, increased efficiency and effectiveness of surgical operations through medical electronics, and experimentation in genetic engineering.

As scientific and technological advances increase man's capabilities to control life, health professionals will be forced to cope with a growing number of moral, ethical, and legal questions.

According to experts, the emphasis on technology, depersonalization, reformulation of work values, and changing roles of men and women will create new types of health problems, including increased stress leading to higher incidence of mental illness, emotional disturbances, and psychosomatic illness.

All of these factors have significant implications for the organization and administration of health care services and the nature and scope of practice of health professionals.

The whole process of futurizing must occur in a relatively short period of time. The accelerated rate of change in today's society makes five and ten year studies of trends and priorities impractical. Moreover, once goals and priorities are identified, the nursing profession must be willing to act immediately. Such an approach implies risk-taking, a chance nurses have been reluctant to take in the past.

The foremost priority must always be the advancement of nursing. Nurses must act in the interest of the profession. This may mean sacrificing individual interests for greater benefits to the profession. Nurses must recognize that there will be times when what is good for the nursing profession may not be immediately advantageous for the membership of this association. Nursing must resolve itself to the fact that what is best for the public welfare may be in direct conflict with nursing's interests on occasion.

If nursing is to remain a viable health profession, nurses must be willing to blaze new trails. I am reminded of the words of an unknown poet who wrote: "Do not follow where the path leads. Rather go where there is no path and leave a trail."

The nursing profession needs risk-takers and leaders who have the ability to chart future directions for the profession and the professional association. The nursing profession must begin to identify the Isabel Hampton Robbs and the Annie Goodrichs in today's society.

In its eighty-year history, the American Nurses' Association has fostered nursing research, promoted nursing practice legislation, encouraged the development of advanced and continuing education programs, stimulated the establishment and implementation of standards of nursing practice, nursing service, and nursing education, and safeguarded the economic and general welfare of nurses. In the next thirty years, under the leadership of futuristically minded nurses, ANA will continue to promote the educational and professional advancement of nurses to the end that the American public will receive quality nursing care.

Seventy-seven years ago, the first president of the American Nurses' Association, Isabel Hampton Robb, stood before convention delegates and declared: "We are the history makers of nurses. Let us see to it that we work so as to leave a fair record as the inheritance of those who come after us." Tonight, I say to each one of you, you are the history makers of nurses. Begin this week to chart a definite course for nursing and the American Nurses' Association, so that, in decades to come, the nursing profession and the American Nurses' Association will emerge with ONE STRONG VOICE—one strong voice for nursing education, one strong voice for nursing practice, one strong voice for nursing service, one strong voice for the economic and general welfare of nurses.

Appendices

Appendix I
In Review

The following pages provide a brief accounting of the numerous activities of the American Nurses' Association as well as significant events affecting the nursing profession between 1896 and 1976.

1896
On September 2, 1896, delegates from ten alumnae associations met near New York City for the purpose of organizing a national professional association for nurses.

1897
On February 11-12, 1897, the constitution and bylaws were completed and the Nurses' Associated Alumnae of the United States and Canada was organized.

1898
The Nurses' Associated Alumnae of the United States and Canada held its first annual convention.

1900
On October 1, 1900, the first issue of the *American Journal of Nursing* was distributed.

1901
The first state nurses' associations were organized to work toward state laws to control nursing practice.

The Nurses' Associated Alumnae helped to secure passage of a bill creating the Army Nurse Corps, Female.

The Nurses' Associated Alumnae of the United States and Canada was incorporated under the laws of the state of New York, making it necessary to drop the reference to Canada in the association's title.

The Nurses' Associated Alumnae affiliated with the American Society of Superintendents of Training Schools for Nurses to form the American Federation of Nurses for the purpose of applying for membership in the National Council of Women.

1902
Lina L. Rogers of New York City became the first school nurse.

1903
The first bills concerning registration for nurses were enacted in North Carolina, New York, New Jersey, and Virginia.

1905
The Nurses' Associated Alumnae joined with Great Britain and Germany to become the three charter members of the International Council of Nurses.

1906
The office of Interstate Secretary was created to handle correspondence and assist in organizing state associations.

1907
Mary Adelaide Nutting was appointed professor of institutional administration at Teachers College, Columbia University, the first nurse to occupy a university chair.

1908
On August 25, 1908, 52 Negro nurses met in New York City and founded the National Association of Colored Graduate Nurses. Martha Franklin of Connecticut, a graduate of the Women's Hospital in Philadelphia, was chosen first president of this group which proposed to work for higher professional nursing standards, the elimination of discrimination, and the development of leadership among Negro nurses.

The Nurses Corps of the United States Navy was founded.

1909
The Nurses' Associated Alumnae cooperated with the American Red Cross in establishing the Red Cross Nursing Service.

The first complete university school of nursing was organized at the University of Minnesota.

1911
The Nurses' Associated Alumnae changed its name to the American Nurses' Association.

ANA established a relief fund for nurses in need of financial assistance.

ANA established an Advisory Council composed of the officers of the national organization and the presidents of state nurses' associations.

1912
ANA purchased all the stock of the American Journal of Nursing Company with the "Journal Purchase Fund" contributed by nurses, plus a note of $1,600.

American Society of Superintendents of Training Schools for Nurses, founded in 1894, changed its name to the National League of Nursing Education. Membership in the league was extended to headworkers of social, educational, and preventive nursing.

ANA helped to organize the National Organization for Public Health Nursing.

ANA accepted into membership the National League of Nursing Education and the National Organization for Public Health Nursing.

1913
The War Department formally accepted the Red Cross enrollment as a reserve for the Army Nurse Corps and the Navy Nurse Corps.

1914
ANA established the Central Information Bureau for Legislation and Information to supply data concerning the work of state boards of nurse examiners.

1916
The membership basis of ANA was changed from that of membership

in the alumnae association to membership in the state association.

Membership in the ANA became a prerequisite for active membership in the National League of Nursing Education.

ANA's annual convention was held in Philadelphia on April 26, 1916, twenty days after the United States declared war on Germany. Delegates were advised to return to their homes to prepare for a call for six reserve hospital units.

Nursing organizations and representatives of allied fields organized the National Emergency Committee on Nursing, later part of the Council of National Defense.

ANA was incorporated in the District of Columbia.

ANA delegates authorized the organization of association sections. The first sections to be established were on private duty nursing and mental hygiene.

Through an amendment to the ANA Bylaws, the House of Delegates was created as the governing body of the organization.

1918

Annie W. Goodrich originated the Army School of Nursing. Miss Goodrich also served as the school's first dean.

Upon request of the Committee on Nursing of the Council of National Defense, ANA completed a census of nursing resources of the country.

The American Red Cross discontinued its Town and Country Nursing Service, establishing in its place a Bureau of Public Health Nursing.

1919

In cooperation with the American Red Cross, ANA, NLNE, and NOPHN helped establish the Bureau of Information which helped nurses returning from overseas readjust to civilian life. In conjunction with these activities, the Red Cross provided headquarters facilities in the office of the Atlantic Division of the American Red Cross.

1920

ANA, with the assistance of NLNE and NOPHN, adopted the Florence Nightingale School of Nursing at Bordeaux, France, as the American

Nurses' Memorial to the nurses who died in World War I. The school's cornerstone was laid on June 5, 1921.

ANA helped secure legislation granting relative rank to members of the Army Nurse Corps.

ANA appointed a Committee on the Status of Colored Graduate Nurses to establish lines of communication with the National Association of Colored Graduate Nurses.

ANA discontinued its annual conventions in order to support state association conventions in alternate years. ANA's first biennial convention was held in Atlanta with 470 delegates from state associations and 2,179 registrants. Between 1920 and 1928 ANA, NLNE, and NOPHN held their conventions at the same time and in the same city.

In September, 1920, ANA and NLNE established headquarters offices at 156 Fifth Avenue. The American Red Cross continued to finance headquarters activities of the two organizations until July 1, 1921.

1921

On April 15, 1921, the ANA, NLNE and NOPHN moved their offices to 370 Seventh Avenue.

512 student nurses, comprising the first class, were graduated from the Army School of Nursing.

ANA organized a legislative section.

1922

ANA increased its dues from 15 cents to 50 cents per member in order to undertake the financial responsibility of maintaining a national headquarters.

1923

The study, *Nursing and Nursing Education in the United States,* was published. Financed by the Rockefeller Foundation, the study identified needs of nursing education and public health nursing.

ANA contributed $16,500 toward the work of the Committee on the Grading of Nursing Schools to study conditions of nursing service, education, and economics.

Agnes Deans was appointed the first paid executive secretary at the national nursing headquarters.

The first special committee on ethical standards was appointed.

Collegiate schools of nursing were established at Yale and Western Reserve Universities.

By the end of 1923, the headquarters operations of the American Nurses' Association and the National League of Nursing Education had been completely separated.

1924
Committees on legislation and organizational self-analysis were appointed by ANA's Board of Directors.

In January, 1924, the Puerto Rico Graduate Nurses' Association was accepted into ANA membership.

ANA organized a government nursing service section.

1925
The first ANA field secretaries were appointed.

The first meeting of the Kentucky Committee for Mothers and Babies, the parent organization of the Frontier Nursing Service, was held on May 28, 1925.

1926
A tentative code of ethics for nurses was adopted by the American Nurses' Association.

As the result of an amendment to the ANA Bylaws, registered nurse status became a prerequisite for membership.

1927
A group of state nurses' associations organized a midwestern conference division.

1928
The Committee on the Grading of Nursing Schools published its study on the supply and demand for nurses entitled *Nurses, Patients and Pocketbooks.*

ANA, NLNE, and NOPHN appointed a Joint Committee on the

Distribution of Nursing Services.

A group of state nurses' associations organized a southern conference division. By 1929, there were five conference divisions: New England, Middle Atlantic, Midwest, Northwestern, and Southern.

ANA organized a federal government nurses section.

1929

ANA began a study of registries and private duty nursing. Tentative standards for registries were formulated.

ANA endorsed a group insurance plan (annuity, life, health, and accident) offered by the Harmon Association for the Advancement of Nursing.

1930

Linda Richards, "America's First Trained Nurse," died on April 16, 1930, at the age of 89.

In June, 1930, ANA's House of Delegates voted that the national relief fund be discontinued and the existing fund be divided among the respective state associations on a per capita basis according to the 1932 membership.

ANA's Special Committee on Reclassification submitted a brief and specifications for civilian nursing service in the federal government to the Personnel Classification Board.

The Committee on the Grading of Nursing Schools published "The Student Body."

As the result of a bylaw amendment, provision was made for male nurses to become members of the American Nurses' Association.

1931

The Committee on the Grading of Nursing Schools published "What Nurses Learn" and "Who Controls the Schools."

In April, 1931, ANA headquarters was relocated at 450 Seventh Avenue with the NOPHN, NLNE, and seventeen other national health agencies.

ANA, through the Joint Committee on Distribution of Nursing Services, formulated standards of employment for private duty nurses, including standards and terms of employment for nurses practicing in institutional settings.

The American Association of Nurse Anesthetists was organized.

1932

The National League of Nursing Education accepted the function of the Department of Education of the American Nurses' Association, while retaining its own organization.

Thc Association of Collegiate Schools of Nursing was organized.

1933

The Joint Committee on Distribution of Nursing Services sponsored a survey on hourly nursing service.

1934

The Committee on the Grading of Nursing Schools published the results of its final studies, *An Activity Analysis of Nursing* and *Nursing Schools—Today and Tomorrow.*

Cooperating with NLNE and NOPHN, ANA established the Nursing Information Bureau under the administration of the American Journal of Nursing Company.

ANA's House of Delegates approved an eight-hour day for nurses and conducted a national campaign to promote better working hours.

ANA, the Federal Emergency Relief Administration, the Civil Works Administration and state nurses' associations collaborated on a survey of unemployed nurses. ANA also assisted states in funding employment for nurses on relief.

In April, 1934, ANA moved their headquarters operation to 50 West 50th Street.

On July 5, 1934, the inaugural meeting of the ICN Florence Nightingale Foundation was held in London.

The National Association of Colored Graduate Nurses established headquarters in New York City.

As of December 31, 1934, ANA membership totalled 110,598.

1935
ANA appointed a committee to study health insurance proposals and programs and their implications for the nursing profession.

The work of ANA's Legislative Section, organized in 1921, was assumed by the Committee on Legislation.

ANA, NLNE, and NOPHN formed a Joint Committee on Community Nursing Service to help communities plan a more complete nursing service.

Congress enacted the Social Security Act.

1936
In 1934, ANA's Board of Directors appointed a special committee to consider a request to move ANA headquarters to Chicago. This committee explored the distribution of nurses across the country, the expense of relocation, and possible relocation sites. In 1936, the Board recommended that ANA retain headquarters offices in New York in close proximity to other health organizations.

ANA undertook a project to review and restate the function of the association as well as the joint functions of the three national nursing organizations.

The three national nursing organizations established a joint committee to examine the issue of subsidiary workers.

ANA appointed a committee to consider the matter of lay membership and lay participation in the American Nurses' Association.

A committee of the National League of Nursing Education and the Division of Nursing of the Council of the American Hospital Association prepared the *Manual of the Essentials of Good Hospital Nursing Service.*

1937
The board of directors of the American Nurses' Association appointed a special committee for the purpose of considering the question of nurse membership in unions.

1938
ANA voted to raise $88,500 for the Florence Nightingale International

Foundation, "a perpetual and living memorial to the undying spirit and influence of nursing's great pioneer."

ANA reported on its study of incomes and employment conditions of nurses. ANA recommended a salary schedule for nurses comparable to those of other women workers, a 48-hour week for nurses practicing in institutions, and vacations with pay.

Delegates voted to allow one delegate for every one hundred members of the state nurses' association. Prior to 1938 the voting body at each convention was based on one delegate for every 50 members.

1939
On January 22, 1939, ANA's Board of Directors appointed a special committee for the purpose of considering the possibility of consolidation of the three national nursing organizations.

ANA adopted a policy favoring the licensure of all who nurse for hire.

1940
ANA's House of Delegates offered President Roosevelt its support in any activity in which nurses could be of service to the country.

ANA organized sections for men nurses and general staff nurses.

ANA proposed and became a member of the Nursing Council on National Defense which was formed to coordinate activities of the profession on national and local levels during the national emergency. The council was renamed the National Nursing Council for War Service in 1942.

ANA headquarters office was relocated at 1790 Broadway in New York City.

ANA and NLNE published a "Digest of Nurse Practice Acts and Board Rules" to facilitate state registration of nurses by reciprocity.

A Joint Committee of the American Hospital Association and the National League of Nursing Education, in cooperation with the American Nurses' Association, published a report on "Administrative Cost Analysis for Nursing Service and Nursing Education."

1941
At the request of the National Nursing Council for War Service, ANA

and NLNE made a study of nursing vacancies in U.S. hospitals.

ANA participated in a national survey of nurses conducted by the U. S. Public Health Service.

In light of the fact that New York City was considered a possible target for enemy attack, ANA made arrangements to store valuable historical records in Chicago.

Between 1941 and 1946, ANA assisted in the recruitment of nurses for military service through state and local committees.

1942

ANA's House of Delegates increased the membership dues from 50 cents to 75 cents, effective January 1, 1943.

At the 1942 biennial convention, delegates adopted a motion that every four years the American Nurses' Association, National League of Nursing Education, and National Organization for Public Health Nursing would hold a joint convention.

ANA endorsed a course for volunteer nurses' aides established by the American Red Cross and the Office of Civilian Defense.

ANA published a *Study of Organization, Control, and Financing of Nurses' Professional Registries.*

The National Association for Practical Nurse Education was organized.

1943

The U. S. Cadet Nurse Corps was created in an attempt to bring more students into nursing schools.

ANA obtained a hearing before the U. S. Commissioner of Internal Revenue which resulted in a ruling that the costs of nursing uniforms could be deducted for income tax purposes.

ANA assisted the War Manpower Commission in a study of civilian hospital services.

ANA established a Clearing Bureau on State Board Problems.

The National League of Nursing Education broadened its membership base to include lay members.

1944

ANA worked to secure passage of legislation granting commissioned rank to nurses in military services.

A Statistics and Research Unit was established at the association headquarters.

ANA made a study of the implications of the Social Security Act for nurses.

The ANA Bylaws were amended in order that no officer be elected to the same office for more than two successive terms.

As a result of the action of ANA's Board of Directors in June, 1944, the name and status of the Clearing Bureau on Problems of State Boards of Nurse Examiners was changed to the Bureau of State Boards of Nurse Examiners. One function of this body was to devise methods and procedures for bringing about desirable and reasonable uniformity in relation to standards, regulations, examinations, and records.

ANA organized sections for industrial nurses and administrators of nursing services in hospitals.

The three national nursing organizations adopted a recommendation favoring the expansion of health insurance plans to provide for nursing service, including nursing care in the home. The organizations expressed the belief that, in addition to voluntary effort, governmental assistance was necessary for obtaining adequate distribution of health services.

ANA delegates adopted an amendment to the bylaws which designated the state association as the constituent association of the American Nurses' Association. According to the bylaw revision, registered nurses belonging to state nurses' associations automatically became members of the ANA.

1945

ANA spearheaded a national collection of uniforms and clothing for nurses in war-devastated countries.

ANA organized a campaign to restore the American Nurses' Memorial at the Florence Nightingale School of Nursing at Bordeaux, France.

ANA intensified efforts to recruit nurses for military service as an alternative to President Roosevelt's proposal to draft nurses into military services.

On May 25, 1945, ANA's Professional Counseling and Placement Service was officially organized and incorporated. The service provided counseling and job placement services without fee to all registered nurses, including non-members, student nurses, practical nurses, and employers. Special attention was given to the needs of nurses demobilized from military service.

On September 1, 1945, the Nurse Placement Service, Midwest Bureau, was acquired and reorganized as the branch office of the Professional Counseling and Placement Service of the American Nurses' Association.

ANA analyzed the postwar plans of approximately 60,000 civilian nurses. ANA also cooperated with the Red Cross in analyzing postwar plans of 41,000 Army and Navy nurses.

The National Nursing Planning Committee published a Comprehensive Program for Nationwide Action in the Field of Nursing.

1946

ANA was successful in obtaining professional status classification for nurses from the U. S. Civil Service Commission.

ANA's Professional Counseling and Placement Service issued criteria to guide state units in developing their own placement services.

ANA established a Committee on Employment Conditions of Nurses to explore the association's resources for assisting nurses to obtain needed improvements in salaries and working conditions.

The ANA House of Delegates voted to inaugurate an Economic Security Program, a long-range comprehensive program to stabilize nursing services, improve working conditions, and provide immediate and long-term economic security for nurses in all fields. State nurses' associations were urged to conduct active programs, including collective bargaining for nurses.

The ANA House of Delegates endorsed the 8-hour day, 40-hour week for all nurses and called for the elimination of discrimination against minority groups.

In April, 1946, Raymond Rich Associates was selected to undertake a detailed study of the organizational structure, functions, and facilities of the six national nursing organizations.

ANA delegates adopted the first association platform.

ANA delegates voted to increase the annual dues from 75 cents to $3.00.

The Hospital Survey and Construction Act (Hill-Burton Bill) was enacted. This bill provided for a five-year federal grant-in-aid program to the states for the purpose of surveying needs, planning, and constructing necessary hospital and health centers.

1947
ANA hosted the Ninth Congress of the International Council of Nurses in Atlantic City.

Army and Navy nurses were granted permanent commissioned officer status.

ANA initiated a long-range public relations program to inform the public and the profession of nursing activities and interests. ANA's public relations department absorbed the Nursing Information Bureau as well as the public relations programs of the other nursing organizations.

The boards of nursing asked ANA to establish a committee of state boards of nursing to devise methods and procedures for bringing about desirable and reasonable uniformity in relation to standards, regulations, records, and examinations.

The first special session of the House of Delegates was convened in Chicago to consider reorganization proposals for the six national nursing organizations.

1948
The Joint Committee on the Structure of National Nursing Organizations presented "A Tentative Plan for One National Nursing Organization."

The World Health Organization was permanently established in Geneva, Switzerland. The International Council of Nurses became the official representative of nurses to the WHO meetings.

ANA celebrated the Diamond Jubilee of Nursing by calling attention to the progress of nursing in the United States.

ANA participated in a study of the Florence Nightingale International Foundation which resulted in the foundation's inclusion as a functional unit of the International Council of Nurses.

ANA delegates adopted measures (bylaw revisions) to provide direct individual membership for Negro nurses restricted from membership in the state nurses' association.

ANA joined with five other nursing organizations to establish a joint board to facilitate official cooperation on mutual projects.

Esther Lucile Brown published the findings of a study on nursing education in the book entitled *Nursing for the Future.*

ANA delegates amended the bylaws to permit state nurses' associations to grant associate membership to certain qualified nurses who were not in active practice.

The Committee on the Function of Nursing (Teachers College) published a book entitled *A Program for the Nursing Profession* which dealt with shortages of nursing personnel.

ANA, at the request of the National Security Resources Board, contracted to establish and maintain a biennial inventory of nurses in the United States, Alaska, Hawaii, and Puerto Rico. The first inventory was completed in 1948.

1949

ANA was accredited as an observer to the United Nations.

The Association of Operating Room Nurses was established.

The joint boards of ANA, NLNE, NOPHN, NACGN, ASCN, and AAIN merged to establish the National Nursing Accrediting Service. The first lists of accredited schools of nursing were issued in October, 1949.

The National Federation of Licensed Practical Nurses was established.

The ANA Board of Directors authorized the establishment of a special committee to study the functions of the National Association of Colored Graduate Nurses as they related to the total program of the association.

The Joint Committee on the Structure of National Nursing Organizations offered two alternate plans for reorganization: a one-organization plan and a two-organization plan.

ANA created a committee on films to review and advise on motion pictures and other audiovisual items of interest to nurses.

1950

ANA's House of Delegates adopted an intergroup relations program to work for full integration of nurses of all racial groups in all aspects of nursing.

ANA endorsed a five-year study of all phases of nursing.

ANA adopted a code of ethics for professional nursing.

ANA appointed a committee on nursing resources to meet civil and military needs.

ANA's House of Delegates approved criteria for the evaluation of state economic security programs in relation to ANA policy.

ANA affirmed the nurse's voluntary relinquishment of the right to strike and insisted that this voluntary no-strike guarantee obligated employers to recognize and deal justly with nurses through their authorized representatives.

ANA's House of Delegates approved a policy to guide nurses as to their proper conduct and professional obligations when labor-management disputes occurred in industry or other agencies where nurses were employed.

ANA established a clearinghouse for studies at its headquarters office which provided a central source of information on research projects, completed and in progress, of interest to the profession.

ANA's House of Delegates endorsed a two-organization plan for reorganization of the national nursing organizations.

Between 1950 and 1951, the functions and responsibilities of the National Association of Colored Graduate Nurses were absorbed by the American Nurses' Association.

1951

In January, 1951, the National Association of Colored Nurse Graduates was officially dissolved.

ANA established a professional liability insurance plan.

ANA expanded its Intergroup Relations Program.

ANA made the first five grants from the Studies of Nursing Functions Funds to assist research projects proposed by state associations or agencies in California, Massachusetts, Minnesota, New York, and Rhode Island.

ANA opened a government relations office in Washington, D.C.

ANA representatives attended the fifth session of the U.N. Commission on Status of Women, where the first item on nursing appeared on the agenda as submitted by the World Health Organization. The commission requested the Secretary-General to draw attention of U.N. members to the importance of raising the status and legal protection of nursing in all countries as an important part of improving the status of women.

Contributions of state associations for restoration of the American Nurses' Memorial at Bordeaux, France, reached $56,138.00.

ANA headquarters were moved to Two Park Avenue, New York City.

On February 6, 1951, ANA filed a statement with the Wage Stabilization Board presenting the views of nurses regarding the establishment of an equitable wage policy to meet the particular problems of professional nurses. On February 20, 1951, General Wage Regulation 7 was issued which substantially exempted employees of nonprofit organizations from wage stabilization controls.

1952

ANA prepared a *Manual for an Economic Security Program.*

The Mary Mahoney Award, initiated and previously bestowed by the National Association of Colored Graduate Nurses, was presented for the first time at the ANA convention.

ANA's House of Delegates amended the constitution and bylaws to implement reorganization of the national nursing organizations. ANA remained the national membership association for professional nurses and endorsed the establishment of the National League for Nursing and provided machinery for cooperative work with this new organization.

The National Organization for Public Health Nursing and the Association of Collegiate Schools of Nursing were dissolved.

ANA established seven sections, representing occupational groups of professional nurses.

ANA delegates approved an increase in dues from $3.00 to $5.00.

ANA's House of Delegates authorized the board of directors to approve legislation for selective service for nurses, if such legislation was introduced during a national emergency.

1953
The National Student Nurses' Association was established.

ANA's Board of Directors adopted a statement on principles of legislation relating to the practice of nursing.

In August, 1953, ANA's PC&PS was reorganized. Major administrative functions were transferred to the Chicago office where counseling and placement activities on the national level were to be centered.

1954
The Virgin Islands Nurses' Association became a constituent association of the American Nurses' Association.

As a result of revision of the ANA Bylaws, the ANA Committee on Economic and General Welfare became a standing committee.

ANA delegates adopted a recommendation to "secure information and to develop a foundation or trust for receiving tax-free funds for desirable charitable, scientific, literary, or educational projects in line with the aims and purposes of the American Nurses' Association."

The ANA Board of Directors approved the maintenance of one national committee on legislation.

ANA's House of Delegates created a Committee on Current and Long-Term Goals to prepare a proposed association platform, to develop a statement of long-term goals of the association, and to make recommendations with regard to services which the association could offer its constituencies. In 1955, the board of directors extended the committee's functions to include an inventory of major problems and goals of ANA in priority arrangement.

The first statements on functions were approved by ANA sections, marking the first step in the program of outlining functions, standards, and qualifications for nursing practice.

By 1954, all but one state nurses' association had changed their bylaws to ban discrimination in accordance with ANA's policy.

1955
The American Nurses' Foundation was established as a separately incorporated ANA subsidiary.

The American College of Nurse Midwives was organized.

ANA's Board of Directors approved a definition of the practice of nursing designed to meet the purposes of licensing legislation.

ANA helped pass a bill to commission male nurses in the Reserve Nurse Corps.

1956
ANA presented the association's first public health nurse award to Pearl McIver.

1957
In January, 1957, the boards of directors of the National Federation of Licensed Practical Nurses and the American Nurses' Association approved a statement on the functions of the licensed practical nurse.

Nondiscrimination in minimum employment standards and in contracts was adopted as an economic security goal.

1958
ANA delegates voted to increase the annual dues from $5.00 to $7.50.

ANA's PC&PS restricted its placement service to ANA membership.

ANA's House of Delegates endorsed health care as a right of all people and urged the extension of social security to include health insurance for beneficiaries of old age, survivors, and disability insurance.

For the first time in the history of the ANA, a liaison committee was formed with the American Medical Association.

Membership in the ANA increased by 9,097 or five percent from 1957 to 1958. The total of 190,463 was the highest recorded since the organization was founded and represented the largest yearly increase in over a decade.

1959

Effective January 1, 1959, ANA's PC&PS operation was restricted to ANA members and first-year professional nurse graduates.

Nurses living abroad were admitted to ANA membership on an individual basis for the first time.

ANA's Board of Directors approved a revised statement on principles of legislation relating to public funds for collegiate nursing education.

In April, 1959, ANA moved its headquarters offices and the PC&PS office, formerly in Chicago, to 10 Columbus Circle.

Requirements for the mandatory licensure of professional nurses were enacted in Maine and New Hampshire.

1960

ANA's Board of Directors authorized the PC&PS committee to conduct a study to evaluate the direct counseling and placement services given to individual members.

ANA published a statement on standards for nursing care in nursing homes.

ANA revised the *Code for Professional Nurses.*

The passage of the Labor-Management Reporting and Disclosure Act of 1959 (Landrum-Griffin Law) necessitated the ANA Bylaws be amended to allow for convention delegates to be selected by secret ballot and the records pertaining to the elections be preserved for one year.

The House of Delegates adopted a motion that the ANA take

immediate steps to secure compulsory social security coverage for nurses in all types of employment.

The House of Delegates adopted a plank to continue to elevate the standards of nursing education by formulating principles of the education essential for effective nursing practice.

1961

ANA's Board of Directors authorized the formation of a committee on nursing service and a committee on nursing education.

ANA's Board of Directors approved a recommendation that a joint committee of the American Nurses' Association and the National Student Nurses' Association for consideration of common interests and goals.

1962

ANA membership dues were increased to $12.50.

ANA held its first clinical sessions.

The House of Delegates amended the bylaws to restate the purposes and functions of the ANA, adding specific provisions for new functions in the areas of nursing education and nursing services.

In June, 1962, the U. S. Public Health Service contracted with ANA to conduct an inventory of professional nurses.

By the end of 1962, all state nurses' associations accepted all qualified registered nurses into membership, regardless of race, color, or creed.

1963

ANA received a special project grant of $10,000 from the National Institute of Mental Health for the purpose of defining the role of the nurse in the community mental health center and making recommendations for continuing education of current practitioners to prepare them to assume this role.

The Surgeon General's Consultant Group on Nursing published a report entitled *Toward Quality in Nursing: Needs and Goals.*

Between 1963 and 1964, ANA conducted pilot projects on central billing.

1964

In February, 1964, the American Nurses' Association and the American Medical Association co-sponsored a two-day conference on "Medical and Nursing Practice in a Changing World."

The House of Delegates adopted a motion that the board of directors appoint a committee to study and report at the 1966 convention on the feasibility of and/or a plan for the establishment of an academy of nursing.

The House of Delegates adopted a recommendation that ANA continue to work toward baccalaureate education as the educational foundation for professional nursing practice.

Congress passed the Nurse Training Act of 1964, the first federal law to give comprehensive assistance for nursing education.

1965

ANA published policies and recommendations on health occupations supportive to nursing.

ANA's Board of Directors developed a position paper on educational preparation for nurse practitioners and assistants to nurses.

ANA's Board of Directors authorized formation of a liaison committee of the American Nurses' Association and the American Hospital Association.

ANA published *Standards for Organized Nursing Services.*

1966

Health insurance for the aged became a benefit of the nation's social insurance system as a result of passage of the Social Security Amendments of 1965.

The House of Delegates adopted an organizational plan calling for divisions on practice and commissions on nursing service, nursing education, and economic and general welfare.

The House of Delegates adopted a recommendation that the principle of central billing and dues collection be adopted by the association.

The name of the association's PC&PS service was changed from Professional Counseling and Placement Service to Professional Credentials and Personnel Service.

In September, 1966, ANA's Board of Directors appointed the organizing committees for the divisions on practice and occupational forums and named the first members of the commissions on nursing education, nursing service, and economic and general welfare.

Legislation for comprehensive health planning was enacted into law.

ANA's Board of Directors approved a statement on family planning.

President Johnson appointed the National Advisory Commission on Health Manpower.

ANA was instrumental in having legislation introduced to raise the rank of chief nurses of the armed services nurse corps to top officer rank and to provide for an increased number of nurse officers to attain the grade of colonel, lieutenant colonel, and major or captain, commander, and lieutenant commander.

1967

In January, 1967, the operations of ANA's Legislative Department and the Washington Office were combined to form the Government Relations Department.

A joint committee of representatives of the American Nurses' Association and the American Society of Hospital Pharmacists was established.

The ANA-NLN Careers Program was initiated.

ANA was awarded a $50,000 grant by the Department of Labor to establish a national program to return inactive licensed nurses to practice through enrollment in refresher courses. To augment this program, ANA entered into a $99,800 informational and educational contract with HEW's Division of Nursing.

ANA's *Statement on Psychiatric Nursing* was published.

ANA's Board of Directors authorized a comprehensive study of the state board test pool examination.

ANA's Board of Directors adopted a resolution to support a program of the U. S. Public Health Service which had as its goal the elimination of measles in the United States by the end of 1967.

ANA published *Avenues for Continued Learning.*

Delegates to the annual National Student Nurses' Association convention voted to support ANA's position paper on nursing education.

ANA published a statement on nursing staff requirements for inpatient health care facilities.

The National Commission for the Study of Nursing and Nursing Education was established.

1968

The Guam Nurses' Association was admitted as a constituent association with "limited constituent status."

The Nurses' Association of the American College of Obstetricians and Gynecologists was established.

ANA's Board of Directors adopted a statement on the health hazards of smoking.

The House of Delegates adopted a recommendation to study state legislation on abortion.

The House of Delegates voted to charge a fee for the association's Professional Credentials and Personnel Service.

The House of Delegates rescinded the association's 18-year-old no-strike policy.

The House of Delegates adopted a new *Code for Nurses* which delineated the ethical principles of practice.

The House of Delegates authorized the establishment of the Congress for Nursing Practice.

ANA published *The Nurse in Research: ANA Guidelines on Ethical Values.*

Interim certification boards held their first meetings.

The American Association of Nephrology Nurses was established.

The American Association of Neurosurgical Nurses was established.

The National Education Association established a Department of School Nurses.

1969

ANA's Board of Directors established a task force to explore more effective ways of meeting the high costs of operating essential association programs.

ANA's Board of Directors appointed an ad hoc committee on ways to enter the academy of nurses.

ANA's Board of Directors established a committee to consider questions of interrelationships between the commissions, congress, and board of directors.

ANA issued a statement on graduate education in nursing.

The American Association of Critical Care Nurses was organized.

1970

ANA's Board of Directors adopted a statement on new careerists.

The National Commission for the Study of Nursing and Nursing Education published *An Abstract for Action,* a series of recommendations concerning the improvement of nursing and nursing education.

The House of Delegates approved measures to create a Commission on Nursing Research.

The House of Delegates voted to increase ANA dues from $12.50 to $25.00.

The House of Delegates approved a bylaw provision for a new associate member category.

The House of Delegates approved a recommendation that a study be undertaken to find the most desirable location for ANA's national headquarters.

A joint committee was established between ANA's Division on Maternal and Child Health Nursing Practice and the American Academy of Pediatrics to provide an official liaison mechanism between these organizations.

The American Urological Association Allied was established.

1971

The boards of directors of the American Academy of Pediatrics and the

American Nurses' Association simultaneously released a joint statement entitled "Guidelines for Short-Term Continuing Education Programs for Pediatric Nurse Associates."

ANA authorized the establishment of a Council of Nurse Researchers and a Council on Continuing Education.

The Nurse Training Act of 1971 included, for the first time, authorization for basic support grants for nursing programs.

ANA was awarded a one-year $42,000 grant for a project entitled "Identification of Need for Continuing Education for Nurses by the National Professional Organization."

ANA utilized a one-year $40,000 grant from the National Institute of Mental Health to develop guidelines for drug abuse curricula in nursing education programs.

ANA endorsed a national moratorium on licensure for new health professionals.

The Council of National Representatives of the International Council of Nurses adopted a resolution endorsing the U.N. Universal Declaration of Human Rights and requesting its member associations "to take the appropriate steps to support and implement the objective" of the statement.

The Commission on Nursing Services developed a statement on the essential elements of a health care system.

The Congress for Nursing Practice issued guidelines for certification.

In the first recorded mass resignation over strictly non-economic issues, registered nurses at an Ames, Iowa, hospital resigned in a body when the hospital administration refused to negotiate on issues, including a patient care committee, an orientation program for new staff members, paid educational leave to attend seminars and workshops, and a nursing care committee.

The National Emergency Department Nurses' Association was established.

1972
In February, 1972, ANA's membership publication, *ANA In Action,*

was renamed *The American Nurse.*

A contract for $355,760 to conduct the project entitled "Training of RNs Providing Patient Care in Nursing Homes" was signed with HEW's Community Health Service on June 2, 1972. This contract was designed to improve patient care in nursing homes by upgrading geriatric nursing care through continuing education.

ANA's Board of Directors established a task force to study the financial structure of the organization.

The Orthopedic Nurses' Association, Inc., was established.

In September, 1972, ANA opened its headquarters in Kansas City, Mo.

ANA-AHA sponsored the first joint institute.

ANA's Task Force for Affirmative Action held its first meeting in November, 1972.

The House of Delegates went on record as opposed to institutional licensure which would cover individual practitioners.

1973

ANA was awarded an 18-month $112,338 contract by the Bureau of Health Manpower Education to obtain statistical and descriptive data on foreign nurse graduate applicants for RN licensure in the United States.

Standards of Community Health, Maternal and Child Health, Geriatric, and Psychiatric and Mental Health Nursing Practice were published. In addition, a generic set of *Standards of Nursing Practice* was published.

ANA's Commission on Nursing Services revised the *Standards for Nursing Services.*

The Council on Continuing Education and the Council of Pediatric Nurse Practitioners held their first business meetings.

The National Association of Pediatric Nurse Associates and Practitioners was organized.

Thirty-six charter fellows were chosen for the American Academy of Nursing.

The Federation of Nursing Specialty Organizations and ANA was established.

ANA filed charges against the nation's largest university pension underwriter on March 2, 1973, for discrimination on the basis of sex.

ANA's National Retirement Plan was established on April 13, 1973.

Criteria were developed for ANA certification of geriatric nurses, pediatric nurses in ambulatory care, and psychiatric nurses.

In November, 1973, the American Nurses' Association was requested by the Senate Subcommittee on Long-Term Care to prepare a report regarding the problems of providing skilled nursing care in intermediate and extended care facilities.

ANA issued a statement on diploma nurse education.

ANA developed guidelines for the establishment of peer review committees.

1974

HEW's Division on Research, Maternal and Child Health Services, approved and funded ANA's project proposal on the "Impact of Pediatric Nurse Practitioner Programs: An Exploratory and Methodological Study."

In January, 1974, the *Standards of Medical-Surgical Nursing Practice* were developed for publication.

On April 1, 1974, the American Nurses' Foundation moved its office from New York City to Kansas City.

The Council of Nursing Service Facilitators, the Council of Family Nurse Practitioners and Clinicians, the Council of Advanced Practitioners in Medical-Surgical Nursing, and the Council of Advanced Practitioners in Psychiatric and Mental Health Nursing held their first business meetings at the ANA convention.

The first ANA Honorary Practitioner Award was presented at the forty-ninth convention.

ANA's Task Force on Affirmative Action established an ombudsman's office at ANA headquarters.

ANA's Board of Directors approved the establishment of a Council of School Nurses.

ANA published *Standards for Continuing Education in Nursing* and *ANA Continuing Education Guidelines for SNAs.*

ANA issued a statement on the scope of practice of pediatric nurse practitioners.

The Nurses' Coalition for Action in Politics was established as a political action arm of the American Nurses' Association.

The Congress for Nursing Practice issued definitions of the terms "nurse practitioner," "nurse clinician," and "clinical nurse specialist."

ANA's Commission on Economic and General Welfare issued a statement on third-party payments for the services of independent nurse practitioners.

The House of Delegates adopted a position on national health insurance which called for a comprehensive system of health insurance benefits for all Americans.

The House of Delegates adopted a motion to examine the feasibility of accreditation of basic and graduate nursing education.

The first ANA Trans-Pacific Nursing Conference was held.

ANA held one invitational conference on accreditation to prepare a formal proposal for a study of the feasibility of accreditation of basic and graduate education for nursing by the ANA.

ANA expanded its programming to offer additional support to constituent associations in implementing economic and general welfare activities.

Ninety-nine registered nurses were certified by ANA for excellence in clinical nursing practice in geriatric and pediatric nursing in ambulatory care.

Three sets of standards were developed jointly by ANA's Division on Medical-Surgical Nursing Practice and specialty organizations: *Standards of Cardiovascular Nursing Practice, Standards of Nursing Practice: Operating Room,* and *Standards of Orthopedic Nursing Practice.*

The Commission on Nursing Education drafted standards for nursing education.

Twenty-six ANA members were selected for admission to the American Academy of Nursing.

ANA was awarded a major contract to develop criteria for measuring the quality and effectiveness of nursing care and to recommend ways in which nursing can participate in professional standards review organizations.

ANA received a $1 million grant to provide thirty-five graduate fellowships in nursing for registered nurses who are members of ethnic minorities. It is a six year project.

1975

ANA held formal ceremonies on January 6, 1975, to honor the first nurses certified by the association.

ANA hosted a second invitational conference on accreditation.

The Commission on Nursing Education completed details on a mechanism to approve nurse practitioner programs which are non-degree granting.

The Commission on Nursing Education formed a National Accreditation Board for Continuing Education Programs and a National Review Committee for Expanded Role Programs.

ANA's report, "Nursing and Long-Term Care: Toward Quality Care of the Aging," was officially presented to the Senate Subcommittee on Long-Term Care.

ANA established a fund to be used to promote ratification of the Equal Rights Amendment.

ANA's Division on Maternal and Child Health Nursing Practice and the Nurses' Association of the American College of Obstetricians and Gynecologists initiated a joint certification program in maternal, gynecological and neonatal nursing.

Ninety-two registered nurses in psychiatric and mental health nursing and twenty-six registered nurses in community health nursing were certified by the association.

ANA was approved for a general institutional assurance for the protection of human subjects by the Department of Health, Education, and Welfare, Office of Protection from Research Risks.

ANA endorsed a campaign for immunization update.

The International Council of Nurses accepted the invitation of the American Nurses' Association to host the council's quadrennial congress in 1981 in Kansas City, Missouri.

The American Academy of Nurses admitted thirty-three members.

1975 marked the seventy-fifth anniversary of the American Journal of Nursing Company.

At the request of the White House and the U. S. Department of State, ANA formed the Advisory Committee on Vietnamese Nursing Personnel.

ANA's Affirmative Action Task Force published "Affirmative Action Programming for the Nursing Profession Through the American Nurses' Association," a brochure outlining a model affirmative action plan.

The Congress for Nursing Practice revised the statements on scope of practice and the model practice act.

ANA's Division on Medical-Surgical Nursing Practice and the Emergency Department Nurses' Association published *Standards of Emergency Nursing Practice.*

ANA's Board of Directors established the Shirley Titus Award in recognition of individual nurse contributions to the association's economic and general welfare program.

In accord with a directive from the 1974 House of Delegates, ANA's Board of Directors approved a fee schedule for accreditation of continuing education activities of state nurses' associations, organizations with approval processes, colleges, and universities.

The Commission on Nursing Education and the Congress for Nursing Practice sponsored a meeting on the accreditation of continuing education programs in nursing and the implementation of standards of nursing practice.

ANA's Division on Medical-Surgical Nursing Practice formed a Task Force on Nursing in High Blood Pressure Control under the National Blood Pressure Education Program.

The executive committees of the ANA and the AMA met in Chicago to explore common concerns. The discussions included national health insurance, PSROs, National Joint Practice Commission and Joint Commission on Accreditation.

ANA's Affirmative Action Task Force held two regional conferences which focused on improving nursing care and health care delivery for ethnic/minority consumers and on promoting affirmative action programs in nursing.

During 1975, ANA published the following documents: *Standards for Nursing Education, Accreditation of Continuing Education in Nursing, Accreditation of Continuing Education Programs Preparing Nurses for Expanded Roles, Continuing Education in Nursing—Guidelines for State Voluntary and Mandatory Systems, Continuing Education in Nursing—Guidelines for Staff Development,* and *A Plan for Implementation of the Standards of Nursing Practice.*

Appendix II

Necessity of an American Nurses' Association

By Edith A. Draper
Superintendent of Illinois Training School, Chicago

I know that to every thinking woman amongst us the needs for a national organization are becoming more and more strongly realized, until now our success for the future depends upon our unity.

We have had a notable example set us, and should be willing to follow the lead of our cousins across the water, in the advancement of nursing.

We have, as a profession, just emerged from infancy and attained our majority, it being twenty-one years since first an English woman introduced the system of training nurses in this country. A passing tribute to Sister Helen, the first superintendent of Bellevue, would not come amiss now, and could she see to what proportions her seedling has grown she would, I am convinced, feel amply repaid for her endeavors.

We have gathered here from East and West, from far and near, actuated by the desire to take part in the World's Exhibition. It would be fitting to commemorate the time by adding our mite to the history of the Exhibition, and becoming a united organization, a body of women trained to be of unquestioned benefit to mankind and not lacking in love and sympathy for each other.

We represent a number of schools, our English friends are here to give us their experience and advice, the medical fraternity are ready to offer their support, and the way seems clear; our combined efforts will surely be crowned with success.

The difficulties to be encountered, one must truthfully admit, will be mainly of our own manufacture. What we need is energy of purpose, enthusiasm, a spirit of philanthropy more developed, and ambition to lift our profession to a height to which the eyes of the nation shall look up and not down. Nothing is more conducive to the ruination of a project than lukewarmness and a conservatism which does not look beyond individual benefits. These are our main hindrances, but not insurmountable ones, for though acknowledging these faults, we are aware of counterbalancing virtues and know that the day will come when America will be justly proud of this association of her countrywomen.

By a national association we mean a society with legal recognition, that every nurse who is a member of the same will be guaranteed for by the association and entitled to its benefits; and that we will be a recognized profession just as doctors are.

The objects to be attained would be schemes for professional and financial assistance and arrangements for conferences and lectures by meeting as frequently as possible we might gain a better knowledge of each other, which would result most undoubtedly in mutual appreciation, and consequently aid in the advancement of other schemes.

We have been accused, and with some justice, of envy, malice, and all uncharitableness toward each other; schools of one system antagonistic to schools of another, and nurses of the larger cities and hospitals looking with contempt upon nurses trained in the smaller places. Upon this petty, narrow-minded state, a quietus might be placed by the system of registering (for a standard of equality would be exacted), so that all members of the association would be considered equally competent as far as their technical knowledge went. To protect the public, the medical profession and ourselves, no better means have been suggested than this.

People may be spared, if they so desire, the imposition of the ignorant woman, who, not fit for anything else, is good enough for a nurse; from the so-called "natural nurse," who believes herself endowed from above with the necessary knowledge to undertake any case, no matter how critical, without wasting time on a preliminary training; from the rejected probationer, who endangers life with the infinitesimal scraps of information she has gleaned in a short stay in the hospital; and, lastly, from the woman who, expelled from her school for cause, pursues unchecked this means of livelihood.

To the many excellent women who have nursed successfully for years, without thorough training, it may seem an arbitrary measure that they should be excluded from the association; but if we are aiming at beneficial results to the many, the inconvenience to the few we may regret but cannot avoid.

I imagine we would all concur readily in deciding that the standard for membership be high; a certified diploma, at least two years training in a hospital, endorsements of work well done and testimonials of character above reproach, should be required.

As a means of discipline this association would prove a power. We might imitate the Society of Loyal Orangewomen, whose regulations state that a member will be fined or expelled who does not "behave as becometh a Orangewoman." An even more laudable undertaking would be the scheme for benefiting nurses in a financial way.

Notwithstanding the objections which have been raised on the score of patronage and the repugnance of the self-respecting toward anything savoring of charity, the assurance of material aid when overtaken by sickness, of a sufficiency to keep the wolf from the door when growing old and unable to discharge the arduous duties of a nurse any longer, would bring consolation and relief to many a weary worker.

In this country, though fairly well paid, nurses are not able to save to any great extent; whether the calls upon their slender means are too great or possibly through sickness or their own improvidence, the fact cannot be controverted that pecuniary aid is not infrequently needed by members of our profession, and I imagine would be received without any loss of self-respect.

The Alumnae Associations furnish help by drawing upon members, and such help is not considered degrading: why should a larger and more far-reaching fund be so regarded?

If we can help others by lending our aid to this undertaking we must put aside all feelings which may tend to obstruct its advance. The endowment of beds for nurses in hospitals would meet with the approval of any nurse who has been ill in a boarding-house, and those of us who have not experienced this nightmare should, selfishly speaking, be most anxious to give our aid, as fortune may not always deal so kindly with us, and the vicissitudes which have overtaken others may in time overtake us.

Another and equally important aim would be the promotion of conferences and lectures as often as practicable. Those thoroughly interested in the work would find a way to attend occasional meetings, and each State association might send one or more representatives, so that in business matters all might have a voice; and through the medium of a publication, those unable to attend might keep up their interest. To advance we must unite! Otherwise, factions will arise and stagnation result. We know that nurses who have graduated ten or twelve years ago feel that they are not keeping pace with the advancement of medicine and science; that the recent graduate is oftentimes preferred before them, though in experience she may be a child. What better help can we give these nurses than the promotion of lectures, theoretical and practical, the encouragement of publications pertaining to our needs, and the free interchange of all the newest and best ideas?

I have only touched lightly upon the many advantages to be obtained, and have not attempted any plan of organization. The subject is of vital interest to us all, and if I have succeeded in promoting its discussion my object has been attained.*

Biographical Note: Edith A. Draper was an 1884 graduate of Bellevue School of Nursing in New York City. Miss Draper participated in the organizational meeting of the Society of Superintendents of Training Schools for Nurses and was a member of the Society's Committee for the Organization of a National Association for Nurses which developed the constitution and bylaws of the Nurses' Associated Alumnae. She was also a contributor to the first volume of the *American Journal of Nursing.*

Upon leaving the Illinois Training School in Chicago in 1893, Miss Draper became the superintendent of nurses at the Royal Victoria Hospital in Montreal.

*Miss Draper's paper is printed in *Nursing of the Sick, 1893* by Isabel A. Hampton and others, published by McGraw-Hill Book Company, Inc. in 1949.

Appendix III

Executive Directors of the American Nurses' Association

In 1923, the American Nurses' Association appointed the first administrative officer of the national headquarters operation. Although the title of the position has varied from executive secretary to director of headquarters to executive director, the responsibilities of the position have remained the same: to administer the long and short-range plans and programs of the association as adopted by the House of Delegates and the board of directors, to oversee and coordinate staff activities, and to facilitate effective relations with constituent associations, government agencies, health and nursing organizations, and consumer groups.

Since 1923, six individuals have served in this capacity. Each one has made a significant contribution to the growth and development of the association. These individuals and their years of service are:

Agnes Deans, R.N. (1922 - 1927)

The first director of the American Nurses' Association was a pioneer in the field of public health nursing as well as in the development of the association. After graduation from the Farrand Training School, Harper Hospital, Detroit, Miss Deans held several supervisory positions in Detroit hospitals and established the Central Directory for Nurses in Detroit. During World War I, she served as assistant to the director of the American Red Cross Nursing Service. Miss Deans then became director of the Social Service Department of Washington University, St. Louis.

Miss Deans held a variety of positions in the Michigan State Nurses' Association, and was active in developing a nurse practice act in that state. She held several positions with the national association and was one of the leaders in the reorganization of ANA and its component units.

Miss Deans died March 14, 1948, after a long illness.

Janet Geister, R.N. (1927 - 1933)

Born in Illinois, Janet Geister graduated from the Sherman Hospital School of Nursing, Elgin, Illinois, and studied further at the Chicago School of Civics and Philanthropy. Her nursing practice included private duty nursing as well as public health nursing. She participated in conducting several major surveys related to nursing, and served as field secretary and educational secretary of the National Organization for Public Health Nursing.

Miss Geister's interests also included journalism. She was editor of *Trained Nurse and Hospital Review,* and she later served as consultant and contributor to *RN Magazine.* Miss Geister served the American Nurses' Association in a variety of capacities, including first vice president and member of the board of directors, as well as director of the headquarters office.

Miss Geister died December 8, 1964, after a short illness.

Alma H. Scott, R.N. (acting, 1933 - 1934; 1935 - 1946)

Alma Scott is a native of Indiana and a graduate of the Presbyterian Hospital School of Nursing in Chicago. She worked as a private duty nurse and hospital supervisor and served with the Army Nurse Corps in France during World War I. She later held positions with the Indiana State Board of Examination and Registration for Nurses and with the Indiana State Nurses' Association before joining the staff of the American Nurses' Association as field secretary in 1929.

Following her years as director of headquarters, Mrs. Scott served on the ANA Board of Directors and on several ANA committees, notably as chairperson of the committee dealing with the ANA Professional Counseling and Placement Service, Inc., which she was instrumental in establishing.

Ella Best, R.N. (1946 - 1958)

Ella Best came to the American Nurses' Association from Chicago, where she had graduated from St. Luke's Hospital School of Nursing and had worked as an administrator and a teacher. Her postgraduate education included work at both Teachers College, Columbia University, and the University of Chicago.

Miss Best joined the ANA staff in 1930 as field secretary and retired after twelve years as headquarters director (executive secretary) in 1958. During her 28 years of service to the Association, she traveled extensively in this country and abroad, representing ANA to the International Council of Nurses and serving as a consultant to the Surgeon General of the United States Air Force and as a civilian consultant to the Army Nurse Corps.

Judith Whitaker, R.N. (1958 - 1969)

Judith Whitaker is a graduate of the Nebraska Methodist School of Nursing and earned both her baccalaureate and master's degrees from Teachers College, Columbia University. Her background includes work in public health nursing and in several positions on the staff of the Nebraska Nurses' Association.

Mrs. Whitaker traveled extensively in her work for ANA as both deputy executive secretary and executive director. She served as a member of the Department of Defense Advisory Committee, as a consultant to the Army Nurse Corps, and as a board member of the National Citizens Committee for the World Health Organization. From 1961 to 1963, she served on the Surgeon General's Consultant Group on Nursing which produced the report, *Toward Quality in Nursing: Needs and Goals.*

Mrs. Whitaker is currently associate professor of continuing education in the School of Nursing at the State University of New York.

Eileen M. Jacobi, Ed.D., R.N. (1970 - 1976)

Eileen Jacobi received her diploma in nursing from Cumberland Hospital School of Nursing, Brooklyn, New York, and was awarded her baccalaureate and master's degrees from Adelphi University. In 1968, Dr. Jacobi was awarded a doctorate of educational administration from Teachers College, Columbia University. She pursued postgraduate studies at the New York University and William Alanson White

Institute of Psychiatry. Dr. Jacobi has held faculty positions at Teachers College, Columbia University, and at Adelphi University, where she also served as professor and dean of the School of Nursing. She has served as psychiatric nursing consultant at both Columbia Teachers College and the New York City Veterans Administration Hospital, and has been associated with several other health agencies in the New York area.

Prior to joining ANA staff as assistant executive director in 1969, Dr. Jacobi was an active participant in the work of the New York State Nurses' Association and several other professional associations as well as in the work of the American Nurses' Association. She has served as consultant to various agencies, including the National Center for Health Services Research and Development and the World Health Organization, and to the Surgeons General of both the Army and the Navy Nurse Corps.

In November, 1975, Boston University's School of Nursing presented Dr. Jacobi with a Merit Award for Distinguished Service.

Dr. Jacobi served as executive director from 1970 to 1976. She accepted an appointment as professor and dean of the School of Nursing at the University of Texas in El Paso, effective September 1976.

Appendix IV

Characteristics of the Six National Nursing Organizations

(as of April, 1950)

Organization	Year Established	Types of Membership	Membership Count	State and Local Units	Voting Body	Governing Body
NLNE	1893	Individual Nurse and Non-Nurse	10,000	42 states, District of Columbia, Hawaii, and Puerto Rico 59 local leagues	Membership	Board of Directors 4 officers 8 directors 4 ex-officio directors
ANA	1897	Individual Nurse	171,000	48 states, District of Columbia, Hawaii, and Puerto Rico	House of Delegates	Board of Directors 5 officers 8 directors Chairmen of sections
NACGN	1908	Individual Nurse and Non-Nurse	1,700	12 states 106 local units	Membership	Board of Directors 7 officers 9 directors
NOPHN	1912	Individual Nurse and Non-Nurse Agencies	10,000 400	19 states	Membership	Board of Directors 31 directors of whom 5 are officers
ACSN	1933	Collegiate Schools	43	–	Membership (delegate from each school)	Board of Directors 4 officers 3 directors
AAIN	1942	Individual Nurse	2,500	6 state associations and 40 local chapters working in harmony with AAIN, but not as units of AAIN	Membership	Executive Board 7 officers 12 directors

Appendix V

Joint Statements of ANA and NLN

Working Relationships Between American Nurses' Association and National League for Nursing

The American Nurses' Association and the National League for Nursing as cooperating organizations in the field of nursing have the need to examine periodically the fundamental premises on which they will work together and serve society. While they are totally different organizations in both responsibilities and structure, they are complementary in purpose and function.

The American Nurses' Association, as the professional organization, is moving to fulfill those functions of standard setting for education, practice and organized services traditionally carried by professional organizations. In the development and modification of such standards, ANA secures consultation and advice from NLN and elsewhere, but retains responsibility for deciding the final content. Normally, standards are in advance of current practice. They are authoritative, based on the expertise of the profession. ANA works through its members and its constituencies, with NLN, and with a variety of organizations and governmental bodies to implement these standards.

The National League for Nursing, composed of individuals, educational institutions, and nursing service agencies, is the organization to which the profession and the public look for services to promote and to improve nursing education programs and organized nursing services.

These activities of NLN include among others accreditation, consultations, and involvement of educational programs and service agencies in programs of self-improvement. In planning and conducting such services, NLN involves its appropriate membership in the development of criteria for the purpose of evaluation. Such criteria and related guides must reflect the broad standards enunciated by ANA and the goals of the profession. NLN studies the application of criteria and their implications for standards and practice for education and for organized nursing services. These findings are shared with ANA. In these ways, the two organizations are complementary, each with distinctive responsibilities and both necessary in meeting society's needs for nursing service.

The needs of the profession and the needs of the public for nursing service are different in 1966 from those of 1952 when a design for function and structure of both organizations was adopted. Change in the demands upon both organizations has caused each to examine its own functions and structure, and its relationship with the other. It is essential that ANA and NLN work cooperatively in areas of common concern as each builds its program in full recognition of the role of the other.*

Complementary Relationship of American Nurses' Association and National League for Nursing

The American Nurses' Association and the National League for Nursing as cooperating organizations in the field of nursing have the need to examine periodically the fundamental premises on which they will work together and serve society. While they are totally different organizations in both responsibilities and structure, they are complementary in purpose and function.

The American Nurses' Association, as the professional organization of registered nurses, sets standards for nursing education, nursing practice and organized nursing services. In the development and modification of standards, ANA secures consultation and advice from

*Approved by ANA and NLN Boards of Directors, January 1966.

NLN and other sources, but retains responsibility for deciding the final content. ANA works to implement these standards through its members and its constituents, with the NLN, and with a variety of other organizations and government bodies.

ANA represents the official voice of American nurses with other professions, community organizations, and the International Council of Nurses. ANA speaks for registered nurses on legislative matters concerning health, education, and general welfare of people. ANA protects the economic and general welfare of nurses and promotes their professional development.

The National League for Nursing links the interests of organized nursing with those of the community through its membership of *individuals,* drawn from all ranks of nursing personnel, the allied professions, and the community, and *agencies,* which are educational institutions and providers of nursing service. NLN works to help communities improve the nursing services and education programs they need by offering services in accreditation, consultation, testing, research, and publications. The programs carried out by its constituent leagues foster community planning for nursing as a primary component of comprehensive health care. NLN observes nursing in action and shares its findings with ANA.

The needs of the profession and the needs of the public for nursing service are different from those of 1952 when a design for function and structure of both organizations was adopted. Change in the demands upon both organizations has caused each to examine its own functions and structure, and its relationship with the other. It is essential that ANA and NLN work cooperatively in areas of common concern as each builds its program in full recognition of the role of the other.*

*Adopted by ANA and NLN Boards of Directors, September 1970.
Reaffirmed by ANA and NLN Boards of Directors, May 1973.

Appendix VI

ANA's Stand on National Health Insurance and Related Issues

(Note: In order to fully comprehend ANA's involvement in national health insurance, it is important to review ANA's position on issues directly related to health insurance coverage and the restructuring of the health care system.)

Since it was organized in 1896, the American Nurses' Association has demonstrated an interest in and concern for the provision of health services, as well as for the giving of nursing care.

1. ANA and the Social Security System

The ANA has always supported the Old Age, Survivors and Disability Insurance Program. With the exception of those nurses employed as occupational health nurses in covered industries, nurses were not eligible to participate in the Social Security Retirement Program until 1950. This was made possible in some measure by the continued and determined efforts of the ANA. A plank in the association's platform committed the association to support the extension and improvement of the Social Security System.

2. ANA and Prepaid Health Insurance

As early as 1936, the ANA began studying and formulating principles in regard to the inclusion of nursing services in prepaid health care. In conjunction with the National Organization for Public Health Nursing, ANA organized (in 1946) a Joint Committee on Nursing in Prepayment

Health Plans. In 1950, the committee published the *Guide for the Inclusion of Nursing Service in Medical Care Plans.* At that time, both the ANA and the NOPHN stated they did not support or oppose legislation then in Congress to establish a government health insurance program. Earlier, belief in the principle of prepayment for health services had been affirmed, as well as the belief that the consumer, the American public, should decide the mechanism for providing health insurance.

In 1952, the ANA House of Delegates adopted the following resolution:

WHEREAS, the ANA in its 1952 platform has reiterated the policy adopted in 1950 of "promoting the inclusion of nursing benefits in prepaid health and medical care plans," and

WHEREAS, significant developments have occurred since 1950 in our efforts to provide health protection for the American people, as evidenced by the fact that 21 states now have committees on nursing in medical care plans, and

WHEREAS, another significant development has been the introduction by several large insurance companies of a new medical care insurance policy which includes as one of its benefits the services of registered nurses, and

WHEREAS, the American nurses desire to remain free to provide nursing service in any prepaid health and medical care plan the American people adopt, be it therefore

Resolved, That this House of Delegates reaffirm the principle that registered nurses shall, without fear or favor, enjoy their rights and privileges as individual citizens to express their views and to make decisions regarding any prepaid health and medical care plan which is consistent with the basic American Nurses' Association policy of promoting and improving nursing care for the American people.

3. Extension of the Social Security System to Provide Health Insurance for Recipients of Old Age and Survivors Insurance.

Between 1952 and 1957, no legislation was introduced that proposed a governmental program of prepaid health insurance. In 1957, legislation was introduced that would have provided a means of payment for the hospital, nursing home, and surgical services of recipients of old age and survivors insurance. During the productive working years, employer and employee would contribute like amounts, and, on retirement, the employee would have a paid up health insurance policy.

The ANA Committee on Legislation reviewed the 1952 position of the association, studied the legislation, and introduced the following resolution which was adopted by the House of Delegates at the 1958 convention:

> WHEREAS, necessary health services should be available to all people in this country without regard to their ability to purchase, and
>
> WHEREAS, prepayment through insurance has become a major and an effective method of financing health services, and
>
> WHEREAS, certain groups in our population, particularly the disabled, retired and aged, are neither eligible nor able to avail themselves of voluntary health insurance, be it therefore
>
> **Resolved,** That the American Nurses' Association support the extension and improvement of the contributory social insurance to include health insurance for beneficiaries of Old Age, Survivors and Disability Insurance; and be it further
>
> **Resolved,** That nursing services, including nursing care in the home, be included as a benefit of any prepaid health insurance program.

During the two-year interval between conventions, individual nurses and the constituent state nurses' associations of the ANA were again subjected to considerable pressure by members of the American Nurses' Association. At the convention in 1960, a resolution was brought to the House of Delegates by one state nurses' association asking that ANA change its position in support of the principle included in the 1958 resolution. However, the House reaffirmed the 1958 position by an overwhelming majority of the 1,200 voting delegates, with less than 50 dissenting votes.

In 1962, the ANA House of Delegates indicated its continuing interest in the extension of the social security system by reaffirming the 1958 resolution.

Several changes were made in the social security program in 1965. A major change was the addition to the system of a health insurance program for persons age 65 and over (Medicare) and the related program for medically indigent known as Medicaid.

At the 1966 convention, the House of Delegates adopted the following resolution recommended by the ANA board supporting implementation of the Social Security Amendments enacted in 1965:

WHEREAS, The American Nurses' Association develops and works for implementation of standards to insure high quality nursing services for all, and

WHEREAS, The American Nurses' Association actively supported the extension of the social security system to include health insurance for the aged, and promoted the inclusion of payment for nursing services in the health insurance program, and

WHEREAS, The Social Security Amendments of 1965 were enacted and include payment for nursing services, and

WHEREAS, The law provides safeguards to protect quality care and the regulations governing the legislation carry through this intent of Congress, and

WHEREAS, The American Nurses' Association has a continuing commitment in the implementation of this program and an obligation to work with agencies of government and providers of services to advance the program of health insurance for the aged, and

WHEREAS, The Social Security Amendments of 1965 further commit the nation to health care as a right of all people, of all ages, without regard to their ability to pay, therefore be it

Resolved, That the American Nurses' Association work for the efficient utilization of all nursing personnel and continue its efforts to provide the means whereby practitioners may render high quality nursing service, and be it further

Resolved, That the American Nurses' Association support the efforts of agencies of government as they administer the Social Security Amendments of 1965 and work with other governmental, community, and professional groups in planning for the establishment of needed services.

Over the period when hearings were held by committees of Congress on legislation based on the principle of extending the social security system to provide health insurance for the aged, ANA presented testimony supporting the principle. Specific proposals were critically analyzed. With some of these ANA disagreed or suggested modification or refinement.

Throughout the years, the ANA, in supporting the principle of the Social Security System to provide health insurance for the aged and disabled, has reiterated its belief that all health insurance programs should provide nursing service and that the nursing service should be provided by or under the supervision of professional registered nurses. Furthermore, the ANA has stated its belief that funds collected through the social security mechanism should not be used to pay the cost of inferior services. Quality standards should be set up that must be adhered to by the venders of service. This position has been maintained to date.

4. Comprehensive Health Planning and Partnership for Health

The passage of Medicare in 1965 pinpointed problems in the delivery of health services. In an effort to help health agencies to strengthen and expand services to the public, legislation was introduced in Congress in 1966. The proposals authorized grants for comprehensive health planning and public health services and required that each state set up one agency to administer the planning programs. It also provided project grants for regional or local planning; training and demonstration projects to schools of public health; consultation service to state or local public health agencies; training of personnel for state or local health work; and exchange of personnel between the states and the Department of Health, Education, and Welfare.

ANA endorsed the principles inherent in the Comprehensive Health Planning Act which became law in November 1966. The statement in support of the bill called attention to the need for an integrated generalized program.

The Comprehensive Health Planning Act was amended in 1967 by the Partnership for Health Amendments, and the provisions of the bill which ANA supported were: grants for comprehensive health planning and public services; the extension and expansion of formula grants to schools of public health; improvement and broadening of the authorization for research and demonstration projects relating to the delivery of health services; and cooperation of medical care facilities and resources.

At the 1968 biennial convention, a resolution regarding nurses in comprehensive health planning, which called for the assistance of state and district nurses' associations in implementing the Comprehensive

Health Planning and Public Health Services Amendment of 1966, was adopted:

WHEREAS, Nurses have broad and diversified knowledge and competencies with a strong sense of responsibility for the health needs of the community, and

WHEREAS, Nurses represent the largest health manpower groups, and

WHEREAS, Comprehensive health planning legislation has serious implications for nursing and health care, therefore be it

Resolved, That ANA support comprehensive health planning and recognize the necessity for providing effective leadership and participation, and be it

Resolved, That this House of Delegates urge state and district nurses' associations to strive for official representation on the advisory councils for comprehensive health planning, and be it

Resolved, That this House of Delegates urge state and district nurses' associations to take active steps insuring the participation of nurses as consultants or staff in state and regional planning agencies, and be it further

Resolved, That all levels of this Association utilize educational opportunities for preparing nurses to participate in comprehensive health planning.

5. Restructuring of the Health Care System

At the 1970 biennial convention, a number of resolutions, including one on national health insurance, were adopted. These resolutions called for a restructuring of the health care system and greater utilization of nurses.

Resolution on National Priority

WHEREAS, The delivery of health care is not currently available to all citizens, and

WHEREAS, Current fiscal allowances in the federal budget do not permit adequate delivery of health care, be it therefore

Resolved, That (a) The ANA again emphasize its belief that quality health care is a right for all persons, not a privilege for the few, and continue to visibly support all measures to obtain this end, and that (b) The ANA vigorously pressure the government to redefine its priorities so that health care for its citizens be a first priority.

Resolution on Availability and Utilization of Nursing Personnel

WHEREAS, Every person in this society has a right to optimum care when he needs it, and

WHEREAS, The profession of nursing historically has acted to meet health needs of people in all times and places, when and wherever needed, civilian and military, therefore be it

Resolved, That the American Nurses' Association affirm once again its primary responsibility and ever-continuing commitment to serve the people of this nation at all times and in all places, and be it further

Resolved, That all levels of the American Nurses' Association redouble efforts to assure availability and effective utilization of nursing personnel toward the worthy aim that the health care needs of all men be met.

Resolution Regarding National Health Insurance Program

WHEREAS, Nursing care is an essential component of health care, and

WHEREAS, The American Nurses' Association has long recognized health care as a right of all people, and

WHEREAS, High costs of essential health services stand in the way of effective delivery of health services to large numbers of people in this country, and

WHEREAS, There are limitations to coverage now provided through voluntary and other social insurance and tax-funded medical care programs, and

WHEREAS, On a national basis the present provision of health services is fragmentary, uncoordinated and incomplete, therefore be it

Resolved, That the ANA be responsible for the introduction of legislation on a national health insurance program, and be it

Resolved, That such insurance program include a restructuring of our present system so that there will be improved utilization of manpower and more effective incentives for the delivery of health care services into a national, cohesive base for meeting the health needs of society.

Resolution Regarding Nurses' Involvement in Delivery of Ambulatory Health Care Services

WHEREAS, Awareness and consideration of consumers' needs by providers of service in relation to the amounts, types, hours, and locations of health services can result in improved health practices and better use of these services, and

WHEREAS, Coordination of health care services can overcome further barriers to use of needed health facilities, and

WHEREAS, There is a need for the development of a variety of types of ambulatory health programs and services that are available, accessible and acceptable to the people, therefore be it

Resolved, That the American Nurses' Association urge nurses to participate actively in stimulating and developing effective systems of delivery of ambulatory care services, and

Resolved, That the American Nurses' Association urge nurses to share their knowledge of community needs and to take an active role in devising and implementing practical and realistic approaches to delivery of ambulatory care services.

Resolution Regarding Use of Registered Nurses in Supervision of Nursing

WHEREAS, It is the stated objective of the American Nurses' Association to promote high standards of nursing practice in order to provide the public with quality nursing services, and

WHEREAS, The safety of patients will be jeopardized if assessing, supervising, planning, and directing of nursing care for patients is provided by persons with less preparation than that of a registered nurse, and

WHEREAS, Persons other than registered nurses are being utilized in leadership positions such as head nurse and team leader positions, all of which carry a direct responsibility for evaluating nursing needs of patients, therefore be it

Resolved, That the American Nurses' Association opposes the use of persons other than registered nurses in leadership positions such as head nurse, charge nurse and team leader positions, and

Resolved, That the American Nurses' Association strongly supports nursing service administrators in utilizing only registered nurses in leadership positions.

Resolution on Utilization of Nurses in Hospital Settings

WHEREAS, Society is entitled to the optimum in quantity and quality of nursing care, and
WHEREAS, Hospitalized persons are being denied skilled nursing services because systems existing in hospitals require that nurses spend a large part of their time in activities not related to direct patient care, and
WHEREAS, The public is being denied adequate nursing services because the present system commonly denies nurses the opportunities to practice at the level of their preparation, and
WHEREAS, Nurses are expected to assume their nursing responsibilities, therefore be it
Resolved, That ANA support nurse practitioners and nursing service administrators in exercising their prerogatives to determine the functions of nurses appropriate to the level of their preparation and their demonstrated capabilities, and be it further
Resolved, That ANA support the nurse practitioner in refusing to accept responsibility for those functions which should be carried by other departments or groups in hospital settings.

Resolution on Health Care Costs

WHEREAS, There is concern over health care costs, and
WHEREAS, Increasing use of health facilities and professional services, increasing salaries for personnel, and rising costs of equipment and supplies are factors in the rising costs, and
WHEREAS, Many components of health care costs are beyond the control of nursing, there are cost factors which nurses directly or indirectly affect, and
WHEREAS, The members of the ANA are concerned that safe and effective nursing care be available at reasonable costs to all persons, therefore be it
Resolved, That the ANA encourage every member to consider the following ways in which nurses may help to control the costs of health care:

1. Seek more efficient and economical systems for the delivery of nursing services based upon careful study and research,
2. Exercise responsibility for controlling costs in terms of supplies and equipment and utilization of health care facilities,
3. Improve personnel utilization through study, education and implementation of more efficient staffing patterns,
4. Interpret cost factors to the consumer regarding essential and nonessential services.

Resolution on the Extended Role of the Nurse

WHEREAS, The traditional roles of the physician and the nurse have become blurred and less circumscribed as the demands of people for a multiplicity of health care services have burgeoned, and

WHEREAS, The acute critical shortage of health professionals will continue for some time to come, and

WHEREAS, A variety of health careers, supportive to medicine and nursing, continue to evolve in response to health manpower needs, and

WHEREAS, The supervisory controls essential to quality health care of people are needed, and

WHEREAS, The appropriate roles and functions of these emerging health careerists are ill-defined and tend to infringe upon the practice of medicine and of nursing, be it

Resolved, That the American Nurses' Association intensify dialogue with members of the American Medical Association and other professional societies to examine the respective roles of physicians and nurses and those of the other health careerists, in order to utilize all health personnel more safely, effectively, productively, and economically in meeting the total health needs of people.

Resolution on Planning for Health Manpower

WHEREAS, Planning for comprehensive health care involves development of new approaches to the delivery of health services, and

WHEREAS, Provision of adequate health manpower is an essential

component for effective health care planning, and
WHEREAS, Critical shortages exist in all areas of health manpower, and
WHEREAS, New types of health workers are being introduced without any evidence of coordinated, long-range planning or clearly defined roles, which often results in fragmentation of patient care, and
WHEREAS, The assessment of the need for assistants to nursing and the removal of non-nursing activities from the practice of nursing is essential for effective utilization of nursing skills, therefore be it
Resolved, That the ANA seek active participation with groups studying new approaches to the delivery of health services, and be it further
Resolved, That the ANA seek active involvement in assessing the need for and defining the scope of practice for new health workers, and be it further
Resolved, That the ANA take positive action in the following areas:

1. Establishing the right of the nursing profession to determine its own scope of the practice of nursing with continued efforts to remove non-nursing activities from the practice of nursing,
2. Defining appropriate education and training for assistants to nursing,
3. Retaining for nurses the responsibility for nursing care.

As a result of the resolutions passed by the 1970 House of Delegates, one of ANA's main objectives between 1970 and 1972 was to develop a comprehensive position and plan of action on the issue of national health insurance. (Unfortunately, ANA's financial problems between 1970-72 precluded the substantial commitment of staff and financial resources required to write legislation.)

In 1971, *A Statement of Essential Elements of a Health Care System* was developed. The statement's thirteen points charged the federal government with the responsibility to guarantee adequate health care through legislation and to establish national standards governing health insurance coverage. ANA further recommended a partnership between government and the private sector to finance the health care system. Addressing itself to the general educational system, the statement called for health manpower of all types in sufficient numbers and joint planning by all health professions for recruitment, preparation, utilization, and compensation. It pointed out the need for special incentives to bring about deployment of health manpower to those areas where there is scarce supply. And it supported a continued system of state licensure to facilitate interstate movement and optimum utilization of the professional nursing function.

In 1971, a *Statement on Catastrophic Health Insurance* was developed which stressed the need to make catastrophic health insurance as one element of a comprehensive health insurance program.

During 1971 and 1972, ANA presented testimony regarding national health insurance on several occasions. ANA's testimony made the primary point that a national program must be comprehensive and include preventive, health maintenance, diagnostic, treatment, restorative, and protective services. ANA pointed out that the nation's total health system could be made more economical and more effective by promotion of all kinds of preventive and maintenance services, by expansion of the nurse's role in primary care and by enlargement of the health manpower complement and its potential through increased public support for both basic and continuing education. To implement a fully integrated and equitable system, the association made several specific recommendations:

—Federal funding and greater authority should be given to health care planning agencies.

—Consumer participation should be sought in identifying health needs.

—Any corporate structure set up to coordinate and deliver health care should have an overall board composed of consumers and providers of services and should be free of domination by any one institution, agency, or group of professional practitioners.

—A major effort should be made to deliver health care to those who have been denied it for economic, social, or geographic reasons.

—Provision should be made for peer review of quality of care. Standards of care for each profession would be developed by its practitioners, but assessment of the total effectiveness of care would be a collaborative responsibility.

—Any program for health maintenance should be under public or non-profit auspices.

At the 1972 convention, a number of resolutions were adopted which dealt with issues of comprehensive health care services:

Resolution on Protecting the Rights of Children and Adolescents

WHEREAS, The ANA and NLN Boards of Directors have gone on record as supporting the major recommendations and goals of the Joint Commission on Mental Health of Children, and

WHEREAS, At least 10 million persons under the age of 25 are thought to suffer from mental and emotional disorders, and

WHEREAS, Nursing professionals have not been utilized in accord with their potential for maintaining and delivering health care to children and adolescents, and

WHEREAS, Nurses have numerous points of entry to influence the care of children which can become strategic positions for working with children, families and community agencies, and

WHEREAS, Nurses have not been sufficiently involved in planning for social and legislative change, be it therefore

Resolved, That the American Nurses' Association encourage the development of educational programs through the appropriate agencies which will prepare nurses to function as child advocates and to assume responsibility for a primary role in health assessment, planning intervention and evaluation, and be it

Resolved, That the American Nurses' Association vigorously promote and support the implementation of quality health care programs, especially mental health for school and preschool-age children, and be it further

Resolved, That the American Nurses' Association move promptly to require that the present Administration and legislative officials quickly develop legislation and funding for an effective comprehensive health care program which includes provision for dental and mental health and day care programs for school and preschool-age children.

Resolution on Peer Review

WHEREAS, There is a nationwide problem of malpractice in

health care that is commanding the attention of providers and consumers of health care, of government, the legal profession, and the insurance industry, and

WHEREAS, Serious questions are being raised about the impact of claims upon the cost and quality of health care, the costs of insurance and methods of handling allegations of substandard treatment and care, and

WHEREAS, The Code for Nurses provides that the nurse act to safeguard the patient, assume responsibility for maintaining competence, and use individual competence as a criterion in accepting delegated responsibilities and in assigning nursing activities to others; therefore be it

Resolved, That in every health care facility in which nurses practice, there be provisions for continuing peer review as one means of maintaining standards of nursing practice, and be it further

Resolved, That in every health care facility there be provisions for nurses to participate in utilization review activities related to facilities, personnel, and services and other arrangements for monitoring health care practices, and be it further

Resolved, That where arbitration is the method used to arrive at judgments on questions of malpractice, nurses serve on arbitration panels in those instances where the actions of nurses are in any way involved.

Resolution on Third-Party Payment for Nurses' Services

WHEREAS, The independent practice of professional nurses is expanding in many areas, and

WHEREAS, It is the right of professional nurses to order and direct nurses' services, and

WHEREAS, The public is entitled to contract for and know the charges made for nurses' services they receive, therefore be it

Resolved, That all health care organizations and representative individuals be urged to identify the charges made for nurses' services, and further, insurers be urged to include provisions in prepaid health plans for the payment of charges for nurses' services.

Resolution on Preparation for Primary Health Care Practice

WHEREAS, Health care is the right of all people, and

WHEREAS, Professional nursing includes promotion of health, prevention of illness and disability, and actions which help in the restoration to maximum wellness and function, and

WHEREAS, Primary health care encompasses these functions of professional nursing, therefore be it

Resolved, That all programs in nursing which prepare nurses for professional practice provide learning opportunities in the basic curriculum for competence in primary health care practice, and be it further

Resolved, That schools of nursing education for professional practice provide learning opportunities through programs of continuing education to enable registered nurses, active and inactive, to augment their knowledge and skills sufficiently to be competent as practitioners who give primary health care.

6. Health Maintenance Organizations

As a means of reforming the health delivery system, both the Administration and several members of Congress have promoted legislation to stimulate the development of health maintenance organizations through planning and development grants.

Health maintenance organizations are, in effect, prepaid group practice plans. Though they provide the full range of health and illness services, they stress prevention and health maintenance, as a practical means of reducing the burden of illness, decreasing the use of intensive care facilities, and cutting the overall cost of health services.

In testimony delivered in 1972, ANA expressed its approval of health maintenance organizations under public or nonprofit auspices that incorporate the recommendations outlined in ANA testimony on national health insurance.

A number of different bills were developed during the past two years to encourage the development of Health Maintenance Organizations. ANA has to closely monitor HMO legislation as it went through numerous changes and drafts in order to see that nurses were named specifically in the final version as one of the health professional groups essential for the basic health services to be offered by HMOs.

7. National Health Insurance Legislation

Between 1972 and early 1974, many proposals for a national health insurance program were introduced, but other concerns occupied the attention of Congress. There was little action in regard to national health insurance in 1973, though brief hearings of a general nature were held late in the year by the House Subcommittee on Health. The Senate Finance Committee, to which national health insurance bills are referred on the Senate side, was preoccupied throughout much of 1972 with proposals for a massive revision of the Social Security Act.

In February, 1974, the Administration completed its long-awaited health insurance proposal, and it was introduced in Congress by Rep. Wilbur Mills (D-Ark.), Chairman of the House Ways and Means Committee. The proposal, the Comprehensive Health Insurance Plan, actually includes three plans: (1) an employee plan to be offered by employers who would pay 75 percent of premium costs and the employee 25 percent; (2) an assisted plan for low-income, unemployed or high-risk individuals and (3) Medicare which would be continued and revised for those 65 years of age and older.

One of two other proposals considered likely to receive the most attention was the National Health Security Act introduced by Senator Edward M. Kennedy (D-Mass.) and Rep. Martha Griffiths (D-Mich.). The most comprehensive of the bills, it would establish a broad system for health care to cover the entire population, federally administered and financed by general revenues and payroll taxes. Another proposal, the Catastrophic Health Insurance and Medical Assistance Reform Act introduced by Senators Russell Long (D-La.), Chairman of the Senate Finance Committee, and Abraham Ribicoff (D-Conn.), would provide a catastrophic illness coverage to social security enrollees and their dependents, and would replace Medicaid with a uniform program for low-income persons, administered by the Social Security Administration.

At the 1974 biennial convention, the ANA House of Delegates endorsed a set of 1974-76 association priorities which would enable ANA to assume a more aggressive role in the development and execution of national health policy. Delegates also adopted a specific resolution on national health insurance:

WHEREAS, Health, a state of physical, social and mental well-being, is a basic right, and

WHEREAS, Government at all levels must act to insure that health care services are provided for all citizens, and
WHEREAS, There is a need for integrated systems to deliver comprehensive health care services that are accessible and acceptable to all people without regard to age, sex, race, social, or economic condition, and
WHEREAS, There is a need for a national program designed to correct serious inadequacies in present health care delivery systems, and
WHEREAS, Nursing care is an essential component of health care, therefore be it
Resolved, That the American Nurses' Association aggressively work for the enactment of legislation to establish a program of national health insurance benefits, and be it further
Resolved, That the national health insurance program guarantee coverage of all people for the full range of comprehensive health services, and be it further
Resolved, That the scope of benefits be clearly defined so that they can be understood by beneficiaries and providers alike, and be it further
Resolved, That the national health program clearly recognize the distinctions between health care and medical care; and that the plan provide options in utilization of health care services that are not necessarily dependent on the physician, and be it further
Resolved, That nursing care be a benefit of the national health program, and be it further
Resolved, That the data systems necessary for effective management of the national insurance program protect the rights and privacy of individuals, and be it further
Resolved, That the plan include provisions for peer review of services that will protect the right and the responsibility of each health care discipline to monitor the practice of its own practitioners, and be it further
Resolved, That there continue to be a system of individual licensure for the practice of nursing, and be it further
Resolved, That provision be made for consumer participation in periodic evaluation of the national health insurance program, and be it further

Resolved, That the national health insurance program be financed through payroll taxes or payment of premiums by the self-employed, and purchase of health insurance coverage for the poor and unemployed from general tax revenues, and be it further

Resolved, That ANA strongly urge the designation of nurses as health providers in all pending or proposed legislation on national health insurance.

Other relevant resolutions adopted at the 1974 biennial convention include:

Resolution on Participation of Nurses in Professional Standards Review Programs

WHEREAS, Nurses contribute a major way to the health and illness care of people, and

WHEREAS, Nurses are responsible, accountable and liable for the quality of their practice, and

WHEREAS, The outcomes of medical care are frequently influenced by the contribution of nursing, and

WHEREAS, Medical care is but one part of the totality of health care, therefore be it

Resolved, That the American Nurses' Association identify and seek legislative support for the participation and contribution of nurses on behalf of their own practice in Professional Standards Review Organization Programs, as currently established by P.L. 92-603, and, be it further

Resolved, That ANA encourage state and district nurses' associations to actively participate at all levels of PSRO.

Resolution on the Nurse as a Primary Health Care Provider

WHEREAS, It has been recognized at the highest levels of government and by the professional nurses' association that society has a right to optimal health care and health maintenence, and

WHEREAS, A major focus of professional nursing is the promotion of high-level wellness, and

WHEREAS, Professional nurses are prepared to provide this dimension of health care, and

WHEREAS, Members of society are entitled to the most effective and economical use of highly skilled health manpower; therefore be it

Resolved, That the American Nurses' Association vigorously support the concept of the nurse as a primary health care provider and, be it further

Resolved, That the ANA Congress for Nursing Practice be directed to establish guidelines for nursing practice in primary care-giving situations; and be it further

Resolved, That the American Nurses' Association and the constituent associations actively work to effect legislation which recognizes nursing as a major discipline for meeting the health needs of society's members.

Resolution on Third-Party Payment

WHEREAS, The state of being sound in body, mind, and spirit constitutes the condition of good health, and health care should be a basic human right, and

WHEREAS, Nursing care is an essential component of comprehensive health care consisting of preventive, health maintenance, diagnostic treatment, and restorative and preventive services, and

WHEREAS, It is in the public interest to provide to all people unrestricted access to nursing services, and the nursing profession bears primary responsibility for guaranteeing to all people unconditional access to nursing services, and

WHEREAS, Access to nursing services is currently severely restricted by reimbursement policies and procedures used by public and private third-party payors for reimbursing consumers and providers, and

WHEREAS, In January 1974, the ANA Commission on Economic and General Welfare at its meeting adopted a statement supporting third-party payments for reimbursing nursing care services rendered by independent nurse practitioners, therefore be it

Resolved, That the American Nurses' Association and its constituents vigorously continue efforts to pursue all avenues at the federal and state level to effect unconditional recognition of direct fee-for-service reimbursement for nursing practitioners by both public and private third party payors.

In November 1973, ANA accepted a request from Sen. Frank E. Moss (D-Utah) to prepare a report regarding the problems of providing skilled nursing care in intermediate and extended care facilities. Sen. Moss' request came after a hearing October 10 by the Senate Subcommittee on Long-Term Care, Special Committee on Aging, at which ANA presented testimony on proposed regulations for skilled nursing care in intermediate and skilled nursing care facilities.

In 1974, ANA presented testimony before the House Ways and Means Committee urging coverage of nursing services of qualified independent nurse practitioners, primary care services by nursing service agencies and professional nurses practicing in health care agencies.

ANA testimony pointed out that nursing care is the critical component of services provided by hospitals and by nursing facilities and urged that no institution be considered a hospital for purposes of implementing national health insurance legislation unless there is an organized service under the direction of a registered professional nurse, and unless all nursing care is rendered and/or supervised by registered professional nurses 24 hours of each day.

In 1975, ANA presented testimony on legislative proposals regarding professional standards review organizations, nursing cost differential, health planning, national health insurance, and the Nurse Training Act.

Bibliography

CHAPTER ONE

Aftab, Shirley Hathaway. "Sixty Years of *Trained Nurse*," *The Trained Nurse*, Vol. CXXII (January, 1949), 14-15.

Alcott, Louisa May. *Hospital Sketches*. Boston: James Redpath, 1863.

Austin, Anne L. *History of Nursing Source Book*. New York: G. P. Putnam's Sons, 1957.

Austin, Anne L. "Nurses in American History: Wartime Volunteers, 1861-1865," *American Journal of Nursing*, Vol. LXXV (May, 1975), 816-818.

Bailey, Thomas A. *The American Pageant, A History of the Republic*. Boston: D. C. Heath and Company, 1966.

Banfield, Maud. "Progress in the Work and Organization of Nurses During the Past Year," *Philadelphia Monthly Medical Journal*, Vol. I (November, 1899), 645-650.

Beck, Harvey G. "The Evolution of Nursing," *Maryland Medical Journal*, Vol. LIX (July, 1916), 157-164.

A Century of Nursing. New York: G. P. Putnam's Sons, 1950.

Cooper, Page. *The Bellevue Story*. New York: Thomas Y. Crowell Company, 1948.

Cooper, Signe Skott. "A Century of Nursing Education," *Journal of Continuing Education in Nursing*, Vol. III (September-October, 1972), 3-4.

Dickens, Charles. *Martin Chuzzlewit*. New York: Dodd, Mead and Company, 1944.

Dietz, Lena Dixon. *History and Modern Nursing*. Philadelphia: F. A. Davis Company, 1963.

Dock, Lavinia L. and Isabel M. Stewart. *A Short History of Nursing*. New York: G. P. Putnam's Sons, 1938.

Dolan, Josephine A. *History of Nursing*. Philadelphia: W. B. Saunders Company, 1968.

Dolan, Josephine A. "Nurses in American History: Three Schools, 1873," *American Journal of Nursing*, Vol. LXXX (June, 1975), 989-992.

Gelinas, Agnes. *Nursing and Nursing Education*. New York: The Commonwealth Fund, 1946.

Goodnow, Minnie. *Outlines of Nursing History*. Philadelphia: W. B. Saunders Company, 1940.

Goodnow, Minnie. *Nursing History in Brief*. Philadelphia: W. B. Saunders Company, 1938.

Jensen, Deborah MacLurg. *History and Trends of Professional Nursing*. St. Louis: C. V. Mosby Company, 1959.

Johnstone, Mary M. "The History of Nursing," *Women's Medical Journal of Toledo*, Vol. XIII (November, 1903), 220-222.

Nightingale, Florence, *Notes on Nursing: What It Is and What It Is Not*. New York: D. Appleton and Company, 1860.

Nutting, M. Adelaide and Lavinia L. Dock. *A History of Nursing: The Evolution of Nursing Systems from the Earliest Times to the Foundation of the First English and American Training Schools for Nurses*, Vol. I-IV. New York: G. P. Putnam's Sons, 1907-1912.

Perry, Charlotte, "A Brief History of Nursing," *The Trained Nurse and Hospital Review*, Vol. XXXIV (August, 1904), 75-79.

Rawnsley, Marilyn M. "The Goldmark Report: Midpoint in Nursing History," *Nursing Outlook*, Vol. XXI (June, 1973), 380-383.

Richards, Linda. "How Trained Nursing Began in America," *American Journal of Nursing*, Vol. II (November, 1901), 88-89.

Richards, Linda. *Reminiscences of Linda Richards, America's First Trained Nurse*. Boston: M. Barrows and Company, 1929.

Roberts, Mary M. *American Nursing: History and Interpretation*. New York: The Macmillan Company, 1959.

Selevan, Ida Cohen. "Nurses in American History: The Revolution," *American Journal of Nursing*, Vol. LXXV (April, 1975), 592-594.

Seymer, Lucy Ridgely. *A General History of Nursing*. New York: The Macmillan Company, 1956.

Sharp, Benita Hall. "The Beginnings of Nursing Education in the U. S.: An Analysis of the Times," *Journal of Nursing Education*, Vol. XII (April, 1973), 26-31.

Staupers, Mable Keaton. *No Time for Prejudice: A Story of the Integration of Negroes in Nursing in the United States*. New York: The Macmillan Company, 1961.

Stewart, Isabel M. and Anne L. Austin. *A History of Nursing: From Ancient to Modern Times, A World View*. New York: G. P. Putnam's Sons, 1962.

Stimson, Julia C. "Earliest Known Connection of Nurses with Army Hospitals in the United States," *American Journal of Nursing*, Vol. XXV (January, 1925), 18.

Whitman, Walt. *The Wound Dresser: Letters Written to His Mother from the Hospitals in Washington During the Civil War*. New York: The Bodley Press, 1949.

CHAPTER TWO

Abdellah, Faye G. "Evolution of Nursing as a Profession: Perspective on Manpower Development," *International Nursing Review*, Vol. XIX (September, 1972), 319-327.

American Journal of Nursing. *Thirty Fruitful Years, The Story of the American Journal of Nursing*. New York: American Journal of Nursing, 1930.

Carr-Saunders, A. M. "Professionalization in Historical Perspective" in *Professionalization* ed. by Howard Vollmer and Donald Mills. New Jersey: Prentice Hall, 1966.

Christy, Teresa E. "Nurses in American History: The Fateful Decade, 1890-1900," *American Journal of Nursing*, Vol. LXXV (July, 1975), 1163-1165.

Dolan, Josephine A. *History of Nursing*. Philadelphia: W. B. Saunders Company, 1968.

Dolan, Josephine A. "1893-1912 Fusing the Past for Future Action" in *Three Score Years and Ten, 1893-1963* ed. by National League for Nursing. New York: National League for Nursing, 1963, 5-13.

"Editor's Table," *The Trained Nurse,* Vol. IV (January, 1890), 37.

"Editor's Table," *The Trained Nurse,* Vol. IV (February, 1890), 89-93.

Fenwick, Ethel Gordon. "Editorial," *British Journal of Nursing,* Vol. XXIX (July 5, 1902), 1.

Fenwick, Ethel Gordon. "Our Silver Jubilee Number," *British Journal of Nursing,* Vol. L (March 29, 1913), 241-242.

Fenwick, Ethel Gordon. "Our Silver Jubilee Number," *British Journal of Nursing,* Vol. L (April 19, 1913), 301.

Fenwick, Ethel Gordon. "Editorial on the British Journal of Nursing," *Nursing Record and The Hospital World,* Vol. XXVIII (April 12, 1902), 281-282.

Goodnow, Minnie. *Outlines of Nursing History.* Philadelphia: W. B. Saunders Company, 1940.

Goodrich, Annie W. "The Evolution of the Nurse—Building Our Future on Our Past," *The Trained Nurse and Hospital Review,* Vol. LXXIV (1925), 142-147.

Gordon, Edith. "Letter to the Editor," *The Trained Nurse,* Vol. II (January, 1889), 26.

Gould, George M. "The Duties and the Dangers of Organization in the Nursing Organization," *Bulletin of the Johns Hopkins Hospital,* Vol. X (June, 1899), 103-108.

Hampton, Isabel and others. *Nursing of the Sick,* 1893. New York: McGraw-Hill Book Company, 1949.

Hampton, Isabel Adams. *Nursing: Its Principles and Practice for Hospital and Private Use.* Philadelphia: W. B. Saunders, 1893.

Jensen, Deborah MacLurg. *History and Trends of Professional Nursing.* St. Louis: C. V. Mosby Company, 1959.

Merton, Robert K. "Issues in the Growth of a Profession," presented at the 41st convention of the American Nurses' Association (June 10, 1958), Kansas City, Mo.: American Nurses' Association, 1958, 1-11.

Merton, Robert K. "The Functions of the Professional Association," *American Journal of Nursing,* Vol. LVIII (January, 1958), 50-54.

Moore, Wilbert E. *The Professions: Roles and Rules.* New York: Russel Sage Foundation, 1970.

Munson, Helen W. with collaboration of Katharine Stevens. *The Story of the National League of Nursing Education.* Philadelphia: W. B. Saunders Company, 1934.

"New York State Nurses' Association: What Is Proposed and What the Association Will Seek to Do for Nurses," *The Trained Nurse,* Vol. III (December, 1889), 227-234.

Pfefferkorn, Blanche. "Nursing Organization in the U. S., Their Origin, Purpose, and Source of Their Results," *Modern Hospital,* Vol. VIII (1917), 131-134.

Proceedings of the First (January 10, 1894) and Second (February 13, 1895) Annual Conventions of the American Society of Superintendents of Training Schools for Nurses. Harrisburg: Pa.: Harrisburg Publishing Company, 1897.

Proceedings of the Third (February 11-14, 1896) Annual Convention of the American Society of Superintendents of Training Schools for Nurses. Harrisburg, Pa.: Harrisburg Publishing Company, 1896.

Proceedings of the Convention of Training School Alumnae Delegates and Representatives from the American Society of Superintendents of Training Schools for Nurses (September 2-4, 1896). Harrisburg, Pa.: Harrisburg Publishing Company, 1896.

Proceedings of the Convention of Training School Alumnae Delegates and Representatives from the American Society of Superintendents of Training Schools for Nurses (February 11-12, 1897).

Proceedings of the Fourth (February 10-12, 1897) Annual Convention of the American Society of Superintendents of Training Schools for Nurses. Harrisburg, Pa.: Harrisburg Publishing Company, 1897.

Proceedings of the First Annual Convention of the Associated Alumnae of Trained Nurses of the U. S. and Canada (April 28-29, 1898). New York: O'Donnell Bros., 1898.

Proceedings of the Second Annual Meeting of the Associated Alumnae of Trained Nurses of the U. S. and Canada (May 1-3, 1899). Cleveland: J. B. Savage, 1899.

Proceedings of the Third Annual Convention of the Associated Alumnae of Trained Nurses of the U. S. (May 3-5, 1900). Cleveland: J. B. Savage, 1900.

Proceedings of the Fourth Annual Convention of the Nurses' Associated Alumnae of the U. S. (September 16-17, 1901), *American Journal of Nursing,* Vol. II (February, 1902), 303-330.

Proceedings of the Fifth Annual Convention of the Nurses' Associated Alumnae of the U. S. (May 1-3, 1902), *American Journal of Nursing,* Vol. II (July, 1902), 745-898.

Proceedings of the Sixth Annual Convention of the Nurses' Associated Alumnae of the U. S. (June 10-12, 1903), *American Journal of Nursing,* Vol. III (August, 1903), 829-918.

Proceedings of the Seventh Annual Convention of the Nurses' Associated Alumnae of the U. S. (May 12-14, 1904), *American Journal of Nursing,* Vol. IV (July, 1904), 749-816.

Robb, Isabel Hampton. *Nursing Ethics: For Hospitals and Private Use.* Cleveland: E. C. Koeckert, 1922.

Robb, Isabel Hampton. *Educational Standards for Nurses with Other Addresses on Nursing Subjects.* 1907.

Roberts, Mary M. *American Nursing: History and Interpretation.* New York: The Macmillan Company, 1959.

"Shall We Organize? A Symposium on the Ideal of a National Association," *The Trained Nurse,* Vol. III (September, 1889), 111-119.

Stewart, Isabel M. and Lavinia L. Dock. *A Short History of Nursing.* New York: G. P. Putnam's Sons, 1938.

"The Trained Nurse and Organization," *The Trained Nurse,* Vol. III (October, 1889), 153.

Todd, Arthur J. "Nursing As A Learned Profession: A Sociologist's View," *Public Health Nurse,* Vol. XI (1919), 13-18.

Vollmer, Howard and Donald Mills, eds. *Professionalization.* New Jersey: Prentice Hall, 1966.

Worcester, A. "Is Nursing Really A Profession," *American Journal of Nursing,* Vol. II (August, 1902), 908-917.

CHAPTER THREE

Constitution and By-Laws of the Nurses' Associated Alumnae of the United States and Canada, 1897.

Proceedings of the Third Annual Convention (May 3-5, 1900) of the Nurses'

Associated Alumnae of the United States, *American Journal of Nursing,* Vol. I (October, 1900), 68-95.

Proceedings of the Fourth Annual Convention (September 16-17, 1901) of the Nurses' Associated Alumnae of the United States, *American Journal of Nursing,* Vol. II (February, 1902), 304-330.

Proceedings of the Fifth Annual Convention (May 1-3, 1902) of the Nurses' Associated Alumnae of the United States, *American Journal of Nursing,* Vol. II (July, 1902), 743-898.

Proceedings of the Sixth Annual Convention (June 10-12, 1903) of the Nurses' Associated Alumnae of the United States, *American Journal of Nursing,* Vol. III (August, 1903), 829-916.

Proceedings of the Seventh Annual Convention (May 12-14, 1904) of the Nurses' Associated Alumnae of the United States, *American Journal of Nursing,* Vol. IV (July, 1904), 749-815.

Proceedings of the Eighth Annual Convention (May 4-5, 1905) of the Nurses' Associated Alumnae of the United States, *American Journal of Nursing,* Vol. V (August, 1905), 725-836.

Proceedings of the Ninth Annual Convention (June 5-7, 1906) of the Nurses' Associated Alumnae of the United States, *American Journal of Nursing,* Vol. VI (August, 1906), 731-828.

Proceedings of the Tenth Annual Convention (May 14-16, 1907) of the Nurses' Associated Alumnae of the United States, *American Journal of Nursing,* Vol. VII (August, 1907), 787-911.

Proceedings of the Eleventh Annual Convention (May 5-8, 1908) of the Nurses' Associated Alumnae of the United States, *American Journal of Nursing,* Vol. VIII (July, 1908), 833-872.

Proceedings of the Twelfth Annual Convention (June 10-11, 1909) of the Nurses' Associated Alumnae of the United States, *American Journal of Nursing,* Vol. IX (September, 1909), 877-991.

Proceedings of the Thirteenth Annual Convention (May 19-20, 1910) of the Nurses' Associated Alumnae of the United States, *American Journal of Nursing,* Vol. X (August, 1910), 799-918.

Proceedings of the Fourteenth Annual Convention (May 31-June 3, 1911) of the Nurses' Associated Alumnae of the United States, *American Journal of Nursing,* Vol. XI (August, 1911), 878-985.

CHAPTER FOUR

American Nurses' Association Handbook. January, 1935.

Deans, Agnes G. *American Nurses' Association Historical Sketch.* New York: ANA, 1925.

Proceedings of the Fourteenth Annual Convention (May 31-June 3, 1911) of the American Nurses' Association, *American Journal of Nursing,* Vol. XI (August, 1911), 878-985.

Proceedings of the Fifteenth Annual Convention (June 5-7, 1912) of the American Nurses' Association, *American Journal of Nursing,* Vol. XII (August, 1912), 859-986.

Proceedings of the Sixteenth Annual Convention (June 25-27, 1913) of the American Nurses' Association, *American Journal of Nursing,* Vol. XIII (September, 1913), 905-1000.

Proceedings of the Seventeenth Annual Convention (April 23-29, 1914) of the American Nurses' Association, *American Journal of Nursing,* Vol. XIV (July, 1914), 775-935.

Proceedings of the Eighteenth Annual Convention (June 20-25, 1915) of the American Nurses' Association, *American Journal of Nursing,* Vol. XV (August, 1915), 899-1066.

Proceedings of the Nineteenth Annual Convention (April 27-May 3, 1916) of the American Nurses' Association, *American Journal of Nursing,* Vol. XVI (June, 1916), 787-957.

Proceedings of the Twentieth Annual Convention (April 26-May 2, 1917) of the American Nurses' Association, *American Journal of Nursing,* Vol. XVII (July, 1917), 845-1018.

Proceedings of the Twenty-First Annual Convention (May 7-11, 1918) of the American Nurses' Association, *American Journal of Nursing,* Vol. XVIII (August, 1918), 939-1128.

Proceedings of the Twenty-Second Convention (April 12-17, 1920) of the American Nurses' Association, *American Journal of Nursing,* Vol. XX (July, 1920), 757-866.

Proceedings of the Twenty-Third Convention (June 26-July 1, 1922) of the American Nurses' Association, *American Journal of Nursing,* Vol. XXII (September, 1922), 968-1098.

Roberts, Mary. *American Nursing History and Interpretation.* New York: Macmillan Company, 1954.

CHAPTER FIVE

American Nurses' Association. *Handbook* (Formerly President's Portfolio). New York: American Nurses' Association, 1935.

Bailey, Thomas A. *The American Pageant.* Boston: D. C. Heath and Company, 1966.

Best, Ella. *Brief Historical Review and Information About Current Activities of the American Nurses' Association.* New York: American Nurses' Association, 1940.

Burgess, May Ayres. "The Distribution of Nursing Service," *American Journal of Nursing,* Vol. XXX (July, 1930), 857.

Burgess, May Ayres. *Nurses, Patients and Pocketbooks.* New York: Committee on the Grading of Nursing Schools, 1928.

Committee on the Grading of Nursing Schools. *Nursing Schools—Today and Tomorrow.* New York: Committee on the Grading of Nursing Schools, 1934.

Department of Health, Education, and Welfare, Public Health Service. *Health Resources Statistics, Health Manpower and Health Facilities, 1968.* Washington, D. C.: National Center for Health Statistics, 1968.

Flexner, Abraham. *Medical Education in the United States and Canada.* New York: Carnegie Foundation for Advancement of Teaching, 1910.

Issues in Nursing, eds. Bonnie Bullough and Vern Bullough. New York: Springer Publishing Company, 1966.

Jamieson, Elizabeth M. and Mary F. Sewall. *Trends in Nursing History.* Philadelphia: W. B. Saunders Company, 1949.

Johns, Ethel and Blanche Pfefferkorn. *An Activity Analysis of Nursing.* New York:

Committee on the Grading of Nursing Schools, 1934.
Proceedings of the Twenty-Fourth Convention (June 16-21, 1924) of the American Nurses' Association. New York: American Nurses' Association, 1924.
Proceedings of the Twenty-Fifth Convention (May 17-22, 1926) of the American Nurses' Association. New York: American Nurses' Association, 1926.
Proceedings of the Twenty-Sixth Convention (June 4-8, 1928) of the American Nurses' Association. New York: American Nurses' Association, 1928.
Proceedings of the Twenty-Seventh Convention (June 9-14, 1930) of the American Nurses' Association. New York: American Nurses' Association, 1930.
Proceedings of the Twenty-Eighth Convention (April 10-15, 1932) of the American Nurses' Association. New York: American Nurses' Association, 1932.
Proceedings of the Twenty-Ninth Convention (April 22-27, 1934) of the American Nurses' Association. New York: American Nurses' Association, 1934.
Winslow, C. E. A. and Josephine Goldmark. *Nursing and Nursing Education in the United States.* New York: The Macmillan Company, 1923.

CHAPTER SIX

Advisory Council Reports of the Thirty-Second Convention (May 12-17, 1940) of the American Nurses' Association. New York: American Nurses' Association, 1940.
Advisory Council Reports of the Thirty-Third Convention (May 17-22, 1942) of the American Nurses' Association. New York: American Nurses' Association, 1942.
Advisory Council Reports of the Thirty-Fourth Convention (June 4-7, 1944) of the American Nurses' Association. New York: American Nurses' Association, 1944.
American Nurses' Association. *Study of Organization, Control, Policies, and Financing of Nurses' Professional Registries.* New York: American Nurses' Association, 1942.
Bailey, Thomas A. *The American Pageant.* Boston: D. C. Heath and Company, 1966.
Best, Ella. *Brief Historical Review and Information About Current Activities of the American Nurses' Association.* New York: American Nurses' Association, 1940.
Division on Nursing of the Council of the American Hospital Association and a Committee of the National League of Nursing Education. *Manual of the Essentials of Good Hospital Nursing Service.* New York: National League of Nursing Education, 1936.
Excerpts from Proceedings of the Thirty-Third Convention (May 17-22, 1942) of the American Nurses' Association. New York: American Nurses' Association, 1942.
General Staff Nurses' Section Reports of the Thirty-Fourth Convention (June 4-7, 1944) of the American Nurses' Association. New York: American Nurses' Association, 1944.
House of Delegates Reports of the Thirty-Second Convention (May 12-17, 1940) of the American Nurses' Association. New York: American Nurses' Association, 1940.
House of Delegates Reports of the Thirty-Third Convention (May 17-22, 1942) of the American Nurses' Association. New York: American Nurses' Association, 1942.
House of Delegates Reports of the Thirty-Fourth Convention (June 4-7, 1944) of the American Nurses' Association. New York: American Nurses' Association, 1944.
Jamieson, Elizabeth M. and Mary F. Sewall. *Trends in Nursing History.* Philadelphia:

W. B. Saunders Company, 1949.

Joint Committee on Auxiliary Nursing Service. *Practical Nurses and Auxiliary Workers for the Care of the Sick*. New York: American Nurses' Association, 1947.

Joint Committee of the American Nurses' Association, National League of Nursing Education, and National Organization for Public Health Nursing. *Subsidiary Workers in the Care of the Sick*. New York: American Nurses' Association, 1941.

Men Nurses' Section Reports of the Thirty-Fourth Convention (June 4-7, 1944) of the American Nurses' Association. New York: American Nurses' Association, 1944.

McIver, Pearl. "Registered Nurses in the U.S.A.," *American Journal of Nursing*, Vol. XLII (July, 1942), 769.

National Nursing Planning Committee. *A Comprehensive Program for Nation-Wide Action in the Field of Nursing*. New York: National Nursing Council for War Service, Inc., 1945.

Nursing Information Bureau. *Professional Nursing and Auxiliary Services*. New York: American Nurses' Association, 1942.

Private Duty Section Reports of the Thirty-Second Convention (May 12-17, 1940) of the American Nurses' Association. New York: American Nurses' Association, 1940.

Private Duty Section Reports of the Thirty-Third Convention (May 17-22, 1942) of the American Nurses' Association. New York: American Nurses' Association, 1942.

Private Duty Section Reports of the Thirty-Fourth Convention (June 4-7, 1944) of the American Nurses' Association. New York: American Nurses' Association, 1944.

Proceedings of the Thirtieth Convention (June 21-26, 1936) of the American Nurses' Association and Institute for Registrars (June 27-28, 1936). New York: American Nurses' Association, 1936.

Proceedings of the Thirty-First Convention (April 24-29, 1938) of the American Nurses' Association. New York: American Nurses' Association, 1938.

Proceedings of the Thirty-Fourth Convention (June 4-7, 1944) of the American Nurses' Association. New York: American Nurses' Association, 1944.

Proceedings of the Thirty-Fifth Biennial Convention (September 22-27, 1946) of the American Nurses' Association. Volume I: *House of Delegates*. New York: American Nurses' Association, 1946.

Proceedings of the Thirty-Fifth Biennial Convention (September 22-27, 1946) of the American Nurses' Association, Volume II: *Advisory Council, Section Meetings, Joint and Special Sessions*. New York: American Nurses' Association, 1946.

Report of the Thirty-Second Convention (May 12-17, 1940) of the American Nurses' Association. New York: American Nurses' Association, 1940.

Roberts, Mary M. *American Nursing: History and Interpretation*. New York: The Macmillan Company, 1954.

Technical Committee on Medical Care. *Report of the Technical Committee on Medical Care*. Washington, D.C.: Interdepartmental Committee to Coordinate Health and Welfare Activities, 1938.

"The Subsidiary Worker," *American Journal of Nursing*, Vol. XXXVII (March, 1937), 283-286.

CHAPER SEVEN

"Aggressive Unionism," *The Modern Hospital*, Vol. L (May, 1938), reprint.

Ballard, Berton J. "The Nurses' Staunchest Friend Could Be the Public," *American Journal of Nursing*, Vol. XLVI (September, 1946), 586-588.

Committee on the Structure of National Nursing Organizations. *1949 Handbook on the Structure of Organized Nursing*. New York: Committee on the Structure of National Nursing Organizations, 1949.

"Criteria for the Evaluation of State Programs in Relation to Official National Policy," *American Journal of Nursing*, Vol. XLIX (October, 1949), reprint.

Economic Security Unit. *Major Official Policies of the Economic Security Program*. New York: American Nurses' Association, 1965.

Economic Security Unit. *Manual for an Economic Security Program: A Guide for State Nurses' Associations*. New York: American Nurses' Association, 1952.

House of Delegates Sections Reports, 1954-1956. New York: American Nurses' Association, 1956.

House of Delegates Sections Reports, 1956-1958. New York: American Nurses' Association, 1958.

Nelson, Josephine, ed. *New Horizons in Nursing*. New York: The Macmillan Company, 1950.

Northrup, Herbert R. "Collective Bargaining and the Professions," *American Journal of Nursing*, Vol. XLVIII (March, 1948), reprint.

Nursing Information Bureau. *Fact Sheet on the Economic Security Program of the American Nurses' Association*. New York: American Nurses' Association, 1947.

"Nurse Membership in Unions," *American Journal of Nursing*, Vol. XXXVII (July, 1937), reprint.

"Nurses' Unions?" *American Journal of Nursing*, Vol. XXXVI (November, 1936), reprint.

Patterson, Lillian B. "The Economic Brief," *American Journal of Nursing*, Vol. XLIX (July, 1949), reprint.

Proceedings of the Thirty-Fifth Biennial Convention (September 22-27, 1946) of the American Nurses' Association, Volume I: *House of Delegates*. New York: American Nurses' Association, 1946.

Proceedings of the Thirty-Fifth Biennial Convention (September 22-27, 1946) of the American Nurses' Association, Volume II: *Advisory Council—Section Meetings, Joint and Special Sessions*. New York: American Nurses' Association, 1946.

Proceedings of the Special Sessions of the Advisory Council, 1947-1948, and the House of Delegates, 1947, of the American Nurses' Association. New York: American Nurses' Association, 1948.

Proceedings of the Thirty-Sixth Biennial Convention (May 31-June 4, 1948) of the American Nurses' Association, Volume I: *House of Delegates*. New York: American Nurses' Association, 1948.

Proceedings of the Thirty-Sixth Biennial Convention (May 31-June 4, 1948) of the American Nurses' Association, Volume II: *Advisory Council—Section Meetings, Joint and Special Meetings*. New York: American Nurses' Association, 1948.

Proceedings of the Special Session of the Advisory Council of the American Nurses' Association, 1949. New York: American Nurses' Association, 1949.

Proceedings of the Special Session of the Advisory Council of the American Nurses' Association, 1950. New York: American Nurses' Association, 1950.

Proceedings of the Thirty-Seventh Convention (May 7-12, 1950) of the American Nurses' Association, Volume I: *House of Delegates*. New York: American Nurses' Association, 1950.

Proceedings of the Thirty-Seventh Convention (May 7-12, 1950) of the American Nurses' Association, Volume II: *Advisory Council—Section Meetings, Joint and Special Meetings*. New York: American Nurses' Association, 1950.

Proceedings of the Special Session of the Advisory Council of the American Nurses' Association, 1951. New York: American Nurses' Association, 1951.

Proceedings of the Special Session of the Advisory Council of the American Nurses' Association, 1952. New York: American Nurses' Association, 1952.

Proceedings of the Thirty-Eighth Convention (June 16-20, 1952) of the American Nurses' Association, Volume I: *House of Delegates*. New York: American Nurses' Association, 1952.

Proceedings of the Thirty-Eighth Convention (June 16-20, 1952) of the American Nurses' Association, Volume II: *Section Meetings, Joint, Special, Student Meetings*. New York: American Nurses' Association, 1952.

Proceedings of the Special Session of the Advisory Council of the American Nurses' Association, 1953. New York: American Nurses' Association, 1953.

Proceedings of the Thirty-Ninth Convention (April 26-30, 1954) of the American Nurses' Association, Volume I: *House of Delegates*. New York: American Nurses' Association, 1954.

Proceedings of the Thirty-Ninth Convention (April 26-30, 1954) of the American Nurses' Association, Volume II: *Section Meetings, General Program Meetings, Special Interest Conferences, Student Meetings*. New York: American Nurses' Association, 1954.

Proceedings of the Special Session of the Advisory Council of the American Nurses' Association, 1955. New York: American Nurses' Association, 1955.

Proceedings of the Special Session of the Advisory Council of the American Nurses' Association, 1956. New York: American Nurses' Association, 1956.

Proceedings of the Fortieth Convention (May 14-18, 1956) of the American Nurses' Association. New York: American Nurses' Association, 1956.

Proceedings of the Special Session of the Advisory Council of the American Nurses' Association, 1958. New York: American Nurses' Association, 1958.

Proceedings of the Forty-First Convention (June 9-13, 1958) of the American Nurses' Association. New York: American Nurses' Association, 1958.

Raymond Rich Associates. "Report on the Structure of Organized Nursing," *American Journal of Nursing*, Vol. XLVI (October, 1946), 648-661.

Staupers, Mabel Keaton. *No Time for Prejudice*. New York: The Macmillan Company, 1961.

"The ANA Economic Security Program," *American Journal of Nursing*, Vol. XLVII (February, 1947), reprint.

"The Structure Study," *American Journal of Nursing*, Vol. XLIX (April, 1949), 236-241.

Thompson, Julia. *The ANA in Washington*. New York: American Nurses' Association, 1972.

Titus, Shirley C. and Sylvia Marrich. "Economic Security for Nurses in Tax-Supported Institutions," *American Journal of Nursing*, Vol. XLIX (July, 1949), reprint.

"Union Membership? No!" *American Journal of Nursing*, Vol. XXXVIII (May, 1938), reprint.

CHAPTER EIGHT

A Blueprint to Build On: A Report to Members, 1966-68. New York: American Nurses' Association, 1968.

Ad Hoc Committee on Implementation of Standards of Nursing Practice. *Peer Review: Guidelines for Establishment of Committees*. Kansas City: American Nurses' Association, 1973.

Ad Hoc Committee on the Future of the National League for Nursing. "Recommended Policy Statement on the Question of One Nursing Organization." January 20, 1955.

American Nurses' Association. *Accreditation of Continuing Education in Nursing: Colleges and Universities*. Kansas City: American Nurses' Association, 1975.

American Nurses' Association. *Accreditation of Continuing Education in Nursing. State Nurses' Associations; National Specialty Nursing Organization; Federal Nursing Services; State Boards of Nursing*. Kansas City: American Nurses' Association, 1975.

American Nurses' Association. *Accreditation of Continuing Education Programs Preparing Nurses for Expanded Roles*. Kansas City: American Nurses' Association, 1975.

American Nurses' Association Bylaws (as amended June, 1966). New York: American Nurses' Association, 1966.

American Nurses' Association Bylaws (as amended May, 1968). New York: American Nurses' Association, 1968.

"American Nurses' Association Blueprint for Research in Nursing." *American Journal of Nursing*, Vol. LXII (August, 1962), 69-71.

American Nurses' Association. *Continuing Education Guidelines for State Nurses' Associations*. Kansas City: American Nurses' Association, 1974.

American Nurses' Association. *Continuing Education in Nursing: An Overview*. Kansas City: American Nurses' Association, 1976.

American Nurses' Association. *Continuing Education in Nursing: Guidelines for Staff Development*. Kansas City: American Nurses' Association, 1976.

American Nurses' Association. *Continuing Education in Nursing: Guidelines for State Voluntary and Mandatory Systems*. Kansas City: American Nurses' Association, 1975.

American Nurses' Association. *Educational Preparation for Nurse' Practitioners and Assistants to Nurses: A Position Paper*. New York: American Nurses' Association, 1965.

American Nurses' Association. *Standards for Continuing Education in Nursing*. Kansas City: American Nurses' Association, 1974.

American Nurses' Association. *Statement of Graduate Education in Nursing*. New York: American Nurses' Association, 1969.

American Nurses' Association. *The Nurse in Research, ANA Guidelines on Ethical Values*. New York: American Nurses' Association, 1968.

Book of ANA Policies, Positions, and Procedures, 1975.

Brown, Esther Lucile. *Nursing for the Future*. New York: Russel Sage Foundation, 1948.

Bylaws: Certificate of Incorporation, Rules of Sections, Branches, and Conference Groups. New York: American Nurses' Association, 1964.

Commission on Nursing Services. *Standards for Nursing Services*. Kansas City: American Nurses' Association, 1973.

Congress for Nursing Practice. *A Plan for Implementation of the Standards of Nursing*

Practice. Kansas City: American Nurses' Association, 1975.

Congress for Nursing Practice. *Standards of Nursing Practice*. Kansas City: American Nurses' Association, 1973.

Department of Health, Education and Welfare. *Report on Licensure and Related Health Personnel Credentialing*. Washington, D.C.: U.S. Government Printing Office, 1971.

Department of Health, Education, and Welfare, Public Health Service. *Toward Quality in Nursing: Needs and Goals* (A Report of the Surgeon General's Consultant Group on Nursing). Washington, D.C.: U.S. Government Printing Office, 1963.

"Establishing Standards for Nursing Practice," *American Journal of Nursing*, Vol. LXIX (July, 1969), reprint.

"Experimentation on Reorganization," Excerpt from Action of ANA Board of Directors, January, 1955, 60-61.

Freeman, Ruth B. "NLN at Twenty: Challenge and Change," *Nursing Outlook*, Vol. XX (June, 1972), 376-382.

House of Delegates Sections Reports, 1956-1958. New York: American Nurses' Association, 1958.

House of Delegates Sections Reports, 1958-1960. New York: American Nurses' Association, 1960.

House of Delegates Sections Reports, 1960-1962. New York: American Nurses' Association, 1962.

House of Delegates Sections Reports, 1962-1964. New York: American Nurses' Association, 1964.

House of Delegates Sections Reports, 1964-1966. New York: American Nurses' Association, 1966.

House of Delegates Reports, 1966-1968. New York: American Nurses' Association, 1968.

House of Delegates Reports, 1968-1970. New York: American Nurses' Association, 1970.

House of Delegates Reports, 1970-1972. New York: American Nurses' Association, 1972.

House of Delegates Reports, 1972-1974. Kansas City: American Nurses' Association, 1974.

Kinney, Lucien B. "Professional Standards: Through Licensure or Certification?" *American Journal of Nursing*, Vol. LXV (October, 1965), reprint.

Lysaught, Jerome P. *An Abstract for Action*. New York: McGraw-Hill Book Company, 1970.

Newton, Mildred E. "As Nursing Research Comes of Age," *American Journal of Nursing*, Vol. LXII (August, 1962), 46-50.

Proceedings of the Forty-First Convention (June 9-13, 1958) of the American Nurses' Association. New York: American Nurses' Association, 1958.

Proceedings of the Forty-Second Convention (May 2-6, 1960) of the American Nurses' Association. New York: American Nurses' Association, 1960.

Proceedings of the Forty-Third Convention (May 14-18, 1962) of the American Nurses' Association. New York: American Nurses' Association, 1962.

Proceedings of the Forty-Fourth Convention (June 15-19, 1964) of the American Nurses' Association. New York: American Nurses' Association, 1964.

Proceedings of the Forty-Fifth Biennial Convention (June 14-17, 1966) of the

American Nurses' Association. New York: American Nurses' Association, 1966.

Proceedings of the Forty-Sixth Convention (May 13-17, 1968) of the American Nurses' Association. New York: American Nurses' Association, 1968.

Proceedings of the Forty-Seventh Convention (May 3-8, 1970) of the American Nurses' Association. New York: American Nurses' Association, 1970.

SASHEP Commission Report. Washington, D.C.: National Commission on Accrediting, 1972.

Study Committee on the Functions of ANA. *Guide to Study of the Functions of ANA.* New York: American Nurses' Association, 1963.

Study Committee on the Functions of ANA. *Proposed Plan for Functions and Structure of ANA.* New York: American Nurses' Association, 1964.

Study Committee on the Functions of ANA. *Proposed Plan for Functions and Structure of ANA, 1965 Supplement.* New York: American Nurses' Association, 1965.

Summary Proceedings of the Forty-Eighth Convention (April 30-May 5, 1972) of the American Nurses' Association. Kansas City: American Nurses' Association, 1974.

Summary Proceedings of the Forty-Ninth Convention (June 9-14, 1974) of the American Nurses' Association. Kansas City: American Nurses' Association, 1975.

Task Force on Organizational Structure. *A Progress Report.* New York: National League for Nursing, 1965.

"Toward One Organization," *American Journal of Nursing,* Vol. LIX (April, 1959), 540-543.

CHAPTER NINE

"A Decade of the Great Society—Success or Failure?" *U. S. News & World Report,* June 9, 1975, 26-31.

Babbie, Earl R. *Science and Morality in Medicine.* Berkeley: University of California Press, 1970.

Brown, Esther Lucile. *Nursing for the Future.* New York: Russel Sage Foundation, 1948.

Brown, Esther Lucile. *Nursing Reconsidered: A Study of Change.* Philadelphia: J. B. Lippincott, 1970.

Changing Patterns of Nursing Practice—New Needs, New Roles compiled by Edith P. Lewis. New York: American Journal of Nursing Company, 1971.

Department of Health, Education, and Welfare, Public Health Service. *Forward Plan for Health, FY 1977-81.* Washington, D.C.: U. S. Government Printing Office, 1975.

Fox, John P., Carrie E. Hall, Lila R. Elveback. *Epidemiology: Man and Disease.* New York: The Macmillan Company, 1970.

Hamburger, J. "Physicians, Biologists, and the Future of Man," *WHO Chronicle,* Vol. XXVIII (1974), 364-368.

"Health Care in America—Progress and Problems," *U. S. News & World Report,* June 16, 1975, 50-67.

Hepner, James O. and Donna M. Hepner. *The Health Strategy Game—A Challenge for Reorganization and Management.* St. Louis: C. V. Mosby Company, 1973.

Judge, Diane. "The New Nurse: A Sense of Duty and Destiny," *Modern Healthcare,* Vol. II (October, 1974), 21-27.

Kennedy, Edward M. *In Critical Condition: The Crisis in America's Health Care.* New York: Simon & Schuster, 1972.

Kramer, Marlene. *Reality Shock—Why Nurses Leave Nursing.* St. Louis: C. V. Mosby Company, 1974.

Levine, Eugene. "Nurse Manpower: Yesterday, Today, and Tomorrow," *American Journal of Nursing,* Vol. LXIX (February, 1969), 290-296.

Lysaught, Jerome P., ed. *Action in Nursing—Progress in Professional Purpose.* New York: McGraw-Hill Book Company, 1974.

Mann, Kenneth W. *Deadline for Survival: A Survey of Moral Issues in Science and Medicine.* New York: Seabury Press, 1970.

Marram, Gwen D., Margaret W. Schlegel, Em O. Bevis. *Primary Nursing, A Model for Individualized Care.* St. Louis: C. V. Mosby Company, 1974.

McHale, John. *The Future of the Future.* New York: George Braziller, Inc., 1969.

Rasmussen, Sandra. "The Expanding Circle," *Nursing Outlook,* Vol. XVI (February, 1968), 29-31.

Report of the Commission on Education for Health Administration. Volume I. Ann Arbor: Ann Arbor Health Administration Press, 1975.

Roberts, Joan T. and Thetis M. Group. "The Women's Movement and Nursing," *Nursing Forum,* Vol. XII (1973), 303-322.

Scott, Jessie M. "The Changing Health Care Environment—Its Implications for Nursing," *American Journal of Public Health,* Vol. LVIV (April, 1974), 365-369.

Storlie, Frances. *Nursing and the Social Conscience.* New York: Appleton-Century-Crofts, 1970.

Teich, Albert H., ed. *Technology and Man's Future.* New York: St. Martin's Press, 1972.

Toffler, Alvin. *Future Shock.* New York: Bantam Books, 1970.

Toffler, Alvin. *Learning for Tomorrow: The Role of the Future in Education.* New York: Vintage Books, 1974.

Index